BEST LOVED HOTELS
OF THE WORLD

ENGLAND ♦ SCOTLAND ♦ WALES ♦ IRELAND

1996

Best Loved Hotels of the World Limited
Thornbury Castle, Thornbury, Avon BS12 1HH, United Kingdom
Telephone: 01454 414786 ♦ Fax: 01454 415796

North America:
C/o DDS 20770 Westwood Drive, Strongsville, OH 44136, USA
Telephone: 216-572-7263 ♦ Fax: (toll free) 800-572-8131

Green is read

I have always thought the saying "it's better to travel hopefully than to arrive" unworthy of Confucius (if he ever said it at all). The idea of travelling hopefully has uncomfortable connotations of doubt; arriving has all the merits of achievement.

My son, Justin, and I were visiting a friend and fellow-hotelier this summer who runs a fine hotel in the Lake District. Justin did most of the driving while I thumbed through the pages of the 1995 Best Loved Directory, now known affectionately as the Big Green Book. Its pages began to absorb me to such a degree that I began to realise that travelling hopefully needs greater understanding.

On our way from Thornbury, I had no idea how many places of interest we were thoughtlessly passing by, indeed had passed by over the years. Whilst this book is not comprehensive, it certainly covers a lot of ground: heritage sites, inns and hotels, country fairs - all the things we take far too much for granted as residents of these islands and all the sorts of places and events our visitors from abroad come here to discover.

So, having put the 'Big Green Book' to good use, we not only enjoyed the pleasures of the journey but the delight of arrival, too.

I hope you find this book as rewarding.

I cannot close this introduction without a word of thanks to American Express who have given us sponsorship far beyond the usual *quid pro quo* of business. They have made a significant contribution to the continuing success of this venture. Our business partners have now become our friends and I am grateful for *all* their support.

Maurice C R Taylor of Portlethen
The Baron of Portlethen
Chairman

How to use this book

> ## "A good book is the best of friends"
>
> *Martin Tapper, Author (1810 - 1889)*

THIS BOOK is about 405 places to stay in the United Kingdom and Ireland: castles, stately homes, country house hotels, city centre hotels, townhouses, leisure resorts, health centres and good, honest inns. Each has its own page with comprehensive details including a recommendation in the form of a "Best Loved" quotation from someone who has been there. When you plan a holiday, a friend's advice is usually helpful; our aim is to provide that kind of quality information.

The hotels are listed in alphabetical order by name within eight regions and an *Island* section; these are shown on the inside cover.

We have set out to make the planning process as easy as possible. This book has a dual role: a description of the hotel and its environment and a source of hard facts about places to stay in England, Scotland, Wales and Ireland.

Colour-coded guide to rates

These Best-Loved rosette's are colour-coded to provide an idea of the hotel's tariff (provided by the hotel) for a standard-type double room for two people for one night including applicable taxes. We have estimated the average of all hotels based on the lowest to highest tariff throughout the year. For Hotels which include meals, an adjustment has been used to arrive at the average rate. A more detailed description of a hotel's tariff appears in the 'Rates' section of each hotel page. We hope this will be a useful guide, however, some hotel rate structures are quite complicated others have special offers and packages so it would be best to check prices when you make your booking.

A word on hotel pages

Best Loved Quotations: We asked each hotel to furnish us with a quotation from one of their guests which would give a verbatim impression of their hotel to our readers. In most cases, we were deluged with notes, letters and guest book entries; from adoring customers to hard-nosed travel writers. In some cases, the quotations may give the reader a better insight into the nature of the hotelier rather than the hotel.

Hotel Ratings (Accolades): For a quick assessment of the establishment's qualities, we have used the four most common rating systems: the **tourist boards**, the **Royal Automobile Club**, the **Automobile Association** and the **Good Hotel Guide**. These systems are self-explanatory but, if you need more information, contact the organisation direct. The *Bibliography* on page 473 will provide addresses and telephone numbers.

These are by no means the only rating systems so a lack of crowns, stars and rosettes does not necessarily convey the whole picture. It is as well to remember that *all* the hotels in this book are best-loved by someone - and for a very good reason!

Phone numbers: For calls from North America and other countries outside Britain and Ireland, other than toll free calls, omit the first 0 in the area code. For example, to dial a British hotel with the number listed as **01202** 555 555 one should dial 011-44-**1202** 555 555. Be sure to include the international country code 44 for Great Britain and Northern Ireland or 353 for the Republic of Ireland.

Charge/Credit Cards: We are pleased to have the continued support for this edition of American Express who have helped us in so many ways. To show our appreciation each hotel accepting the **American Express** card is indicated by the their distinctive logotype. Hotels accepting other credit card facilities are indicated as follows:

DC	=	Diners Club
JCB	=	Japan Credit card
MC	=	MasterCard
VI	=	Visa

Access Codes: These are computer reservation numbers and are intended for the use of travel agents and those who have access to the various airline reservation systems. The great majority of hotels in Great Britain and Ireland do not have this facility, so, in such cases, we have written "Not applicable" under access codes.

Publishers' notes

Calendar. *The calendar on pages 6 - 9 has been extracted from the extensive calendars compiled by the British and Irish Tourist Authorities. The small sample of events is for guidance only. Readers are advised to check with the tourist boards for updated information.*

County boundary changes. *The counties of Avon, Cleveland and Humberside are being abolished from 1st April 1996, and there are some boundary changes in North Yorkshire. The Royal Mail sorts letters by postcode, so please be careful to include the correct postcode (which will not have changed) if you are writing to these areas.*

ISBN 1-898889-05-8

The 1996 Best Loved Hotels of th

Contents

Cover Picture:
A Tranquil Loch by J. S. Dewar, 1878

Published by
Best Loved Hotels of the World Limited
Thornbury Castle, Thornbury,
Avon BS12 1HH
Tel: 01454 414786
Fax: 01454 415796

E-mail: 73321.1370@compuserve.com

Registered Office: 30, St Giles, Oxford

Book sales (see page 384)
Best Loved Hotels of the World Limited
Cowley Bridge Road, Exeter EX4 5HQ
Tel: 01392 429420
Fax: 01392 431025

Joint Publishers
Jeffrey M Epstein
Justin Taylor of Portlethen, Yr

Communications Director
Peter C H Jarvis

Administration
Julie Greatbach

Designed by
Paul Broadbent
The Broadbent Consultancy Limited
134 Lots Road, London SW10 0RJ

Production & Editorial Assistants
Joanne Downey
Brian Jones
Charlotte Murphy

Colour separations by
Colourpath, London

Printed by
RR Donnelly & Sons Company, USA

What to do and when to do it

A four-page ***calendar*** covering 176 events of all kinds and in all regions; arts festivals, book fairs, sporting occasions, flower shows, food festivals and also some inimitably medieval events like Oul' Lammas Fair in Ireland and the Egremont Crab Fair in Cumbria. **Page 6**

Take it or leave it

Three pages we call the ***Pleasure & Leisure Finder***, a miscellany of mostly irrelevant facts about people and places in Britain and Ireland but it may prompt a few ideas. If nothing else, they will take you on an amusing journey through this book!. **Pages 150, 336** and **446**

A word from our sponsors

American Express (whose cards are accepted by almost every hotel in this book) tell us something about the surprisingly wide variety of services they offer. Don't miss **Page 10**

Digging deeper

The information in this book has been drawn from a number of sources. It weighs enough as it is so, of course, there is a limit to its range of detail. For lots more information, we recommend a variety of sources which are listed in the ***Bibliography***. **Page 473**

Where in the world are you?

Whether you are in the United States, Australia or anywhere in between, you could be reading this book. As a matter of fact, no other book of hotels reaches further or in such numbers as this one. So we list all the overseas offices of the ***British Tourist Authority*** and the ***Bord Failte*** (the Irish Tourist Board). So, if you're over there and you want to know more, turn to **Page 480**

A room with a view

Getting down to the serious business of ***where to stay***. The hotels in this book are divided into eight regions and a special section we call *Islands*. And each of these regions are introduced by a character sketch of the people, culture, geography, places of interest and a touring map on which all the hotels are clearly located. The hotels follow, one to a page. **See opposite**

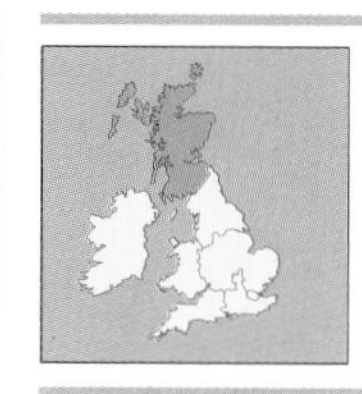

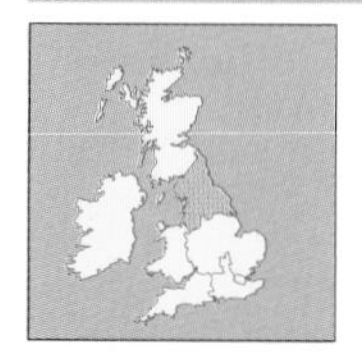

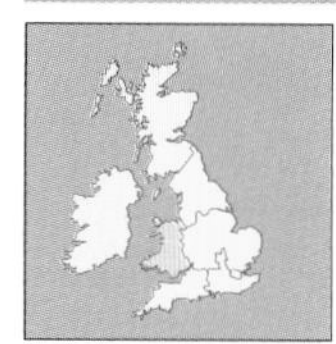

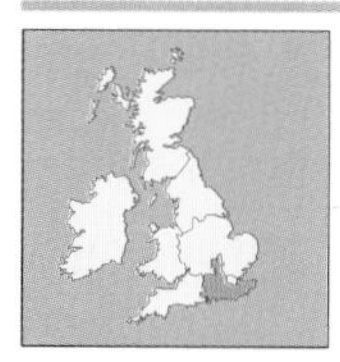

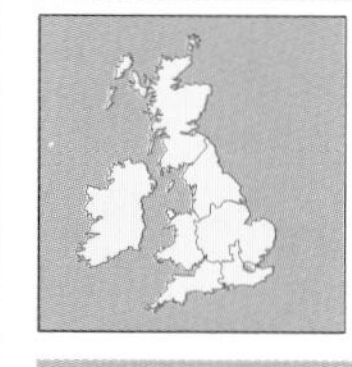

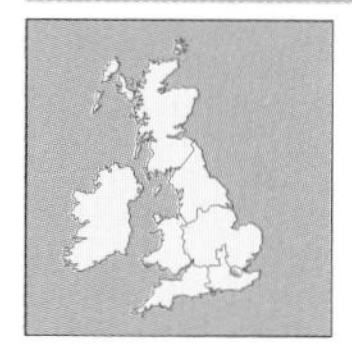

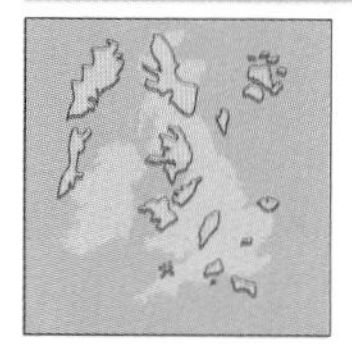

World Directory spread out before you

CONTENTS

Said to be the last great natural environment for leisure and adventure in Europe. The scenery varies dramatically from the majesty of the purple Highlands to the rolling green hills of the Border Country; the misty magic of the Isles to the charm of its cities. As far as food and drink are concerned, Scotland is legendary.

The Vikings left their mark here but, in the Lake District, the culture is decidedly gentler with the influences of Beatrix Potter and Wordsworth. The Yorkshire Moors bring to mind the Brontës and latterly James Herriot; Liverpool is famous for the Beatles and The Grand National, the greatest Steeplechase in the world.

The Welsh are a proud nation and have a lot to be proud about. There are three National Parks and five Areas of Outstanding Natural Beauty. In the distant past, it attracted many unwanted tourists which accounts for Offa's Dyke, a defense system built in 784. Edward I took Wales for his own in 1277 but the Welsh language still persists today.

This region stretches across England from the oyster beds of East Anglia to cathedral bells of Herefordshire. And on the way includes Oxford and Cambridge, Blenheim Palace, the Vales of Aylesbury and Evesham and the Cotswold Hills. At its centre lies Stratford-upon-Avon, the cultural heart of England.

Regarded as the premier holiday resort in the British Isles, this is a region of character vividly portrayed in such novels as Lorna Doone and Tess of the D'Urbervilles. Stonehenge goes back 4000 years; King Arthur lived at Tintagel: Christianity in Britain spread from Glastonbury; and, of course, there were pirates in Penzance!

Some would argue the modern history started here at the Battle of Hastings in 1066. Since then, the south coast has both launched and repelled attacks for centuries. HMS Victory, in Portsmouth, is a proud relic of the Battle of Trafalgar. George III's exotic Pavillion, a tribute to indulgence, stands in Brighton.

London - a cultural treasury without equal. Art galleries, museums, palaces and theatres are gathered close together presenting an array of mankind's achievements and natural sciences: arts and artefacts from all over the world, international music and drama, the list is endless. A cosmopolitan city splendidly expressed by its myriad restaurants.

This is where myth, legend and history are inextricably bound; folklore and faith are part of the same religion. The country has often been harsh on those who live off it and yet the Irish love their homeland with a passion. There's romance in the hills, loughs, rivers and the magnificent ragged coastline.

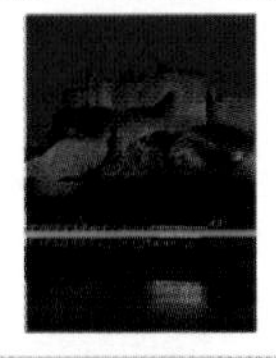

Of the many islands around Britain and Ireland, seven have Best Loved Hotels on them. Their insular cultures vary immensely both naturally and historically: some have their own government, some their own currency, others their own languages; some even have their own unique flora and fauna. Some have a history going back 4000 years.

Index of Indexes

... theatre ... historical re-enactments ...
cultural festivals ... agricultural shows ...
horse racing ... the visual arts ...

CALENDAR *of* EVENTS *1996*

JANUARY	1st - 28th	**Images of Brighton Exhibition**	Paintings, drawings and prints. 18th, 19th and 20th centuries. Admission free. Brighton Museum & Art Gallery. Tel: 01273 603005.	**South**
	1st - 10th Mar	**In Trust for the Nation**	Almost 100 pictures from over 25 National Trust properties. Salisbury Wing, National Gallery, Trafalgar Square, London WC1. Tel: 0171 227 4820.	**London**
	1st - 31st Mar	**Photographs of the Royal Family**	Presenting an Image exhibition. Palace of Holyrood House, Canongate, Edinburgh. Tel: 0131 556 7371.	**Scotland**
	4th - 14th	**London International Boat Show**	Over 600 crafts on show. Earls Court, London SW5. Tel: 01784 473377.	**London**
	6th	**Handel's Messiah**	Philharmonic Hall, Hope Street, Liverpool. Tel: 0151 709 3789.	**North**
	17th - 21st	**LAPADA Antiques and Fine Art Fair**	National Exhibition Centre, Birmingham. Tel: 0121 780 4141.	**Midshires**
FEBRUARY	4th - 9th	**Wordsworth Winter School**	Dove Cottage and Wordsworth Museum, Cumbria. Tel: 01539 435544.	**North**
	10th - 17th	**Jorvik Viking Festival**	Various venues, York, North Yorkshire. Tel: 01904 643211.	**North**
	16th - 18th	**Statoil Galway Rally**	International Car Rally. Tel: +353 (0)91 524557.	**Ireland**
	23rd - 24th	**Sussex Beer Festival**	Real ales, traditional ciders and perries. Hove Town Hall, West Sussex	**South**
	27th - 3rd Mar	**Stampex Philatelic Exhibition**	Royal Horticultural Halls, London SW1. Tel: 0171 490 1005.	**London**
MARCH	1st - 16th	**Bradford Film Festival**	Various venues, Bradford. West Yorkshire. Tel: 01274 727488.	**North**
	5th - 17th	**Chelsea Antiques Fair**	Chelsea Old Town Hall, Chelsea. Tel: 01444 482514	**London**
	3rd - 9th	**National Tree Planting Week**	All over Ireland. Walks, seminars, tree-plantings. Tel: +353 (0)1 6790699.	**Ireland**
	5th - 14th	**Dublin Film Festival**	International and Irish films. Dublin. Tel: +353 (0)1 6792937.	**Ireland**
	12th - 14th	**Cheltenham Gold Cup Meeting**	Major national hunt horse-racing. Tel: 01242 513014.	**Midshires**
	14th - 17th	**Crufts Dog Show**	Over 100 breeds compete. National Exhibition Centre, Birmingham.	**Midshires**
	14th - 11th Apr	**Daily Mail Ideal Home Exhibition**	Earls Court, London. Tel: 0171 373 8141.	**London**
	15th - 18th	**Guinness Roaring Twenties Festival**	Charlestons, flappers and all that's best from the Roaring Twenties. Kenmare, Co Kerry. Tel: +353 (0)64 41170.	**Ireland**
	17th - 19th	**London International Bookfair**	Olympia, Hammersmith Road, London W14. Tel: 0181 948 9828.	**London**
	22nd - 24th	**Galway International Set Dancing Festival**	Galway City. Contact Colie Mullin. Tel: +353 (0)91 753137.	**Ireland**
	24th	**Coca-Cola League Cup Final**	Wembley Stadium. Tel: 0181 900 1234.	**London**
	28th - 30th	**Martell Grand National**	The greatest steeplechase. Aintree, Liverpool. Tel: 0151 523 2600.	**North**
APRIL	1st - 31st May	**Cornwall Gardens Festival**	Various venues throughout Cornwall. Tel: 01872 74057.	**West**
	1st* - Jan 1997	**Shakespeare Theatre Season**	Royal Shakespeare Theatre, Swan Theatre and The Other Place, Stratford-upon-Avon, *To be confirmed. Tel: 01789 295623.	**Midshires**
	4th - 9th	**West Sussex International Youth Music Festival**	Various venues in West Sussex. Tel: 0171 401 9941.	**South**
	5th - 8th	**Lancaster Easter Maritime Festival**	Various venues. Lancaster. Tel 01524 32878.	**North**
	6th	**Oxford v Cambridge Boat Race**	On the River Thames from Putney Bridge to Mortlake.	**London**
	7th	**Annual Horse Races Road Trotting**	Ballydehob, Co Cork. Tel: +353 (0)28 37191.	**Ireland**
	10th - 13th	**Burton-on-Trent Festival of Music and Drama**	Town Hall, Burton-on-Trent, Staffordshire. Tel: 01283 562973.	**Midshires**
	21st	**London Marathon**	Starts Blackheath, finishes The Mall, London. Tel: 0171 620 4117.	**London**
	24th - 28th	**Jersey Jazz Festival**	Various venues. Jersey, Channel Islands. Tel: 01534 617521.	**Islands**
	25th- 28th	**Harrogate Spring Flower Festival**	Valley Gardens, Harrogate, North Yorkshire. Tel: 01423 561049.	**North**
	25th - 5th Oct	**Pitlochry Festival Theatre Season**	Festival Theatre, Pitlochry, Tayside. Tel: 01796 473054.	**Scotland**
	26th - 28th	**Kenmare Literary Weekend**	Kenmare, Co Kerry. Tel: +353 (0)64 41650.	**Ireland**
	27th	**Rugby League Challenge Cup Final**	Wembley Stadium. Tel: 0113 262 4637.	**London**
	27th - 28th	**St George's Spring Festival**	Various venues. Salisbury, Wiltshire. Tel: 01722 434300.	**West**
	29th - 6th May	**Festival of Mime, Dance and Visual Theatre**	Brewery Arts Centre, Highgate, Kendal, Cumbria. Tel: 01539 725133.	**North**
MAY	2nd - 5th	**Mitsubishi Motors Badminton Horse Trials**	Badminton Horse Trials, Badminton, Avon. Tel: 01454 218272.	**West**
	2nd - 5th	**Cork International Choral Festival**	Various venues, Cork. Tel: +353 (0)21 308308.	**Ireland**
	2nd - 25th	**Glasgow Mayfest 1996**	Various venues. Glasgow. Tel: 0141 552 8000.	**Scotland**
	3rd - 6th	**Great Cornwall Balloon Festival**	Various venues. St Austell and Newquay, Cornwall. Tel: 01637 872211.	**West**
	3rd - 26th	**Brighton International Festival**	All aspects of the performing arts. Brighton. Tel: 01273 676926.	**South**
	4th - 6th	**Classic & Sportscar Show**	National Exhibition Centre, Birmingham. Tel: 0171 402 2555.	**Midshires**

1996 CALENDAR *of* EVENTS

	4th, 8th	**Grange Concert Season**	Victoria Hall, Main Street, Grange-over-Sands, Cumbria. Tel: 01539 734375.	**North**
	8th	**Helston Floral Dance**	Dancing in the streets to greet the spring. Cornwall. Tel: 01326 572082.	**West**
	8th - 12th	**Royal Windsor Horse Show**	Showjumping. Home Park, Windsor, Berkshire. Tel: 01753 860633.	**South**
	8th - 1st Sept	**William Morris Exhibition**	Victoria & Albert Museum, South Kensington, London. Tel: 0171 938 8500.	**London**
	9th - 12th	**Beverley Early Music Festival**	Various venues. Beverley, Humberside. Tel: 01904 658338.	**North**
	11th	**FA Cup Final**	Premier soccer competition. Wembley Stadium. Tel: 0171 262 4524.	**London**
	11th - 18th	**Solihull Festival**	Various venues. Solihull, West Midlands. Tel: 0121 704 6961.	**Midshires**
	15th - 24th Aug	**Glyndebourne Festival Opera Season**	Now set in superb new opera house. Glyndebourne.Tel: 01273 812321.	**South**
	17th - 19th	**Keswick Jazz Festival**	Keswick, Cumbria. Tel: 01900 602122.	**North**
	17th - 2nd June	**Bath International Music Festival**	Classical and contemporary music and jazz. Tel: 01225 462231.	**West**
	21st - 24th	**Chelsea Flower Show**	Major flower show. Members only on 21st and 22nd. Tel: 0171 834 4333.	**London**
	24th - 2nd June	**Hay Festival**	Literature, poetry readings and lectures in "Town of Books". Hay-on-Wye, Hereford. Tel: 01497 821299.	**Midshires**
	24th - 8th June	**English Riviera Dance Festival**	Various venues. Torquay, Devon. Tel: 01895 632143.	**West**
	25th - 26th	**Bedford River Festival**	200 river crafts, 80 floats and funfair. Great Ouse. Tel: 01234 221622.	**Midshires**
	25th - 27th	**Liverpool Show**	Wavertree Playground, Liverpool. Tel: 0151 225 6354.	**North**
	26th - 3rd June	**Beaumaris Festival**	Various venues. Beaumaris, Gwynedd. Tel: 01248 750057.	**Wales**
	27th	**Surrey County Show**	Stoke Park, Guildford, Surrey. Tel: 01483 414651.	**South**
	28th - 2nd June	**International Animation Festival**	For film enthusiasts. St David's Hall, The Hayes, Cardiff. Tel: 0171 255 1444,	**Wales**
	29th - 1st June	**Royal Bath and West of England Show**	One of Britain's oldest and largest agricultural shows. Shepton Mallet, Somerset. Tel: 01749 822200.	**West**
	30th - 2nd June	**Rochester Dickens Festival**	He lived at nearby Gad's Hill. Rochester, Kent. Tel: 01634 843666.	**South**
	30th - 2nd	**Jersey Good Food Festival**	International and traditional Jersey cuisine. Tel: 01534 500700.	**Islands**
	31st - 2nd June	**Great Garden & Countryside Festival**	Holker Hall and Gardens, Cark in Cartmel, Cumbria. Tel: 01539 558838.	**North**
	31st - 3rd June	**Queen of the Sea Festival**	Castletownbere, Beara, Co Cork. Tel: +353 (0)27 70054.	**Ireland**
JUNE	1st - 2nd	**Balloon & Vintage Car Fiesta**	In grounds of moated medieval castle. Leeds Castle, Kent. Tel: 01622 765400.	**South**
	1st - 3rd	**Guinness International Cartoon Festival**	Rathdrum, Co Wicklow. Tel: +353 (0)404 46811.	**Ireland**
	1st - 16th	**Much Wenlock Festival**	Theatre, crafts, mixed choirs and a jazz concert. Tel: 01952 727858.	**Midshires**
	5th - 6th	**Beating Retreat**	Household Division, Horse Guards Parade, London.	**London**
	6th - 12th	**Appleby Horse Fair**	Traditional fair for trading of horses. Appleby-in-Westmorland, Cumbria. Tel: 01325 362933.	**North**
	7th - 9th	**Wimborne Folk Festival**	Home to the Kings of Wessex. Tel: 01202 740792	**West**
	7th - 23rd	**Aldeburgh Festival of Music and the Arts**	Premier cultural festival of arts in England. Inspiration for Benjamin Britten. Tel: 01728 452935.	**Midshires**
	8th	**The Vodafone Derby**	World famous race, first held in 1780. Epsom, Surrey. Tel: 01372 726311.	**South**
	8th - 30th	**European Football Championships**	International soccer competition. Games in several English cities. Final at Wembley Stadium, London. Tel: 01782 741996.	**London**
	9th	**Bristol to Bournemouth Car Rally**	Starts at Bristol and finishes in Bournemouth. Tel: 01935 25597.	**West**
	9th - 18th Aug	**Royal Academy of Arts**	World's largest exhibition of contemporary art. Burlington House, Piccadilly, London. Tel: 0171 439 7438.	**London**
	10th - 16th	**Stella Artois Tennis Tournament**	Top men's tennis. Queen's Club, Fulham. Tel: 0171 225 3733.	**London**
	13th - 16th	**Blarney International 3 Day Horse Trials**	Blarney Castle Estate, Co Cork. Tel: +353 (0)21 385252.	**Ireland**
	14th - 16th	**Silloth Victorian Weekend**	Silloth Green, Criffel Street, Silloth, Cumbria. Tel: 016973 32580.	**North**
	15th	**Trooping the Colour**	Her Majesty the Queen takes the salute on her Official Birthday Parade.	**London**
	15th - 16th	**Biggin Hill International Air Fair**	Biggin Hill Airport, Kent. Tel: 01959 572277.	**South**
	15th - 16th	**Middle Wallop Air Show**	Army Air Corps Centre, Middle Wallop, Hampshire. Tel: 01264 384461.	**South**
	15th - 22nd	**Eastbourne International Ladies Tennis Championship**	Top women players on grass. Eastbourne, E. Sussex. Tel: 01323 415442.	**South**
	16th	**Singlehanded Transatlantic Race**	Starts Plymouth, Devon and finishes Rhode Island, USA. Tel: 01752 660077.	**West**
	18th - 21st	**Royal Ascot**	Horse racing and high fashion. Ascot, Berkshire. Tel: 01344 22211.	**South**
	19th - 20th	**Lincoln Show**	Lincolnshire Showground, Grange-de-Lings, Lincoln. Tel: 01522 524240.	**Midshires**
	20th - 23rd	**Royal Highland Show**	Ingliston, Newbridge, Midlothian. Tel: 0131 333 2444.	**Scotland**
	21st - 22nd	**Curtis Cup**	Ladies golf international. Killarney, Co Kerry. Tel: +353 (0)1 269 4111.	**Ireland**

highland games . . . book fairs . . . flower shows . . . arts & crafts exhibitions . . . parades & tattoos . . . country fairs . . .

CALENDAR of EVENTS 1996

	21st - 23rd	**Gwyl Ifan Festival**	The largest Welsh folk dancing festival. Tel: 01222 563989.	**Wales**
	21st - 23rd	**Clans Gathering**	Hosted by the O'Sullivan Bere Clan. Castletown. Tel: 27 70054.	**Ireland**
	21st - 6th July	**Bradford Festival**	Various venues. Bradford, West Yorkshire. Tel: 01274 309199.	**North**
	21st - 7th July	**Swanage Festival of the Arts**	Various venues. Swanage, Dorset. Tel: 01929 426310.	**West**
	22nd - 7th July	**Ludlow Festival**	Centred on the Norman Castle. Ludlow, Shropshire. Tel: 01584 872150.	**Midshires**
	24th - 7th July	**Wimbledon Tennis Championships**	All England Lawn Tennis & Croquet Club. Tel: 0181 946 2244.	**London**
	26th - 27th	**Royal Norfolk Show**	The Showground, Dereham Road, Norwich. Tel: 01603 748931.	**Midshires**
	28th - 30th	**Petworth Park Open Air Concerts**	Petworth Park, West Sussex. Tel: 01372 453401.	**South**
	28th - 30th	**Irish Derby Meeting**	Curragh Racecourse, Kildare. Tel: +353 (0)1 2892888.	**Ireland**
	28th - 7th July	**Glasgow International Jazz Festival**	One of Europe's biggest celebrations of jazz. Tel: 0141 552 3552.	**Scotland**
	29th	**Round the Island Yacht Race**	Starts Cowes, Isle of Wight. Tel: 01983 296621.	**Islands**
	29th - 30th	**National Music Day**	Various venues throughout England. Tel: 0171 491 0044.	**Whole of Britain**
	29th & 6th July	**Open Air Concerts**	Leeds Castle, near Maidstone, Kent. Tel: 01622 765400.	**South**
	30th - 7th July	**Alnwick Medieval Fair**	Stocks and ducking. Alnwick, Northumberland. Tel: 01665 605004.	**North**
	30th - 16th July	**Chichester Festivities**	Concerts, jazz and street entertainments. Tel: 01243 785718.	**South**
JULY	1st - 4th	**The Royal Show**	Britain's premier agricultural show, with over 175,000 visitors. Stoneleigh Coventry. Tel: 01203 696969.	**Midshires**
	3rd - 7th	**Henley Royal Regatta**	International rowing. Oxfordshire. Tel: 01491 572153.	**South**
	4th - 7th	**Irish Open Championship**	Golf at Portmarnock, Co Dublin. Tel: +353 (0)1 2694111.	**Ireland**
	5th - 14th	**York Early Music Festival**	Music ranging from Yorkshire's medieval abbeys to the Georgian splendour of the Assembly Rooms. Various venues in York. Tel: 01904 658338.	**North**
	7th - 10th	**Bernard Shaw Summer School**	Dublin. Tel: 1 4784788.	**Ireland**
	9th - 14th	**Hampton Court Palace Flower Show**	East Molesey, Surrey. Tel: 0171 834 4333.	**London**
	9th - 14th	**Llangollen International Eisteddfod**	Over thirty nationalities in music and dance competitions. Clwyd. Tel: 01978 860236.	**Wales**
	10th - 13th	**Fête Champêtre**	Open-air festivities at Claremont Landscape Garden, Old Portsmouth Road, Esher, Surrey. Tel: 01372 453401.	**South**
	10th - 14th	**Buxton Well Dressing Festival and Carnival**	Ancient custom of decorating wells with flowers. Buxton, Derbyshire. Tel 01298 23114	**Midshires**
	11th - 20th	**Welsh Proms '96**	St David's Hall, The Hayes, Cardiff. Tel: 01222 878444.	**Wales**
	12th - 14th	**British Grand Prix, Silverstone**	Formula One World Championship event. Tel: 01327 857271.	**Midshires**
	13th	**Benson and Hedges Cup Final**	Cricket at Lord's, St John's Wood. Tel: 0171 289 8979.	**London**
	15th - 20th	**Jersey Floral Festival**	Various venues, St Helier, Jersey. Tel: 01534 500700.	**Islands**
	17th - 28th	**Galway Arts Festival**	Galway. Tel: +353 (0) 91 583800.	**Ireland**
	18th - 21st	**The Open Championship**	Principal event in the golfing world calendar. Royal Lytham and St Anne's Club, Royal Lytham & St Anne's, Lancashire. Tel: 01253 724106.	**North**
	19th - 14th Sept	**Henry Wood Promenade Concerts "The Proms"**	Royal Albert Hall, Kensington Gore, Tel: 0171 765 4296.	**London**
	2nd - 25th	**Royal Welsh Show**	Llanelwedd, Builth Wells, Powys. Tel: 01982 553683.	**Wales**
	26th - 28th	**Pickering Traction Engine Rally**	The Showfield, Malton Road, Pickering, North Yorkshire. Tel: 01751 473780.	**North**
	30th - 3rd Aug	**Glorious Goodwood**	Goodwood Racecourse, Tel: 01243 774107.	**South**
AUGUST	2nd - 9th	**Sidmouth Festival of Folk Arts, Music and Dance.**	Participants from all over the world. Devon. Tel: 01296 393293.	**West**
	2nd - 24th	**Edinburgh Military Tattoo**	Pageantry on the ramparts of Edinburgh Castle. Tel: 0131 225 1188.	**Scotland**
	3rd - 10th	**Cowes Week**	All classes of yacht racing. Tel 01983 295744.	**Islands**
	3rd - 10th	**Eisteddfod Genedlaethol Frenhinol**	Music, drama, poetry, arts and crafts. Llandeilo, Dyfed	**Wales**
	4th - 18th	**Buxton Gilbert and Sullivan Festival**	Opera House, Water Street, Buxton, Derbyshire. Tel: 01422 359161.	**Midshires**
	8th	**Battle of Flowers**	Jersey's day of floral floats. St Helier, Jersey. Tel: 01534 500700.	**Islands**
	10th - 12th	**Puck Fair**	County Kerry. Tel: +353 (0)66 61595.	**Ireland**
	10th - 25th	**Edinburgh Film Festival**	Documentaries, special events and lectures. Tel: 0131 228 4051.	**Scotland**
	13th - 2nd Sept	**Edinburgh International Festival**	World's largest festival of the arts. Tel: 0131 226 4001. Festival Fringe Society, tel: 226 5257.	**Scotland**
	17th - 24th	**Three Choirs Festival**	Europe's oldest music festival. Worcester Cathedral. Tel: 01905 616211.	**Midshires**
	17th - 25th Aug	**Llandrindod Wells Victorian Festival**	The clocks turn back to the Victorian age. Tel 01597 823441.	**Wales**
	22nd - 24th	**Southport Flower Show 96**	Ten acres packed to perfection with floral displays and landscape gardens. Tel: 01704 547147.	**North**

	23rd - 27th	**Beatles Festival**	Cavern Club, Liverpool. Tel: 0151 236 9091	**North**
	23rd - 29th	**Rose of Tralee Festival**	"To choose the most beautiful of the most beautiful." Tel: +353 (0)66 21322.	**Ireland**
	25th	**Shark Safari**	Mullaghmore Harbour, Co Sligo. Tel: +353 (0)71 66267.	**Ireland**
	25th - 26th	**Notting Hill Carnival**	Stalls, steel bands, dance and processions. Tel: 0181 964 0544.	**London**
	26th - 27th	**Oul' Lammas Fair**	Ireland's oldest traditional fair. Charter 1606. Try a piece of "yellow man" toffee, or dulse seaweed. Tel: +44 (0)1265 762024.	**Ireland**
	29th - 31st	**Dartmouth Royal Regatta**	West of England Rowing Championships, sailing and many other events. Devon. Tel: 01803 832435.	**West**
	30th - 5th Nov	**Blackpool Illuminations**	A 5-mile spectacular on the Promenade! Tel: 01253 25212.	**North**
	31st - 1st Sept	**Chatsworth Country Fair**	Country sports in the grounds of this famous house. Bakewell, Derbyshire. Tel: 01328 830367.	**Midshires**
SEPTEMBER	7th	**Braemar Royal Highland Gathering**	Cabers, Scottish dancing, bagpipes - attended by the Royal Family. Tel: 01339 755377.	**Scotland**
	7th	**National Westminster Final**	Lord's Cricket Ground, St John's Wood. Tel: 0171 289 8979.	**London**
	8th	**Historic Vehicle Cavalcade**	Fabulous old machines make their way from Helmshore to Townsley Hall, Helmshore, Rossendale, Lancashire. Tel: 01706 226459.	**North**
	13th - 15th	**Great Autumn Flower Show**	Superb autumnal displays. Great Yorkshire Showground, Harrogate, North Yorkshire. Tel: 01423 561049.	**North**
	14th - 22nd	**Southampton International Boat Show**	Largest of its kind in Europe. Tel: 01784 473377.	**South**
	15th	**All Ireland Football Final**	Croke Park, Dublin. Tel: +353 (0)1 363222.	**Ireland**
	18th - 19th	**Dairy Farming Event**	The premier show in Europe for milk producers. Stoneleigh. Nr Coventry, Warwickshire. Tel: 0171 627 2111.	**Midshires**
	19th - 22nd	**Blenheim International Horse Trials**	Lavish equestrian occasion at Blenheim Palace. Woodstock, Oxfordshire Tel: 01993 813335.	**Midshires**
	21st	**Egremont Crab Fair**	Street racing, wrestling, gurning, greasy pole races. Egremont, Cumbria Tel: 01946 821554.	**North**
	21st - 6th Oct	**Waterford Light Opera Festival**	Waterford City. Tel: +353 (0) 51 75437.	**Ireland**
	26th - 29th	**Galway Oyster Festival**	Gastronomic gallivanting around Galway. Tel: +353 (0)91 527282.	**Ireland**
	26th - 5th Oct	**Soho Jazz Festival**	Soho, London. Tel: 0171 437 6437.	**London**
OCTOBER	Early October	**Cork Film Festival**	8-day festival. Tel: +353 (0)21 271711.	**Ireland**
	4th - 6th	**Nottingham Goose Fair**	One of Britain's oldest traditional fairs. Tel: 0115 941 7324.	**Midshires**
	3rd - 6th	**Kinsale Gourmet Festival**	Good Food in abundance. Tel: +353 (0)21 774026.	**Ireland**
	7th - 19th	**Dublin Theatre Festival**	Tel: +353 (0)1 6778439.	**Ireland**
	10th - 20th	**Norwich & Norfolk Festival**	"Ancient World" events, including music and drama. Tel: 01603 614921.	**Midshires**
	11th - 20th	**Daily Telegraph Cheltenham Festival of Literature**	Book displays, play readings and lectures by well-known literary figures. Tel: 01242 521621.	**Midshires**
	17th - 3rd Nov	**Wexford Opera Festival**	Theatre Royal, High Street, Wexford. Tel: +353 (0)53 22144.	**Ireland**
	19th - 27th	**British International Motor Show**	National Exhibition Centre, Birmingham. Tel: 0171 235 7000.	**Midshires**
	25th - 28th	**Guinness Cork Jazz Festival**	Tel: +353 (0)1 6765091.	**Ireland**
	29th - 31st	**Ulster Antiques & Fine Arts Fair**	International collectors' fair. Culloden Hotel, Belfast.	**Ireland**
NOVEMBER	1st - 30th	**Cornwall Dance Festival**	Various venues throughout Cornwall. Tel: 01726 64517.	**West**
	3rd	**London to Brighton Veteran Car Run**	From London's Hyde Park to Brighton. Tel: 01753 681736.	**London & South**
	9th - 27th	**Belfast Festival at Queen's**	International festival of drama, opera and music. Tel: 01232 667687.	**Ireland**
	10th	**Remembrance Day**	Service, parade and wreath-laying ceremony by HM The Queen	**London**
	13th	**Lord Mayor's Show**	Procession from the Guildhall in the City to the Royal Courts of Justice.	**London**
	20th - 1st Dec	**Huddersfield Contemporary Music Festival.**	Renowned festival of dance, film, music and theatre. Tel: 01484 425082.	**North**
	24th - 27th	**Royal Smithfield Show**	Major livestock and farm equipment show. Earls Court Tel: 0171 370 8226.	**London**
DECEMBER	3rd	**Royal Welsh Agricultural Winter Fair**	Sale of livestock, Welsh foods and crafts. Tel: 01982 553683.	**Wales**
	26th	**King George VI Chase**	National Hunt Christmas Festival. Kempton Park. Tel: 01932 782292.	**South**
	31st	**Allendale Baal Festival**	Villagers parade in costume with burning tar barrels on their heads.	**North**

"I'm a creature of impulse. I like to make quick decisions and the American Express Card enables me to do that. It gives me freedom and security"

Glenda Bailey, editor Marie Claire

AMERICAN EXPRESS

Quality financial & travel services

CHARGE CARD OPTIONS

The American Express Card

The American Express Gold Card

The American Express Platinum Card

The American Express Corporate Card

JUST THE FACTS . . .

1850 - Established as an express freight company during US Civil War

1875 - Created first private pension plan in US

1882 - The American Express Money Order was created

1891 - Invented the first Travellers Cheque

1958 - Launched the American Express Card in US

1963 - Launched the American Express Card in UK

INFORMATION

World's largest business travel agent

3,200 travel service and representative office

37,000,000,000 American Express cards in use worldwide

UK CARD SERVICES

24 hr customer service	*01273 696933*
Global Assist	*0181 469 3742*
Travel Line	*0171 930 3121*
Travel Insurance	*0171 930 3121*
Membership Rewards	*01273 863863*
Travellers Cheque Refunds	*0800 521313*
Emergency Help & Advice	*01273 697272*

BECOMING A CARDMEMBER

American Express Cardmembership
0800 700 444

American Express Credit Card
0800 700 717

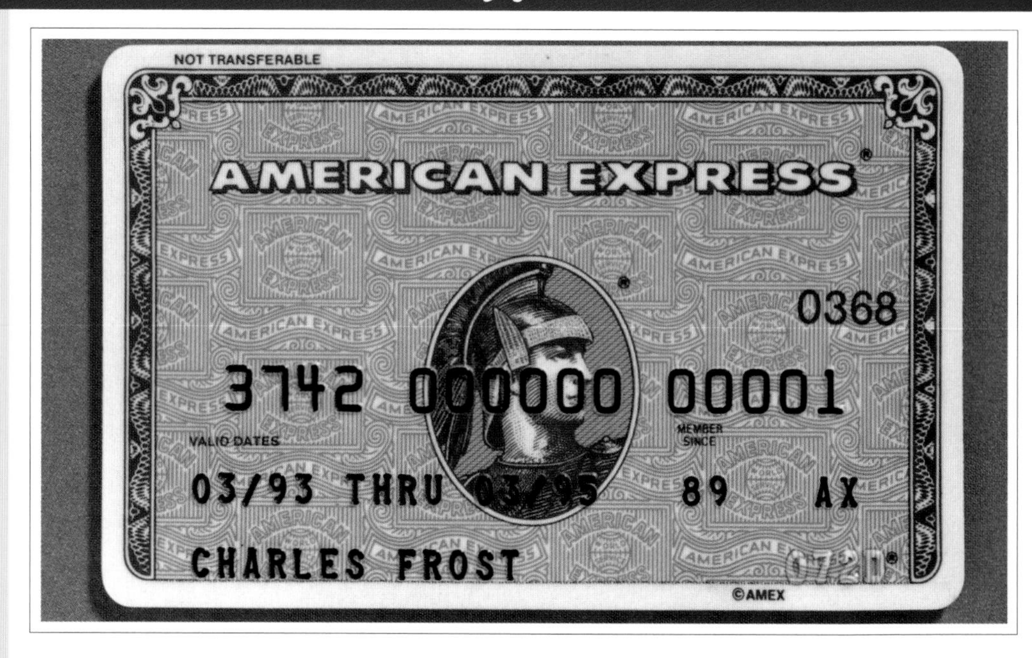

American Express – the smart choice wherever you are in the world

American Express is known throughout the world for offering outstanding quality and high levels of customer service. As a leading global company specialising in travel and financial services, the company has always been one step ahead offering its customers useful and exciting new products and services.

From its beginnings as an express freight company during the US Civil War, American Express today is the world's largest business travel agent and has a network of 3,200 travel service and representative offices, providing expert travel advice and support for Cardmembers.

Today, American Express is probably best known for its charge card, launched in the US in 1958 and in the UK in 1963. There are now some 37 million American Express Cards in use worldwide and American Express offers a range of cards ideal for both business and personal spending.

The American Express Card and the American Express Corporate Card have no pre-set spending limit and are ideal for those who want flexibility, as well as the control that payment in full every month brings.

American Express Cardmembers have access to an emergency card replacement service with Cards normally being replaced within 24 hours in the UK or through any American Express travel service throughout the world. We are proud to have American Express as our 'Best Loved' Financial and Travel Services Company for 1996.

LOCATIONS

American Express Cards are accepted in around 3.6 million establishments and in 160 countries around the world.

Five ways

to know if you're staying at an excellent establishment

Ever wonder why some hotels seem to know exactly who you are and what you want, while others don't have a clue?

The answer lies in exactly how the establishment decides to service you. Here are some ways to determine whether you are getting excellent value for your money:

1 They hold the reservation

even if you arrive later than expected. All you need to do is phone ahead to confirm your booking. In fact, if you book your reservation with the American Express Card, you can always expect a warm welcome even in the evening.

2 Your suite or room is always a comforting surprise.

Whether you're travelling for business or for leisure, your room should feel like a home away from home. The ambience must be appealing and comfortable, with literature on hand to help guide you in getting the service you need.

3 They care about your total experience,

including any special requests you may have. Especially important are great dining experiences - either at the hotel or outside. They should be able to help you with both.

4 The staff can solve all of your problems,

24 hours a day. At a great establishment, the staff are knowledgeable enough to help you with things like getting around town easily, finding a good place to do some shopping, or doing the right thing in an emergency. An excellent establishment will always leverage their prominent role in their community on your behalf, with resolve to "leave no stone unturned" in helping you.

5 Of course, they accept the American Express Card.

An excellent hotel will see the Card as a natural extension of their own great service. Connecting you to the largest travel network in the world (with over 1,700 travel service offices globally), they know that it makes them worthy of the level of service and security that you deserve. Not to mention the fact that you can earn Membership Rewards Points on virtually every purchase you make on the Card,* which can earn you access to free flights and hotel nights - perhaps even at the hotel you're choosing right now!

excluding Travellers Cheques

Scotland

The late 14th century Caerlaverock Castle, south of Dumfries, once the stronghold of the Maxwells, a powerful border family in the 15th century. Robert Burns lived in Dumfries until his death in 1796 and it was here that he wrote 'Auld Lang Syne' and 'Ye Banks and Braes of Bonnie Doon'.

Heritage sites

The following heritage sites can be found on the map overleaf. The key numbers show where they are located.

ARGYLL & BUTE & ARRAN

Dunstaffnage Castle and Chapel	1
Rothesay Castle	2

BORDERS

Jedburgh Abbey	3
Melrose Abbey	4

DUMFRIES & GALLOWAY

Caerlaverock Castle	5
Cardoness Castle	6
Glenluce Abbey	7
New Abbey Corn Mill	8
Sweetheart Abbey	9
Whithorn Priory	10

FIFE & CENTRAL

Aberdour Castle	11
Castle Campbell	12
Inchcolm Abbey	13
Inchmahome Priory	14
St Andrews Cathedral	15
Stirling Castle	16

GRAMPIAN

Balvenie Castle	17
Dallas Dhu Distillery	18
Elgin Cathedral	19
Tolquhon Castle	20

HIGHLANDS & WESTERN ISLES

Fort George	21
Urquhart Castle	22

LOTHIAN

Cairnpapple Hill	23
Edinburgh Castle	24
Linlithgow Palace	25

SOUTH STRATHCLYDE

Bothwell Castle	26
Dumbarton Castle	27

TAYSIDE

Arbroath Castle	28
Claypotts Castle	29
Lochleven Castle	30

COLOUR KEY TO HOTEL SYMBOLS

The rosettes on the map indicate the location of each hotel; the numbers within show the page number of the hotel. The colour of the rosette is a rough guide to the price of a twin or double room (see colour key below).

- Double room: up to £75 per night
- Double room: £76 - £125 per night
- Double room: £126 - £175 per night
- Double room: from £176+ per night

PAGE	HOTEL
18	Achray House Hotel
19	Allt-Chaorain
20	Ardanaiseig
21	Arisaig House
22	Atholl Hotel
23	Auchen Castle Hotel
24	Balbirnie House
25	Balgonie Country House
26	Ballathie House Hotel
27	Baron's Craig Hotel
28	Braemar Lodge
29	Bunchrew House Hotel
30	Channings
31	Chapeltoun House Hotel
32	Collin House
33	Corsemalzie
34	Coul House Hotel
35	Craigellachie
36	Cringletie House Hotel
37	Cromlix House
38	Cross, The
39	Culdearn House
40	Culloden House Hotel
41	Dalmunzie House
42	Darroch Learg
43	Devonshire Hotel, The
44	Dornoch Castle
45	Dunain Park Hotel
46	Enmore Hotel
47	Farleyer House
48	Fernhill Hotel

KEY

- Motorways
- 'A' Roads
- Railways
- Airports
- National Boundaries
- County Boundaries
- Heritage Sites
- English Heritage Sites
- Ferry Routes
- Urban Areas
- National Parks and Areas of Outstanding Natural Beauty

Each grid square equals 30 miles(approx. 50 km)

0 Miles 30
0 Kilometres 50

ORKNEY ISLANDS
From Lerwick
Balfour 451 Shapinsay
Stromness Kirkwall
Hoy
DUNNET HEAD
CAPE WRATH
Scrabster John O' Groats
Durness Melvich Thurso Castletown
Bettyhill Halkirk
Tongue Wick
Laxford Bridge
Stornoway Stornoway
Port of Ness
Kylestrome Altnaharra Kinbrace Latheron
Unapool
WESTERN ISLES
Isle of Lewis
Lochinver
Achiltibuie 86
Helmsdale
Lairg 83 Brora
Tarbert Golspie
Ullapool 44 Dornoch
Harris Scalpay
Bonar Bridge
Rodel
TARBETT NESS
Portmahomack
HIGHLANDS Tain
Gairloch
Invergordon
Moray Firth
Lossiemouth
Cullen Macduff Fraserburgh
Uig 464
Kinlochewe Achnasheen Dingwall Cromarty 71 19
Torridon 68 Contin by Strathpeffer 34 Fortrose 21 51 Nairn Elgin Banff
89 Shieldaig Muir of Ord Inverness 63 Forres 18 Keith
Dunvegan Beauly 29 Bunchrew 40 35 Craigellachie Huntly Mintlaw Peterhead
Portree 45 INVERNESS Charlestown of Aberlour 17 Dufftown
Raasay Lochcarron GRAMPIAN
Stromeferry 81 Grantown-on-Spey 39 72 Glenlivet 66 Insch 20 Ellon 90
Isle of Skye Sconser Kyle of Lochalsh Drummnadrochit 22 Rhynie Oldmeldrum Newburgh
Broadford Kyleakin Carrbridge Boat of Garten Tomintoul 59 Mossat
Inner Hebrides Kinloch 457 Shiel Bridge Invermoriston Aviemore Kildrummy Alford Dyce
Elgol 454 Eilean Iarmain Fort Augustus Aberdeen 22
Canna Ardvasar ABERDEEN
Invergarry 38 Kingussie 42 Ballater Aboyne Peterculter NORTH
Rhum Mallaig Braemar 55 25 53 Banchory
Arisaig 76 21 SCOTLAND 28 Muchalls 74 SEA
Eigg Dalwhinnie Stonehaven
From Lerwick

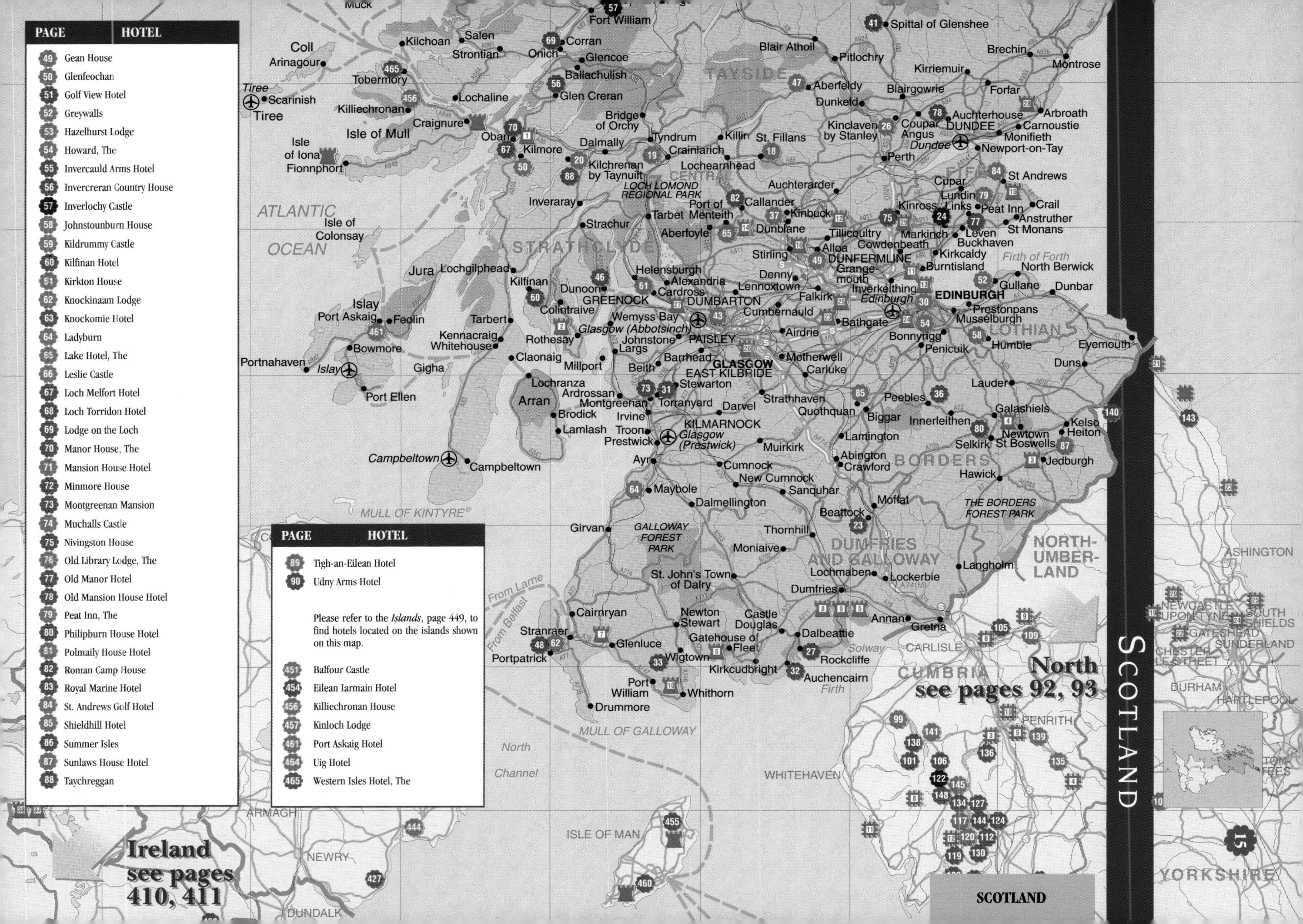

North see pages 92, 93

Ireland see pages 410, 411

PAGE	HOTEL
49	Gean House
50	Glenfeochan
51	Golf View Hotel
52	Greywalls
53	Hazelhurst Lodge
54	Howard, The
55	Invercauld Arms Hotel
56	Invercreran Country House
57	Inverlochy Castle
58	Johnstounburn House
59	Kildrummy Castle
60	Kilfinan Hotel
61	Kirkton House
62	Knockinaam Lodge
63	Knockomie Hotel
64	Ladyburn
65	Lake Hotel, The
66	Leslie Castle
67	Loch Melfort Hotel
68	Loch Torridon Hotel
69	Lodge on the Loch
70	Manor House, The
71	Mansion House Hotel
72	Minmore House
73	Montgreenan Mansion
74	Muchalls Castle
75	Nivingston House
76	Old Library Lodge, The
77	Old Manor Hotel
78	Old Mansion House Hotel
79	Peat Inn, The
80	Philipburn House Hotel
81	Polmaily House Hotel
82	Roman Camp House
83	Royal Marine Hotel
84	St. Andrews Golf Hotel
85	Shieldhill Hotel
86	Summer Isles
87	Sunlaws House Hotel
88	Taychreggan

PAGE	HOTEL
89	Tigh-an-Eilean Hotel
90	Udny Arms Hotel

Please refer to the *Islands*, page 449, to find hotels located on the islands shown on this map.

PAGE	HOTEL
451	Balfour Castle
454	Eilean Iarmain Hotel
456	Killiechronan House
457	Kinloch Lodge
461	Port Askaig Hotel
464	Uig Hotel
465	Western Isles Hotel, The

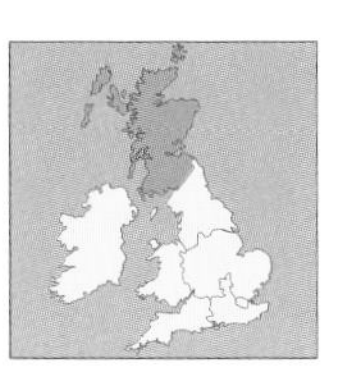

Edinburgh Castle, built on the site of an Iron Age fort, frequently changed hands between the English and the Scots. Today, it is the scene of the thrilling Edinburgh Tattoo.

COUNTIES

Borders

Central

Dumfries & Galloway

Fife

Grampian

Highland

Lothian

Strathclyde

Tayside

Scotland is Europe's last great natural environment for leisure and adventure, and enjoyment of unspoiled, majestic scenery. It is a land enriched by nature and by man, offering extraordinary experiences of discovery. In the Highlands are grand, rugged mountains, moors purple with heather, shimmering lochs and tumbling rivers. The Border country has gentle hills and rich farmland. In the west are the tranquil hills and forests of Dumfries and Galloway, and a magic coastline winding up to Ayrshire and to the Firth of Clyde, Oban and Argyll. Offshore is the lure of the Orkneys, the Shetlands and Bonnie Prince Charlie's Skye.

Scotland has over 600 castles, hundreds of ancient kirks, abbeys, cathedrals and palaces, many clustered around the great cities of Edinburgh, Glasgow, Aberdeen and Dundee. Scotland is a land of names that fire the world's imagination: Bonnie Prince Charlie, Flora Macdonald, Annie Laurie, Robert the Bruce, Robbie Burns and Sir Walter Scott. Above all, Scotland values ideas and invention; the engineer Thomas Telford devoted 44 years to its Caledonian Canal. The combination between pure natural resources and dedicated skills are seen in the wools and tweeds, all the way from the crofters' villages in the Highlands to the Woollen Trail on the Borders. At mealtimes, you can enjoy fine meat and game and local produce, cooked with devotion and care. Don't miss your breakfast, the porridge and kippers are fabulous!

The Scots are a proud people, ever eager to improve the quality of your visit by blending the best of ancient and modern. Highland games, such as the Royal Highland Gathering at Braemar (Sept) trace their origins in the mists of time. Yet the world-renowned Edinburgh Festival (Sept/Oct), originated in 1947. An essential element in Scotland's pride is the way they welcome visitors as friends, and help you enjoy a marvellous ancient and modern country in a unique natural frame.

Castles, Stately Homes, Historic Houses

Balmoral Castle 8 m W of Ballater. The name is the Gaelic word for "majestic dwelling". Holiday home of the Royal Family.

Brodick Castle, Isle of Arran. Once a Viking fortress, parts date from 13th century. Ancient seat of the Dukes of Hamilton.

Brodie Castle, W of Forres. The Brodies were endowed with this land in 1160. Castle built on Z plan in 16th c.

Cawdor Castle, Old central tower of 1372, fortified 1454. Family home for over 600 years. Formal garden.

Culzean Castle, Built by Robert Adam 1772-92. Links with Kennedy family go back to 14th c. Oval Staircase. Eisenhower Room.

Dunrobin Castle, N of Golspie. Built about 1275 by Robert of Sutherland. Great park overlooking the sea.

Dunvegan Castle, Isle of Skye. Seat of the Clan MacLeod for 700 years.

Edinburgh Castle, On Castle Rock at top of Royal Mile. Chapel c1100. Massive Mons Meg canon. Military Tattoo Aug/Sep.

Falkland Palace, Built 1501-1541, on site of 12th century palace. Country home of the Stewart kings.

Fyvie Castle, Its five towers are named after five different families, and together they enshrine five centuries of Scottish history.

Glamis Castle, SW of Forfar. 14th c, rebuilt in 17th c French chateau style. Birthplace of Queen Mother and Princess Margaret.

Manderston, E of Duns. A fine Edwardian country house, with a unique silver staircase.

Museums, Galleries & Attractions

Provost Skene's Home, Guestrow, Aberdeen. A fine museum in a 16th c house.

Burns Cottage & Museum, Alloway, S of Ayr. Robert Burns born here 25 Jan 1759. Relics, songs and poetry manuscripts.

John Paul Jones Birthplace Museum, Arbigland, Kirkbean. Father of the United States Navy.

David Livingstone Centre, Blantyre, NW of Hamilton. 18th c mill tenements where the missionary/explorer was born in 1813.

Culross, nr Dunfermline. A small town built in the 16th and 17th century which has changed little since then.

Andrew Carnegie Birth-place Museum, Dunfermline. The weaver's son won a fortune in America and gave $350 million to benefit mankind.

National Gallery of Scotland, Princes St, Edinburgh.

Royal Scottish Museum, Edinburgh. Britain's most comprehensive museum under one roof.

TOURIST OFFICE INFORMATION

Further information about these areas will be gladly supplied by:

The Scottish Tourist Board,
23 Ravelston Terrace,
Edinburgh EH4 3EU
***Telephone*:** 0131 332 2433

For international offices, please turn to page 480

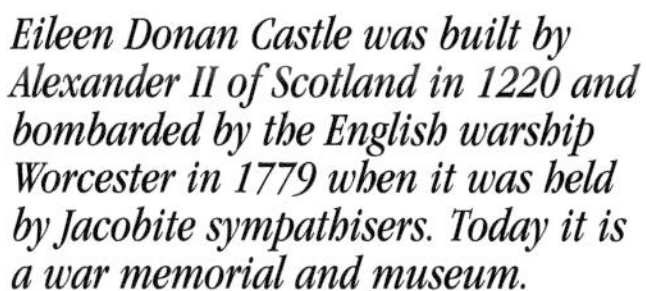

Eileen Donan Castle was built by Alexander II of Scotland in 1220 and bombarded by the English warship Worcester in 1779 when it was held by Jacobite sympathisers. Today it is a war memorial and museum.

Glasgow Art Gallery & Museum, Kelvingrove. Rich collection of Scottish, French and Dutch paintings.

Churches, Cathedrals, Abbeys

St Machar's Cathedral, Aberdeen. 14th c granite building with painted wooden heraldic ceiling dated 1520.

Dornoch Cathedral. Founded in 1224 by Archdeacon of Moray. The fine 13th c stonework is still to be admired.

Dunkeld Cathedral. Refounded in the early 12th century on an ancient ecclesiastical site beside the Tay.

St Giles's Cathedral, Edinburgh. The High Kirk, built in 14th and 15th centuries. Thistle Chapel for Knights of the Thistle.

Elgin Cathedral. The Lantern of the North. Burnt by the Wolf of Badenoch in 1390, but choir and much fine 13th c work survive.

Glasgow Cathedral. Built by St Mungo in AD 543. Rebuilt in 12th century, this is the most complete Gothic medieval church in south Scotland.

Jedburgh Abbey. This great Border Abbey was founded in about 1118. Burnt by Earl of Surrey in 1523, but splendidly restored.

Earl Patrick's and Bishop's Palaces, Kirkwall. Built in 1607, Scotland's supreme example of Renaissance architecture.

Gardens

Hazlehead Park, Aberdeen. Ornamental gardens, maze, nature trail, zoo.

Castle Kennedy Gardens, 3m E of Stranraer. Interesting walks between two historic castles, beautiful views. Disabled welcome.

Linn Park, Glasgow. On the banks of White Park Water. Nature trail and children's zoo.

Glenmore Forest Park. E of Aviemore. 5,000 acres of pine and spruce on slopes of Cairngorms, Loch Morlich in centre of park.

Sport & Outdoors

Angling. Highland lochs and rivers teem with salmon and trout.

Barras Market, Glasgow. Over 100 years old, now with more than 800 stalls, open each weekend.

Glencoe, S of Fort William. This fine forest glen was the scene of Massacre of Glencoe, 1692.

Golf. St Andrews, Fife. The Royal and Ancient. Open to visiting players. Museum. The Old Course dates from the 15th c.

Golf. Carnoustie, Dundee. Visitors are welcome on the Championship course. The same is true on most of Scotland's other great courses.

Motor Racing. The Jim Clark Room, Newton Street, Duns, Berwickshire. Trophies and memorabilia. Opened 1993. Easter - late Oct.

Loch Ness, SW of Inverness. Britain's largest freshwater lake, up to 700 ft deep.

Malt Whisky Trail. Visit distilleries such as Glenlivet, Glenfarclas and Glen Grant in the Highland Grampians.

Skiing. The Cairngorms has the modern Aviemore Centre, Britain's highest restaurant and skiing over 4,000 ft.

Castle Stalker, by Port Appin on loch Linnhe, was built by Duncan Stuart in the 13th century on the proceeds of of arrears of rent owed by the McLeans of te Isle of Mull. It was built for his kinsman, King James IV of Scotland. Ownership changed many times over the centuries as a result of feudal clashes between the Stuarts and the Campbells. The last time was in 1908 when it bought into the ownership of the Stuart family.

"The hotel competes with the scenery – both are superb; to return is a must"

Les & Barbara Owen, Rugby

ACHRAY HOUSE HOTEL

Lochside country house

Loch Earn, St Fillans, Perthshire PH6 2NF

Telephone 01764 685231
Fax 01764 685320

PROPRIETORS
Tony and Jane Ross

ROOM RATES

Single occupancy	*£38*
8 Doubles/Twins	*£50 - £65*
1 Family suite	*£50 - £65*

Includes full breakfast and VAT

CHARGE/CREDIT CARDS

• MC • VI

ACCOLADES
S.T.B. Highly Commended
A.A. ★★ 71%
Taste of Scotland

FACILITIES
Garden, fishing, watersports
Golf, deer stalking and grouse shooting nearby

RESTRICTIONS
Closed Nov-Feb inclusive
No pets

ATTRACTIONS
Drummond Gardens, Scone Palace, Blair, Glamis and Stirling Castles, Glenturret Distillery

AFFILIATIONS
Independent

NEAREST
MAJOR CITY:
Glasgow - 55 miles/1¼ hrs

MAJOR AIRPORT:
Edinburgh - 58 miles/1 hr 20 mins
Glasgow - 63 miles/1¼ hrs

RAILWAY STATION:
Perth - 30 miles/40 mins
Gleneagles - 21 miles/30 mins
Stirling - 30 miles/40 mins

RESERVATIONS
Direct with hotel

ACCESS CODES
Not applicable

The height of home cooking in an idyllic Highland Loch setting

Set in the stunning scenery of the southern central Highlands and overlooking Loch Earn, Achray House Hotel is the ideal setting for a relaxing holiday away from it all. There is no shortage of things to see and do: the hotel's own foreshore and jetty provides access to sailing, windsurfing and trout fishing; there are 14 golf courses within 30 minutes drive; walking in the fresh air of this area of outstanding beauty is nothing short of exhilarating.

The food at Achray House is also a rare delight: the variety offered by the à la carte and table d'hôte menus has attracted good food awards from many leading organisations. It is always fresh and the portions generous, so, in terms of value for money, almost unbeatable. But the pride of Achray is its desserts – whisky syllabubs, Ecclefechan tart and many more – all of which defy description. And after dinner a choice of forty malt whiskies in the bar.

Most of the bedrooms have a loch view and are all prettily decorated and furnished entirely with your comfort in mind. The style is traditional with all the modern amenities: television, direct-dial telephone and an ever ready tray for tea and coffee.

A stay at Achray House with its vast array of activities is a great way to spend and learn about Scotland.

LOCATION

Achray House is situated off the A85 in the village of St Fillans beside Loch Earn, 30 miles west of Perth and 30 miles north of Stirling. A detailed route plan from your starting point can be provided.

“ The perfect Scottish inn – the perfect Scottish host ”

Helen Wade, Massachusetts

Country home

ALLT-CHAORAIN HOUSE HOTEL

Welcome to spectacular Highland scenery and home cooking

Allt-Chaorain House is a small hotel affording guests the amenities, comfort and atmosphere of a private home. “Welcome to my Home” is their motto. Everything possible is done to help you enjoy your stay. The lounge has a log fire burning throughout the year, a trust bar, and an adjoining sunroom which offers one of the most spectacular views of the Highlands, with Ben More dominating the landscape.

The house has eight comfortable bedrooms, each with private facilities, remote control TV, radio, tea and coffee-making facilities, electric blankets, hairdryer, and central heating.

The hotel is a member of “Taste of Scotland” and is proud of its reputation for home-cooked food made from fresh local produce. The menu is discussed with the guests, whether it be a full Scottish breakfast or a traditional evening meal. The wood-panelled dining room seats six people to a table, so it is easy and natural for guests to exchange their experiences with others who have been fishing for trout and salmon in the numerous lochs and rivers, or walking on magnificent mountains such as Ben Lawers, Ben More and Ben Lui. Boats are available for hire nearby, and there are four fine golf courses in the neighbourhood.

Allt-Chaorain is the perfect touring centre from which to visit the towns of Oban, Fort William, Pitlochry and Crieff, the castles of Inverary, Downe, Stirling, Blair and Kilchurn, and outstanding scenic beauty and history that lies on the doorstep such as Glencoe, Glen Lyon, Loch Lomond, Loch Awe and the Trossachs.

LOCATION

Situated 500 yards to the left of the A82 from Crianlarich to Tyndrum, 8 miles north of Loch Lomond.

Crianlarich, Perthshire FK20 8RU

Telephone 01838 300283
Fax 01838 300238

SCOTLAND

PROPRIETOR

Roger McDonald

RATES PER PERSON

Single occupancy £43 - £49
8 Doubles/Twins £33 - £39
Includes full breakfast and VAT

CHARGE/CREDIT CARDS

MC • VI

ACCOLADES

S.T.B. ♛♛♛ Commended
The Good Hotel Guide
Taste of Scotland

FACILITIES

Garden, croquet, bowling green
Fishing, boating and hill walking nearby

RESTRICTIONS

No children under 7 years
No smoking in bedrooms

ATTRACTIONS

Loch Lomond,
Loch Tay,
Loch Awe (Kilchurn Castle),
Loch Earn,
Glencoe,
Stirling Castle,
Rob Roy Country

AFFILIATIONS

Logis of Great Britain

NEAREST

MAJOR CITY:
Stirling - 45 miles/1 hr

MAJOR AIRPORT:
Glasgow - 55 miles/1hr 15 mins

RAILWAY STATION:
Crianlarich - 1 mile/5 mins

RESERVATIONS

Direct with hotel

ACCESS CODES

Not applicable

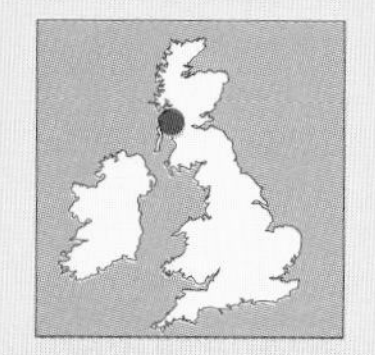

"A little paradise in the middle of Scotland"

Ros & Peter Logan, Croydon, Surrey

ARDANAISEIG

19th century country house

Kilchrenan by Taynuilt, Argyll PA35 1HE

Telephone 01866 833333
Fax 01866 833222

PROPRIETOR
Mrs Julia Smith

GENERAL MANAGER
Nigel W Liston

ROOM RATES

Single occupancy	£78 - £110
10 Doubles/Twins	£96 - £160
3 Four-posters	£142 - £160
1 Suite	£142 - £160

Includes full breakfast and VAT

CHARGE/CREDIT CARDS

• DC • MC • VI

ACCOLADES
S.T.B. ♛♛♛♛ Highly Commended
R.A.C. ★★★ + Merit Awards H C & R
A.A. ★★★ ❀❀ 75%
The Good Hotel Guide

FACILITIES
Croquet, tennis, gardens, boating, fishing, billiards, heli-pad

RESTRICTIONS
No children under 8 years
No facilities for disabled guests

ATTRACTIONS
Oban and the Hebrides, Inveraray Castle, Glen Coe

AFFILIATIONS
Scotland's Commended Hotels
The Celebrated Hotels Collection

NEAREST
MAJOR CITY:
Glasgow - 90 miles/2 hrs

MAJOR AIRPORT:
Glasgow - 80 miles/1½ hrs

RAILWAY STATION:
Taynuilt - 10 miles/15 mins

FERRY PORT:
Oban - 22 miles/30 mins

RESERVATIONS
Toll free in US: 800-322-2403

ACCESS CODES
SABRE LX 158
APOLLO LX 45209
SELECT/DATAS/SAHARA LX G1AAH
SYSTEM 1 LX GIA100
AXESS LX 4670
AMADEUS LX GIAANH

The perfect spot to discover the highlands and islands of Scotland

Ardanaiseig is an oasis on the shores of Loch Awe set in 100 acres of exotic woodland garden, with rhododendron, azalea, magnolia and many other rare shrubs and trees.

Built in the Scottish Baronial style in 1834, the house has retained much of its elegance and character whilst incorporating all the elements of a first-class country house hotel.

Ardanaiseig has 14 bedrooms, each with a private bathroom, central-heating, colour television and direct-dial telephone. The bedrooms have retained their individuality and charm through careful furnishing to achieve a sense of luxury, privacy and peace.

Ardanaiseig is ideally situated for visits to Argyll's many castles and sites of historic interest. Just 22 miles from Oban and ferries to Mull, Iona and the Hebrides.

There are boats for those wishing to fish or just to explore the many islands and castles on the loch. The hotel also offers croquet, billiards, and tennis, or for the less energetic just relax and enjoy the cuisine for which Ardanaiseig is rightly renowned.

LOCATION

On the Scottish west coast, Loch Awe side, 85 miles from Stirling and 90 miles from Glasgow on the B845 to Kilchrenan and on to Ardanaiseig.

" Truly exceptional, amongst the finest: in every respect Arisaig House sets standards that few can approach "

Ashley Courtenay, Chichester

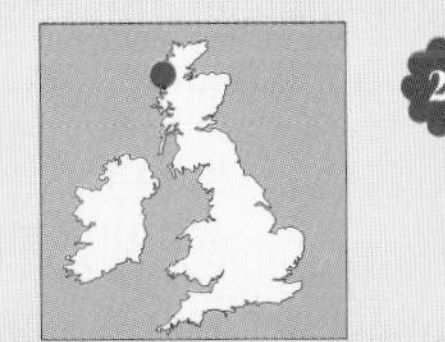

Stately house

ARISAIG HOUSE

Gateway to Ardnamurchan or Skye and the Hebrides

Tucked into a fold of the hills, Arisaig House stands close to the romantic road to the Isles: sentinel of the Prince's beach from which Bonnie Prince Charlie escaped to Skye and thence to France in Jacobean times. The house itself, an impressive stone building superbly restored, stands serene in twenty acres of gardens, facing south and enjoying dramatic views of sea loch and seemingly endless mountain ranges. It has wide terraces, sweeping lawns, mature beech woods, stately sequoia and established banks of rhododendrons and azaleas. There are also three walled gardens in which flowers, fruit and vegetables are gathered daily in season.

Family owned and run, the house has a reputation for good food, fine wine and above all, the warmth of its welcome. The resident owners, Ruth, John and Andrew Smither, maintain the splendid interior of the house with impeccable taste and furnishings to please the most discerning guests.

Head Chef, son-in-law, David Wilkinson, presents a delightful choice of freshly prepared wholesome dishes based upon an abundant local larder. The house and its twenty acres of cultivated peace represents an oasis of natural beauty amongst the rugged splendour of the West Coast.

LOCATION

On A830, Fort William to Mallaig Road, 34 miles. 1 mile past Beasdale Railway Station. 3 miles east of Arisaig village.

Beasdale, by Arisaig
Inverness-shire PH39 4NR

Telephone 01687 450622
Fax 01687 450626

SCOTLAND

PROPRIETORS

The Smither Family

ROOM RATES

1 Single £65
11 Doubles/Twins £155 - £215
2 Suites £215
Includes full breakfast and VAT

CHARGE/CREDIT CARDS

• MC • VI

ACCOLADES

S.T.B. ♛♛♛♛ De Luxe
A.A. ★★★ ❀❀
The Good Hotel Guide

FACILITIES

Garden, croquet, snooker, heli-pad
1 meeting room/max 10 people

RESTRICTIONS

No children under 10 years
No smoking in dining room
No facilities for disabled guests
No pets allowed

ATTRACTIONS

Inner Hebrides Islands and Isle of Skye, Loch Ness, Ben Nevis, Ardnamurchan Peninsula

AFFILIATIONS

Relais et Châteaux

NEAREST

MAJOR CITY:
Fort William - 34 miles/55 mins

MAJOR AIRPORT:
Edinburgh - 165 miles/4 hrs
Glasgow - 135 miles/3½ hrs
Inverness - 100 miles/2½ hrs

RAILWAY STATION:
Beasdale - 1 mile/5 mins

FERRY PORT:
Mallaig - 12 miles/25 mins

RESERVATIONS

Direct with hotel

ACCESS CODES

Not applicable

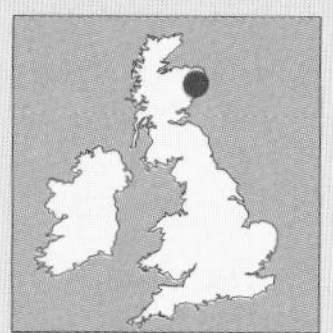

“We could not have been more impressed with the courtesy, friendliness or quality of the hotel team”

Roger Milton

ATHOLL HOTEL

19th century town house

54 King's Gate,
Aberdeen,
Aberdeenshire AB9 2YN

Phone 01224 323505
Fax 01224 321555

PROPRIETOR
David Parkinson

ROOM RATES
11 Singles £44 - £74
24 Doubles/Twins £52 - £84
Family Room £65 - £100
Includes full breakfast, newspaper and VAT

CHARGE/CREDIT CARDS

• DC • MC • VI

ACCOLADES
S.T.B. ♛♛♛♛ *Highly Commended*
A.A. ★★★ *68%*

FACILITIES
Private car park
Golf nearby

RESTRICTIONS
None

ATTRACTIONS
Balmoral Castle,
The Whisky Trail,
The Castle Trail,
Royal Aberdeen Golf Club

AFFILIATIONS
The Tartan Collection

NEAREST
MAJOR CITY:
Aberdeen - 1 mile/5 mins

MAJOR AIRPORT:
Aberdeen - 5 miles/10 mins

RAILWAY STATION:
Aberdeen - 5 miles/10 mins

RESERVATIONS
Direct with hotel

ACCESS CODES
Not applicable

The hotel in Aberdeen where the Aberdonians eat

The Atholl Hotel is located in an attractive leafy residential area only minutes away from the centre of Aberdeen. This immaculate hotel, with its loyal clientele, from Aberdeen itself as well as the international community, has for many years retained a high reputation for its excellent service and first class accommodation, as well as its relaxed and friendly atmosphere.

The hotel, a turreted granite building in the style of the granite city, has fine architectural features, both internally and externally. Each of the 35 tastefully decorated bedrooms has its own private bathroom, colour TV, radio, direct-dial telephone, hair dryer, trouser press, and also tea and coffee-making facilities. You can be sure of a high level of comfort.

Aberdonians appreciate the high standard of cuisine and excellent value. The dining room is a particularly friendly place in which to get to know local people as well as international visitors. The dedicated chef prepares fine dishes from local produce from land and sea. This is the home of Aberdeen Angus steaks, and fine salmon from the rivers Don and Dee.

The Atholl has its own car park. Its excellent location makes it ideal for exploring Aberdeen and Royal Deeside. There are over 150 castles in the immediate neighbourhood, including Braemar, Craigievar and Drum. The grounds of Balmoral, the royal family residence, are open in summer whenever the royal family is not in residence. Golf, salmon and trout fishing are available in the neighbourhood. The Grampian Mountains with their snow-filled gullies and spectacular pinewood forests are within easy reach.

LOCATION

400 yards off the main ring route and 10 minutes from the city centre.

“This is an oasis. It is always just like coming home”

Robert Dunn

Victorian house

AUCHEN CASTLE HOTEL

Genuine Scottish hospitality in an area of great beauty

Named after the early 13th century castle (now a ruin) on the hill behind, Auchen Castle started as a four-bedroomed detached house in about 1840 and was extended during the following two decades. In the 1960's a modern wing was added which is known as Cedar Lodge and which offers comfortable bedrooms – particularly popular with those who just want to stay one night.

The house retains most of its mid-19th century features and the emphasis is on informality and genuine hospitality at sensible prices. The situation is spectacular and no one should visit without taking the time to look at the exceptional collection of trees and shrubs in the 50 acres surrounding the house.

Often overlooked in favour of the Highlands, this is not only an area of historic interest but a countryside full of beauty and variety. Easily reached both east and west, you will find that a little extra time spent will be well rewarded.

Of course, golf, walking, fishing, stalking, and numerous leisure activities are not far from the doorstep.

LOCATION

On main north/south route into Scotland, 55 miles south of Glasgow/Edinburgh.

Beattock, Moffat, Dumfries & Galloway DG10 9SH

Telephone 01683 300407
Fax 01683 300667

PROPRIETOR

Hazel Beckh

ROOM RATES

2 Singles £49.50
13 Doubles/Twins £76 - £84
Includes full breakfast and VAT

CHARGE/CREDIT CARDS

• *DC* • *MC* • *VI*

ACCOLADES

S.T.B. ♛♛♛♛ *Commended*
R.A.C. ★★★
A.A. ★★★ *65%*
The Good Hotel Guide

FACILITIES

Gardens and trout loch with boat
2 meeting rooms/max 50 people
Golf, riding and fishing nearby

RESTRICTIONS

No facilities for disabled guests

ATTRACTIONS

St Mary's Loch,
Drumlanrig Castle,
Hadrian's Wall,
Robert Burns,
Sir Walter Scott
and John Buchan country

AFFILIATIONS

Scotland's Commended Hotels

NEAREST

MAJOR CITY:
Edinburgh - 65 miles/1½ hrs

MAJOR AIRPORT:
Glasgow - 55 miles/1½ hrs
Edinburgh - 55 miles/1½ hrs

RAILWAY STATION:
Lockerbie - 15 miles/20 mins

RESERVATIONS

Toll free in US: 800-989-7676

ACCESS CODES

Not applicable

"We look forward to our next apportunity to visit – Next to excellence is the appreciation of it"

Beryl Barnett

BALBIRNIE HOUSE HOTEL

Georgian mansion

Balbirnie Park, Markinch, Glenrothes, Fife KY7 6NE

Telephone 01592 610066
Fax 01592 610529

PROPRIETORS
Alan, Elizabeth and Nicholas Russell

ROOM RATES

2 Singles	*£99.50 - £125*
25 Doubles/Twins	*£168 - £190*
1 Four-poster	*£198*
2 Suites	*£225*

Includes full breakfast and VAT

CHARGE/CREDIT CARDS

• DC • MC • VI

ACCOLADES
S.T.B. ♛♛♛♛♛ De Luxe
R.A.C. ★★★★ + Merit Awards H & R
A.A. ★★★★ ❀❀
Restaurant of the Year, 1994 - 'Scotland on Sunday'
Regional Hotel of the Year 1995 - Fife
The Good Hotel Guide

FACILITIES
Garden, golf, croquet, snooker, heli-pad
5 meeting rooms/max 150 people
Riding, clay pigeon shooting, off track driving and archery nearby

RESTRICTIONS
Pets by prior arrangement

ATTRACTIONS
Falkland Palace, St Andrews and Ladybank golf courses, Lochleven Castle, St Andrews Cathedral

AFFILIATIONS
Small Luxury Hotels

NEAREST
MAJOR CITY:
Edinburgh - 28 miles/35 mins
MAJOR AIRPORT:
Edinburgh - 25 miles/30 mins
RAILWAY STATION:
Markinch - 1 mile/5 mins

RESERVATIONS
Toll free in US/Canada: 800-525-4800

ACCESS CODES
AMADEUS/SYSTEM 1 LX EDIBHH
APOLLO LX 20905
AXESS LX 1039
DATAS II/SELECT/SAHARA LX EDIBH
SABRE LX 23430

Fine food, fine surroundings – the natural warmth of Scottish hospitality

Balbirnie, a lovely country house in the heart of the Kingdom of Fife, is the centrepiece of a beautiful 400-acre estate and country park overlooking the fairways of Balbirnie golf course.

Steeped in 200 years of history, it is one of Scotland's finest Georgian mansions, circa 1777. Caringly reappointed as a luxury hotel it offers the ambience of a gracious home with many period features.

The dining experience at Balbirnie reflects the wide range of the country's wonderful larder. The co-proprietors provide personal attention, and the friendly staff convey the warmth and welcome of Scottish hospitality.

Balbirnie occupies an unrivalled geographical location. Visit quaint fishing villages, historic Edinburgh and St Andrews, or explore the countryside and heritage of Fife. Varied leisure pursuits can also be arranged.

Lunches and dinners are served each day in the exquisite restaurant. The Gamekeeper's Inn serves bar lunches in a Bistro setting. Both offer tremendous quality and value for money.

LOCATION

Take Junction 3 off the M90. Follow signs for Glenrothes/Tay road bridge (A92). Past Glenrothes, take B9130 to right. Balbirnie House is 2nd on left.

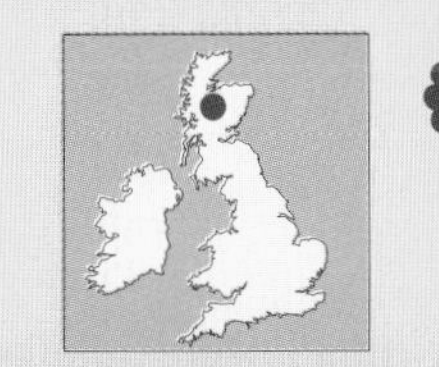

"I should like to sing the praises of this splendid country mansion that combines a marvellous setting, luxurious accommodation, superb food and drink, and friendly service"

Professor David Daiches, Scholar & Academic

Edwardian country house BALGONIE COUNTRY HOUSE HOTEL

Away from it all with a prospect fit for a king

There are some places whose fame has spread across the world, not for their size nor their importance but quite simply for their breath-taking beauty. Royal Deeside is one such place; 'Royal' because the Royal family have made it their home for generations. It is in this setting of splendour that you will find the village of Ballater where many of the shops proudly display the Royal Warrant, the mark of royal patronage. On its edge, sheltered from the occasional traffic by four acres of gardens, is Balgonie House.

The house was built in 1898 next to the golf course commanding a magnificent view of the hills of Glen Muick, right in the heart of the 'Whisky Trail'. This might be enough to have many rushing off to make a booking!

But there is more – the dining room, or more particularly the pleasures it confers, is regarded as the heart of Balgonie. The salmon, beef and game from this area are renowned far beyond the British Isles; the seafood, fresh from the Orkneys and the East Coast, are delights of no lesser merit. Add to this profusion, the skills of the kitchen and an excellent choice of wine, and you have a prospect fit for a king.

John and Priscilla Finnie have a fine sense of style that pervades every aspect of the hotel – no less the pretty, well-appointed en suite bedrooms designed with your comfort in mind.

A most romantic hotel in a glorious setting!

LOCATION

On the outskirts of Ballater just off the A93 towards Braemar, Glenshee and Perth.

Braemar Place, Ballater AB35 5RQ

Telephone 013397 55482
Fax 013397 55482

PROPRIETORS

John and Priscilla Finnie

RATES PER PERSON

Single occupancy £57.50
9 Doubles/Twins £47.50
Includes full breakfast and VAT

CHARGE/CREDIT CARDS

• *DC* • *MC* • *VI*

ACCOLADES

S.T.B. 👑👑👑👑 *De Luxe*
A.A. ★★ ❀❀
The Good Hotel Guide
Taste of Scotland
A.A. Inspector's Selected Scottish Hotel 1994

FACILITIES

Garden, croquet
Golf and fishing nearby

RESTRICTIONS

No facilities for disabled guests
No pets in public rooms or unaccompanied in bedrooms

ATTRACTIONS

Castle Trail, Malt Whisky Trail, Craigievar, Balmoral and Crathes Castles

AFFILIATIONS

Scotland's Commended Hotels
Scotland Deluxe

NEAREST

MAJOR CITY:
Aberdeen - 43 miles/1 hr 10 mins

MAJOR AIRPORT:
Aberdeen - 49 miles/1 hr 20 mins

RAILWAY STATION:
Aberdeen - 43 miles/1 hr 10 mins

RESERVATIONS

Direct with hotel

ACCESS CODES

WORLDSPAN HK BALGO
SABRE HK 31318
APOLLO HT 04063

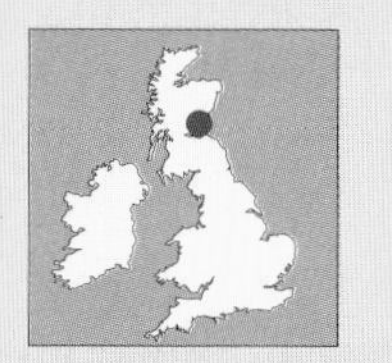

“ Ballathie is not just a fine hotel – it is a civilized haven of rural peace ”

Sir Patrick Cormack, FSA MP

BALLATHIE HOUSE HOTEL

Victorian manor house

Kinclaven by Stanley, Perth, Perthshire PH1 4QN

Telephone 01250 883268
Fax 01250 883396

GENERAL MANAGER
Christopher J Longden

ROOM RATES

9 Singles	£60 - £95
18 Doubles/Twins	£115 - £180
1 Suite	£160 - £200

Includes full breakfast, newspaper and VAT

CHARGE/CREDIT CARDS

• DC • MC • VI

ACCOLADES
S.T.B. ♛♛♛♛ De luxe
R.A.C. ★★★ + Merit Awards C & R
A.A.★★★ ❀❀ 76%
Country House Hotel of the Year 1994
Macallan Taste of Scotland Award

FACILITIES
Croquet, tennis, gardens, fishing, shooting, heli-pad
4 meeting rooms/max 60 people

RESTRICTIONS
None

ATTRACTIONS
Scone Palace, Glamis Castle, Perth, Blairgowrie, Rosemount Golf Course

AFFILIATIONS
Scotland's Heritage Hotels
Independent Innkeepers Association

NEAREST
MAJOR CITY:
Perth - 10 miles/15 mins

MAJOR AIRPORT:
Edinburgh - 60 miles/1 hr

RAILWAY STATION:
Perth - 10 miles/15 mins

RESERVATIONS
Toll free in US: 800-323-5463

ACCESS CODES
Not applicable

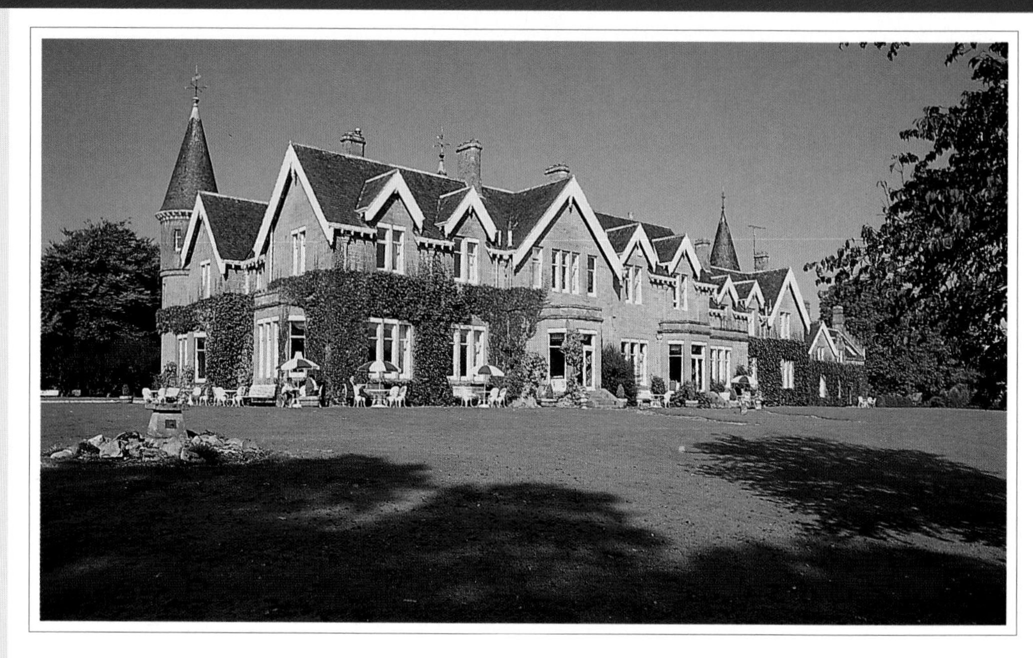

Dine on salmon overlooking the famous River Tay

Situated on its own 1500-acre estate overlooking the River Tay, Ballathie House offers Scottish hospitality in a house of character and distinction dating from 1850. The original public rooms are elegantly furnished and spacious master bedrooms retain antique furniture with period bathrooms featuring modern facilities.

Standard rooms are cosy and charmingly decorated. On the ground floor there are rooms suitable for disabled guests and a suite opening out on to the lawns which slope gently to the river.

Menus specialise in local produce with Tay salmon, beef, lamb and west coast seafood featuring regularly. Asparagus, game and soft fruits are available seasonally. The Macallan Taste of Scotland 1994 has been awarded to the dining room and the food is recommended in the major guides.

Activities include fishing, tennis, croquet, putting, walking and touring. Major golf courses at Rosemount, Carnoustie and St. Andrews are within reach and local courses are nearby. Ballathie House is an ideal touring centre with visits to Glamis Castle, Scone Palace, Perth, Blairgowrie and Edinburgh within a pleasant hour's drive.

LOCATION

From Edinburgh, take the M90 to Perth, off A9, 2 miles north of Perth take the B9000 through Stanley, turn right at a sign for Kinclaven (and Ballathie).

"Having worked in hotels, I can honestly say that your's is the most friendly, well-run and comfortable in my experience"

Jennifer Gordon, Blackford

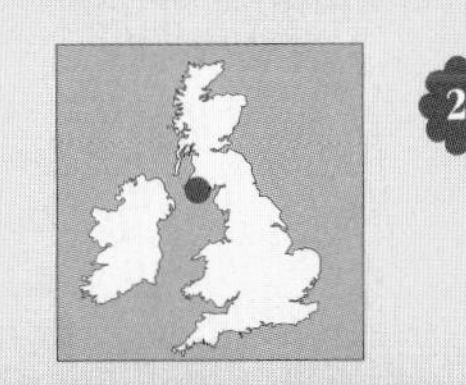

19th century country house

BARON'S CRAIG HOTEL

A seventh heaven overlooking the Solway and Rough Firth

Few hotels can boast of a setting as beautiful as that in which Baron's Craig is situated. It stands in wooded country overlooking the expanse of the Solway and Rough Firth, a tidal inlet biting deep into tree-covered and heathered hills. The grounds themselves are equally attractive, being virtually a clearing in a twelve acre wooded area with lush lawns and gardens abounding in colour, especially in spring and early summer, with masses of rhododendrons.

The imposing granite structure of 1880 has since been extended for comfort and convenience, while retaining its character and interest. The well appointed lounges and restaurant are airy and spacious, as are the twenty two rooms, all with private bathroom and shower, and all are well heated. Furnishing is in keeping with the quality evident throughout the hotel while the atmosphere is friendly and relaxed.

Preparation and serving of food, as with everything else, is under the personal supervision of the resident owner and his staff offering tempting and interesting menus, while selected wines can be chosen from the comprehensive wine list. Special three day breaks are available.

LOCATION

Take the A75 from Dumfries, immediately turning left on to the A710. Follow this road around the coast and turn left for Rockcliffe after Colvend.

Rockcliffe, by Dalbeattie, Kirkcudbrightshire DG5 4QF

Telephone 01556 630225
Fax 01556 630328

OWNER
Alberto Capaccioli

RATES PER PERSON

Single occupancy	£57
22 Doubles/Twins	£49

Includes full breakfast and VAT

CHARGE/CREDIT CARDS

• MC • VI

ACCOLADES
S.T.B. ♛♛♛♛ Commended
R.A.C. ★★★

FACILITIES
Garden, putting green
1 meeting room/max 20 people
Riding, sea fishing and coarse fishing nearby

RESTRICTIONS
None

ATTRACTIONS
Robert Burns House,
Shambellie House,
Sweetheart Abbey,
Gemrock Museum

AFFILIATIONS
Independent

NEAREST
MAJOR CITY:
Edinburgh - 100 miles/2 hrs
Glasgow - 100 miles/2 hrs

MAJOR AIRPORT:
Glasgow - 100 miles/2 hrs

RAILWAY STATION:
Dumfries - 20 miles/30 mins

RESERVATIONS
Direct with hotel

ACCESS CODES
Not applicable

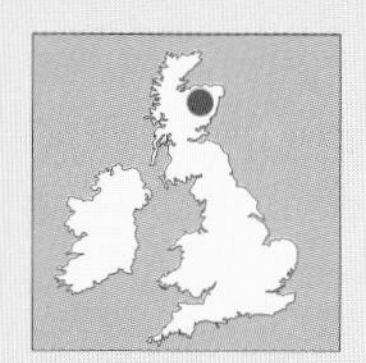

"The first of what we hope will be more visits to a bit of heaven in the highlands"

Monte Ackerman, New York

BRAEMAR LODGE HOTEL

Victorian shooting lodge

Glenshee Road,
Braemar,
Grampian AB35 5YQ

Telephone 013397 41627
Fax 013397 41627

PROPRIETORS

Edna and Sarah Coyne

ROOM RATES

2 Singles £36
4 Doubles/Twins £72
Includes full breakfast and VAT

CHARGE/CREDIT CARDS

ACCOLADES

A.A. ★★ ❀ 72%
Taste of Scotland

FACILITIES

Garden
Golf, fishing, stalking, riding and skiing nearby

RESTRICTIONS

No facilities for disabled guests

ATTRACTIONS

Balmoral,
Braemar Castle,
Royal Lochnagar Distillery,
Braemar Highland Heritage Centre,
Glenshee,
Whisky Trail

AFFILIATIONS

Independent

NEAREST

MAJOR CITY:
Aberdeen - 60 miles/1½ hrs

MAJOR AIRPORT:
Aberdeen - 66 miles/1¾ hrs

RAILWAY STATION:
Perth - 52 miles/1 hr 10 mins

RESERVATIONS

Direct with hotel

ACCESS CODES

Not applicable

Set in extensive grounds where shooting parties return year after year

Summer and winter, Braemar attracts visitors from every nation. Some for its world-famous highland games, some for the winter sports (Glenshee, Scotland's largest ski area is only eight miles away). And then there are the cognoscenti following their noses up the 'Whisky Trail'. This is Royal Deeside, one of the finest areas for field sports in Britain: deer-stalking, grouse shooting, salmon fishing, golf . . . and this is why Braemar Lodge could be your ideal place to stay: arrangements can be made for you to indulge in the pursuit of your choice at three local estates.

Best described as an hotel of character, it has the air of a large family house that has not forgotten its sporting origins – every window has a fine mountain view and the reception rooms are well-stocked with magazines, books and games should the weather close in. The bedrooms have ample space and lots of welcoming touches to make one feel at home.

Standards are high and this is especially evident in the dining room. The area is world famous for its Aberdeen Angus beef, Scottish salmon and game of all sorts. The chef exploits this natural abundance, having earned a rosette for the hotel and the accolade of being the only Taste of Scotland restaurant in Braemar.

For those too lazy to take the Whisky Trail there's a splendid selection of malt whiskies in the wood-panelled bar where they can be enjoyed in front of a roaring log fire.

LOCATION

Travelling south on the A93, at the southern edge of Braemar village on the right hand side.

" Relaxation personified "

Ken & Caroline Venters

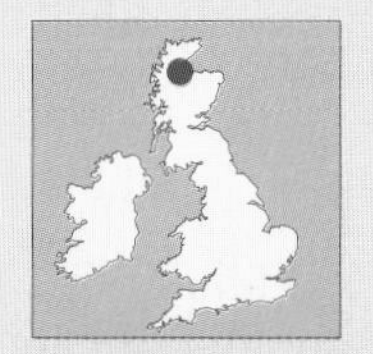

Baronial mansion

BUNCHREW HOUSE HOTEL

Timelessness and tranquillity by the banks of the Beauly Firth

Steeped in history and tradition, this beautiful 17th century Scottish mansion stands in 20 acres of landscaped gardens whose wall is lapped by the sea in the Beauly Firth. It was built by Simon Fraser, the eighth Lord Lovat, whose marriage to Jean Stewart in 1621 is commemorated by a stone marriage lintel above the fireplace in the drawing room.

Magnificent views from the hotel include the Black Isle and Ben Wyvis. While the dining room – filled with contemporary paintings of the Frasers – overlooks the sea.

Traditional cuisine includes prime scottish beef, fresh lobster and langoustines, local game and venison, and fresh vegetables. These superb dishes are complemented by a comprehensive 92-bin wine list.

Guest accommodations offer 11 luxury suites, including two with four-posters and one with a sumptuous half-tester and jacuzzi; all are furnished to an extremely high standard and all benefit from the availability of 24-hour room service.

This is an area offering a number of outdoor sporting activities and a diversity of castles, glens, gardens, and, of course, the intriguing legend of the Loch Ness Monster.

LOCATION

A short distance from both Inverness Airport and railway station, off the A862 between Inverness and Beauly.

SCOTLAND

By Inverness, Inverness-shire IV3 6TA

Telephone 01463 234917
Fax 01463 710620

PROPRIETORS

Stewart and Lesley Dykes

ROOM RATES

Single occupancy	*£55 - £82*
8 Doubles/Twins	*£65 - £98*
2 Four-posters	*£80 - £115*
1 Suite	*£90 - £115*

Includes full breakfast and VAT

CHARGE/CREDIT CARDS

• MC • VI

ACCOLADES

S.T.B. ♛♛♛♛ Highly Commended
R.A.C. ★★★ + Merit Awards H C & R
A.A. ★★★ ❀ 73%
Morrison Bowmore Scottish Field Restaurant of the Year Award

FACILITIES

Garden, croquet, fishing, heli-pad
3 meeting rooms/max 100 people
Golf and riding nearby

RESTRICTIONS

No facilities for disabled guests

ATTRACTIONS

Loch Ness, Culloden Battlefield, Glens of Affric, Cawdor Castle, Strathglass and Strathcanon

AFFILIATIONS

Scotland's Commended Hotels

NEAREST

MAJOR CITY:
Inverness - 3 miles/10 mins
Edinburgh - 125 miles/ 2½ hrs

MAJOR AIRPORT:
Inverness - 9 miles/20 mins
Edinburgh - 125 miles/ 2½ hrs

RAILWAY STATION:
Inverness - 3 miles/10 mins

RESERVATIONS

Direct with hotel

ACCESS CODES

Not applicable

"You have achieved a simple perfection. Thank you. P.S. Great staff"

Kenneth H Millstein

CHANNINGS

Edwardian town house

South Learmonth Gardens, Edinburgh EH4 1EZ

Telephone 0131 315 2226
Fax 0131 332 9631

PROPRIETOR
Peter Taylor

GENERAL MANAGER
Simon Williams

ROOM RATES
6 Singles £85 - £97
42 Doubles/Twins £115 - £160
Includes full breakfast and VAT

CHARGE/CREDIT CARDS

• DC • MC • VI

ACCOLADES
S.T.B. ♛♛♛♛ Highly Commended
A.A. ★★★ ❀ 70%

FACILITIES
Gardens
2 meeting rooms/max 40 people

RESTRICTIONS
No facilities for disabled guests
No pets

ATTRACTIONS
Botanical gardens
Edinburgh Castle,
Holyrood House, Royal Mile,
National Art Gallery of Scotland

AFFILIATIONS
Selected British Hotels
Scotland's Commended Hotels

NEAREST
MAJOR CITY:
Edinburgh

MAJOR AIRPORT:
Edinburgh - 6 miles/20 mins

RAILWAY STATION:
Waverley or Haymarket - 1½ miles/3 mins

RESERVATIONS
Toll free in US: 800-323-5463

ACCESS CODES
AMADEUS/SYSTEM 1 UI EDICHA
APOLLO/GALILEO/GEMINI UI 22312
AXESS UI 5588
SABRE UI 22560
SAHARA UI EDI14126
WORLDSPAN UI 14126

A privately owned hotel with a club like atmosphere

Walk through the quiet cobbled streets of Edinburgh city centre, just a little way from the castle and push open the door of a row of five beautifully maintained Edwardian town houses.

Together, these make up Channings, a privately-owned hotel with a cosy, old fashioned club-like atmosphere right in the heart of historic Edinburgh. The style of Channings is rarely found today: a feeling of classic care from the peaceful, fire-lit lounges to any one of the 48 individually designed guest rooms, several of which offer wonderful panoramic views over the Firth of Forth to the hills of Fife.

The Brasserie is one of the popular haunts of the city. A restaurant that prides itself on honest food and personable service. After dinner, the bar welcomes you with an interesting range of malt whiskies and the odd game of chess. In the warmer months, take your lunch outside where the hotel's terraced garden captures the heat of the sun.

The quiet, classical feel of the hotel makes it the ideal venue for a corporate dinner or small conference. Any such gathering can be held in one of two different rooms – the oak-panelled library or the Kingsleigh Suite.

LOCATION

Channings is only ½ mile from the city centre (10 minutes walk) and only 20 minutes from the airport by taxi.

" Great food, great people, great golfing . . . just great! "

James Wilmerton, Atlanta

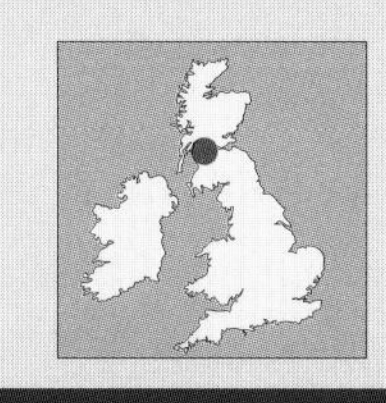

Country house and restaurant CHAPELTOUN HOUSE HOTEL

The very best of hospitality and only 30 minutes from Glasgow airport

Hugh Neilson made his fortune in coal and shipping, married a beautiful young English girl and built Chapeltoun in 1900 as a fine home where he could raise his family. Chapeltoun's Victorian magnificence is still to be seen in the large staircase, solid oak-panelled hall with its log fire, and dining rooms with floors made of shipbuilders' quality teak. The hotel has a simple philosophy: to provide good food in a pleasant atmosphere, and to look after the guests.

Each bedroom has its individual style and character. All have large and cosy bathrooms, bathrobes, colour TV, radio, direct-dial telephones, hair dryer and trouser press, and thoughtful little extras including fresh fruit.

The dining rooms feature rich colours, oak panelling and magnificent views across the gardens to the river. The menus are memorable, and the cuisine has regularly been held in high esteem by food guides and writers, and most importantly, by discerning guests. The wine list includes wines from all the world's great wine-producing regions.

Chapeltoun is set in 20 acres of private gardens, looking out over the lovely Ayrshire countryside. It offers a peaceful haven for guests wishing to relax in great style and comfort, yet also to be within easy reach of Glasgow, with its cathedral, its wealth of art galleries and museums, and its bustling shops and leisure facilities.

LOCATION

From Fenwick exit on A77 take B778 to Stewarton Cross. Turn left under the railway viaduct, the second right on to B769 for 2 miles. Chapeltoun is off to the right.

Irvine Road,
Nr Stewarton,
Ayrshire KA3 3ED

Telephone 01560 482696
Fax 01560 485100

PROPRIETOR
Mr G McKenzie

ROOM RATES

Single occupancy	*£70 - £89*
2 Standard Doubles/Twins	*£80 - £99*
3 Superiors	*£89 - £119*
2 Masters	*£99 - £139*
1 Four-poster	*£99 - £139*

Includes full breakfast and VAT

CHARGE/CREDIT CARDS

• MC • VI

ACCOLADES
S.T.B. 4 Crowns Highly Commended
A.A. ★★★ 75%
The Good Hotel Guide

FACILITIES
Garden, fishing, heli-pad
Golf, riding and fishing nearby

RESTRICTIONS
No children under 12 years
No smoking in dining room
Pets by prior arrangement

ATTRACTIONS
Royal Troon Golf Course, Old Prestwick, Turnberry, Arran Island

AFFILIATIONS
Scotland's Commended Hotels

NEAREST
MAJOR CITY:
Glasgow - 18 miles/30 mins

MAJOR AIRPORT:
Glasgow - 18 miles/30 mins
Prestwick - 15 miles/25 mins

RAILWAY STATION:
Stewarton - 2 miles/5 mins

RESERVATIONS
Toll free in US: 800-43-SCOTS

ACCESS CODES
Not applicable

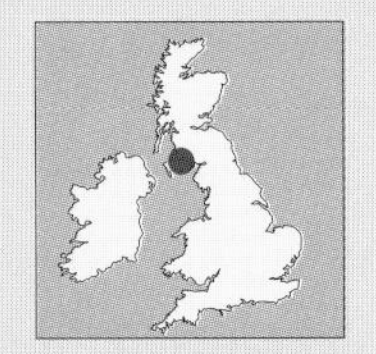

"Informal, extremely friendly and completely peaceful"

Bernard Spratt

COLLIN HOUSE

Georgian house

Auchencairn,
Castle Douglas,
Kirkcudbrightshire DG7 1QN

Telephone 01556 640292
Fax 01556 640276

OWNERS
John Wood and Pam Hall

ROOM RATES
6 Doubles/Twins £78 - £84
Includes full breakfast and VAT

CHARGE/CREDIT CARDS

• *MC* • *VI*

ACCOLADES
S.T.B. ♛♛♛ De Luxe
A.A. ★★ ❀❀❀
The Good Hotel Guide
Taste of Scotland

FACILITIES
Gardens
Golf, riding, fishing and beach nearby

RESTRICTIONS
No children under 11 years in dining room at night
No facilities for disabled guests
Pets by prior arrangement

ATTRACTIONS
Hornell Art Gallery,
Broughton House,
Drumlanrig Castle,
Southerness – championship golf course

AFFILIATIONS
Independent

NEAREST
MAJOR CITY:
Glasgow - 100 miles/2¼ hrs

MAJOR AIRPORT:
Glasgow - 100 miles/2¼ hrs

RAILWAY STATION:
Dumfries - 20 miles/30 mins

RESERVATIONS
Direct with hotel

ACCESS CODES
Not applicable

An exclusive country home set in Robbie Burns' romantic landscape

Collin House, situated on south west Scotland's unspoiled Galloway coast amidst a landscape of outstanding beauty, looks out from its hillside setting across the Solway Firth to the Cumbrian hills beyond.

Originally built around 1750, the house was sympathetically extended and renovated in 1991 to create a small exclusive hotel. Throughout the refurbishment every care was taken to preserve the style and character of a country home. The bedrooms, each with a well-appointed spacious bathroom, maintain the generous proportions of the house; they are furnished with many period pieces.

Collin House, featured in leading restaurant guides, offers guests a menu that changes daily, making extensive use of the excellent fresh local produce for which the region is renowned.

Galloway, in the south west corner of Scotland remains tranquil and unspoilt. The varied coast ranges from cliffs to estuaries, picturesque fishing ports and pretty beaches. Along the coastal lowlands is a rolling landscape of vivid green pastures and, inland, one enters the under-populated heather clad moors and dark forests described by John Buchan in The Thirty Nine Steps.

For those of a historic or cultural bent; this is 'Burns country' (a former excise man, when smuggling was a way of life here), 'Robert de Bruce country' (he ambushed the Sassenachs in Glen Trool), 'early-Christian country' (archaeologists at Whithorn are uncovering Britain's earliest Christian settlement).

LOCATION

Between Dalbeattie and Kircudbright. Turn right off the A711, ¼ mile east of Auchencairn where signposted.

" We stayed here once and have been back twelve more times! "

Sally Huntley, golfing and fishing widow

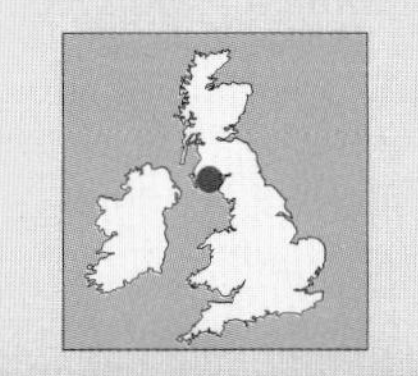

19th century mansion CORSEMALZIE HOUSE HOTEL

The epitome of the Scottish country life

Corsemalzie House Hotel, set in forty acres of garden and woodland, symbolises the very essence of a Scottish country mansion. Built during the 19th century, the hotel has retained all the elegance of the era. Careful restoration has ensured that every facility is provided for guests without altering the intimate atmosphere of the original house.

Entering the hotel, a sense of tranquillity and comfort sets the tone for guests looking for that feeling of something different. The drawing room has expansive views over lawns and putting green. The cocktail bar is stocked with an extensive range of carefully selected wines and malt whiskies, and makes an ideal meeting place prior to dinner. Scottish fayre, locally produced, enhances the excellent cuisine provided by the hotel. Under the personal supervision of resident proprietor, Peter McDougall, an extensive and varied menu of interesting dishes is offered in the dining room and cocktail bar.

Bedrooms enjoy en suite facilities furnished to reflect the design of each room. Direct dial telephones, remote control television and tea or coffee making facilities are provided for guests.

The hotel has extensive private salmon/brown trout fishing on the rivers Bladnoch and Tarff, which offers good sport to hotel guests. We also have an exciting new trout loch for boat fishing. Shooting can be organised over 8,000 acres of neighbouring woods and estate. Golfing arrangements are available on two local courses.

LOCATION

From the roundabout on A75 at Newton Stewart, drive south 8 miles on A714 to Wigtown. Cross the River Bladnoch at the Bladnoch Distillery and proceed ¼ mile to junction of B7005 to Glenluce. Turn right and continue 5 miles to hotel.

Port William,
Newton Stewart,
Wigtownshire DG8 9RL

Telephone 01988 860254
Fax 01988 860213

SCOTLAND

PROPRIETOR

Peter and Elaine McDougall

ROOM RATES

Single occupancy	*£45 - £55*
12 Doubles/Twins	*£68 - £86*
2 Family	*£65 - £86*

Includes full breakfast and VAT

CHARGE/CREDIT CARDS

• *MC* • *VI*

ACCOLADES

S.T.B. ♛♛♛♛ *Commended*
R.A.C. ★★★ *+ Merit Awards H & R*
A.A. ★★★ *65%*

FACILITIES

Garden, croquet, putting
Fishing and shooting nearby

RESTRICTIONS

No facilities for disabled guests
No pets in public rooms

ATTRACTIONS

Castle Kennedy,
Logan Gardens, Whithorn Dig,
Gem Rock Museum

AFFILIATIONS

Logis of Great Britain
Scotland's Commended Hotels

NEAREST

MAJOR CITY:
Glasgow - 95 miles/2½ hrs

MAJOR AIRPORT:
Glasgow - 90 miles/2½ hrs

RAILWAY STATION:
Stranraer - 23 miles/35 mins

RESERVATIONS

Toll free in US: 800-43-SCOTS
Toll free in US: 800-987-7676

ACCESS CODES

APOLLO HT 25925
SABRE HK 31060
WORLDSPAN HK CORSE

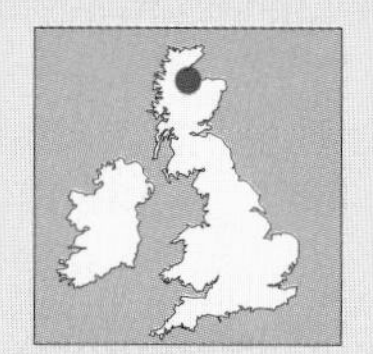

"Very much the country house with a relaxed and welcoming atmosphere, and refreshingly unpretentious"

D J Robertson, AA Inspector

COUL HOUSE HOTEL

Highland mansion

Contin, by Strathpeffer, Ross-shire IV14 9EY

Telephone 01997 421487
Fax 01997 421945

PROPRIETORS
Martyn and Ann Hill

RATES PER PERSON

3 Singles	*£46 - £58*
14 Doubles/Twins	*£35 - £47*
1 Triple	*£35 - £47*
1 Suite	*£35 - £47*
1 Family Room	*£35 - £47*

Includes full breakfast and VAT

CHARGE/CREDIT CARDS

• DC • JCB • MC • VI

ACCOLADES
S.T.B. Highly Commended
A.A. ★★★ 72%
Taste of Scotland

FACILITIES
Garden, 9 hole golf course
1 meeting room/max 60 people
Golf and fishing nearby

RESTRICTIONS
None

ATTRACTIONS
Strathpeffer Spa Victorian village, Loch Ness, Strathconon, Cromarty Firth, Loch Achonachie salmon lift, Rogie Falls and Turachilty Forest Trail, Beauly Priory, Castle Leod

AFFILIATIONS
Scotland's Commended Hotels
Minotel

NEAREST
MAJOR CITY:
Inverness - 20 miles/30 mins

MAJOR AIRPORT:
Glasgow - 180 miles/4 hrs

RAILWAY STATION:
Inverness - 20 miles/30 mins

RESERVATIONS
Toll free in US: 800-43-SCOTS

ACCESS CODES
WORLDSPAN/AMADEUS/ SYSTEM 1 HK COULH
SABRE HK 30594

So much to see in such a perfect setting

The ancient Mackenzies of Coul picked the supreme situation for this secluded country mansion, with magnificent, uninterrupted views over forest and mountain. For almost 20 years, it has been the home of Martyn and Ann Hill, whose warm Highland welcome is matched only by that of 'Skye' and 'Raasay', their two lovable Labradors, and an evening piper in summertime.

The hotel's emphasis is on friendly personal service and high standards, both of food and accommodation. The candlelit restaurant is well appointed for Taste of Scotland cooking, which is personally supervised by Chris Bentley, the long-standing head chef. Smoked seafoods, fresh salmon and succulent roasts are on the menu. The wine list is equally superb, and the Mackenzie's Bar has a fine selection of single malts. The three elegant lounges all have log fires. The bedrooms are individually designed and decorated, and thoroughly well equipped; there is even an iron for dresses and shirts.

The hotel is a favourite with anglers and golfers. It has its own salmon and trout fishing, and offers a 5-course golf package that includes Royal Dornoch. It has its own 9-hole pitch and putt course. There's much, much more besides in this lovely county of Ross and Cromarty. You can use the hotel's Highland Passport to cruise Loch Ness, visit Macbeth's Cawdor Castle, and sail to the Summer Isles. You can pony-trek and go on guided 'Insight' rambling, or follow the Highland Heritage Trail.

LOCATION

From the south: by-passing Inverness, continue on A9 over Moray Firth Bridge. After 5 miles, take second exit at roundabout on to A835. Follow to Contin. Hotel is ½ mile up private drive to the right.

" The warmth of the welcome is unsurpassed. You really know how to make your guests feel good! "

Annmarie and Richard Burdett, Caithness

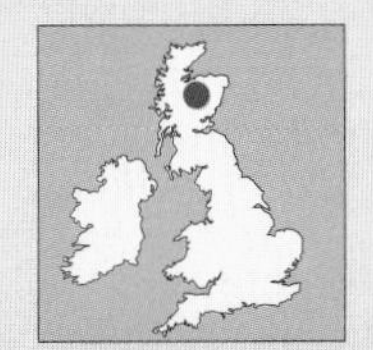

Victorian hotel

CRAIGELLACHIE HOTEL

The quality hotel in the heart of the Highlands

The Craigellachie Hotel is a haven of Highland hospitality in a lovely wooded valley. Located in the beautiful village of the same name, at the confluence of the rivers Spey and Fiddich, the hotel has an atmosphere of peaceful luxury. Dating from 1893, it offers the rare opportunity to savour the style and elegance of a bygone era, and the comforts of a first-class hotel.

The Craigellachie has been beautifully refurbished. The 30 elegantly appointed bedrooms, some with four-poster beds, feature subtle and interesting colour combinations, quality fabrics and fine furniture.

The Ben Aigan restaurant sets exemplary standards for cuisine and service. The care and thought taken in preparing your meals is matched by the attention to detail which the staff provides in serving them.

The library offers the perfect setting for you to enjoy a pre-dinner drink, or you may wish to relax with a book from the finely crafted bookcases adorning the walls. An equally warm welcome awaits you in the Quaitch cocktail bar, where you can choose from an extensive range of local malt whiskies. The Fiddich and drawing room have blazing log fires, fine antique curios and deep-cushioned comfort. There are also sauna, solarium, snooker and games rooms.

Within the picturesque setting, you can enjoy many leisure activities, including hill-walking, viewing wildlife such as pheasant, grouse and deer, historic castles and buildings, malt whisky distilleries, tennis, golf, riding, mountain-biking and fishing for salmon, king of the River Spey.

LOCATION

Craigellachie is in the heart of the Highlands, where the A95 meets the A941.

Craigellachie, Speyside, Banffshire AB38 9SR

Telephone 01340 881204
Fax 01340 881253

SCOTLAND

GENERAL MANAGER

Ian A Fleming

ROOM RATES

5 Standard singles	*£58 - £60*
Single occupancy	*£81 - £85*
19 Standard Doubles/Twins	*£99*
6 Master Doubles/Twins	*£119 - £125*

Includes full breakfast and VAT

CHARGE/CREDIT CARDS

• DC • MC • VI

ACCOLADES

S.T.B. ♛♛♛♛ Highly Commended
R.A.C. ★★★ + Merit Awards H & R
A.A. ★★★ ❀ 72%

FACILITIES

Garden, tennis, games room, exercise room, sauna, snooker
3 meeting rooms/max 50 people
Golf and fishing nearby

RESTRICTIONS

No facilities for disabled guests

ATTRACTIONS

Ballindalloch, Balvenie, Cawdor and Brodie Castles,
Malt Whisky Trail,
Culloden Battlefield,
Ben Aigan, Ben Rinnes

AFFILIATIONS

Small Luxury Hotels,
Scotland's Commended Hotels

NEAREST

MAJOR CITY:
Aberdeen - 60 miles/75 mins

MAJOR AIRPORT:
Aberdeen - 55 miles/70 mins

RAILWAY STATION:
Elgin - 12 miles/15 mins

RESERVATIONS

Toll free in US/Canada: 800-525-4800

ACCESS CODES

LX

"You've either got, or you haven't got style. Cringletie House has got more than its fair share of the stuff"

Bill Clapperton, Edinburgh Evening News

CRINGLETIE HOUSE HOTEL

Country mansion

Peebles,
Borders EH45 8PL

Telephone 01721 730233
Fax 01721 730244

PROPRIETORS

Mr and Mrs Stanley Maguire

ROOM RATES

1 Single £52.50 - £65
12 Doubles/Twins £98 - £104
Includes full breakfast and VAT

CHARGE/CREDIT CARDS

• MC • VI

ACCOLADES

S.T.B. ♛♛♛♛ Highly Commended
A.A. ★★★ ❀ 71%
The Good Hotel Guide

FACILITIES

Croquet, gardens, tennis
Golf, riding and fishing nearby

RESTRICTIONS

No facilities for disabled guests

ATTRACTIONS

Edinburgh,
Traquair,
Abbotsford,
Melrose Abbey,
Jedburgh Abbey

AFFILIATIONS

Independent

NEAREST

MAJOR CITY:
Edinburgh - 20 miles/35 mins

MAJOR AIRPORT:
Edinburgh - 25 miles/40 mins

RAILWAY STATION:
Edinburgh - 20 miles/30 mins

RESERVATIONS

Direct with hotel

ACCESS CODES

Not applicable

Splendidly romantic – and the food comes highly recommended

Cringletie House Hotel is a romantically splendid mansion house, set in 28 acres of gardens and woodland, twenty miles south of Edinburgh, and two miles north of Peebles. Its location, just half an hour's drive from Edinburgh, makes it a convenient overnight stop from which to visit the city, and return to peaceful rural surroundings.

Cringletie has retained the same atmosphere of a private country house which is owned and run by the Maguire family. The bedrooms are all tastefully decorated and furnished to a high standard of comfort with en suite bathrooms. There are magnificent views from every room. There is an all weather tennis court, putting green and croquet lawn.

Recommended for good food since 1971, Aileen Maguire and her kitchen team provide imaginative dishes. Fresh local produce is used, including fruit and vegetables from the two acre walled kitchen garden featured in Geraldene Holt's 'The Gourmet Garden'.

Quotes from independent guidebooks include: 'Excellent in every way. Friendly, efficient service and outstanding food. Probably the best country house hotel we have visited during the past five years.' 'A very peaceful place; the only noise is the sheep and the birds.'

LOCATION

20 miles from Edinburgh, 2 miles north of Peebles, on A703.

" A magical experience! By far our best ever in many years of quality travel. A must on any quality itinerary "

Sally Miller, California

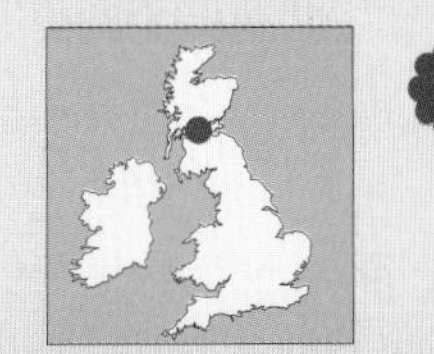

Baronial mansion and estate — CROMLIX HOUSE

A country pursuits heaven and so close to Edinburgh and Glasgow

Built in 1874 as a family residence, Cromlix retains its original character and features, including a charming chapel – perfect for weddings.

The imposing exterior belies a 'comfortable' and 'homely' interior. The feeling is that of a much loved home which invites relaxation. In the true traditions of country house hospitality, nothing is 'too precious' or pretentious – everything about Cromlix is genuine, including the sense of history.

As you would expect, Cromlix is furnished throughout with antiques, fine furniture and paintings. The six bedrooms and eight very spacious suites with private sitting rooms, offer comfort and luxury. Two of the five public rooms are typical of a Victorian shooting lodge.

Dining at Cromlix is an experience to be savoured. Our award winning staff prepare a fresh menu daily. Vegetarian, special and lighter diets are readily catered for.

Country pursuits are extensive, whether it be fishing, shooting or simply enjoying the land which is rich in wildlife. By advance arrangement: trout and salmon fishing; sporting, clay shooting. Nearby: 10 golf courses, Glenturret Distillery and a wealth of historical treasures. Day trips can easily embrace much of the Lowlands, Southern Highlands, Oban, The Trossachs and many other areas of beauty.

LOCATION

5 minutes off the A9 north of Dunblane through Kinbuck Village on the B8033.

Kinbuck By Dunblane, Nr Stirling Perthshire FK15 9JT

Telephone 01786 822125
Fax 01786 825450

PROPRIETORS

David and Ailsa Assenti

ROOM RATES

Single occupancy	*£80 - £100*
6 Doubles/Twins	*£120 - £180*
8 Suites	*£160 - £260*

Includes full breakfast and VAT

CHARGE/CREDIT CARDS

 • *DC* • *MC* • *VI*

ACCOLADES

S.T.B. ♛♛♛♛ *De Luxe*
A.A. ★★★ ❀❀
The Good Hotel Guide
Taste of Scotland

FACILITIES

Garden, croquet, tennis, riding, fishing, heli-pad
3 meeting rooms/max 40 people
Golf, riding and salmon fishing nearby

RESTRICTIONS

No facilities for disabled guests
Dogs in bedrooms only

ATTRACTIONS

Stirling Castle, Scone Palace, Glenturret Distillery, The Trossachs

AFFILIATIONS

Pride of Britain
Scotland's Heritage Hotels

NEAREST

MAJOR CITY:
Glasgow - 30 miles/35 mins
Edinburgh - 38 miles/45 mins

MAJOR AIRPORT:
Edinburgh - 35 miles/40 mins
Glasgow - 40 miles/55 mins

RAILWAY STATION:
Dunblane - 4 miles,/10 mins

RESERVATIONS

Toll free in US: 800-98-PRIDE

ACCESS CODES

Not applicable

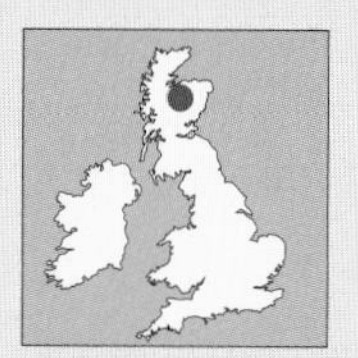

"Now I know what they mean by the Inner Smile"

Neil McLean, Sunday Times

THE CROSS

19th century tweed mill

Tweed Mill Brae,
Ardbroilach Road,
Kingussie, PH21 1TC

Telephone 01540 661166
Fax 01540 661080

PROPRIETORS
Ruth and Tony Hadley

RATES PER PERSON
9 Doubles/Twins £85
Includes dinner, breakfast and VAT

CHARGE/CREDIT CARDS

• MC • VI

ACCOLADES
A.A. ★★ 80%
The Good Hotel Guide
Ackerman Heidseick Clover Leaf Award
Scottish Restaurant of the Year Award 1993/94

FACILITIES
Garden
Golf, fishing, shooting, gliding, 4x4 driving and riding nearby

RESTRICTIONS
No children under 12 years
Facilities for disabled guests in the restaurant only
No smoking in bedrooms and restaurant

ATTRACTIONS
Highland Folk Park,
Cairngorm Mountains,
Malt Whisky Distilleries,
Highland Wildlife Centre

AFFILIATIONS
Independent

NEAREST
MAJOR CITY:
Inverness - 40 miles/45 mins

MAJOR AIRPORT:
Inverness - 45 miles/45 mins

RAILWAY STATION:
Kingussie - ½ mile/3 mins

RESERVATIONS
Direct with hotel

ACCESS CODES
Not applicable

Superb comfort, sensational food in the heart of the Cairngorms

Built as a tweed mill in the 1800s when the local Laird wanted to create more income, The Cross at Kingussie opened in 1993 as a "Restaurant with Rooms". Its original character and features have been carefully preserved: rough stone walls and heavy beams in the restaurant, coombed ceilings in the upstairs lounge.

The nine bedrooms are styled individually, with a mixture of canopied, twin and king bedded rooms. Each has its own private bathroom and controllable heating. Books and paintings are there to help you relax; there are no TVs. Each bedroom has a direct-dial telephone, and a fax is also available.

The spacious restaurant uses only the finest ingredients, with an emphasis on Scottish products: venison, mountain hare, salmon, scallops, to name but a few, cooked to produce dishes with a deceptive simplicity. Ruth Hadley's love and passion for food shines through as you breakfast with freshly baked croissants, lunch on the terrace, enjoy a glass of champagne and peruse the award-winning wine list, and dine from the cuisine that won the Macallan Decanter Scottish Restaurant of the Year 1993/4 award.

The Cross stands in four idyllic waterside acres, 250 metres from the centre of Kingussie, with its Highland Folk Museum. This village is the capital of Badenoch, "the drowned land". The Gynach which flows beside the old mill varies from a gentle burn in summer to a raging torrent in spring when the snows melt. On the hotel's semi-wilderness site are many native trees and wild flowers, and an absolute abundance of wildlife. You may see dipper, tree creeper, red squirrel and even roe deer. All around is the mountain grandeur of the Cairngorms.

LOCATION

At the junction of the A9 and A86.

"A great place to stay"

Alun J Edwards, Newport

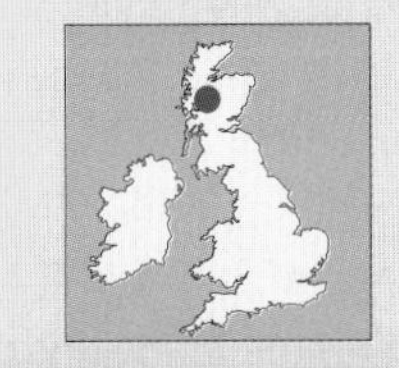

Country house

CULDEARN HOUSE

True Scottish warmth, hospitality and a kilted laird

Following extensive refurbishment this elegant house has been awarded "Scotland's Best Small Hotel for 1995" (RAC). With such a recommendation "This had to be worth a visit; so we included Culdearn House in our tour of Scotland" said a recent guest.

Situated in the heart of the Scottish highlands, Grantown on Spey is an ideal base for exploring this most beautiful area. A perfect complement to the lush surroundings is the highly individualistic Culdearn House. A small hotel where personal service and attention to detail are typified by Alasdair Little, the kilted laird himself, the perfect host. Culdearn has just nine immaculate guestrooms: each is unique with romantic names like Dunrobin Castle.

Stays at Culdearn House are fully inclusive of room and meals which gives Alasdair and his staff a chance to indoctrinate guests into the ways of true Scottish hospitality. On a typical stay, relaxing in the lounge before dinner, the laird takes it upon himself to introduce your fellow guests, serves drinks and discusses the evening's menu. All the food is prepared by Isobel and her staff from fresh produce obtained from the local estates and the Moray coast.

In the well appointed dining room, service is informal and friendly, but correct, and deftly handled by smiling kilted girls while Alasdair tends to the wine. Occasionally a piper and highland dancing girl in traditional dress perform for the guests after dinner.

LOCATION

Approaching Grantown from south west on A95 turn left at the 30 mph sign. Culdearn faces you.

SCOTLAND

Woodlands Terrace, Grantown on Spey, Moray PH26 3JU

Telephone 01479 872106
Fax 01479 873641

PROPRIETORS

Isobel and Alasdair Little

ROOM RATES

1 Single £49.50
8 Doubles/Twins £99
Includes full breakfast, dinner and VAT

CHARGE/CREDIT CARDS

 *• DC • JCB • MC • VI*

ACCOLADES

S.T.B. ♛♛♛ De Luxe
R.A.C. Highly Acclaimed
A.A. Q Q Q Q Q Premier Selected
R.A.C. Scotland's Best Small Hotel 1995
Taste of Scotland

FACILITIES

Croquet, garden
Golf, fishing and birdwatching nearby

RESTRICTIONS

No children under 5 years old
No facilities for disabled guests
No pets

ATTRACTIONS

Ballindalloch, Cawdor and Brodie Castles, Culloden Battlefield, Malt whisky distilleries

AFFILIATIONS

Logis of Great Britian

NEAREST

MAJOR CITY:
Inverness - 30 miles/35 mins

MAJOR AIRPORT:
Inverness - 35 miles/40 mins

RAILWAY STATION:
Aviemore -15 miles/20 mins

RESERVATIONS

Direct with hotel

ACCESS CODES

Not applicable

“ Our first taste of the spacious beauty of Scotland ”

Elizabeth Ortiz, Gourmet Magazine, USA

CULLODEN HOUSE HOTEL

Country house

Inverness, Highland IV1 2NZ

Telephone 01463 790461
Fax 01463 792181

OWNERS

Ian and Marjory McKenzie

ROOM RATES

2 Singles	£125 - £175
11 Doubles/Twins	£175 - £220
4 Four-posters	£205
6 Suites	£205 - £220

Includes full breakfast and VAT

CHARGE/CREDIT CARDS

• DC • MC • VI

ACCOLADES

S.T.B. 🏠🏠🏠🏠🏠 De Luxe

A.A. ★★★★ ❀ 67%

FACILITIES

Garden, tennis, sauna, snooker, heli-pad
2 meeting rooms/max 75 people
Golf, fishing, shooting and sailing nearby

RESTRICTIONS

No children under 10 years
No facilities for disabled guests
Pets by arrangement

ATTRACTIONS

Cawdor Castle, Clava Cairns, Loch Ness, Culloden Battlefield

AFFILIATIONS

Small Luxury Hotels

NEAREST

MAJOR CITY:
Aberdeen - 100 miles/2½ hrs

MAJOR AIRPORT:
Glasgow - 150 miles/3½ hrs
Inverness - 5 miles/10 mins

RAILWAY STATION:
Inverness - 3 miles/10 mins

RESERVATIONS

Toll free fax in US: 800-373-7987

ACCESS CODES

SABRE LX 4539
APOLLO LX 21661
SAHARA LX INVCH
AXESS LX 5602
SYSTEM1/AMADEUS LX INVCHH

Praised to the heights nearby Scotland's most famous battlefield

“Magnificent house, magnificent food”, said the prince.

“Finest meal we have had in Scotland”, said the king. And a thick file of letters from satisfied guests testify that the warmth and welcome of Culloden House is spread right across the board. Ian and Marjory are happiest when guests say, “It wasn't like a hotel at all – more like being a guest in someone's home”. The house is supremely comfortable. No-smoking garden suites are available. On summer evenings, a piper plays on the lawn.

The 20-bedroom mansion has a lively history, both for boundless hospitality and for events. Armies, spies, sieges, touchy Highland chieftains, dungeons and romance all feature in the story. Bonnie Prince Charlie ran from the house buckling on his sword to fight his last battle. And what happened when the wicked Duke of Cumberland moved in is best learned over a fine old brandy in the gracious drawing room.

The house sits in forty acres of stately parkland close to Inverness. Ideally placed for playing famous golf courses, touring the beautiful highland glens, or visiting castles, distilleries and gardens. Loch Ness with its mysterious monster is a short car-ride away. Lovely walks radiate from the house, such as along the shore of the Moray Firth, or to the “Clootie Well” where old Druid customs still survive, or to the massive bronze-age burial chambers, the Clava Cairns. Easy access by car or rail, with several flights a day from London Heathrow.

LOCATION

From Inverness, take A96 (airport/Aberdeen road). After one mile turn right at sign “Culloden”. After another mile, turn left at Culloden House Avenue.

"Much appreciated your consideration which enabled us to enjoy a real holiday. Our only regret was that our stay was all too short"

Mr Fujii, London

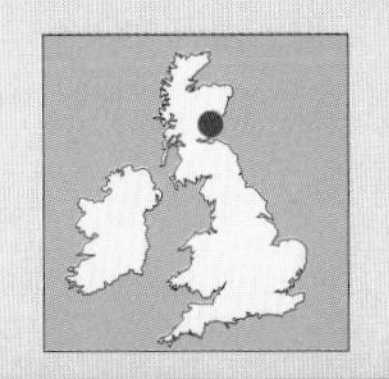

Highland house hotel

DALMUNZIE HOUSE

A warm Scottish family welcome in stupendous Highland scenery

The 17-bedroom Dalmunzie House Hotel is small enough to ensure guests are welcomed as part of the family. Yet when you stay there, your "garden" has to be one of the biggest of any British hotel: the hotel's private driveway leads on to a 6,500-acre Highland estate amidst some of Scotland's finest mountains.

Dalmunzie is run by the Winton family. Every detail is fully attended to, yet they are unobtrusive with their service. They know how their guests value a real log fire. The food, fresh from the hills and lochs, is cooked in traditional Scottish style and served to the accompaniment of fine wines from the well stocked cellar, and when you fancy a snack, a coffee or a cocktail, that's no problem.

Sixteen of the seventeen bedrooms have en-suite facilities. All are of individual character and all are centrally heated. Their charming decor and restful tranquillity reflect the ambience found everywhere at Dalmunzie. For the not-so-nimble there is a lift to the first floor.

In addition to the magnificent mountain walking, the other leisure facilities are superb. Right on the doorstep is the hotel's 9-hole golf course, the highest in Britain. There is tennis, river and loch fishing, shooting for grouse, ptarmigan and blackcock, stalking for red and roe deer, an automated clay pigeon shoot, table tennis, darts and bar billiards.

Dalmunzie is an ideal base for touring Royal Deeside, nearby castles and the Whisky Trail.

LOCATION

Turn left from A93 18 miles north of Blairgowrie at signs for Spittal O' Glenshee and Dalmunzie.

Spittal O'Glenshee,
Blairgowrie,
Perthshire PH10 7QG

Telephone 01250 885224
Fax 01250 885225

SCOTLAND

PROPRIETORS
Simon and Alexandra Winton

ROOM RATES
Single occupancy £48 - £54
17 Doubles/Twins £72 - £88
Includes full breakfast and VAT

CHARGE/CREDIT CARDS
MC • VI

ACCOLADES
S.T.B. ♛♛♛ Commended
A.A. ★★ 65%

FACILITIES
Garden, croquet, tennis, walking, fishing, clay-pigeon shooting, stalking, grouse and rough shooting, heli-pad
1 meeting room/max 20 people
Golf nearby

RESTRICTIONS
None

ATTRACTIONS
Glamis Castle,
Braemar,
Balmoral Castle,
Blair Atholl Castle,
The Whisky Trail,
Pitlochry Salmon Ladder,
Pitlochry Theatre,
Royal Deeside

AFFILIATIONS
Independent

NEAREST
MAJOR CITY:
Perth - 35 miles/55 mins

MAJOR AIRPORT:
Edinburgh - 80 miles/2 hrs

RAILWAY STATION:
Perth - 35 miles/55 mins

RESERVATIONS
Direct with hotel

ACCESS CODES
Not applicable

"Amid tall trees on a hillside, the Darroch Learg is everything a Scottish country house hotel should be"

Gilbert Summers, Fodor's

DARROCH LEARG

Country house

Braemar Road, Ballater, Aberdeenshire AB35 5UX

Telephone 013397 55443
Fax 013397 55252

PROPRIETOR
Nigel and Fiona Franks

ROOM RATES

1 Single	£43
15 Doubles/Twins	£70 - £85
3 Masters	£100

Includes full breakfast and VAT

CHARGE/CREDIT CARDS

• DC • MC • VI

ACCOLADES
S.T.B. ♕♕♕♕ Highly Commended
R.A.C. ★★★ + Merit Awards H C & R
A.A. ★★★ ❀❀ 72%
The Good Hotel Guide

FACILITIES
Garden
Golf and fishing nearby

RESTRICTIONS
Pets not allowed in public rooms

ATTRACTIONS
Balmoral Castle, Lochnagar Distillery, Crathes, Drum and Craigievar Castles, Grampian Mountains, Cairngorms

AFFILIATIONS
Scotland's Commended Hotels
The Tartan Collection

NEAREST
MAJOR CITY:
Aberdeen - 42 miles/1 hr

MAJOR AIRPORT:
Aberdeen - 42 miles/1 hr

RAILWAY STATION:
Aberdeen - 42 miles/1 hr

RESERVATIONS
Direct with hotel

ACCESS CODES
Not applicable

A "truly relaxing country house" on Royal Deeside

The Darroch Learg is everything a Scottish country house hotel should be. It was built in 1888 as a country residence on Royal Deeside, and stands in 4 acres of tall trees on the side of the rocky hill which dominates the charming town of Ballater. This fine vantage point gives panoramic views over the golf course, River Dee and Balmoral estate to the Grampians and Lochnagar, one of Scotland's highest peaks.

Five of the 20 bedrooms are in the adjacent mansion of Oakhall, built in Scottish baronial style in 1880. All are individually decorated and furnished to give each its own character.

The dining room and spacious conservatory offer a wonderful outlook to the hills of Glen Muick. A daily-changing modern Scottish dinner menu is created using the finest fresh ingredients: Aberdeen Angus beef, Scottish lamb, local game, fresh fish and seafood. It starts with delicately flavoured soups and terrines and finishes with superb Scottish cheeses. The wine list is 120 bins long, with tasting notes.

The wealth of outdoor activities includes bird watching, clay pigeon and game shooting, gliding, golf, hang gliding, hill walking, riding and pony trekking, loch and river fishing, mountain biking and skiing. The area is justly famous for its castles, the Highland Games, Royal Deeside and Balmoral Castle.

LOCATION

Take the A93 to Ballater. The Darroch Learg is situated at the western edge of the town on the main road to Braemar.

" Loved it! "

Neil Sedaka

Victorian town house

THE DEVONSHIRE HOTEL

An establishment of distinction and stylish splendour

The Devonshire Hotel of Glasgow is set in the West End of the city, only minutes from the impressive city centre's many famous attractions; The Burrell Collection, Glasgow University, Kelvingrove Art Gallery & Museum to name a few.

A majestic central staircase, painstakingly restored to the carved glory of a bygone era, sweeps the guest to the upper floors past a charming conservatory on the half-landing highlighted by original stain glass windows. Against this splendid backdrop, guests are assured individual, traditional grand country-style hospitality. Throughout, the splendour of the decor, subdued lighting and countless original paintings, reflect the status of the Devonshire Hotel.

All the rooms are individually designed with luxurious en suite facilities.

There is an intimate dining room for residents only which has superb standards and quality of food.

Loch Lomond is just twenty minutes drive from the hotel. Edinburgh is forty five minutes by train, which runs twice-hourly.

The hotel is the ideal place to relax and enjoy some of the vast collection of malt whiskies and hear all the exciting stories of their famous past guests – Michael Jackson, Whitney Houston, Bryan Adams to name a few.

LOCATION

M8 exit at Junction 17. Turn right at traffic lights at end of slip-road onto the A82, travel 1½ miles. Straight on at traffic lights by Grosvenor Hotel and turn left at 2nd traffic lights into Hyndland Road. Take first right and turn right at roundabout. The hotel is at end of the road on the right.

5 Devonshire Gardens, Glasgow G12 0UX

Telephone 0141 339 7878
Fax 0141 339 3980

PROPRIETOR
Robert C Hyndman

GENERAL MANAGER
Jeanette Montgomery

ROOM RATES

Single occupancy	*£90 - £115*
10 Doubles	*£95 - £165*
2 Four-posters	*£115 - £165*
2 Suites	*£115 - £175*

Includes VAT

CHARGE/CREDIT CARDS

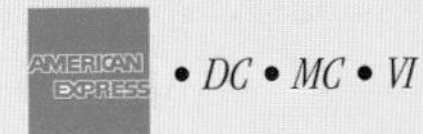

• DC • MC • VI

ACCOLADES
S.T.B. ♛♛♛♛ De Luxe
A.A. Townhouse ❀ 76%

FACILITIES
Private and exclusive dining
2 meeting rooms/max 40 people
Golf and riding nearby

RESTRICTIONS
No facilities for disabled guests
Pets at manager's discretion

ATTRACTIONS
Burrell Collection, Macintosh House, Dumbarton and Bothwell Castles, Glasgow University

AFFILIATIONS
Scotland's Commended Hotels
The Celebrated Hotels Collection

NEAREST
MAJOR CITY:
Glasgow - 1½ miles/10 mins

MAJOR AIRPORT:
Glasgow - 12 miles/20 mins

RAILWAY STATION:
Glasgow - 1½ miles/10 mins

RESERVATIONS
Toll free in US: 800-322-2403

ACCESS CODES
Not applicable

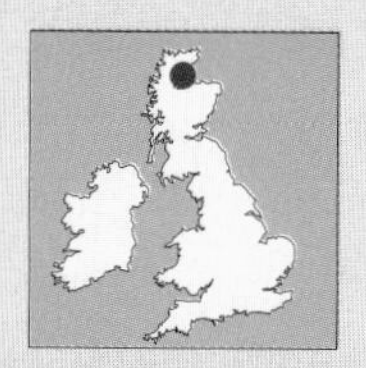

"Our short stay in the Dornoch Castle was a highlight in our tour of Scotland"

Sylvia Bromley, Kent

DORNOCH CASTLE

Former Bishop's palace

Castle Street,
Dornoch,
Sutherland IV25 3SD

Telephone 01862 810216
Fax 01862 810981

PROPRIETOR
Michael Ketchin

ROOM RATES
3 Singles £37 - £39
14 Doubles/Twins £65 - £82
Includes full breakfast and VAT

CHARGE/CREDIT CARDS

• *MC* • *VI*

ACCOLADES
S.T.B. ♛♛♛♛ Commended
R.A.C. ★★ + Merit Awards H & C
A.A. ★★ 66%

FACILITIES
Garden
Golf nearby

RESTRICTIONS
Pets allowed in bedrooms only

ATTRACTIONS
Dunrobin Castle,
Timespan Visitor's Centre,
Dornoch Cathedral,
Dornoch Town Jail

AFFILIATIONS
Scotland's Commended Hotels

NEAREST
MAJOR CITY:
Aberdeen - 140 miles/2 hrs 30 mins

MAJOR AIRPORT:
Aberdeen - 140 miles/2 hrs 30 mins
Inverness - 50 miles/1 hr 30 mins

RAILWAY STATION:
Tain - 8 miles/10 mins

RESERVATIONS
Toll free in US: 800-43-SCOTS

ACCESS CODES
Not applicable

Living history, golf and magnificence in the far north of Scotland

Formerly the Palace of the Bishops of Caithness, the present building probably dates from the late 15th or early 16th century. At different times it has served as palace, garrison, courthouse, jail, school and private residence for the Earls of Sutherland. The tower, dungeon and spiral staircase are original, the upper part of the main wing was rebuilt in the first part of the 19th century, and a new wing of 13 bedrooms was added in 1974. The hotel is personally managed by its owner Michael Ketchin.

History surrounds you, from the panelled cocktail bar to the elegant lounge, to the restaurant set in what was once the kitchen of the Bishop's Palace. Today the restaurant is one of Sutherland's finest, and so is the wine list.

Sutherland has fewer people per square mile than anywhere else in Britain, and few counties are more suited to "getting away from it all". There are high mountain peaks, rugged cliffs, spectacular seascapes, over 2,000 lochs and lochans, fresh air and wide open spaces. There is safe bathing and miles of peaceful golden sand on the beach 10 minutes' walk from the hotel. Stone circles and other prehistoric remains abound in the area. Dornoch is Sutherland's county town: 16 Earls are buried at its magnificent cathedral.

The Royal Dornoch Golf Club is one of the finest links courses in the world. It hosted the 1980 home international championships, and Tom Watson said of the course: "This is the most fun I have ever had playing golf."

LOCATION

From Inverness, take A9 north. Cross Dornoch Firth Bridge. Turn right on to A949 to Dornoch.

"We travel around a great deal. No other hotel in the British Isles has so invariably combined caring service and beautiful cooking all in a completely relaxed atmosphere"

Sonia and Patrick Stevenson

Georgian shooting lodge

DUNAIN PARK HOTEL

Secluded in six acres of gardens and woodlands

Dunain Park Hotel was originally a shooting lodge, built in Georgian times by the Duke of Gordon, and extended in Victorian times.

Edward and Ann Nicoll have owned and run Dunain Park as a hotel for ten years, which they constantly upgrade and refurbish to the highest standard. In the original part of the house there are six bedrooms all with private facilities. The Nicolls then added on six de-luxe king-bedded suites each with its own lounge and bathroom. There are also two garden cottages which are fully serviced and furnished to the same high standard of the main building and overlook the walled garden. The hotel has full central heating and there are real log fires in both main lounges.

Mrs Nicoll is in charge of the kitchen and is a Master Chef of Great Britain. The à la carte menu changes daily and uses the best local produce such as salmon, venison and highland beef. Accompanied by soft fruits, lettuce, vegetables and herbs from the kitchen garden, as well as home-made jams, jellies and chutneys, the meals prove to be innovative and irresistible.

Dunain Park is set in six acres of gardens and woodlands. Although in the countryside it is just a short trip from Inverness crossing over the Caledonian Canal. The hotel is on the A82 Fort William Road one mile from Inverness on the left hand side and only three miles from Loch Ness.

LOCATION

Heading south from Inverness on the A82, one mile from the town boundary on the left hand side.

SCOTLAND

Inverness
Inverness-shire IV3 6JN

Telephone 01463 230512
Fax 01463 230512

PROPRIETORS

Ann and Edward Nicoll

RATES PER PERSON

4 Doubles/Twins	*£55 - £69*
1 Superior Double	*£60 - £75*
1 Four-poster	*£60 - £70*
6 Suites	*£65 - £79*
2 Cottages	*£55 - £69*

Includes full breakfast and VAT

CHARGE/CREDIT CARDS

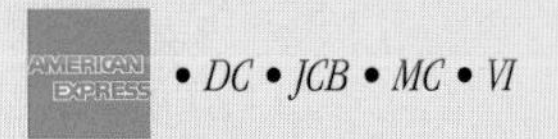

• DC • JCB • MC • VI

ACCOLADES

S.T.B. ♛♛♛♛ Highly Commended
A.A. ★★ ❀
The Good Hotel Guide

FACILITIES

Garden, croquet,
indoor pool, sauna
1 meeting room/max 8 people
Golf and fishing nearby

RESTRICTIONS

Well behaved children allowed

ATTRACTIONS

Loch Ness, Cawdor Castle,
Culloden battlefield,
Whisky Trail,
Edencourt Theatre

AFFILIATIONS

Independent

NEAREST

MAJOR CITY:
Inverness - 2 miles/5 mins

MAJOR AIRPORT:
Glasgow - 188 miles/3¾ hrs

RAILWAY STATION:
Inverness - 3 miles/10 mins

RESERVATIONS

Direct with hotel

ACCESS CODES

WORLDSPAN HK DUNAI
SABRE HK 32491

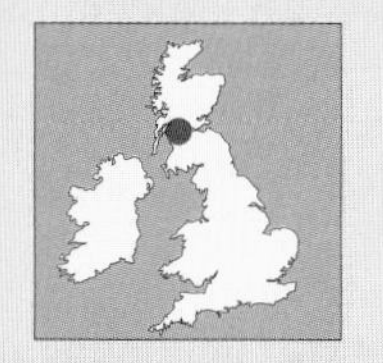

" At the Enmore Hotel everything doth gel "

Anne & John Mancino, Plymouth

ENMORE HOTEL

Gentleman's retreat

SCOTLAND

Marine Parade, Dunoon
Argyll PA23 8HH

Telephone 01369 702230
Fax 01369 702148

OWNER
Angela and David Wilson

ROOM RATES
2 Singles £41 - £85
4 Doubles/Twins £79 - £99
4 Four-posters £150
Includes full breakfast and VAT

CHARGE/CREDIT CARDS

• MC • VI

ACCOLADES
S.T.B. ♛♛♛♛ Highly Commended
A.A. ★★ ❀ 76%
A.A. Courtesy & Care Award
Taste of Scotland

FACILITIES
Garden, squash,
private shingle beach
2 meeting rooms/max 40 people
Golf, riding and fishing nearby

RESTRICTIONS
No facilities for disabled guests

ATTRACTIONS
Dunoon Golf Course,
Inverary, Loch Lomond,
Stirling, Dumbarton Castle,
Rothesay Castle

AFFILIATIONS
Scotland's Commended Hotels

NEAREST
MAJOR CITY:
Glasgow - 70 miles/1 hr

MAJOR AIRPORT:
Glasgow - 50 miles/1 hr

RAILWAY STATION:
Glasgow - 40 miles/40 mins

FERRY PORT:
Gourock - 20 mins ferry

RESERVATIONS
Toll free in US: 800-43-SCOTS
800-322-2403
800-201-7620

ACCESS CODES
Not applicable

A lot of love has been lavished on this luxury home by Holy Loch

The Enmore Hotel, set on the shore hugging A815 from Dunoon and yet only minutes away from the golf course, must surely have the best situation in the area.

Originally built in 1875 as a gentleman's retreat for a wealthy Glasgow businessman (named Wilson but absolutely no connections with the present Wilsons), the house has been enlarged over the years to now present the very best in accommodation with no less than four honeymoon/luxury suites some with jacuzzi and waterbed. The warmth and hospitality of this small but luxurious hotel is very evident – a family run hotel of the best kind.

Angela and David Wilson came to the Enmore in 1979 to find a "way of life" running their own hotel with their two children. They have spent the intervening years lovingly restoring this very pretty house into one of the best-loved hotels and restaurants in the area. For many years until 1992, the principal US naval base was just a few miles away at the beautiful Holy Loch, so the hotel is well used to American ways with even French toast and cinnamon on the breakfast menu.

David Wilson is the chef/patron who puts the same amount of care into the menu as Angela does in creating a very special place for the traveller. So leave the busy world behind and be cosseted in this beautiful but largely unknown part of Scotland – and only one hour from Glasgow Airport via the 20 minute ferry crossing.

LOCATION

On coastal route between the two ferries, one mile north of Dunoon. Travel from Glasgow either on the M8/A8 through Greenock and Gourock and over on one of the two ferries or via Loch Lomond and the A815 to Dunoon.

"It was really the highlight of our honeymoon tour in Scotland. One cannot express in words the excellence of the dinners we took and the service was as perfect"

Mr & Mrs H Seiderssticker, Germany

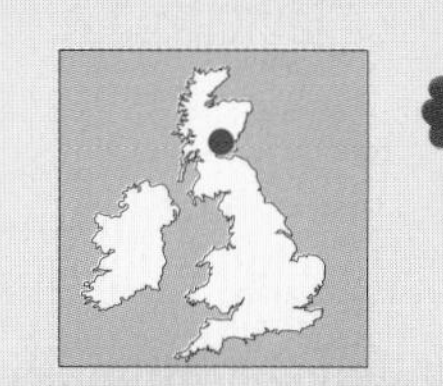

16th century dower house

FARLEYER HOUSE

An ancient croft situated in the heart of the old Castle Menzies Estate

Following the 1745 rebellion, when Charles Stuart was given refuge in the Castle, the croft was enlarged to become the bailiff's residence. Later, when Lady Stair married Sir Neil Menzies, Farleyer, by then the dower house, was again enlarged to its present size to be the main residence for the head of the Clan Menzies.

As such, historically Farleyer became known far and wide for its own particular style of exceptional hospitality, tranquillity and warmth. A flavour of that special hospitality awaits you at Farleyer today, only greatly enhanced by some of the most imaginative and exciting cuisine to be found in Britain.

Farleyer stands in some of the most beautiful scenery in Scotland. A leisurely stroll in the grounds, or a quick fun round of golf on the novel, yet challenging six-hole course will produce the most wonderful feeling of peace. Farleyer can truly host the international traveller whether on business or simply for relaxation with the family.

Situated in the centre of Scotland, Farleyer House provides a perfect base from which to visit numerous attractions and beauty spots.

Although discreetly hidden away in the beautiful Tay Valley, Farleyer is surprisingly easy to reach, approximately 1½ hours drive from Scotland's major airports at Edinburgh and Glasgow, and only 12 miles from the major A9 arterial route through Scotland.

LOCATION

A9 to Ballinghuig, A827 to Aberfeldy, then the B846 out of Aberfeldy 1 mile past Menzies Castle. (The hotel is the Dower House.)

Aberfeldy, Perthshire PH15 2JE

Telephone 01887 820332
Fax 01887 829430

OWNER

Mrs Janice Reid

MANAGING DIRECTOR

Nick White

RATES PER PERSON

5 Doubles/Twins	*£90 - £100*
4 Deluxe	*£100 - £110*
1 Family	*£100 - £110*

Includes full breakfast, dinner and VAT

CHARGE/CREDIT CARDS

• DC • MC • VI

ACCOLADES

S.T.B. ♛♛♛♛ De Luxe
The Good Hotel Guide

FACILITIES

Garden, croquet, golf, heli-pad
2 meeting rooms/max 35 people
Golf, riding, swimming pool, hunting and fishing nearby

RESTRICTIONS

No pets (kennels by prior arrangement)

ATTRACTIONS

Pitlochry, Loch Ness, The Locus Trails, Blair and Menzies Castles

AFFILIATIONS

Scotland's Commended Hotels
The Virgin Collection

NEAREST

MAJOR CITY:
Glasgow/Edinburgh - 75 miles/1½ hrs

MAJOR AIRPORT:
Glasgow/Edinburgh - 70 miles/1½ hrs

RAILWAY STATION:
Pitlochry - 15 miles/30 mins

RESERVATIONS

Toll free in US: 800-43-SCOTS

ACCESS CODES

Not applicable

“Everything was excellent – facilities, food and its presentation and we cannot speak too highly of the staff”

C & M Price

FERNHILL

Coastal hotel

Heugh Road,
Portpatrick,
Dumfries & Galloway DG9 8TD

Telephone 01776 810220
Fax 01776 810596

PROPRIETORS
Anne and Hugh Harvie

ROOM RATES

2 Singles	£55 - £85
18 Doubles/Twins	£79 - £99

Includes full breakfast and VAT

CHARGE/CREDIT CARDS

• DC • MC • VI

ACCOLADES
S.T.B. ♛♛♛♛ Highly Commended
R.A.C. ★★★
A.A. ★★★ 66%
Taste of Scotland

FACILITIES
Garden
Golf, fishing, indoor leisure centre, swimming pool, bowls, rough shooting, sailing, water skiing and scuba diving nearby

RESTRICTIONS
No children
No pets allowed in public rooms

ATTRACTIONS
Culzean Castle, Logan Botanical Gardens, southwest coastline

AFFILIATIONS
Scotland's Commended Hotels

NEAREST
MAJOR CITY:
Glasgow - 90 miles/2 hrs

MAJOR AIRPORT:
Prestwick - 50 miles/1 hr 15 mins

RAILWAY STATION:
Stranraer - 8 miles/10 mins

RESERVATIONS
Toll free in US: 800-43-SCOTS

ACCESS CODES
Not applicable

The 4-crown hotel that remembers it was once a family home

The Harvie family has loved Fernhill for many years. As they have improved and cosseted it, the Fernhill has grown from a boarding house into a fully licensed, four crown, highly commended hotel. The individual attention of owners Anne and Hugh Harvie, with the backing of their friendly, helpful staff continues to ensure that guests lack for nothing. Little wonder that people return time and again.

All 20 bedrooms are high quality, with the luxury rooms fully living up to their names. The Restaurant has an international reputation for the excellence of its cuisine. Like the cocktail bar and lounge, it provides panoramic views over Portpatrick and the sea. As well as full restaurant service, the Fernhill has an extensive bar meals menu. Packed lunches, vegetarian meals and children's high teas are provided on request.

Portpatrick village is rich in history and legend, and well deserves its title as the jewel in the crown of Galloway. This region of south west Scotland is a magic land of picturesque villages, majestic mountains and secluded glens. The coast offers an astonishing array of cliffs, bays and golden-sanded, family-safe beaches. The warmth of the Gulf Stream encourages some of Britain's finest sub-tropical gardens and palm trees: Logan Botanical Gardens and three other superb gardens are within 10 miles of the hotel.

This is ideal golfing country: spring comes early and the light stays playably longer in the autumn evenings. The hotel has five clubs nearby, and offers special golfing breaks.

LOCATION

Just after entering Portpatrick village, fork right at the war memorial. Drive along Heugh Road, the hotel is on the left.

“ As a 'professional' hotel resident, I can confidently say that The Gean House is one of the outstanding British hotel experiences ”

Bob Cheshire, England

Edwardian country house

THE GEAN HOUSE

Originally a wedding present, this house can now be appreciated by all

The Gean House was commissioned in 1910 by Alexander Forrester-Paton, a leading industrialist, as a wedding gift for his son. Now fully restored and beautifully furnished, this architecturally significant house features an elegant reception hall with inglenook fireplace and a minstrels gallery which offers fine views of the nearby Ochil Hills.

The team of young chefs pursue excellence in the kitchen, where meals are dictated by the availability of good quality Scottish produce. Mouthwatering dishes are prepared with skill and flair using seafood, beef, venison and game, however the speciality of the house is the “Bread and Butter Pudding” – presented like a soufflé and highly recommended!

The Gean enjoys a central location, situated 45 minutes equidistant from Edinburgh and Glasgow International Airports, and offers an ideal base for touring or golfing holidays. The championship courses of St. Andrews and Carnoustie are within easy driving distance with many inland courses in the immediate locale. Additional local attractions are the interesting historic town of Stirling and a wealth of woollen mills where visitors have the opportunity to purchase cashmeres direct from the manufacturer. Hill walking, falconry, riding and fishing can all be arranged at Gean House. Truly a magnificent discovery.

LOCATION

From Edinburgh take M9 leaving at Junction 7. Take the A876 to Kincardine, the A907 to Alloa and B9096 to Tullibody. Gean House is 1 mile along on the left. From Glasgow take M8 leaving at Junction 9 take A91, then A907 to Alloa, B9096 via Tullibody as before.

Gean Park, Tullibody Road, Alloa, Clackmannanshire FK10 2HS

Telephone 01259 219275
Fax 01259 213827

PROPRIETORS

Dr and Mrs P L Frost

ROOM RATES

Single occupancy £80
6 Doubles £120 - £140
Includes full breakfast, fruit, shortbread and VAT

CHARGE/CREDIT CARDS

• DC • MC • VI

ACCOLADES

S.T.B. ♛♛♛♛ De Luxe
The Good Hotel Guide
'Overall Excellence' award-winner from Taste of Scotland

FACILITIES

Gardens
Golf, riding and fishing nearby
3 meeting rooms/max 100 people

RESTRICTIONS

No pets

ATTRACTIONS

Stirling Castle, The Trossachs, Loch Lomond, Edinburgh, Glasgow, Mill Trail

AFFILIATIONS

McFarland Ltd, USA
The Celebrated Hotels Collection

NEAREST

MAJOR CITY:
Edinburgh - 22 miles/45 mins
Glasgow - 24 miles/1 hr

MAJOR AIRPORT:
Edinburgh - 22 miles/45 mins

RAILWAY STATION:
Stirling - 7 miles/10 mins

RESERVATIONS

Toll free in US: 800-322-2403

ACCESS CODES

Not applicable

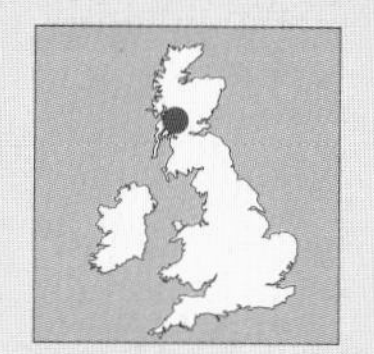

"An exquisite private home in a breathtaking setting"

C Battacharyya, Northampton

GLENFEOCHAN HOUSE

Victorian country mansion

Kilmore, by Oban, Argyllshire PA34 4QR

Telephone 01631 770273
Fax 01631 770624

OWNERS
Mr and Mrs David Baber and James Petley

ROOM RATES
3 Doubles £128 - £134
Includes full breakfast and VAT

CHARGE/CREDIT CARDS

• MC • VI

ACCOLADES
S.T.B. ♛♛♛ De Luxe
The Good Hotel Guide

FACILITIES
Croquet, gardens, heli-pad, Victorian arboretum, Salmon/sea trout fishing in season
Golf nearby

RESTRICTIONS
No children under 10 yrs
No pets
No smoking

ATTRACTIONS
Inverary Castle, Crarae and Arduaine Gardens, Oban Distillery, Islands of Mull, Iona and Staffa

AFFILIATIONS
Independent

NEAREST
MAJOR CITY:
Glasgow - 95 miles/2 1/2 hrs
MAJOR AIRPORT:
Glasgow - 90 miles/2 1/2 hrs
RAILWAY STATION:
Oban - 5 miles/10 mins
FERRY PORT:
Oban - 5 miles/10 mins

RESERVATIONS
Direct with hotel

ACCESS CODES
Not applicable

A discreet and personal private house with an unrivalled garden

Glenfeochan House is a listed, turreted Victorian country mansion at the head of Loch Feochan, built in 1875 and set amidst a 350-acre estate of hills, lochs, rivers and pasture. The house is surrounded by a mature six-acre garden (open to the public) and a one and half-acre walled garden with herbaceous borders, vegetables, fruit and herb beds.

The house has recently been carefully restored. Beautiful fabrics and family antiques fill the rooms. Original ornate plasterwork and the carved American pine staircase with parget-ed canopy lead guests to three large comfortable bedrooms. The views over the garden and through to the Loch are spectacular.

The Victorian arboretum is 'one of the great gardens of the Highlands'. Trees, some planted in 1840, make a wonderful canopy for tender rhododendron and rare shrubs. The herbaceous borders are a blaze of colour providing many of the flowers that fill the house.

The superb cuisine is provided by Patricia, who taught at the London Cordon Bleu. Excellent fresh food, mainly found on the estate – wild salmon, sea trout, either served fresh or smoked traditionally, is a speciality. Game fishing in season is available to guests.

David and Patricia Baber, and her son James Petley, are always at hand to make guests feel at home in their beautiful house. A superb place to stay while touring the Highlands and Islands.

LOCATION

At the head of Loch Feochan, 5 miles south of Oban.

" A dolphin is a pretty sight from a bedroom window "

The Honourable James Stuart, Morayshire, Scotland

Leisure club

THE GOLF VIEW HOTEL

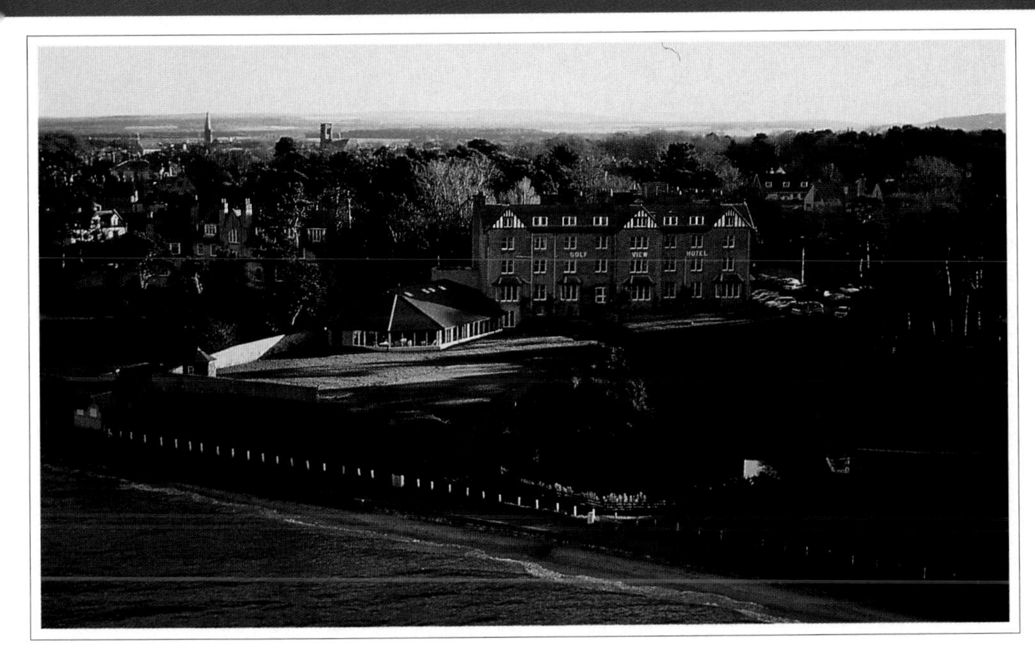

A sporranful of things to eat, drink, see and do

Watching dolphins at play in the sea in front of the Golf View is not the only reason guests choose to stay here.

There are 47 lovely rooms, many with sea views, each with private bathroom, satellite television, and direct dial telephones. Not to mention the acclaimed restaurant and bar serving fine food and drink drawn from the countryside around. A stunning conservatory has been added (early '96) overlooking the Moray Firth.

This is a golfers' dream; next to the Nairn Championship Course, there are another 17 gems within one hour's drive – including Royal Dornoch. You can relax beside the indoor swimming pool with spa, sauna and steam room, work out in the Nautilus Fitness Centre or mix it with a tour of one of the many historic houses and sites for which the area is famous.

From Edwardian times, Nairn has appealed to a variety of outdoor sport lovers; its climate is comparatively benign and the landscape a picture – miles of sandy beaches at the foot of a hinterland of mixed farming, forests and heather-covered moorland interlaced with lochs and rivers. There is a pair of Scotland's finest woollen mills, a clutch of famous distilleries, a trio of celebrated salmon smokeries, and a brace of world-famous sites – Cawdor Castle and Loch Ness – virtually on the doorstep. Two-centre breaks are available with our sister hotel, The Royal Golf Hotel at Dornoch (*see page 46*).

LOCATION

Travelling from Inverness to Nairn on A96 turn left at Parish church into Seabank Road. Drive to bottom of road and hotel is on the right.

Seabank Road, Nairn, Nr Inverness IV12 4HD

Telephone 01667 452301
Fax 01667 455267

OWNERS

The Sword family

ROOM RATES

5 Singles	*£57 - £79*
38 Doubles/Twins	*£80 - £120*
1 Suite	*£100 - £140*
3 Family	*£80 - £120*

Includes full breakfast and VAT

CHARGE/CREDIT CARDS

• DC • MC • VI

ACCOLADES

S.T.B. ♛♛♛♛♛ Commended
A.A. ★★★★ 61%

FACILITIES

Garden, indoor pool, tennis, jacuzzi, sauna, gym, heli-pad
2 meeting rooms/max 120 people
Golf, riding and fishing nearby

RESTRICTIONS

No facilities for disabled guests
Pets by prior arrangement

ATTRACTIONS

Loch Ness, Aviemore, Cawdor Castle, Whisky Trail, Culloden Battlefield

AFFILIATIONS

Scotlands Commended Hotels
Taste of Scotland

NEAREST

MAJOR CITY:
Inverness - 16 miles/20 mins

MAJOR AIRPORT:
Glasgow - 160 miles/3½ hrs
Inverness - 9 miles/15 mins

RAILWAY STATION:
Nairn - 2 miles/3 mins

RESERVATIONS

Toll free in US: 800-43-SCOTS

ACCESS CODES

Not applicable

"Long live Greywalls, so dear in our hearts"

Edouard Van Vyve, Antwerp

GREYWALLS

Country retreat

Muirfield,
Gullane,
East Lothian EH31 2EG

Telephone 01620 842144
Fax 01620 842241

PROPRIETORS
Giles and Ros Weaver

ROOM RATES

4 Singles	£95 - £143.50
17 Doubles/Twins	£155 - £170
1 Four-poster	£170

Includes full breakfast and VAT

CHARGE/CREDIT CARDS

• DC • MC • VI

ACCOLADES
S.T.B. ♛♛♛♛ Highly Commended
R.A.C. ★★★ + Merit Awards H C & R
A.A. ★★★ ❀❀

FACILITIES
Garden
Golf and beaches

RESTRICTIONS
None

ATTRACTIONS
Tantallon Castle,
Dirleton Castle,
Edinburgh,
Edinburgh Castle,
Holyrood House,
numerous golf courses

AFFILIATIONS
Pride of Britain

NEAREST
MAJOR CITY:
Edinburgh - 18 miles/35 mins

MAJOR AIRPORT:
Edinburgh - 25 miles/40 mins

RAILWAY STATION:
Drem - 2 miles/5 mins

RESERVATIONS
Toll free in US: 800-544-9856

ACCESS CODES
Not applicable

Follow in the footsteps of Nicklaus, Faldo, Edward VII and King Hussein

Sir Edward Lutyens, architect of the British Embassy in Washington and the Cenotaph in Whitehall, designed Greywalls in 1901. King Edward VII stayed here: you can write your postcards in the panelled library he loved. King Hussein of Jordan is a more recent royal visitor.

Greywalls is next to Muirfield golf course. Past guests including Arnold Palmer, Jack Nicklaus, Lee Trevino, Greg Norman and Nick Faldo are all part of the Greywalls story.

Greywalls still feels like a family home. The warmth of hospitality from Giles and Ros Weaver today makes guests feel like honoured family friends.

There are 22 comfortable, cosy bedrooms each with its own bathroom; many are furnished with antiques. There is a Steinway grand piano, a sunny Edwardian tea room and a small blue bar with a fine stock of whiskies.

Dedicated chefs use the very best of local produce to create outstanding meals worthy of the acclaim they receive. There are hearty breakfasts, rich afternoon teas – all leading up to dinner!

Outside are the gardens that Lutyens himself helped meticulously plan. Within 8 miles are 10 golf courses, long sandy beaches, nature reserves renowned for bird life, and ancient ruined castles. For a change of pace, the city of Edinburgh with its fascinating shops and cultural wealth is 25 minutes' drive away.

LOCATION

Link from M8, M9 or M90 Motorways to A198 Edinburgh City Bypass.

" Thank you for the delightful visit to your lovely inn. You have made our trip to Scotland very special "

Russ & Diane Curtis, Cedar Falls, Iowa

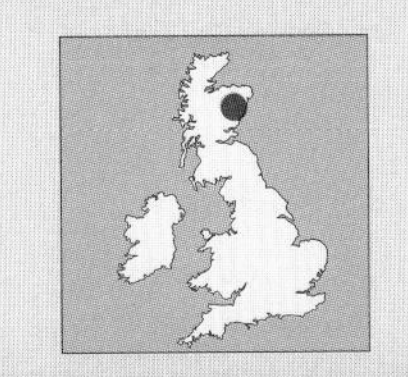

19th century highland lodge

HAZLEHURST LODGE

The definitive B & B that reflects the creative spirit of the Highlands

Hazlehurst was built in 1880 as coachman's lodge to Aboyne Castle, seat of the Marquis of Huntly, chief of Clan Gordon. Once it was home to Robert Milne, photographer to Queen Victoria at nearby Balmoral.

Anne Strachan, with her family origins on Deeside, has created an intriguing place to stay. Hazlehurst is the epitome of traditional Victorian Highland architecture, built in rose granite with crowstepped gables. It offers an unusually high standard of accommodation, with an unexpected mix of old and new. The specially commissioned cherrywood furniture reflects a continuing tradition of Scottish craft and design.

Hazlehurst is a noted "restaurant with rooms". A different menu is created every day, each one special. Anne's love of real cooking derives from her years of experience of fine European cuisine, combined with her memories of the Scottish country kitchen. She uses game from the ancient forests, fish fresh from the sea and rivers, and herbs, fruit and wild mushrooms gathered from an unpolluted countryside.

Hazlehurst is a creative environment in the heart of Royal Deeside with its many castles and access to the finest whisky distilleries. For the sports minded there is salmon fishing, deer stalking, grouse and pheasant shooting, horse riding and trekking. Hazlehurst is accredited by Gleneagles Hotel and golfing holidays can be extended to enjoy the Highland courses which are close at hand.

LOCATION

Hazlehurst Lodge stands in a wooded garden in the village of Aboyne, 30 miles west of Aberdeen on the A93 road to Perth.

Ballater Road, Aboyne, Aberdeenshire AB34 5HY

Telephone 013398 86921
Fax 013398 86660

E Mail *hazlehurst.lodge@nest.org.uk*

SCOTLAND

PROPRIETOR

Anne Strachan

ROOM RATES

Single occupancy	*£35 - £64*
5 Doubles/Twins	*£64 - £80*
1 Suite	*£90 - £110*

Includes full breakfast and VAT

CHARGE/CREDIT CARDS

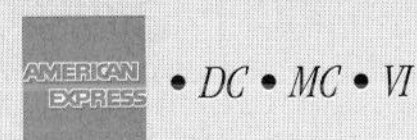

• DC • MC • VI

ACCOLADES

S.T.B. De Luxe
Taste of Scotland

FACILITIES

Garden
Golf, fishing, riding, hunting, gliding, biking, trekking and skiing nearby

RESTRICTIONS

Disabled facilities in restaurant only

ATTRACTIONS

Balmoral Castle,
Crathes Castle,
Drum Castle,
Nature conservation area,
Whisky Trail

AFFILIATIONS

The Tartan Collection

NEAREST

MAJOR CITY:
Aberdeen - 32 miles/55 mins

MAJOR AIRPORT:
Aberdeen - 38 miles/1 hr
Glasgow - 150 miles/3¼ hrs
Edinburgh - 119 miles/2 hrs 40 mins

RAILWAY STATION:
Aberdeen - 32 miles/55 mins

RESERVATIONS

Direct with hotel

ACCESS CODES

Not applicable

"Absolutely fantastic in every way – many, many thanks"

Lady Clare Macdonald, Skye

THE HOWARD

Georgian town house

32-36 Great King Street
Edinburgh EH3 6QH

Telephone 0131 557 3500
Fax 0131 557 6515

GENERAL MANAGER
Jonathan Phillips

ROOM RATES

4 Singles	£80 - £140
10 Doubles/Twins	£140 - £180
2 Suites	£255

CREDIT CARDS

• DC • MC • VI

ACCOLADES
S.T.B. ♛♛♛♛ Highly Commended
A.A Townhouse 71%
The Good Hotel Guide

FACILITIES
No. 36 Restaurant
2 meeting rooms/max 30 people
Gardens nearby

RESTRICTIONS
Pets by arrangement

ATTRACTIONS
Edinburgh, Edinburgh Castle,
Holyrood House,
National Gallery,
Fringe Festival, Military Tattoo,
Edinburgh 'Old Town',
Edinburgh 'New Town'

AFFILIATIONS
The Celebrated Hotels Collection

NEAREST
MAJOR CITY:
Edinburgh

MAJOR AIRPORT:
Edinburgh - 8 miles/25 mins

RAILWAY STATION:
Waverley - 1 mile/5 mins

RESERVATIONS
Toll free in US: 800-322-2403

ACCESS CODES
Not applicable

Select, intimate and beautifully furnished

The Howard is situated in the heart of Edinburgh's New Town, an area built in an extraordinary explosion of creativity between 1766 and 1840. This part of the city is one of the biggest Georgian developments on earth and features wide cobbled streets and private gardens.

The hotel is a conversion of three houses to form sixteen luxurious and delightfully furnished bedrooms. From the discreet front entrance through to the drawing room and reception lounge with their comfortable chairs and sofas, the feeling is of being in someone's home.

The bedrooms and suites have been decorated with inspired taste using rich, co-ordinated colour schemes. Many bathrooms feature free-standing claw feet baths, individual power showers, thick towels and bathrobes.

The No. 36 Restaurant, with large round tables as well as intimate tables for two, is open for dinner every night. Both à la carte and set menus are available featuring modern interpretations of classical dishes such as herb-crusted salmon with green lentils and plum sauce, medallions of beef with polenta, bell peppers and madeira sauce. The wine list, like the menu changes with great frequency in order to retain balance and harmony with the cuisine.

LOCATION

Travelling east along Princes Street, turn left into St Davids Street. Go to end of road. Turn left, first right at lights. Great King Street is 3rd on right.

“I took the high road in a snowy storm and found a real Scottish hotel. A cheerful welcome, a wee dram, mouthwatering food and a cosy bed”

Gareth Roberts, North Carolina

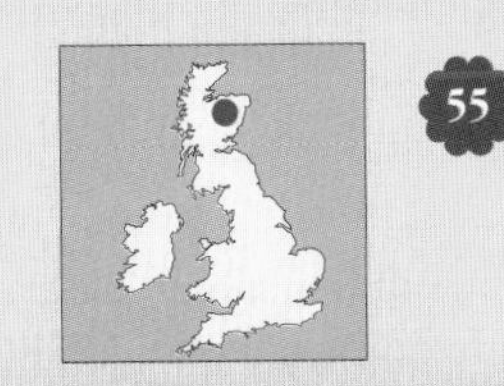

17th century coaching inn

INVERCAULD ARMS HOTEL

Its reputation is only surpassed by the breathtaking mountain views

This 17th century coaching inn is a well known establishment not least because it marks the site where the Earl of Mar raised the standard during the famous 1715 uprising. It has always been an inn/hotel, except when taken over as a Belgian School during the 2nd World War.

It was purchased by Mount Charlotte Investments in 1985, and a major £2.8 million refurbishment was completed in 1990. All 68 bedrooms now have bath and shower, colour television, hospitality tray, hair dryer and direct dial telephones. A drying room is provided for skiers, shooters and hill walkers.

The ‘Colonels Bed’ (named after a local rock formation) provides an excellent conference and banqueting facility. The hotel's cocktail bar has an impressive range of whiskies from around Scotland.

The hotel now enjoys an excellent reputation locally with a wide variety of dishes with both Scottish and international influences. The Castleview Restaurant, with its breathtaking mountainous scenic views, overlooks Braemar Castle, part of the vast Invercauld Estate.

A vast array of local activities make it an excellent base for skiing (Glenshee), hill walking, mountain biking, abseiling, off road driving, pony treking, clay-pigeon shooting, as well as more passive pursuits, such as whisky and castle trails, the Braemar Highland Heritage Centre and golf courses.

It all adds to an idealistic tranquil location for business or pleasure.

LOCATION

On the eastern edge of Braemar on the main A93 Perth-Aberdeen road.

Braemar,
Aberdeenshire AB35 5YR

Telephone 013397 41605
Fax 013397 41428

SCOTLAND

GENERAL MANAGER

Kathy McKeown

ROOM RATES

5 Singles	*£70*
62 Doubles/Twins	*£95*
1 Studio	*£110 - £125*

Includes full breakfast and VAT

CHARGE/CREDIT CARDS

• *DC* • *JCB* • *MC* • *VI*

ACCOLADES

S.T.B. ♛♛♛♛ Commended
R.A.C. ★★★
A.A. ★★★ 68%

FACILITIES

1 meeting room/max 70 people
Golf, riding, fishing and mountain biking nearby

RESTRICTIONS

No pets in public areas

ATTRACTIONS

The Braemer Highland Heritage Centre, Balmoral, Braemar Castle, Royal Lochnagar

AFFILIATIONS

A Thistle Country House Hotel

NEAREST

MAJOR CITY:
Aberdeen - 57 miles/1 hr 10 mins

MAJOR AIRPORT:
Edinburgh - 120 miles.2 hrs
Aberdeen - 60 miles/1 hr

RAILWAY STATION:
Perth - 58 miles/1 hr 10 mins
Aberdeen - 57 miles/1 hr 10 mins

RESERVATIONS

Toll free in US/Canada: 800-847-4358
Toll free in Australia: 800-062-055

ACCESS CODES

AMADEUS/SYSTEM 1 TI ABZINV
APOLLO TI 16950
SABRE TI 24206
WORLDSPAN TI 8556

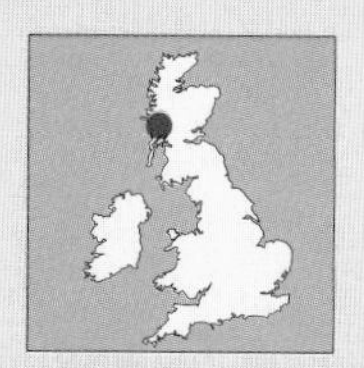

" Superlatives are often over-used, but not here. This is a gem of a place, strikingly different, wonderful "

Jack Macmillan MBE, Chairman, Taste of Scotland

INVERCRERAN COUNTRY HOUSE HOTEL *Country mansion*

Glen Creran, by Oban, Appin, PA38 4BJ

Telephone 01631 730414
Fax 01631 730532

E-Mail *tin@novalink.com*

PROPRIETORS
The Kersley family

GENERAL MANAGER
Colin Kersley

ROOM RATES

2 Singles	£50 - £62
6 Doubles	£94 - £124
1 Suite	£138

Includes full breakfast and VAT

CHARGE/CREDIT CARDS

• MC • VI

ACCOLADES
S.T.B. ♛♛♛♛ De Luxe

FACILITIES
Gardens,sauna, fishing, heli-pad
Heated kennels for dogs
1 meeting room/max 40 people
Fishing and clay-pigeon shooting nearby

RESTRICTIONS
No children under 5 years
No pets allowed in hotel

ATTRACTIONS
West Highlands, Fort William, Glen Coe, Dunstaffnage Castle, Oban, Islands of Mull, Iona, Lismore, Staffa

AFFILIATIONS
Scotland's Heritage Hotels

NEAREST
MAJOR CITY:
Oban - 18 miles/30 mins

MAJOR AIRPORT:
Glasgow - 95 miles/1 1/4 hrs

RAILWAY STATION:
Oban - 18 miles/30 mins

RESERVATIONS
Toll free in US: 800-43-SCOTS
Toll free fax in US: 800-646-1620

ACCESS CODES
SABRE HK 30591
APOLLO HT 06886
WORLDSPAN HK INVER

Elegance and luxury in a wild and beautiful landscape

Set in the wild, beautiful landscape of Glen Creran, the Invercreran Country House Hotel commands one of the most sensational mountain views in Scotland.

In contrast to the mountains of Ben Sgulaird and Ben Fhionnlaidh, the uniquely-styled mansion house stands in 25 acres of mature gardens and woodlands. Beyond the delightful seclusion of the grounds you overlook Glen Creran with a panorama of mountains beyond.

Three generations of the Kersley family are your hosts and are involved in all aspects of what is truly a family hotel.

Invercreran enjoys a deserved reputation as an outstanding country house hotel, with all the comforts and service of a first class hotel.

The cuisine at Invercreran is wonderful, being blessed with a marvellous wild larder of shellfish, game birds, and prime meats, all presented to delight the eye and please the palate.

Two to three hours drive north of Glasgow and Edinburgh, Invercreran is ideally located for touring the West Highlands and Islands, Argyll and Mull of Kintyre.

The surrounding area offers all manner of possibilities, providing peaceful walks among mountains and meadows or along river banks. While further afield the romantic islands of Mull, Lismore and Iona beckon. The towns of Oban, Fort William and Inverness are also of interest.

LOCATION

Just off the A828 Oban to Fort William Road, 14 miles north of the Connel bridge, 18 miles south of the Ballachulish bridge. Travelling to Invercreran at the head of Loch Creran, continue on the minor road running north-east into Glen Creran. The hotel is 3/4 mile on the left.

"I never saw a lovelier or more romantic spot"

Queen Victoria, 1873

Stately manor

INVERLOCHY CASTLE

Torlundy,
Fort William,
Inverness-shire PH33 6SN

Telephone 01397 702177
Fax 01397 702953

OWNER/PROPRIETOR
Grete Hobbs

GENERAL MANAGER
Michael Leonard

ROOM RATES
14 Doubles/Twins £200 - £280
3 Suites £285 - £350
Includes VAT

CHARGE/CREDIT CARDS

• MC • VI

ACCOLADES
S.T.B. ♛♛♛♛♛ De Luxe
R.A.C. Blue Ribbon Award ★★★★
A.A. ★★★★ ❀❀❀
The Good Hotel Guide

FACILITIES
Garden, croquet, tennis, snooker, heli-pad
Golf, fishing, skiing, riding,
stalking, guided hill walking,
yachting and hunting/shooting nearby

RESTRICTIONS
No children
No facilities for disabled
No pets

ATTRACTIONS
Glencoe, Glenfinnan, Culloden,
Isle of Skye, Blair Castle

AFFILIATIONS
Relais & Châteaux

NEAREST
MAJOR CITY:
Glasgow - 100 miles/2½ hrs

MAJOR AIRPORT:
Glasgow - 100 miles/2½ hrs
Inverness - 70 miles/1¾ hrs

RAILWAY STATION:
Fort William - 4 miles/15 mins

RESERVATIONS
Direct with hotel

ACCESS CODES
Not applicable

A passionate commitment to your needs in the grandeur of the Highlands

Inverlochy was built by the first Lord Abinger in 1863, near the site of the original 13th century fortress. It is set against a backdrop of some of the most magnificent scenery in the Western Highlands, and stands amongst the foothills of Ben Nevis (Scotland's highest mountain) in its own 500-acre estate. The manor is surrounded by landscaped gardens and rhododendrons.

The baronial Great Hall has beautiful frescoed ceilings, with crystal chandeliers and a handsome staircase. Fine decorations throughout befit the Victorian proportions of the rooms and reflect the atmosphere of a bygone era. There are 17 apartments with private bathroom, colour TV, telephone and all modern amenities.

Centrepiece of the dining room is an elaborate carved breakfront, presented as a gift to Inverlochy by the King of Norway. The menu changes every day, featuring international cuisine with a Highland flair. The wine cellar is of the highest standard.

Tennis, loch fishing and many beautiful walking paths are within the grounds. Highland scenic attractions, and sports and leisure activities are situated within a short drive. Please note: such is the reputation of Inverlochy that it is advisable to book well in advance!

LOCATION

From Fort William, take the A82 heading north. 4 miles up this road, pass Fort William Golf Club. Take next turning on your left to Inverlochy – the hotel is clearly signposted.

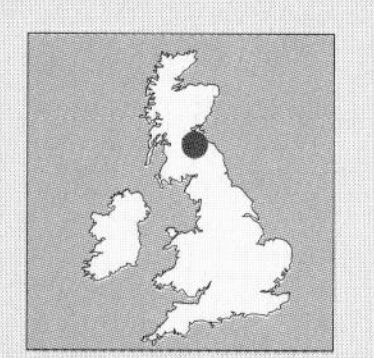

“ Whenever I come to Johnstounburn, the rest of the world disappears ”

Brian Mitchell, Nottingham

JOHNSTOUNBURN HOUSE

17th century country estate

Humbie,
East Lothian EH36 5PL

Telephone 01875 833696
Fax 01875 833626

GENERAL MANAGER
Ken Chernoff

ROOM RATES

1 Single	£99 - £110
13 Doubles/Twins	£130 - £135
1 Four-poster	£160
1 Triple from	£150
4 Quads from	£160

Includes full breakfast and VAT

CHARGE/CREDIT CARDS

• DC • MC • VI

ACCOLADES
S.T.B. ♛♛♛♛ Commended
R.A.C. ★★★
A.A. ★★★ 64%
Taste of Scotland

FACILITIES
Gardens, croquet, fishing
3 meeting rooms/max 60 people

RESTRICTIONS
No facilities for disabled guests

ATTRACTIONS
Lennoxlove House, Edinburgh Castle, Thirlestane Castle, Mellerstain House

AFFILIATIONS
A Thistle Country House Hotel

NEAREST
MAJOR CITY:
Edinburgh - 17 miles/30 mins
MAJOR AIRPORT:
Edinburgh - 20 miles/30 mins
RAILWAY STATION:
Edinburgh Waverley - 17 miles/30 mins

RESERVATIONS
Toll free in US/Canada: 800-847-4358
Toll free in Australia: 800-062-055

ACCESS CODES
AMADEUS/SYSTEM1 TI EDIJOH
APOLLO TI 16951
SABRE TI 7884
WORLDSPAN TI 8681

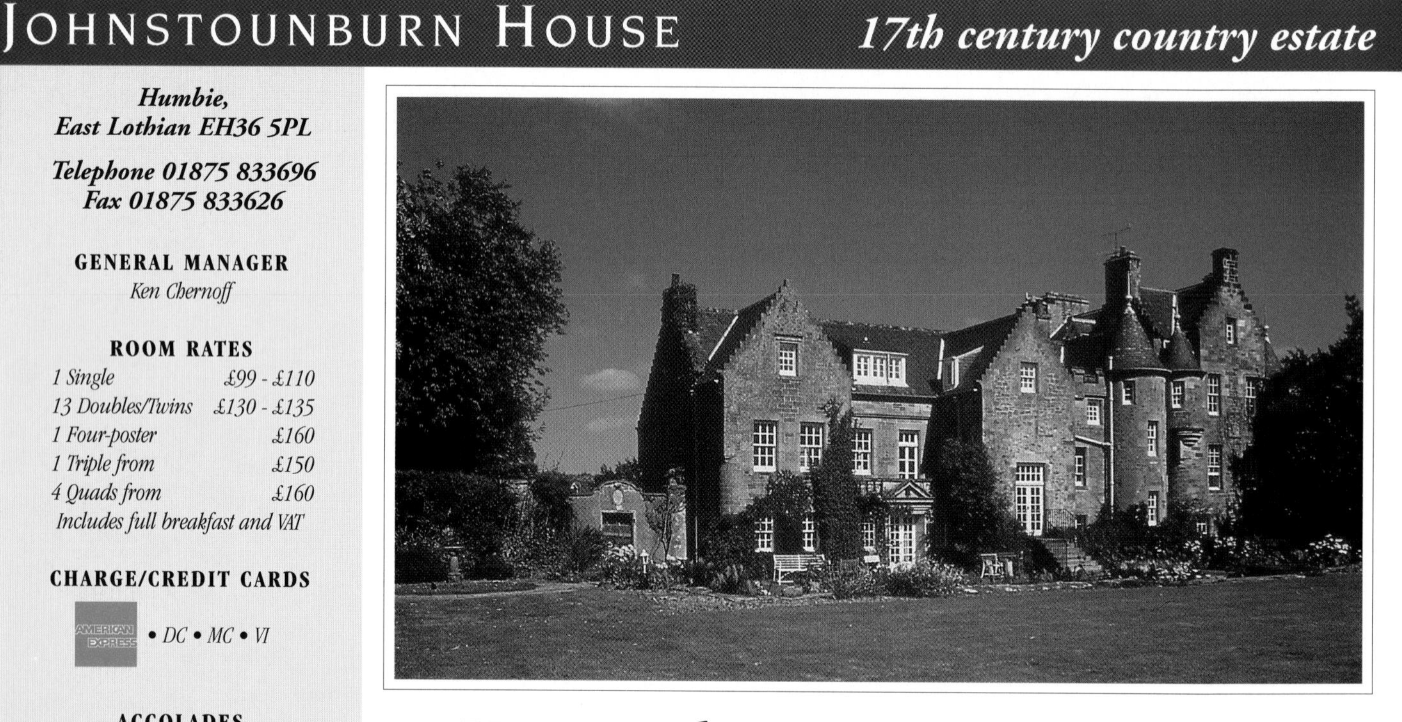

Very much a country estate; yet so close to Royal Edinburgh

Dating from 1625, Johnstounburn House sits proudly in a private estate of some 300 acres at the foot of the Lammermuir Hills, 15 miles to the south east of Edinburgh. The house has been the home to Borthwicks, Brouns and Ushers throughout its history, and today continues the traditions of Scottish hospitality by offering fine food, drink and comfort in an environment of outstanding natural beauty and peaceful relaxation.

The house is ideally located for an extended visit to Edinburgh and the south of Scotland. Both airport and city centre are thirty minutes by car, as is the beautiful border region with its castles, gardens, stately homes and picturesque rolling hills. Again, 30 minutes will take you to the Championship golf courses on East Lothian's coast – Muirfield, North Berwick, Gullane and Dunbar. Day trips to St Andrews, Glasgow and Pitlochry add further scope to your stay.

On the estate at Johnstounburn is Mavis Hall Park, where you can engage in off road driving, clay pigeon shooting, trout fishing or practicing your golf swing. And you can stroll through the gardens or walk for miles through the unspoilt countryside.

But more than anything else, your visit will be remembered by the warmth and friendliness of the people you will meet, who will welcome you to a house that is there for you to enjoy and appreciate – and to which you will long to return.

LOCATION

Situated off A68. Turn off at Fala onto B6457. After 1½ miles at the "T" junction, turn right and the hotel is on the left.

"Clients loved their visit. Everyone very helpful. A very special place"

Travex, Illinois

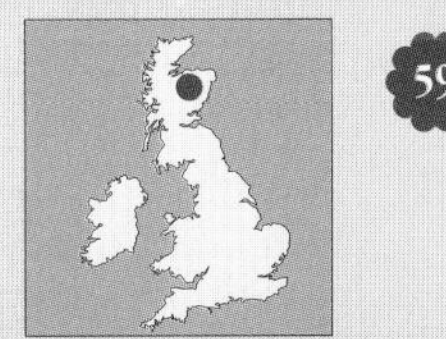

Castle hotel

KILDRUMMY CASTLE

Style and elegance of first class proportions

Set in the heart of Donside adjacent to the renowned Kildrummy Castle Gardens, and overlooking the ruins of the original 13th century castle from which it takes its name, Kildrummy Castle Hotel offers a rare opportunity to enjoy the style and elegance of a by-gone era combined with all the comforts and service of a first-class hotel.

Recent modern improvements have not detracted from the turn of the century interior featuring the original wall tapestries and oak-panelled walls and ceilings.

The restaurant, which specialises in the use of fresh local produce, fish and shellfish from the Moray Firth, local game and of course Aberdeen Angus beef, enjoys a deservedly high reputation for the quality of its food and service.

Three hours drive north of Edinburgh, Kildrummy Castle is ideally located for touring Royal Deeside and Balmoral, the Spey Valley, the "Granite City" of Aberdeen and Inverness.

The surrounding Grampian region offers the visitor a wealth of places of interest to visit with more castles than any other part of Scotland. Nearby lies the "whisky country", the home of most of Scotland's finest malt whiskies, whose distilleries welcome the visitor with a sample "dram" of their famous produce.

The sportsman too will find much on offer around Donside, with over 20 golf courses within one hour's drive of the hotel.

LOCATION

Off A97 Huntly/Ballater Road, 35 miles west of Aberdeen, 3 hours drive north of Edinburgh.

Kildrummy, by Alford, Aberdeenshire AB33 8RA

Telephone 019755 71288
Fax 019755 71345

***E-Mail** kildrummy.hotel@nest.org.uk*

SCOTLAND

PROPRIETOR

Thomas Hanna

ROOM RATES

1 Single	*£90*
12 Doubles/Twins	*£115 - £145*
2 Four-posters	*£125 - £145*

Includes full breakfast and VAT

CHARGE/CREDIT CARDS

• *MC* • *VI*

ACCOLADES

S.T.B. ♛♛♛♛ *De Luxe*
R.A.C. ★★★ + *Merit Awards H C & R*
A.A. ★★★ ❀
The Good Hotel Guide

FACILITIES

Garden, snooker
Golf and fishing nearby

RESTRICTIONS

No smoking in dining room
No facilities for disabled guests

ATTRACTIONS

Balmoral Castle,
Crathes Castle,
Craigievaar Castle,
Malt whisky distilleries,
Grampian Transport Museum

AFFILIATIONS

Select British Hotels
Scotland's Heritage Hotels

NEAREST

MAJOR CITY:
Aberdeen - 35 miles/45 mins

MAJOR AIRPORT:
Aberdeen - 35 miles/45 miles

RAILWAY STATION:
Huntly - 17 miles/20 mins

RESERVATIONS

Toll free in US/Canada: 800-323-5463

ACCESS CODES

Not applicable

“What a peaceful haven with fantastic food and wild walks to work it off! I could have run away with that venison!”

Clement and Juliet Salaman, London

KILFINAN HOTEL

17th century coaching inn

Kilfinan, Nr Tighnabruaich, Argyll PA21 2EP

Telephone 01700 821201
Fax 01700 821205

GENERAL MANAGER
Lynne Mueller

ROOM RATES

2 Singles	£48
9 Doubles/Twins	£72 - £92
1 Cottage	£300 - £420

Includes full breakfast and VAT

CHARGE/CREDIT CARDS

• MC • VI

ACCOLADES
S.T.B. ♛♛♛ Highly Commended
R.A.C. ★★ + Merit Awards H C & R
A.A. ★★ ❀❀ 76%
Taste of Scotland

FACILITIES
Garden, stalking, fishing, clay pigeon shooting, heli-pad, 6000 acre private estate
1 meeting room/max 10 people
Fishing nearby

RESTRICTIONS
No children under 10 yrs
No facilities for disabled guests
No pets

ATTRACTIONS
Inveraray, Loch Lomond, Argyll Forest Park, Highlands
Mount Stuart House, Isle of Bute

AFFILIATIONS
Independent

NEAREST
MAJOR CITY:
Glasgow - 50 miles/2 hrs

MAJOR AIRPORT:
Glasgow - 50 miles/2 hrs

RAILWAY STATION:
Gourock - 30 miles/1½ hrs

RESERVATIONS
Direct with hotel

ACCESS CODES
Not applicable

Exquisite cuisine inspired by the beauty of the Highlands

Set amongst thousands of acres of unspoilt highland countryside is the Kilfinan Hotel, an ideal centre for all kinds of outdoor activities and, of course, for relaxation. This 17th century coaching inn is situated on the Eastern shore of Loch Fyne. It is comfortable, friendly and warm, with blazing log fires in the colder months complemented by efficient central heating. There are 11 bedrooms each with their own bathroom, colour TV, and direct-dial telephone. The public rooms are all tastefully furnished and full of character.

The hotel is famed for its gourmet food; Rolf Mueller, the owner chef, is a member of the Master Chefs of Great Britain. His table d'hôte dinners are inspired by, and created from fresh seasonal produce like wild duck, pheasant and venison from the adjacent estate and from local seafood and salmon from the loch. Bar lunches are served every day. A well-chosen wine list enables diners to have a variety of memorable meals.

There is plenty to do at Kilfinan. It is an ideal centre for lovely forest walks, birdwatching or just relaxing in peaceful, beautiful surroundings. The hotel offers free golf and fishing, while shooting of various kinds can also be arranged.

LOCATION

From Glasgow M8 west to Gourock Ferry to Dunoon B836/B8003 to Tighnabruaich B8000 to Kilfinan.

" Most impressive stay I've made worldwide – fantastic set up – 200% welcome, comfort and food . . . "

Jane Buchanan, France

18/19th century farmhouse

KIRKTON HOUSE

Darleith Road, Cardross, Dunbartonshire G82 5EZ

Telephone 01389 841951
Fax 01389 841868

***E-Mail** 100535.424@compuserve.com*

PROPRIETORS

Stewart and Gillian Macdonald

ROOM RATES

Single occupancy	*£37.50*
6 Doubles/Twins	*£59*
Family	*£69 - £75*

Includes full breakfast and VAT

CHARGE/CREDIT CARDS

• MC • VI

ACCOLADES

S.T.B. ♛♛♛ Highly Commended
R.A.C. Highly Acclaimed
A.A. QQQQ Selected
The Good Hotel Guide

FACILITIES

Garden
Golf, riding and fishing nearby

RESTRICTIONS

None

ATTRACTIONS

Loch Lomond, The Trossachs, Hill House, Glasgow, Burrell Collection, Scottish Exhibition Centre, West Highlands, golf courses

AFFILIATIONS

Logis of Great Britain
Taste of Scotland

NEAREST

MAJOR CITY:
Glasgow - 18 miles/35 mins

MAJOR AIRPORT:
Glasgow - 14 miles/25 mins

RAILWAY STATION:
Cardross - 1 mile/2 mins

RESERVATIONS

Toll free in US: 800-989-7676

ACCESS CODES

Not applicable

A great little country place in easy reach of Glasgow Airport

Commanding panoramic views of the River Clyde and the Argyll Hills, Kirkton House is situated in tranquil countryside, handy for Glasgow Airport, Loch Lomond, the West Highlands and Glasgow City. There are excellent local walks and golf courses.

Kirkton House is a tasteful conversion of a traditional 18/19th century Scottish farmhouse and barns around a courtyard – retaining its old world charm. The lounge and dining areas have exposed stone walls and rustic fireplaces (including the original 'swee' for hanging the pots). Guests can enjoy a drink and convivial conversation in the guest lounge (beside a roaring open fire on chilly evenings), and savour the 'homey', informal and unpretentious ambience. Your well-travelled proprietor hosts provide an unobtrusive and personal service.

All the well-appointed bedrooms (two on the ground floor) have a bath and/or shower and toilet, direct dial telephones, television, writing table, hairdryer, and hospitality tray.

Wholesome home cooked dinners for residents and their guests are served at individual tables per party: orders are taken at about 7 pm from the extensive menu.

Here are just some remarks from the 'Niggles and Giggles' guest comment leaflets in each room:

"A luxurious and delightful experience" JF, Mass, USA. "How does one improve on perfection?" HH, Pinner, UK.

LOCATION

Turn north off A814 at west end of Cardross village, up Darleith Road. Proceed ½ mile out of housing line and Kirkton House drive is on right after 3 cottages.

" The epitome of what a fine country house hotel should be – warm, inviting and totally enjoyable "

Helen Worth & Michael Angelis

KNOCKINAAM LODGE

19th century hunting lodge

SCOTLAND

Portpatrick, Nr Stranraer, Wigtownshire, Dumfries & Galloway DG9 9AD

Telephone 01776 810471
Fax 01776 810435

PROPRIETORS
Michael Bricker and Pauline Ashworth

MANAGER
Lorna McMiken

ROOM RATES

1 Single	£80
5 Twins/Doubles	£116
4 Master Rooms	£160

Includes full breakfast and VAT

CHARGE/CREDIT CARDS

• DC • MC • VI

ACCOLADES
S.T.B. ♛♛♛♛ De Luxe
A.A. ★★ ❀❀❀
The Good Hotel Guide

FACILITIES
Garden, croquet, fishing, heli-pad
1 meeting room/max 20 people
Fishing, shooting, golf and walking nearby

RESTRICTIONS
No facilities for disabled guests
Dogs allowed with own bedding

ATTRACTIONS
Logan, Ardwell and Glenwhan gardens, Castle Kennedy, Culzean Castle, Galloway Forest

AFFILIATIONS
Pride of Britain

NEAREST
MAJOR CITY:
Stranraer - 8 miles/15 mins

MAJOR AIRPORT:
Glasgow - 98 miles/2 hrs

RAILWAY STATION:
Stranraer - 8 miles/15 mins

RESERVATIONS
Direct with hotel

ACCESS CODES
Not applicable

One of Churchill's and Eisenhower's best kept secrets

In its beautiful 30-acre setting beside the Irish Sea, Knockinaam enjoys one of Scotland's most romantic settings. Built in 1869 as a hunting lodge by Lady Hunter-Blair and extended to its present size in 1901, it has marvellous sea views and sunsets, gardens, public rooms with open log fires and 10 comfortable en-suite bedrooms. It is the ideal place for a relaxing getaway.

Sir Winston Churchill chose Knockinaam as his secret meeting place with General Dwight D. Eisenhower during the Second World War.

The AA 3-rosette restaurant serves the most delicious and innovative cuisine, using only the freshest ingredients available. The 4-course menu changes daily and it features Scottish beef and lamb, as well as local seafood. To complement the food, Knockinaam's wine list has over 400 varieties. One of the highlights of the Lodge is to be found in the oak-panelled bar. Here, over 96 single malt whiskies are on display for connoisseurs and novices alike to sample a warming "wee dram" before and after dinner.

Knockinaam has an international reputation for service, hospitality and attention to details, provided by owners Pauline Ashworth, Michael Bricker and their wonderful staff.

There is superb fishing and shooting nearby, and for golfers, within driving distance are Turnberry, Royal Troon, Prestwick, Brunston Castle, Southerness, Stranraer and Portpatrick Golf Clubs.

LOCATION

From the A75 or the A77, follow signs to Portpatrick. 2 miles west of Lochans, turn left at sign to Knockinaam Lodge, pass Colfin Smokehouse and follow signs for 3 miles to the Lodge.

"We came wondering. We went in wonderment"

George & Florence Wilson, Musselburgh

19th century house

KNOCKOMIE HOTEL

Pampered comfort surrounded by a wealth of sights and sports

Overlooking the Royal Burgh of Forres, Knockomie is ideally situated to conquer castles, distilleries and golf courses, while salmon and deer await the keen sportsman.

The interior varies from room to room. The front hall is panelled in Scots Pine, while all 14 bedrooms are individually decorated with soft furnishings and period furniture. Some have four-poster or half-tester beds, others patios, and are on the ground floor, including one for the disabled.

Knockomie House was built in 1821, added to in the Arts and Crafts style in 1914 and extended in 1993. The restaurant uses the best of Scottish produce to specialise in the Taste of Scotland. This is complemented by an extensive wine list and a large collection of malt whiskies. After dinner, guests can relax in one of the lounges in front of the fire savouring a dram.

An ideal location to go east or west, to visit the many castles, including Cawdor, Brodie and Ballindalloch or the unique whisky trail in the Spey Valley. Loch Ness is less than an hour away waiting to reveal its secret. Other opportunities include golfing on a selection of courses, stalking and shooting in the glens or fishing in the lochs and rivers.

Local golf courses include Lossiemouth, Hopeman, Forres, Nairn (championship) and Dornoch (championship).

Above all, a warm welcome is assured.

LOCATION

1 mile south of Forres on A940.

Grantown Road, Forres, Moray IV36 0SG

Telephone 01309 673146
Fax 01309 673290

DIRECTOR

Gavin Ellis

ROOM RATES

1 Single	*£65*
11 Doubles	*£75 - £95*
1 Four-poster	*£125*
1 Suite	*£165*
1 Family Room	*£65 - £75*

Includes full breakfast and VAT

CHARGE/CREDIT CARDS

• DC • MC • VI

ACCOLADES

S.T.B. ♛♛♛♛ Highly Commended
A.A. ★★★ ❀ 66%
Taste of Scotland

FACILITIES

Garden, croquet, heli-pad
3 meeting rooms/max 40 people
Golf, fishing, shooting and stalking nearby

RESTRICTIONS

None

ATTRACTIONS

Brodie Castle, Cawdor Castle, Ballindalloch Castle, Johnston's of Elgin

AFFILIATIONS

Scotland's Commended Hotels

NEAREST

MAJOR CITY:
Inverness - 27 miles/30 mins

MAJOR AIRPORT:
Aberdeen - 75 miles/1 hr 25 mins
Inverness - 25 miles/30 mins

RAILWAY STATION:
Forres - 1 mile/5 mins

RESERVATIONS

Toll free in US: 800-43-SCOTS

ACCESS CODES

APOLLO HT 14861
SABRE HH 32407
WORLDSPAN HW WNOCW

"Ladyburn exemplifies life as it used to be lived and ought to be lived"

Jack Macmillan MBE, Edinburgh

LADYBURN

Country house

**by Maybole,
Ayrshire KA19 7SG**

**Telephone 01655 740585
Fax 01655 740580**

OWNER

David and Jane Hepburn

ROOM RATES

Single occupancy £60 - £90
5 Doubles/Twins £130 - £160
Includes full breakfast and VAT

CHARGE/CREDIT CARDS

• MC • VI

ACCOLADES

S.T.B. ♛♛♛ De Luxe
R.A.C. Blue Ribbon Award ★★
A.A. ★★ ❀

FACILITIES

Garden, croquet, heli-pad
Golf, fishing and
clay pigeon shooting nearby

RESTRICTIONS

No children under 16 years
Smoking in library only
No pets

ATTRACTIONS

Burns' Centre,
Tam O'Shanter Experience,
Culzean Castle, Glentrool,
Crossraguel Abbey

AFFILIATIONS

Independent

NEAREST

MAJOR CITY:
Glasgow - 45 miles/1 hr

MAJOR AIRPORT:
Glasgow - 50 miles/1 hr 10 mins
Prestwick - 17 miles/30 mins

RAILWAY STATION:
Ayr - 12 miles/20 mins

RESERVATIONS

Direct with hotel

ACCESS CODES

Not applicable

A blue ribbon of excellence and a warm glow of satisfaction

Ladyburn, family home of the Hepburns, lies nestling at the head of the most beautiful valley in Ayrshire. Peace, tranquility and gracious living are the words most often used to describe a visit to Ladyburn.

From the moment that you arrive until the time that you leave, you are made to feel welcome and very special. The accommodation is superb, furnished throughout with inherited antiques, and the house is filled with fresh flowers from the garden.

The food is purely traditional: Jane Hepburn uses only fresh garden and local produce and, combined with old family recipes handed down through the generations, produces such favourites as 'Great Aunt May's Chicken Casserole' and 'Tai-Tai's fish pie'.

1996 is going to very special in this part of Scotland; it's the 300th anniversary of the death of Robert Burns, born not far away, so there will be all kinds of celebrations throughout the year. Also nearby is Culzean Castle and, further afield, are Glasgow, a mere one hour's drive, the magnificent Burrell Collection and ferries to the Scottish islands.

Sportsmen will find golf at Turnberry, Royal Troon and Prestwick all within 45 minutes and fine salmon and trout fishing within a few minutes drive. For racing enthusiasts, Scotland's premier race course is only 20 minutes away, with a full flat and National Hunt programme.

Ladyburn epitomises gracious living and the whole experience there will send you home with a warm glow of satisfaction.

LOCATION

Follow the A77 Glasgow-Stranraer road to Maybole. Turn left onto B7023 to Crosshill and right at War Memorial. 2 miles further along, turn left – Ladyburn is ¾ mile on right.

" This is a magical place "

Dr & Mrs A Mitchell, Bray -on-Thames

THE LAKE HOTEL

Fine foods, and a grandstand vista of lake and mountains

The Lake Hotel is set in a splendid sheltered position on the banks of Lake Menteith in the Trossachs. Its lawn runs down to the edge of the lake. As a guest, you are assured of all the amenities of an STB four crown hotel. A thorough refurbishment programme has recently been completed, so the interiors have fresh decoration and new furnishings. All bedrooms have en-suite facilities, with all the little details that will make your stay much more comfortable. From the elegant lounge and the large conservatory, the vista of lake and mountains is stunning.

The à la carte and table d'hôte menus offer a varied choice of imaginatively prepared dishes. The table d'hôte menus are particularly good value: start with pheasant terrine topped with slivers of smoked venison, followed by a sorbet, then, after a main course of halibut cooked in fennel and cream sauce, enjoy a light Drambuie parfait before your coffee and home-made petits fours. Special rates are available for mini-breaks of two nights or more.

In winter the lake often freezes over, and it is not unusual for locals to bring out their skates for a skim over the ice. Throughout the year the hotel is within easy reach of mountain, wildlife and other leisure activities, including golf. Nearby are Stirling Castle and Loch Lomond. In Port Menteith is the well-preserved ruined 13th century Inchmahome Priory that gave shelter to Robert the Bruce and Mary Queen of Scots.

LOCATION

Take the A85 to Port of Menteith, then the B8034 to Arnprior. After 250 metres, turn right to Lake Hotel.

Port of Menteith, Perthshire FK8 3RA

Telephone 01877 385258
Fax 01877 385671

OWNER
John L Leroy

MANAGER
Douglas Little

RATES PER PERSON
Single occupancy £51 - £90
16 Doubles/Twins £41 - £80
Includes dinner, full breakfast and VAT

CHARGE/CREDIT CARDS

• MC • VI

ACCOLADES
S.T.B. ♛♛♛♛ Highly Commended
A.A. ★★ ❀❀ 75%
The Good Hotel Guide

FACILITIES
Garden, fishing
Golf and riding nearby

RESTRICTIONS
No children under 14 years
No facilities for disabled guests
No pets in public rooms

ATTRACTIONS
Inchmahome Priory, The Trossachs, Stirling Castle, Rob Roy Centre, Loch Katrine

AFFILIATIONS
Logis of Great Britain

NEAREST
MAJOR CITY:
Glasgow - 33 miles/50 mins

MAJOR AIRPORT:
Glasgow - 35 miles/50 mins

RAILWAY STATION:
Stirling - 17 miles/25 mins

RESERVATIONS
Direct with hotel

ACCESS CODES
Not applicable

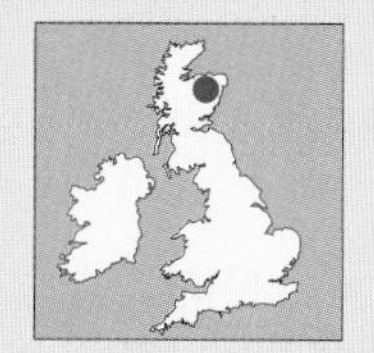

"Splendour and intimacy filled a magical moment"

Misha & Lea Plees, Massachusetts

LESLIE CASTLE

17th century baronial fortified house

By Insch,
Aberdeenshire AB52 6NX

Telephone 01464 820869
Fax 01464 821076

PROPRIETORS
The Baron and Baroness of Leslie

ROOM RATES

Single occupancy	*£93 - £95*
2 Double/sTwins	*£132*
2 Four-posters	*£136*

Includes full breakfast and VAT

CHARGE/CREDIT CARDS

• *MC* • *VI*

ACCOLADES
S.T.B. ♛♛♛♛ Highly Commended

FACILITIES
Garden, heli-pad
Golf nearby

RESTRICTIONS
No facilities for disabled guests
No smoking in dining room
No pets

ATTRACTIONS
Castle Trail,
Whisky Trail,
Falconry Centre,
Balvenie Castle,
Dallas Dhu Distillery

AFFILIATIONS
The Tartan Collection

NEAREST
MAJOR CITY:
Aberdeen - 30 miles/40 mins

MAJOR AIRPORT:
Aberdeen - 25 miles/30 mins

RAILWAY STATION:
Insch - 3 miles/5 mins

RESERVATIONS
Direct with hotel

ACCESS CODES
Not applicable

Once a roofless ruin, now a unique fairytale place

Leslie Castle is situated at the west end of the Bennachie Range, in the fertile valley of Gadie Burn. The original seat of Clan Leslie, the castle is the 3rd fortified building on the site since 1070. In 1979, the present owners and hosts, David and Leslie (Baron and Baroness of Leslie) acquired it as a decaying, roofless ruin. Ten years of careful, painstaking, detailed restoration have transformed it into a fairytale, turreted 17th century fortified house.

The Baronial Hall with timber-beamed ceiling, large fireplace and stone-flagged floor creates a fitting atmosphere in which to enjoy splendid Scottish and international cuisine prepared personally by the Baroness in the best tradition of Scottish hospitality. Specialities include smoked and fresh fish, game, lamb and Aberdeenshire beef. The best local produce is chosen, according to season. You can also dine in the Kitchen Dining Room, the original kitchen of the castle.

Amid the winding staircases and open fireplaces, you need not sacrifice modern comforts. The four bedrooms are beautifully furnished, and spacious enough for family use. Nor should you feel nervous about the titles. David and Leslie Leslie are friendly down-to-earth folk who immediately set guests at their ease in their unique home. A holiday or short break at Leslie Castle is truly unforgettable.

LOCATION

Take A96 30 miles north west from Aberdeen. Turn left on to B992 to Insch.

" It is the kind of view you could watch all day and it accompanies everything you do in the hotel like silent music – the food matches the setting "

Iain Crawford, freelance journalist

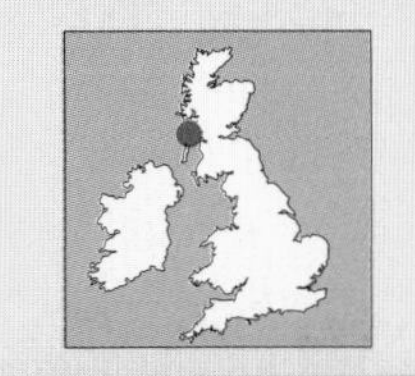

Coastal hotel

LOCH MELFORT

Spectacular location on the west coast with uninterrupted views

The finest location on the west coast of Scotland awaits visitors to this award-winning hotel. The first ever to be chosen as the Scottish Hotel of the Year by the AA, Loch Melfort is the perfect place for a relaxing holiday or short break. It is personally run by Philip and Rosalind Lewis, with their friendly and attentive staff.

Comfortable bedrooms all have private bathrooms, TV and telephones. Most have stunning views across Asknish Bay to the islands of Shuna, Scarba and Jura.

Philip Lewis, the head chef, and his dedicated team combine the best of fresh local produce including meat and cheeses, and particularly locally caught fish and shellfish. Mouth-watering home-made puddings and ice-creams provide the perfect finale to a five-course menu that changes each day. A carefully chosen and comprehensive wine list offers an excellent choice. Light lunches, suppers and afternoon teas are served in the Chartroom Bar.

The hotel lies next to the National Trust of Scotland's famous Arduaine Garden, one of 20 within easy reach, all revelling in the mountain grandeur of Argyll.

Scotland's romantic isles are easily accessible from Oban, a scenic 19 miles away.

LOCATION

Midway between Oban and Lochgilphead on A816.

Arduaine,
By Oban,
Argyll PA34 4XG

Telephone 01852 200233
Fax 01852 200214

SCOTLAND

PROPRIETORS

Philip and Rosalind Lewis

ROOM RATES

Single occupancy	£50 - £62
24 Doubles/Twins	£75 - £99
2 Superior Doubles	£100 - £124

CHARGE/CREDIT CARDS

• *MC* • *VI*

ACCOLADES

S.T.B. ♛♛♛♛ Commended
A.A. ★★★ ❀ 71%
The Good Hotel Guide
César Award 1996

FACILITIES

Garden
1 meeting room/max 20 people
Fishing, riding, sailing, windsurfing, walking and mountain biking nearby

RESTRICTIONS

None

ATTRACTIONS

Arduaine Gardens, Mull, Iona, Kerra, Gigha and Arran Islands, Inveraray, Glencoe, Dunstaffnage Castle and Chapel

AFFILIATIONS

Independent

NEAREST

MAJOR CITY:
Glasgow - 110 miles/2 hrs

MAJOR AIRPORT:
Glasgow - 100 miles/2 hrs

RAILWAY STATION:
Oban - 19 miles/30 mins

RESERVATIONS

Direct with hotel

ACCESS CODES

Not applicable

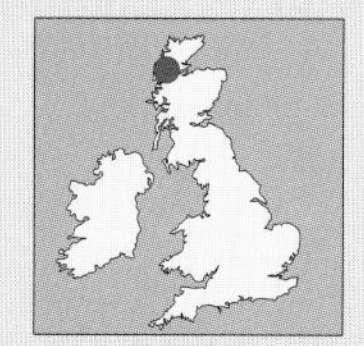

“ I can't wait to return with my family ”

Ted Dansen, actor

SCOTLAND

LOCH TORRIDON HOTEL

19th century shooting lodge

Torridon, Achnasheen
Ross-shire IV22 2EY

Telephone 01445 791242
Fax 01445 791296

PROPRIETOR
David Gregory

ROOM RATES

2 Singles	*£40 - £90*
2 Doubles/Twins	*£60 - £90*
8 Superior	*£80 - £120*
3 Deluxe	*£100 - £140*
5 Master	*£120 - £180*
1 Suite	*£130 - £220*

Includes full breakfast and VAT

CHARGE/CREDIT CARDS

• *MC* • *VI*

ACCOLADES
S.T.B. ♛♛♛♛ Highly Commended
A.A.★★★ ❀❀ 73%
A.A. Best Newcomer Scotland 1993
The Good Hotel Guide

FACILITIES
Garden, croquet, lift, heli-pad, fishing
1 meeting room/max 20 people

RESTRICTIONS
No pets

ATTRACTIONS
Isle of Skye,
Deer Museum,
Torridon Mountains,
Inverewe Gardens

AFFILIATIONS
Scotland's Commended Hotels
Small Luxury Hotels

NEAREST
MAJOR CITY:
Inverness - 64 miles/1½ hrs

MAJOR AIRPORT:
Glasgow - 230 miles/4½ hrs
Inverness - 70 miles/1¾ hrs

RAILWAY STATION:
Inverness - 64 miles/1½ hrs

RESERVATIONS
Toll free in US/Canada: 800-525-4800

ACCESS CODES
Not applicable

Where spirits soar and eagles fly

The hotel, once a shooting lodge built for the first Earl of Lovelace in 1887, is now a family owned and run country house hotel. A total refurbishment programme, including the installation of a lift has recently been completed. This and other improvements have created one of the finest hotels to be found on the west coast. From the impressive entrance lounge with its magnificent Zodiac crest ceiling, to bedrooms which set standards of luxury rarely found in such wild regions. The bathrooms are equally superb.

With log fires, cosy chairs and cordon bleu cuisine this is a must for those who appreciate good food and good company in a 'Highland Paradise'.

Set amidst some 58 acres of mature trees and parkland at the foot of majestic mountains on the shores of Loch Torridon, the area is renowned for being one of nature's marvels and undoubtedly has the most striking skyline in Scotland. Glittering snow-tipped pinnacles, rocky turrets and spires – a massive fortress of mountains which is at once both breathtaking and awe-inspiring.

There is excellent fishing on numerous hill lochs and rivers, and sea angling on Loch Torridon. For the hill walkers and mountaineer the area is a natural paradise.

LOCATION

Only hotel on A896. Do not turn off to Torridon Village.

“ I wish I could ‘bottle’ my experience here and share it with others ”

Judith Kaye-Howard

Lochside country house

LODGE ON THE LOCH

A spellbinding blend of elegance, informality and high standards

Looking south across the water to Argyll, or west to the near and distant hills of Morvern and Mull, The Lodge on the Loch enjoys one of the finest panoramas in Scotland. A strategic location on the A82 allows easy access to the Scottish Islands – Mull, Iona, Skye and the Small Isles – and to Inverness.

Formerly the country home of Sir John and Lady MacPherson, The Lodge on the Loch has been designed to take advantage of its superb situation with wide bay windows in drawing, dining and bedrooms, presenting views across five acres of grounds to the bay beyond. Palm trees grow in the sheltered grounds and wild rhododendron flourish on a hillside where you can feel the magic of the Gulf Stream brushing by. Such a memorable setting inspires a special quality of service and a rich ambience of tranquillity.

Savour fine connoisseur malt whiskies in the intimate cocktail bar. Enjoy “Taste of Scotland” cuisine at its best, selected from a range of fresh, local produce. Choose from local salmon, seafood, game, venison, wholefoods, home baking and, of course, there is the discerning wine list. Later, relax by the log fire or retire to the gentle elegance of your individually designed bedroom.

Benefit from a unique “dine around the loch” experience during your stay and sample the culinary delights of their two nearby sister hotels, together with complimentary membership of pool and leisure club.

LOCATION

Situated on the shores of Loch Linnhe, just off A82 road, 5 miles north of the pass of Glencoe and 10 miles south of Fort William.

Onich, Nr Fort William, Inverness-shire PH33 6RY

Telephone 01855 821237
Fax 01855 821463

PROPRIETORS
The Young Family

GENERAL MANAGER
Iain R Coulter

ROOM RATES

2 Singles	£56
14 Doubles/Twins	£112
2 Family	£112

Includes full breakfast and VAT

CHARGE/CREDIT CARDS
MC • VI

ACCOLADES
S.T.B. ♛♛♛♛ Highly Commended
R.A.C. ★★★ + Merit Award H
A.A. ★★★ 65%
Taste of Scotland

FACILITIES
Garden
1 meeting room/max 50 people
Leisure facilities, riding, climbing, watersports and mountain biking nearby

RESTRICTIONS
None

ATTRACTIONS
Glencoe Visitor Centre, Nevis Range Ski Resort, Mull and Iona, Loch Ness, Highland Mysteryworld

AFFILIATIONS
Scotland's Commended Hotels

NEAREST
MAJOR CITY:
Glasgow - 100 miles/2 hrs

MAJOR AIRPORT:
Glasgow - 100 miles/2 hrs
Inverness - 80 miles/1½ hrs

RAILWAY STATION:
Fort William - 10 miles/15 mins

RESERVATIONS
Toll free in US: 800-43-SCOTS

ACCESS CODES
Not applicable

“ Once again superb. Lovely flowers on our return ”

Mr & Mrs Rouke, Glasgow

THE MANOR HOUSE

Duke's residence

Gallanach Road,
Oban,
Argyll PA34 4LS

Telephone 01631 562087
Fax 01631 563053

MANAGER
Gabrielle Wijker

RATES PER PERSON
Single £59 - £74
11 Doubles/Twins £41 - £72
Includes dinner, full breakfast and VAT

CHARGE/CREDIT CARDS

• *MC* • *VI*

ACCOLADES
S.T.B. Highly Commended
A.A. ★★ 76%

FACILITIES
Garden
Golf, fishing and riding nearby

RESTRICTIONS
No children under 14 years
No facilities for disabled guests
No pets in public rooms

ATTRACTIONS
Ferries to the Western Isles,
Distilleries,
Glencoe,
Rare Breeds Park,
Salmon Centre,
Mull of Kintyre

AFFILIATIONS
Logis of Great Britain

NEAREST
MAJOR CITY:
Glasgow - 95 miles/2 hrs 10 mins

MAJOR AIRPORT:
Glasgow - 90 miles/2 hrs

RAILWAY STATION:
Oban - ¼ mile/2 mins

RESERVATIONS
Direct with hotel

ACCESS CODES
Not applicable

The elegance of bygone days and gateway to the Western Isles

Late Georgian style, The Manor House was built in 1780 as the principal residence of the Duke of Argyll's Oban estate. It later became a dower house, residence of a Duke's widow. Today it is a hotel where great consideration has been taken to preserve the elegance of bygone days. The Manor House Hotel occupies a prime position overlooking Oban Bay, the adjacent islands and the mountains of Movern and Mull.

The elegant dining room offers guests a fine blend of Scottish and French cooking, with an emphasis on local seafood and game in season. The table d'hôte menus take pride of place and are changed daily to present a choice of starters, intermediate fish course or soup, home-made sorbet, choice of puddings, and to round off, coffee and mints. The hotel has a fine cellar of wines and wide selection of malt whiskies.

All bedrooms are twin or double bedded, and all have en suite bathrooms, TV and tea-making facilities.

The hotel is quietly located on the outskirts of Oban, yet within easy walking distance of the town. Oban is Scotland's main port for trips to the Western Isles, and the varied day trips are a splendid way of discovering this beautiful area. Towering above Oban is McCaig's Folly, an unfinished replica of the Roman Colosseum, built by a local banker in the 19th century. On the mainland, nearby Glencoe is one of Scotland's wildest and most celebrated glens.

Special mini-breaks are available for stays of two nights or more. Please note that the hotel is closed in January.

LOCATION

Follow signs to MacBrayne Ferries. Continue past ferry entrance for 300 metres. Manor House is on the right hand side.

“ A fantastic stay-over within our multi-centre honeymoon ”

Richard and Karen White, London

Baronial mansion

MANSION HOUSE HOTEL

Peaceful yet active in the heart of Elgin

Set within private woodland, the 19th century baronial Mansion House is only a minute's walk from the centre of the ancient city of Elgin. Newly refurbished to offer a superb range of indoor facilities, it has a character and atmosphere all of its own, from the moment you step into the oak-panelled entrance hall with its antique curiosities. The majestic staircase leads to high-quality bedroom accommodation, and a welcoming glass of sherry.

In the elegant restaurant, the most creative food awaits those who enjoy the simple and delicious things in life. The piano lounge is a favourite pre-diner gathering point, and so is the Wee Bar. The Still Room features a unique collection of whiskies.

Expansive lawns dotted with mature trees and fine views over the tranquil River Lossie rekindle the romance of holidaying in the heart of the countryside. For the energetic, the country club has a warm, inviting pool, with spa, sauna, steam room and sunbed, and a gym with computerised coaches. There is the Dip Inn all-day snack bar to re-stock the calories. The golfer will enjoy an unbelievable choice of courses within 10 miles. There is fishing on the Spey, stag, pheasant and grouse on the moors, horse riding stables and unlimited water sports in Findhorn Bay. Moray is famed for the Whisky Trail. The Mansion House now provides the ideal base from which to cover such a challenging and enjoyable adventure.

LOCATION

Situated on A96 between Inverness and Aberdeen. The hotel is situated behind the Lady Hill monument near the centre of Elgin.

The Haugh,
Moray, Elgin
Grampian IV30 1AW

Telephone 01343 548811
Fax 01343 547916

SCOTLAND

PROPRIETORS

Jim and Joan Stirrat

ROOM RATES

Single occupancy £75 - £90
8 Doubles/Twins £110 - £150
15 Superior four-posters £150
Includes VAT

CHARGE/CREDIT CARDS

• *DC* • *JCB* • *MC* • *VI*

ACCOLADES

S.T.B. ♛♛♛♛♛ *Highly Commended*
A.A. ★★★ ❀ *73%*

FACILITIES

Garden, indoor pool, health & beauty, jacuzzi, gym, sauna, steam room, snooker
2 meeting rooms/max 200 people
Golf and fishing nearby

RESTRICTIONS

No pets in hotel

ATTRACTIONS

Whisky Trail, Elgin Cathedral, Johnston's Wool Mill, Baxters Factory, Brodie Castle

AFFILIATIONS

Scottish Heritage Hotels
Tartan Collection

NEAREST

MAJOR CITY:
Inverness - 30 miles/45 mins

MAJOR AIRPORT:
Inverness - 30 miles/45 mins

RAILWAY STATION:
Elgin - ½ mile/5 mins

RESERVATIONS

Direct with hotel

ACCESS CODES

Not applicable

“ If paradise exists, Minmore cannot be far away

Gordon & Maureen Stewart, Fife

SCOTLAND

MINMORE HOUSE

19th century family home

Glenlivet,
Banffshire, AB37 9DB

Telephone 01807 590378
Fax 01807 590472

PROPRIETOR
Belinda Luxmoore

RATES PER PERSON
2 Singles £38
8 Doubles/Twins £38
Includes full breakfast and VAT

CHARGE/CREDIT CARDS

• MC • VI

ACCOLADES
S.T.B. Highly Commended
The Good Hotel Guide
Taste of Scotland

FACILITIES
Garden, croquet, tennis, swimming pool, fishing
2 meeting rooms/max 10 people

RESTRICTIONS
Well behaved pets but not in public rooms
No smoking in dining room

ATTRACTIONS
Castle Trail,
Whisky Trail,
Birdwatching, walking,
20 golf courses within 1 hour's drive,

AFFILIATIONS
Independent

NEAREST
MAJOR CITY:
Inverness - 50 miles/1 hr

MAJOR AIRPORT:
Aberdeen - 60 miles/1¼ hrs
Inverness - 60 miles/1¼ hrs

RAILWAY STATION:
Aviemore - 35 miles/45 mins

RESERVATIONS
Direct with hotel

ACCESS CODES
Not applicable

The former home of Glenlivet whisky distillery in the heart of Speyside

Minmore House is a family run hotel with a very relaxed atmosphere: log fires, an abundance of fresh flowers and plenty of peace and quiet. The house was the home of George Smith, founder of the Glenlivet Whisky. It is situated above the River Livet and surrounded by four acres of secluded walled garden.

The ten en-suite bedrooms each have central heating and gallons of hot water. The bedrooms are all individually and comfortably furnished. Each is named after a local Speyside malt. You can take your hearty breakfast at ease in your room or downstairs. Picnic lunches can be provided on request. Sumptuous afternoon teas are served in the sunny drawing room with glorious views over the glen. The grand finale is a five-course dinner, the main course of which can vary from fresh salmon to fillet of venison. The hotel grows its own herbs and has other excellent sources of fresh produce. Minmore House has a specially selected wine cellar, and an impressive range of single malt whiskies on display in the oak-panelled bar.

Minmore House has a hard tennis court, croquet lawn, an outdoor pool for sunny days and plenty of space for you to curl up with a good book. Nearby activities include exploring, walking, fishing, birdwatching, uncrowded golf courses within an easy drive, a grand variety of castles, art galleries, local museums and crafts, horse-riding and gardens, and the famous Whisky Trail. Slainte Mhath! – you can be sure of a warm welcome at Minmore House.

LOCATION

From London via M1, M6, A74 Glasgow Bypass, Stirling, Perth, A9 to Aviemore, A95 to Grantown, and turn right on to B9008 at Delanshaugh Inn.

"My stay was all too short, look out for me next time"

Sir Harry Secombe

SCOTLAND

Georgian mansion — MONTGREENAN MANSION HOUSE

Parkland seclusion surrounded by a wealth of top golf courses

Built in 1817 by a wealthy tobacco baron, and set in 50 acres of secluded parklands and beautiful gardens, Montgreenan still retains the impressive architecture and decorative features of the period. Indeed travellers who visit the mansion may be forgiven for feeling they have travelled back in time. Montgreenan is a family owned and managed establishment and prides itself on its high standards of personal service and genuine warm hospitality.

The mansion house has 10 beautifully appointed bedrooms which are furnished to a high standard, some having antique furniture. The surroundings are perfect for relaxing and enjoying the culinary skills of Chef Allan McColl; seasonal and local specialities include salmon, lobster, game and Ayrshire beef, all of which can be complemented by the largest wine cellar in Ayrshire.

Montgreenan is close to Glasgow, Ayr and Royal Troon. Attractions nearby include Culzean Castle, the Burrell Collection and the cottage where Robert Burns was born. Montgreenan is surrounded by a wealth of top golf courses, in fact there are over 30 within 45 minutes of the estate, including Turnberry, Old Prestwick and Royal Troon. They are happy to arrange golf for guests on request.

Guests who prefer to be active in other ways can enjoy horse riding, clay pigeon shooting and fishing, all of which can be booked for you by the hotel.

LOCATION

Montgreenan can be found 4 miles north of Irvine on the A736.

Montgreenan Estate, Torranyard, Nr Kilwinning, Ayrshire KA13 7QZ

Telephone 01294 557733
Fax 01294 850397

PROPRIETOR

Darren Dobson

ROOM RATES

2 Singles	£66
6 Doubles/Twins	£92
1 Four-poster	£146
1 Suite	£146

Includes full breakfast and VAT

CHARGE/CREDIT CARDS

• DC • MC • VI

ACCOLADES

S.T.B. ♛♛♛♛ Highly Commended
R.A.C. ★★★ + Merit Awards H C & R
A.A. ★★★ ❀ 71%

FACILITIES

Croquet, tennis, gardens, 5 hole practice course, snooker, heli-pad
2 meeting rooms/max 100 people
Golf, riding and fishing nearby

RESTRICTIONS

No facilities for disabled guests
Pets by arrangement

ATTRACTIONS

Burns Cottage and Memorials, Culzean Castle, Isle of Arran, The Burrell Collection, Maritime Museum

AFFILIATIONS

Scotland's Heritage
Virgin Collection

NEAREST

MAJOR CITY:
Glasgow -19 miles/40 mins

MAJOR AIRPORT:
Glasgow - 19 miles/40 mins

RAILWAY STATION:
Irvine - 4 miles/10 mins

RESERVATIONS

Direct with hotel

ACCESS CODES

Not applicable

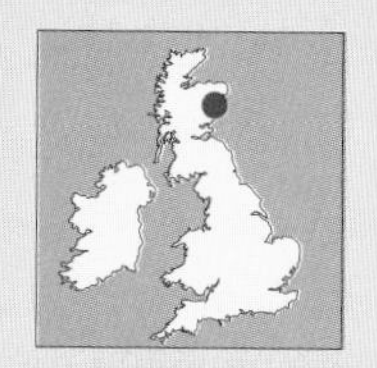

“A truly magical place”

Laurie Werner, New York

MUCHALLS CASTLE

17th century fortified house

By Stonehaven,
Kincardineshire AB3 2RS

Telephone 01569 731170
Fax 01569 731480

PROPRIETORS
Mrs Glenda Nicol Cormack
and Mr Michael Acklom

ROOM RATES

1 Single	*£90*
5 Doubles/Twins	*£135*
1 Four-poster	*£145*

Includes full breakfast and VAT

CHARGE/CREDIT CARDS
Cash or cheque only

ACCOLADES
S.T.B. ♛♛♛♛ Highly Commended
The Good Hotel Guide

FACILITIES
Garden
3 meeting rooms/max 30 people
Golf, riding and fishing nearby

RESTRICTIONS
Dinner by arrangement
No children under 12 years
No facilities for disabled guests
No pets allowed
No smoking in bedrooms

ATTRACTIONS
Crathes, Drum, Craigevar,
Fraser, Fyvie, Dunnotar,
Balmoral and Glamis Castles

AFFILIATIONS
The Tartan Collection

NEAREST
MAJOR CITY:
Aberdeen - 10 miles/15 mins

MAJOR AIRPORT:
Aberdeen - 10 miles/15 mins

RAILWAY STATION:
Stonehaven - 4 miles/8 mins

RESERVATIONS
Toll free in US: 800-43-SCOTS

ACCESS CODES
Not applicable

A fortress that whets the appetite for mystery and stylish high-life

“Gracious”, “Memorable”, and “A fantasy fulfilled” have all been used to describe Muchalls Castle. Overlooking the North Sea and built in 1619 on the remains of a 15th century fortress, it stands in five acres of grounds and is a most fascinating and original example of a Scottish early 17th century fortified house. Its famed interiors include magnificent Renaissance plaster ceilings, which are reputed to be some of the finest in Scotland.

The reception rooms are all available to visitors and the bedrooms, with antique furniture, bathrooms en suite and central heating, are individual and characteristically unusual, for this intriguing house still guards the secret of a hidden staircase, and a smuggler's passage supposedly leading to the sea.

After nearly four centuries Muchalls today remains a delightful private home, and now its history, seclusion and modern comfort may be shared by visitors from all over the world. All guests are personally and warmly welcomed with emphasis placed upon excellent food, wine, and individual requirements. Additionally, the hotel is perfect for special occasions, such as weddings, anniversaries, and private residential parties, where much care is given to every detail.

LOCATION

From Aberdeen-Dundee Road (A90) turn off at foot of large Z bend 3 miles north of Stonehaven. This is signposted 'Netherley'. Go up hill for 1 mile, turn right at top, signposted Muchalls Castle.

"Maureen, Alan and Michael went well beyond the call of duty for us and we truly appreciate their efforts"

Richard Rome, Dallas, Texas

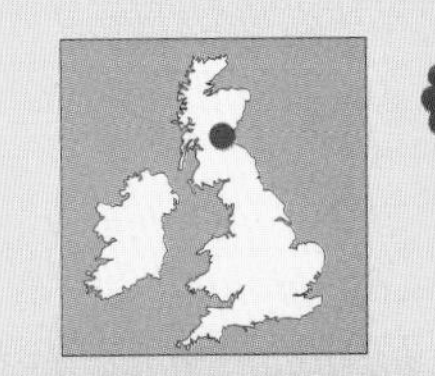

18th century country house

NIVINGSTON HOUSE

Award-winning food, great golf, in landscaped peace and quiet

Nestling at the foot of the Cleish Hills and dating back to the year 1725, Nivingston is a peaceful haven within easy reach of Edinburgh, Glasgow and Perth. Situated in 12 acres of landscaped grounds in which guests can try their hand at golf, putting and croquet, the hotel provides every comfort and modern convenience.

The hotel has an enviable reputation for the high quality of its cuisine, much of which is based on fresh local ingredients. Chef Michael Thompson selects the best Scottish products, cooking and serving them in delightful, unusual sauces. The wine list has been chosen with great care, offering over 100 different wines to suit all tastes and pockets. The bar, in the oldest part of the hotel, has around 50 different malt whiskies from which guests can make their selection.

Nivingston is the ideal base for many different types of holiday. Placed as it is within an easy drive of the famous courses of St Andrews, Gleneagles and Ladybank, there is particular emphasis on golfing holidays. The hotel will happily book tee times for guests. Please be sure to take your handicap certificate with you.

There is much to attract in terms of history. The area is famous for its salmon trout, the international angling competitions and Falkland Palace, the setting for Sir Walter Scott's novel, The Fair Maid of Perth.

LOCATION

Take Junction 5 from M90 on to B9097 towards Crook of Devon. Nivingston is 2 miles from the motorway on the left hand side of the road, clearly signposted.

Cleish Hills,
Nr Kinross,
Kinross-shire KY13 7LS

Telephone 01577 850216
Fax 01577 850238

SCOTLAND

PROPRIETOR

Allan Deeson

RATES PER PERSON

2 Singles £75
15 Doubles/Twins £50 - 65
Includes full breakfast and VAT

CHARGE/CREDIT CARDS

• *MC* • *VI*

ACCOLADES

S.T.B. ♛♛♛♛ Highly Commended
A.A. ★★★ ❀ 68%
Taste of Scotland

FACILITIES

Garden, croquet, putting, snooker
Golf and fishing nearby

RESTRICTIONS

None

ATTRACTIONS

Kinross,
Loch Leven,
Falkland Palace,
St Andrews, Gleneagles and
Ladybank golf courses

AFFILIATIONS

Scotland's Commended Hotels

NEAREST

MAJOR CITY:
Edinburgh - 22 miles/40 mins

MAJOR AIRPORT:
Edinburgh - 24 miles/45 mins

RAILWAY STATION:
Waverley - 23 miles/40 mins

RESERVATIONS

Toll free in US: 800-43-SCOTS

ACCESS CODES

Not applicable

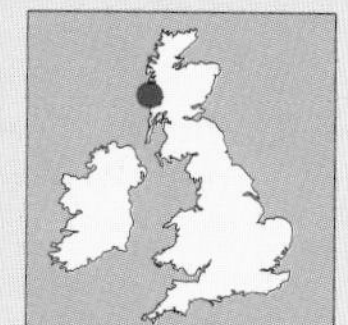

" Came recommended, left recommending "

David & Louise Brown, Newcastle

THE OLD LIBRARY LODGE

Restaurant with rooms

Arisaig, Inverness-shire PH39 4NH

Telephone 01687 450651
Fax 01687 450219

OWNERS
Alan and Angela Broadhurst

ROOM RATES
6 Doubles/Twins £70
Includes full breakfast and VAT

CHARGE/CREDIT CARDS

• MC • VI

ACCOLADES
S.T.B. ♛♛♛ Commended
The Good Hotel Guide
Les Routiers Casserole Award
Taste of Scotland

FACILITIES
Garden
Golf, riding and fishing nearby

RESTRICTIONS
No facilities for disabled guests
No pets

ATTRACTIONS
Glenfinnan,
Isle of Skye,
Clan MacDonald Centre,
"Local Hero" beach,
Inner Hebredian Islands

AFFILIATIONS
Independent

NEAREST
MAJOR CITY:
Glasgow - 150 miles/3 hrs

MAJOR AIRPORT:
Glasgow - 150 miles/3 hrs
Inverness - 100 miles/2½ hrs

RAILWAY STATION:
Arisaig - ½ mile/5 mins

RESERVATIONS
Direct with hotel

ACCESS CODES
Not applicable

An exceptional restaurant – and definitely a "local hero"

Situated in the tranquil village of Arisaig, which is justly famous for its magnificent white sandy beaches and secluded rocky bays, The Old Library has been owned for the past 12 years by Alan and Angela Broadhurst.

Originally a 200 year old stable, it has been tastefully converted into an award-winning restaurant with a high standard of accommodation. The restaurant, which has an enviable reputation with locals and visitors alike, makes full use of the finest local meat, fish and game, and the atmosphere of friendly informality, coupled with the high standard of cuisine, makes dining an unforgettable experience.

The en suite bedrooms are beautifully furnished and provide every facility to make your stay as pleasant as possible.

Arisaig and the surrounding area (the film Local Hero was made here) is especially suitable for walking, touring and making trips to the Inner Hebridian Islands of Eigg, Rum and Muck. Arisaig is also just 20 minutes from the Mallaig Ferry Terminal to the Isle of Skye, and can also be reached by direct rail link from London, Euston or Glasgow.

LOCATION

Proceed north along the A82 for one mile out of Fort William following the signs to Inverness. Turn left down the A830, signposted "The Road to the Isles", for 34 miles until reaching the village. The Old Library is in the centre facing the sea.

" Thank you for a great game of golf at Lundin Links and providing us with a very pleasant stay at the Old Manor "

Royston J Palmer, New Zealand

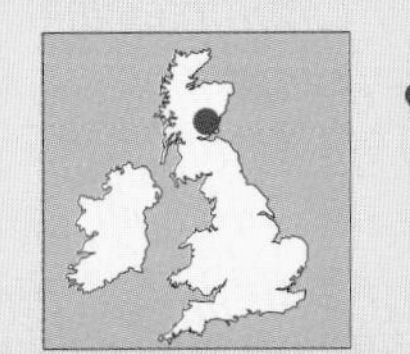

Country house hotel

OLD MANOR HOTEL

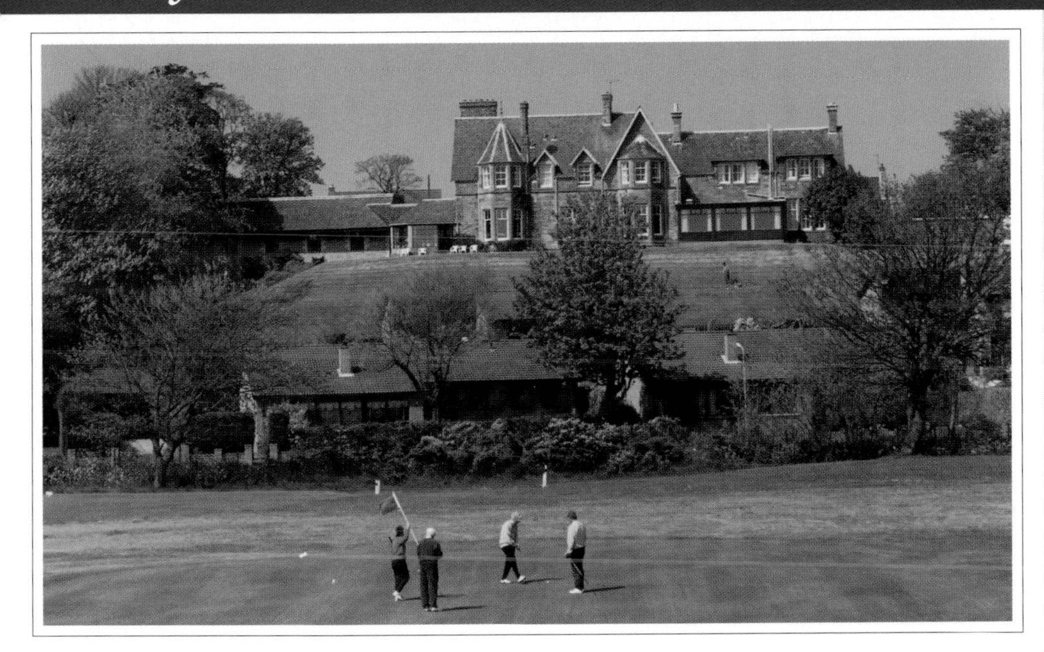

The birthplace, the Mecca and the heartland of golf

Situated in the golfers' mecca, this pleasant hotel is 15 minutes from St Andrews itself, looking out on to the Lundin Links and Leven Open qualifying golf courses. By booking "golf à la carte", you can choose convenient tee times at over 30 courses within an hour's drive. Staff will, on receipt of a small deposit, pay booking fees and deposits where required and confirm in writing to the golf clubs. Please be sure to bring your current handicap certificate.

The hotel is a fine old country house, situated in its own grounds with impressive views over Largo Bay. All public rooms are comfortably furnished. Many bedrooms have delightful sea views; all are en-suite with TV, Teletext, direct-dial telephone and hospitality tray.

Chef Alan Brunt and his team have won an AA rosette and credits in top guides for their imaginative use of local produce and seafood. Menus change each day, and there is an excellent wine list. The old coachman's cottage in the grounds offers fine chargrilled steaks and seafood when you want a less formal meal and a hand-pulled beer; in the cocktail bar looking out to the links and the sea you can choose from over 100 different malt whiskies.

There is also a great deal for non-golfers. St Andrews has beautiful beaches and Scotland's oldest university. Leisure parks, museums, castles, stately homes and gardens easily reached.

LOCATION

From M90, leave at Junction 3 on to A92 to St Andrews. At roundabout take third exit and follow A915 to St Andrews. Lundin Links is 1 mile past Leven. The Old Manor is on the right as you enter the village.

Lundin Links, Nr St Andrews, Fife KY8 6AJ

Phone 01333 320368
Fax 01333 320911

PROPRIETOR
Clark Family

ROOM RATES

2 Singles	*£65*
8 Standard Doubles/Twins	*£90*
15 Superior Doubles/Twins	*£105*

Includes full breakfast and VAT

CHARGE/CREDIT CARDS

• JCB • MC • VI

ACCOLADES
A.A. ★★★ ❀ 69%
Consort/RAC Scottish Hotel of the Year 1995
Taste of Scotland

FACILITIES
Garden
2 meeting rooms/max 80 people
Golf, fishing, riding and beaches nearby

RESTRICTIONS
Pets not allowed in public areas

ATTRACTIONS
Deep Sea World, Crail, Anstruther, St Andrews Cathedral, St Andrews Golf Course, Falkland Palace

AFFILIATIONS
Scotland's Commended Hotels
Consort Hotels

NEAREST
MAJOR CITY:
St Andrews - 12 miles/15 mins

MAJOR AIRPORT:
Edinburgh - 30 miles/45 mins

RAILWAY STATION:
Markinch - 6 miles/10 mins

RESERVATIONS
Direct with hotel

ACCESS CODES
SABRE CN 05340
AMADEUS CN DNDOLD
WORLDSPAN CN OLDMA

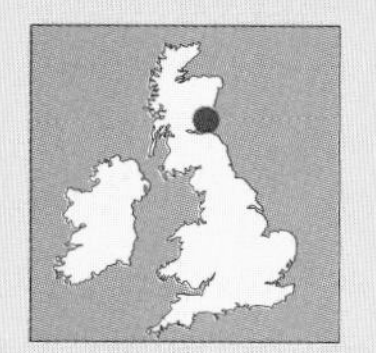

" Lovingly and beautifully restored "

Nancy Roberts Lonsdale, Oakland, California

OLD MANSION HOUSE

16th century baronial home

Auchterhouse, By Dundee, Angus DD3 0QN

Telephone 01382 320366
Fax 01382 320400

PROPRIETORS
Nigel and Eva Bell

ROOM RATES
4 Doubles/Twins £80 - £100
2 Four-posters £80 - £125
Includes full breakfast and VAT

CHARGE/CREDIT CARDS

• DC • MC • VI

ACCOLADES
S.T.B. ♛♛♛♛ Highly Commended
A.A. ★★★ ❀ 70%
The Good Hotel Guide
Taste of Scotland

FACILITIES
Garden, croquet, squash, tennis, outdoor pool
Golf and riding nearby

RESTRICTIONS
No facilities for disabled guests

ATTRACTIONS
Glamis Castle, The Glens, Affleck Castle, Arbroath Castle, Claypotts Castle, Blair Castle, Glenshee, Carnoustie and Gleneagles golf courses

AFFILIATIONS
Scotland's Commended Hotels

NEAREST
MAJOR CITY:
Dundee - 7 miles/10 mins

MAJOR AIRPORT:
Edinburgh - 60 miles/1 hr

RAILWAY STATION:
Dundee - 7 miles/10 mins

RESERVATIONS
Toll free in US: 800-43-SCOTS

ACCESS CODES
Not applicable

Good food, wine, breakfasts and a generous helping of Scottish history

The Mansion House, skilfully converted by its present owners Nigel and Eva Bell to a small luxury hotel, specialises in the quality of its food and the excellence of its wine cellar. The staff are friendly and attentive. At the same time the hotel retains the atmosphere and character of this magnificent 16th century baronial home.

The lands and the house, steeped in Scottish history, have been owned by several noted families, namely the Ogilvies, Strathmores and the Earls of Buchan. William Wallace is reputed to have stayed here; the tower to the east is named "the Wallace Tower". 17th century additions include ornate plasterwork in the original drawing room with its open Jacobean tower. The vaulted entrance hall dates back even earlier.

All bedrooms have private bathroom, TV, telephone, and central heating. Within the 10-acre grounds are landscaped gardens, croquet and tennis lawns, squash court and outdoor swimming pool.

The superb Scottish breakfast is served in the stately dining room. There is a bar in the first floor library, where you can choose from the excellent dinner menu whose specialities include local angus beef and fresh salmon. All vegetables are fresh, many from the mansion's own garden.

Auchterhouse village is seven miles from Dundee with its museums, art gallery, and famous railway bridge across the River Tay.

LOCATION

Take the A923 (Coupar Angus) road out of Dundee. Cross the Kingsway and fork right at Muirhead. Hotel is on the left, 2½ miles along the Alyth road.

“ The complete Scottish dining experience, worth travelling a long way for and worth staying ”

Raymond Gardner, The Glasgow Herald

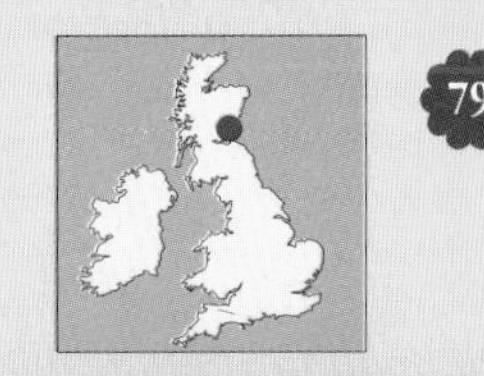

Country inn

THE PEAT INN

“In a class of its own.” “Wine cellar of the year” What more could you ask?

The Peat Inn is one of Scotland's most celebrated restaurants. David Wilson, Chef Laureate, Master Chef and Proprietor, is well known to viewers of the television series 'Master Chef' and 'Hot Chefs'. Food lovers the world over are attracted to his restaurant in the tiny rural village named after the inn.

There they are presented with innovative dishes, imaginatively reflecting the region and making excellent use of its produce.

The Peat Inn has won innumerable distinctions including a Catey Award – an 'Oscar' of the catering industry – and a unique Taste of Scotland Award 'In a Class of its Own'.

David Wilson's wine list is legendary, winning a leading guide's 'Wine Cellar of the Year' award, and offering variety, interest and good value.

The residence, built in 1987, satisfies a growing demand for those who wish the pleasure of the table to be prolonged by an overnight stay.

Sympathetically designed and built to the highest standard in garden grounds to the rear of the restaurant, the residence offers eight luxury suites, seven split level and one single level suite.

Patricia Wilson, a design graduate, has furnished each suite individually with quality fabrics and period French furniture. Each suite has a comfortable sitting room and luxurious bathroom and bedroom with a choice of double, kingsize or twin beds.

LOCATION

Situated in the village of Peat Inn at the junction of the B940/B941, 6 miles south west of St Andrews.

by Cupar,
Fife KY15 5LH

Telephone 01334 840206
Fax 01334 840530

PROPRIETORS

David and Patricia Wilson

ROOM RATES

8 Suites £135 - £145
Includes continental breakfast and VAT

CHARGE/CREDIT CARDS

• DC • MC • VI

ACCOLADES

A.A. ★★ ❀❀❀
Andrew Harper Award – Hideaway Report
Taste of Scotland

FACILITIES

Garden
Riding nearby

RESTRICTIONS

None

ATTRACTIONS

St Andrews,
East Neuk fishing villages,
Falkland Palace,
Aberdour Castle,
Inchcolm Abbey

AFFILIATIONS

Independent

NEAREST

MAJOR CITY:
Edinburgh - 40 miles/1 hr

MAJOR AIRPORT:
Edinburgh - 40 miles/1 hr

RAILWAY STATION:
Cupar - 6 miles/10 mins

RESERVATIONS

Direct with hotel

ACCESS CODES

Not applicable

"They've thought of everything in their rambling house.... And they have the light touch that makes you feel at home, with enough going on to make you feel on holiday"

Peter Irvine, "Scotland the Best!"

PHILIPBURN HOUSE

18th century dowager house

Selkirk, Borders TD7 5LS

Telephone 01750 20747
Fax 01750 21690

PROPRIETOR
Jim C M Hill

RATES PER PERSON

Single occupancy	*£58.50*
11 Doubles/Twins	*£48.50*
5 Superior Doubles/Twins	*£55*

Includes full breakfast and VAT

CHARGE/CREDIT CARDS

• *DC* • *MC* • *VI*

ACCOLADES
S.T.B. ♛♛♛♛ Highly Commended

FACILITIES
Garden, swimming pool, badminton, children's adventure area
1 meeting room/max 12 people
Golf and fishing nearby

RESTRICTIONS
Pets by prior arrangement

ATTRACTIONS
Abbotsford, Bowhill House, Floors Castle "Greystoke", Dryburgh, Melrose, Jedburgh and Kelso Abbeys

AFFILIATIONS
Scotland's Commended Hotels
Independent Innkeepers Association

NEAREST
MAJOR CITY:
Edinburgh - 40 miles/1 hr

MAJOR AIRPORT:
Edinburgh - 46 miles/1 hr

RAILWAY STATION:
Waverley - 45 miles/1 hr

RESERVATIONS
Direct with hotel

ACCESS CODES
SABRE HK 30582
APOLLO HT 25904
WORLDSPAN HK PHILP

A Shangri-La high in the hills of the Border Country

During the routine pressures of everyday life, have you dreamt of escaping to a cosy little hostelry up in the hills? At Philipburn you may find your Shangri-La.

In former times the Dowager House to the Philiphaugh Estate, Philipburn was built in 1751, not long after Covenanters and Royalists fought the bloody battle of Philiphaugh, a few yards from the now tranquil lawns, flowers and woodlands in which the friendly old house lies.

Owned and personally managed by the Hill family for 25 years, they have lovingly fashioned Philiphaugh into exactly what a Scottish country house hotel should be. Chef Patron Jim Hill and his Claridges-trained younger son mastermind the innovative and delicious cooking that is known and respected throughout Scotland. The Garden and Poolside Restaurants are leafy places with low ceilings, mellow pine panelling and delightful table settings in nooks and crannies, each looking out across the flowers and gardens to the hills beyond.

Situated in the heart of Sir Walter Scott's historic Borderland, Philipburn is barely an hour's drive from Edinburgh through rolling hills, sparkling rivers, peel towers, and castles.

A great walking centre, Philipburn has its own craggy fun-loving and knowledgeable hill guides. The "Walker's Wall" and the cosy Souters bar help you relax and reflect on the day's golf, fishing or riding, or to examine the mouth-watering menus in the blissful realisation that a holiday at Philipburn lies ahead.

LOCATION

M6 to northern end (Junction 44). Follow A7 past Longtown, Langholm and Hawick to Selkirk. Then A707 (Peebles road). Hotel is at the next junction ¾ mile from Selkirk.

" An inspired decision "

Anne & John Lenting

Country house

POLMAILY HOUSE HOTEL

A country house of great character, comfort and informal atmosphere

Such distinctive character and atmosphere is only possible in a privately-owned, well-run establishment where your hosts are committed to the highest standards. Polmaily House is just such a place. Set in 18 acres of gardens, the house looks southwards, across the slope of Glen Urquhart, to the mysterious Loch Ness.

All the bedrooms are individually decorated and tastefully furnished, each having en suite bathroom, radio, direct-dial telephone, colour television and tea-making facilities with a choice of fine teas. A ground floor room suitable for elderly and disabled guests is also available.

The menus, composed under the personal supervision of your host, reflect an abundant larder of fresh wild game, salmon and Aberdeen Angus beef together with locally grown herbs, vegetables and soft fruit.

Throughout the year, the hotel provides unrivalled recreational opportunities and is the gateway to the last great wilderness area in Europe. The local sports facilities include some of the finest championship golf courses in the country, fly-fishing and horse back trails through the hills and glens. There is access to deer stalking using the hotel's four-wheel drive vehicles. Skiers have the choice of the two principal ski resorts in the country: Aviemore or Aonoch Mor, both only 50 minutes drive away.

Families are especially welcome. There are well-equipped play areas, separate children's meals and a baby listening and sitting service.

LOCATION

From Inverness, take the A82 signposted to Fort William, after 16 miles turn onto the A831 signposted to Cannich. Remain on this road for about 2 miles and the hotel will be seen on the right.

SCOTLAND

Loch Ness, Drumnadrochit, Inverness-shire IV3 6XT

Telephone 01456 450343
Fax 01456 450813

PROPRIETORS

John and Sonia Whittington-Davis

RATES PER PERSON

2 Singles	*£29.50 - £45*
9 Doubles	*£29.50 - £45*
1 Suite	*£36.50 - £52.50*

Includes full breakfast and VAT

CHARGE/CREDIT CARDS

• *MC* • *VI*

ACCOLADES

S.T.B. ♛♛♛♛ *Highly Commended*
R.A.C. ★★★
A.A. ★★★ *69%*

FACILITIES

Garden, croquet, tennis, heated indoor pool
Riding, skiing and deer stalking nearby
Extensive facilities for children

RESTRICTIONS

None

ATTRACTIONS

Glen Affic, Loch Ness, Cawdor Castle, Isle of Skye, Cairngorms, Nevis Range

AFFILIATIONS

Independent

NEAREST

MAJOR CITY:
Inverness - 16 miles/20 mins

MAJOR AIRPORT:
Glasgow - 180 miles/ 3½ hrs
Inverness - 20 miles/25 mins

RAILWAY STATION:
Inverness - 16 miles/20 mins

RESERVATIONS

Direct with hotel

ACCESS CODES

Not applicable

" If there's anywhere better than here then it must have pearly gates "

Lyn Foggo & Walter Butler, Edinburgh

ROMAN CAMP COUNTRY HOUSE *17th century hunting lodge*

Off Main Street, Callander, Perthshire FK17 8BG

Telephone 01877 330003
Fax 01877 331533

PROPRIETORS

Eric and Marion Brown

ROOM RATES

Single occupancy	*£60 - £80*
4 Doubles/Twins	*£80 - £105*
7 Superior Doubles	*£105 - £135*
3 Suites	*£120 - £150*

Includes full breakfast and VAT

CHARGE/CREDIT CARDS

• DC • MC • VI

ACCOLADES

S.T.B. Highly Commended
R.A.C. ★★★ + Merit Awards H C & R
A.A. ★★★ 69%
The Good Hotel Guide

FACILITIES

Garden, fishing, heli-pad
1 meeting room/max 30 people
Golf, fishing and shooting nearby

RESTRICTIONS

No children under 4 years
Pets by prior arrangement

ATTRACTIONS

Rob Roy country, Castle Campbell, Inchmahome Priory, Stirling Castle, Loch Lomond

AFFILIATIONS

Selected British Hotels

NEAREST

MAJOR CITY:
Edinburgh - 52 miles/1 hr

MAJOR AIRPORT:
Edinburgh - 46 miles/50 mins

RAILWAY STATION:
Stirling - 17 miles/30 mins

RRESERVATIONS

Toll free in US: 800-323-5463

ACCESS CODES

Not applicable

Historic house centrally situated for Callander and the Trossachs

The house takes its name from earth works to the east of its walled gardens, believed to be the site of a Roman fort. It was built originally as a hunting lodge in 1625 for the Dukes of Perth. It passed into the ownership of Viscount Esher in 1897. The turrets that give the building its unique character were added at that time. The house became a hotel in 1939.

Each of the 14 bedrooms has its own distinctive style and character. Some have coombed walls and furniture dating back 200 years. All are equipped with the little thoughtful extras that make your stay comfortable and enjoyable.

The library, panelled in 16th century oak, takes on a mellow atmosphere in the evening with the glow of a log fire, lit even in summer. The drawing room is bright and soft, with silk-lined walls. The recently remodelled restaurant with a painted 16th century style ceiling features tapestries of English cathedrals woven by Elizabeth Esher in the 1930s. Menus change daily and are prepared from local ingredients in season. There are tasting and à la carte and vegetarian menus.

Beyond the 20 acres of tranquil parkland and gardens with views of the River Teith are the Trossachs and the Highlands. This is a land of mountain and glen, rolling pasture and heather moor. It is a marvellous base for your Scottish holiday. Owners Eric and Marion Brown look forward to welcoming you, and hope that The Roman Camp becomes your favourite country retreat.

LOCATION

From M9 Junction 10, head north on the A84 through the village of Callander, then turn left down a 300-yard drive at the east end of Callander main street.

"What a joy it is for world weary travellers to find an oasis of such calm and caring attention"

Sarah Lord, Calvin Klein Inc

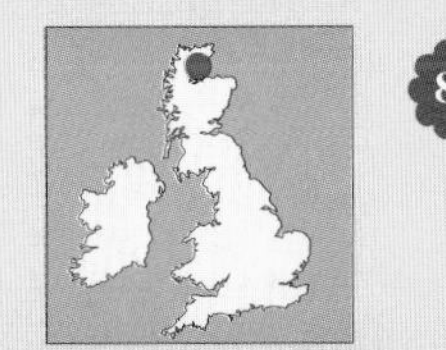

Edwardian house

ROYAL MARINE HOTEL

A warm oasis amongst a wild and beautiful environment

The renowned Scottish architect, Sir Robert Lorimer, originally designed this as a private country house in the 1900's. A recent extensive restoration has taken place, however the buildings rich character and ambience have been retained whilst now providing the modern amenities expected of a quality hotel. Features include a number of carved wooden fireplaces and an elegant stairway and reception foyer, all complemented by the chef's cuisine in the traditionally styled dining room.

Since Brora is thriving with golf and fishing possibilities the hotel is especially attractive to sportsmen. Nearby are local championship links golf courses including Brora, Golspie, Royal Dornoch and Tain.

The hotel has its own boat on Loch Brora for fly fishing, a heated indoor swimming pool and sauna, a full sized snooker table and access to the four lane curling rink during the winter months.

Situated midway between Inverness and John O'Groats, Brora is ideal as a centre, from which to tour the Northern Highlands and the Orkney Islands. The region is the least densely populated area in Europe and abounds with birds and wild life which can be seen in their natural habitat. The rock formations are of particular interest to geologists and provide excellent hill walking.

LOCATION

One hour north of Inverness, just off A9 adjacent to James Braid's 18 hole links golf course.

Golf Road, Brora, Sutherland KW9 6QS

Telephone 01408 621252
Fax 01408 621181

GENERAL MANAGER
Robert Powell

ROOM RATES

Single occupancy	*£55*
8 Doubles	*£90*
2 Suites	*£120*
1 Family	*£120*

Includes full breakfast and VAT

CHARGE/CREDIT CARDS

• DC • MC • VI

ACCOLADES
S.T.B. ♛♛♛♛ Commended
R.A.C.★★★
A.A. ★★★ 66%
Taste of Scotland

FACILITIES
Garden, croquet, petanque, curling, tennis, indoor pool, snooker, sauna, fishing, heli-pad
2 meeting rooms/max 60 people
Fishing nearby

RESTRICTIONS
None

ATTRACTIONS
Dunrobin Castle, Clynelish Malt Whisky Distillery, Hunters of Brora Woollen Mills, Orkney Islands

AFFILIATIONS
Scotland's Commended Hotels

NEAREST
MAJOR CITY:
Inverness - 60 miles/1 hr

MAJOR AIRPORT:
Glasgow - 220 miles/4 hrs
Inverness - 70 miles/1 1/4 hrs

RAILWAY STATION:
Brora - 1/4 mile/2 mins

RESERVATIONS
Toll free in US: 800-43-SCOTS

ACCESS CODES
Not applicable

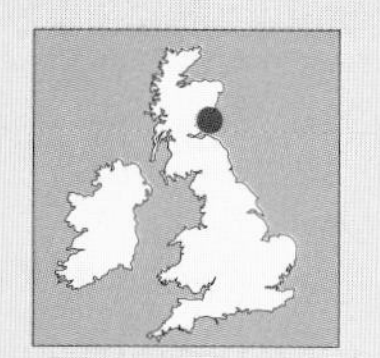

“ The Hughes family's hospitality is second to none ”

Severiano Ballesteros, Golf Champion

ST ANDREWS GOLF HOTEL

Victorian hotel Castle

40 The Scores, St Andrews, Fife KY16 9AS

Telephone 01334 472611
Fax 01334 472188

PROPRIETORS
Brian and Maureen Hughes

MANAGER
Justin Hughes

ROOM RATES

2 Singles	£74 - £80.50
17 Doubles	£122 - £135
1 Four-poster	£148
3 Masters	£148

Includes full breakfast and VAT

CHARGE/CREDIT CARDS

• *DC* • *MC* • *VI*

ACCOLADES
S.T.B. ♛♛♛♛ Highly Commended
R.A.C. ★★★ + Merit Awards H C & R
A.A. ★★★ ❀ 73%
Taste of Scotland

FACILITIES
Garden
2 meeting rooms/max 200 people
Golf and riding nearby

RESTRICTIONS
No facilities for disabled guests
Pets by prior arrangement

ATTRACTIONS
The East Neuk fishing villages, The Medieval Old Town, Falkland Palace, Glamis Castle, Golf courses including the 'Old Course'

AFFILIATIONS
Scotland's Heritage Hotels

NEAREST
MAJOR CITY:
Edinburgh - 55 miles/1 ¼ hrs

MAJOR AIRPORT:
Edinburgh - 50 miles/1 hr

RAILWAY STATION:
Leuchars - 4 miles/15 mins

RESERVATIONS
Toll free in US: 800-344-5257

ACCESS CODES
Not applicable

Spectacular sea views and wonderful food at the ancient home of golf

St Andrews Golf Hotel is privately owned and run and is situated on the cliff overlooking St Andrews Bay and Links, 200 yards from the world famous 'Old Course'.

A tastefully modernised Victorian building, the hotel has 23 individually decorated, very comfortable bedrooms all with en suite facilities, telephone, radio, satellite TV, trouser press and iron, hairdryer, tea-maker and, of course, fresh fruit and flowers. Many superior rooms and the four magnificent master bedrooms have sea views.

The spacious public rooms include the oak-panelled restaurant which also has a spectacular sea view. Award-winning chef, Adam Harrow, prepares table d'hôte and à la carte menus daily featuring the best of local meats, fish and game. The menus are complemented by a superb list of more than 100 wines selected from all over the world.

This pleasant town, with its fine shops, dates from the Middle Ages and boasts a ruined castle and cathedral. The University with its many lovely buildings is more than 500 years old. Golf is the junior member being here in serious intent for only 250 years.

Today, golf is the life-blood of the town; there are 5½ courses and excellent practice facilities in St Andrews and another 30 courses within 40 minutes drive. Your golfing holiday can be arranged here by the hotel or anywhere in Scotland.

LOCATION

St Andrews, on the cliff overlooking the sea and links. M8 from Glasgow to Forth Bridge, then M90 and A91 to St Andrews.

" A very special part of our trip. Great place, fantastic food and marvellous hospitality "

S Cantor, California

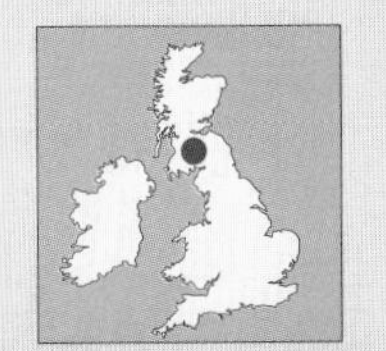

12th century manor house

SHIELDHILL HOTEL

Quothquan, Biggar, Lanarkshire ML12 6NA

Telephone 01899 220035
Fax 01899 221092

PROPRIETORS
Neil and Joan Mackintosh

ROOM RATES

Single occupancy	*£68 - £89*
4 Doubles/Twins	*£104*
4 Four-posters	*£114*
3 Jacuzzi Doubles	*£124 - £152*

Includes full breakfast and VAT

CHARGE/CREDIT CARDS

• DC • MC • VI

ACCOLADES
S.T.B. Highly Commended
R.A.C. ★★★ + Merit Award C
A.A. ★★★ 70%
The Good Hotel Guide

FACILITIES
Garden, jacuzzi, heli-pad
2 meeting rooms/max 70 people
Golf, riding and fishing nearby

RESTRICTIONS
No children under 12 years
No facilities for disabled guests
No pets

ATTRACTIONS
New Lanark, Wanlock Head Lead Mine and gold panning, Neidpath & Traquaire Castle, Edinburgh and border towns, Linlithgow Palace

AFFILIATIONS
Virgin Hotels
Scotland's Commended Hotels

NEAREST
MAJOR CITY:
Edinburgh - 30 miles/45 mins
Glasgow - 36 miles/1 hr

MAJOR AIRPORT:
Edinburgh - 32 miles/45 mins
Glasgow - 38 miles/1 hr

RAILWAY STATION:
Edinburgh - 30 miles/45 mins

RESERVATIONS
Toll free in US: 800-43-SCOTS

ACCESS CODES
SABRE HK 30584
APOLLO HK 04061
WORLDSPAN HK SHIEL

Comfort, warmth and elegance en route to Edinburgh

Shieldhill has stood amidst the rich farmlands and rolling hills of the Clyde Valley since 1199 and was the home of the Chancellor family until 1959.

The castle-style country house sits in five acres of parkland and woodland. The 'Old Keep' with its turreted roof and secret stairway, panelled rooms and open fires all help to create an atmosphere that allows guests to imagine life during Scotland's turbulent past.

Each of the eleven spacious bedrooms has been individually designed and refurbished with four-poster, king, queen or twin beds. Some rooms have jacuzzi, some fireplaces but all have been furnished with great attention to comfort and detail.

Shieldhill is managed by the owners, Neil and Joan Mackintosh. Their award winning kitchen uses only the finest of Scottish produce to create meals, a feast for the eye as well as the palate.

For the energetic this is walking, golfing and fishing country but it has to be a great place to relax with a good book. As a touring base, Sheildhill is perfect for visiting Edinburgh, only 45 minutes away or alternatively, touring the Scottish border country with its many ancient abbeys and ruins.

LOCATION

From Edinburgh take the A702 (direction Carlisle) to Biggar (29 miles), then B7016 (direction Carnwath), 2 miles to Shieldhill Road, then left to Shieldhill Hotel (1½ miles). From the south take Junction 44 of the M6.

“ The views over the Summer Isles are still stunning and the food remains a major attraction ”

Derek Cooper, Scotland on Sunday

Summer Isles

19th century fishing inn

Achiltibuie,
Ross-shire IV26 2YG

Telephone 01854 622282
Fax 01854 622251

PROPRIETORS
Mr and Mrs M Irvine

ROOM RATES
12 Doubles/Twins £77 - £95
1 Log House suite £124 - £190
Includes full breakfast and VAT

CHARGE/CREDIT CARDS
Cash or cheque only

ACCOLADES
S.T.B. ♛♛♛ Highly Commended
The Good Hotel Guide
Taste of Scotland

FACILITIES
Birdwatching, walking fishing, scuba diving and sailing nearby

RESTRICTIONS
No facilities for disabled guests
Pets not allowed in public rooms

ATTRACTIONS
Inverewe Gardens,
Inverpolly nature reserve,
Sutherland coast,
Western Isles,
Highlands

AFFILIATIONS
Independent

NEAREST
MAJOR CITY:
Inverness - 85 miles/2 hrs

MAJOR AIRPORT:
Edinburgh - 220 miles/5 hrs

RAILWAY STATION:
Garve - 60 miles/1½ hrs

RESERVATIONS
Direct with hotel

ACCESS CODES
Not applicable

An oasis of civilisation in wild, untouched landscape

Mark and Geraldine Irvine run this individual but sophisticated hotel which has belonged to the family since the late 1960s. It has established itself as an oasis of civilisation hidden away in a stunningly beautiful, but still wild and untouched landscape.

Nearly everything you eat there is home produced or locally caught. Scallops, lobsters, languoustines, crabs, halibut, turbot, salmon, venison, big brown eggs, wholesome brown bread fresh from the oven – the list of real food is endless. With such fresh ingredients, chef Chris Firth-Bernard provides delicious, healthy fare. Most guests like to change for dinner but there is no formality. A single balanced menu dinner is served at 8 pm; special diets can be accommodated given prior notice.

After breakfast Mark and Geraldine are happy to talk to you about fishing, walking or birdwatching. A collection of favourite walks, from 3 to 30 miles, is beside every bed. A local boat, the Hectoria, sails round the islands to show off seals and rare birds. You can also explore the scenery sub-aqua with the local diving school. Inverewe Gardens, Inverpolly Nature Reserve and the Sutherland coast are all within easy reach.

Take your wellingtons, sensible shoes, sunglasses, cameras, paint boxes, binoculars and comfortable old clothes. The gulf stream is at the foot of the croft: the weather may vary from Arctic to Aegean inside a week. Make the most of this beautiful wilderness of islands and mountains. Eating well, sleeping well and living in beautiful surroundings is a therapy for which many return year after year.

LOCATION

10 miles north of Ullapool, turn left on to a single track road. After 15 miles you reach the village of Achiltibuie. The hotel is just past the post office.

" Drinks mysteriously appeared on silver trays and waiters attended to our every need. Had I coughed or sneezed, one of them would surely have proffered a perfumed handkerchief "

Giles Milton, The Mail on Sunday

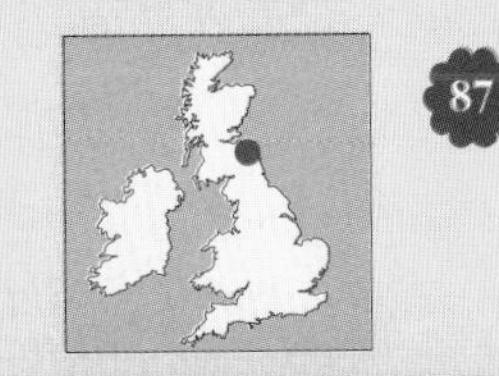

18th century country house

SUNLAWS HOUSE HOTEL

In 200 acres, an old country house with modern-day comforts

Sunlaws is a beautiful country house hotel situated in the heart of the Scottish Borders. The hotel is owned by the Duke of Roxburghe and has all the quality and charm of an 18th century gentleman's retreat.

In such a setting, where log fires crackle and reflect the qualities of an earlier age, discover a high level of comfort complemented by discreet and personal attention. Enjoy that special service that only a small, intimate country hotel like Sunlaws House can provide.

Each of the 22 bedrooms is fully equipped to care for today's discerning guest. To match the exacting international standards now expected, each room is well fitted with en suite bathrooms, direct-dial telephone, radio and television. Some of the bedrooms have four-poster beds with open log fires and several bedrooms are located in the delightful stables courtyard.

Relax in over 200 acres of secluded woodlands. Enjoy the many leisure activities on the estate such as the clay shooting school or stocked trout loch.

You will find excellent cuisine and a warm Scottish welcome. Visit Sunlaws and enjoy the Borders at its best.

LOCATION

From the A68 Edinburgh-Newcastle route, take the A698 Jedburgh-Kelso road. The Sunlaws Estate is 3 miles south of Kelso on the outskirts of Heiton village.

SCOTLAND

Heiton, Kelso, Roxburghshire TD5 8JZ

Telephone 01573 450331
Fax 01573 450611

PROPRIETOR
The Duke of Roxburghe

GENERAL MANAGER
David A Webster

ROOM RATES

2 Singles	£95
15 Doubles/Twins	£140
4 Four-posters	£155
1 Suite	£175

Includes full breakfast and VAT

CHARGE/CREDIT CARDS

• DC • MC • VI

ACCOLADES
S.T.B. Highly Commended
R.A.C. ★★★ + Merit Awards H C & R
A.A. ★★★ 76%
Taste of Scotland

FACILITIES
Croquet, tennis, gardens, health and beauty, trout loch, clay pigeon shooting school, helipad
3 meeting rooms/max 150 people
Fishing nearby

RESTRICTIONS
Dogs accepted but extra charge of £6 per night

ATTRACTIONS
Floors Castle, Kelso Abbey, Jedburgh Abbey, Edinburgh

AFFILIATIONS
Pride of Britain

NEAREST
MAJOR CITY:
Edinburgh - 58 miles/1 hr
Newcastle - 60 miles/1 hr

MAJOR AIRPORT:
Edinburgh - 58 miles/1 hr

RAILWAY STATION:
Berwick-upon-Tweed - 20 miles/35 mins

RESERVATIONS
Direct with hotel

ACCESS CODES
Not applicable

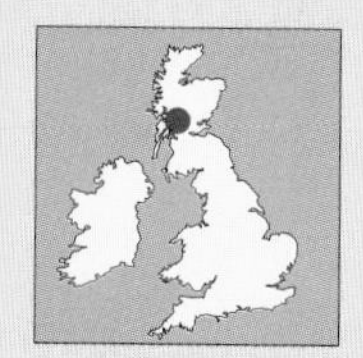

"It is not just the food, but everything else at this hotel which will convince any visitor to return time and again"

J P Sharp, West Yorkshire

TAYCHREGGAN

Drovers inn

Kilchrenan,
By Taynuilt,
Argyll PA35 1HQ

Telephone 01866 833211
Fax 01866 833244

PROPRIETOR
Annie C Paul

RATES PER PERSON
Doubles/Twins £65 - £80
Includes dinner, full breakfast and VAT

CHARGE/CREDIT CARDS

• *MC* • *VI*

ACCOLADES
S.T.B. ♛♛♛♛ Highly Commended
R.A.C. ★★★ + Merit Award H
A.A. ★★★ ❀❀ 72%
A.A. Courtesy & Care Award 1995
The Good Hotel Guide
Taste of Scotland

FACILITIES
Garden, fishing
2 meeting rooms/max 14 people
Walking and gliding nearby

RESTRICTIONS
No children under 12 years
No facilities for disabled guests
Pets by arrangement

ATTRACTIONS
Kilchurn Castle, Inveraray, loch cruises, forest walks

AFFILIATIONS
Scotland's Commended Hotels
Virgin Hotels
Les Routiers

NEAREST
MAJOR CITY:
Glasgow - 90 miles/2 hrs

MAJOR AIRPORT:
Glasgow - 90 miles/2 hrs

RAILWAY STATION:
Taynuilt - 7 miles/15 mins

RESERVATIONS
Direct with hotel

ACCESS CODES
Not applicable

Mountain grandeur, fascinating wildlife and lochside beauty

With its own backdrop of beautiful Scottish countryside and surrounded by the grandeur of Argyll's mountains and forests, Taychreggan Hotel has nestled on the shores of magnificent Loch Awe for the past 300 years. Originally a cattle drovers' inn, the old stone house and its cobbled courtyard form the centrepiece of the hotel where the aim is to woo visitors into feeling like house guests. Most of the beautiful en suite bedrooms overlook the loch; all offer high standards of quality, style and comfort.

Owner Annie Paul and her friendly and experienced staff have scooped two top UK awards for 1995: "Newcomer of the Year" Award from Les Routiers and the "Most Romantic Hotels" nomination awarded to only eight Scottish hotels by the AA. The magnificent view from the dining room is matched by superb Scottish cuisine, a comprehensive list of French wines and fine Scotch whiskies.

After the breakfast of your choice, you can visit historic places such as Inveraray or Kilchurn Castle, or choose from many outdoor activities. For hill walkers there are 13 peaks over 3,000 feet within an hour's drive. You can fish for brown or rainbow trout, salmon, pike, char and perch. The hotel has its own fishing rights, boats and ghillie. You can see birds of prey and rare species in breathtaking surroundings. Horse riding, deer stalking, water sports, golf and rough shooting can all be arranged. Sitting and doing nothing in utter tranquillity is also encouraged at Taychreggan.

LOCATION

From Edinburgh M9 to Stirling (exit 10). Take A84 through Callander, after Lochearnhead take A85 signposted Crianlarich/Oban. 1 mile before Taynuilt turn left on to B845 signposted Kilchrenan/Taychreggan. Hotel is 7 miles down this single track road (pass with care) at very end on shores of Loch Awe.

"Wonderful . . . an unexpected gem"

Barry Smith, Wiltshire

Seaside house

TIGH-AN-EILEAN

A highland inn surrounded by dramatic sea and landscapes

Tigh-an-Eilean (House of the Island) is on the edge of the sea at the centre of the small fishing village of Shieldaig in the Torridon hills of Ross-shire. The quiet village, bypassed by the A896, faces the Scottish National Trust's "Isle of Pines" with glorious views over Loch Shieldaig to Loch Torridon and the open sea beyond. The simple white-washed hotel is in the centre and a few minutes stroll from the jetty where the fishing boats unload their catch.

Calum and Elizabeth Stewart greet you with a warm welcome to their comfortable hotel. There are two lounges and a cosy self-service residents' bar. The dining room, looking across the sea towards the sunset is the setting for a memorable evening.

Calum's dinner menus emphasise the finest quality local and Scottish produce. The reasonably priced wine list is short but comprehensive.

All bedrooms are en suite, most with a sea view. No two are the same, each having its own individual charm. A wealth of prints and paintings complete the welcoming atmosphere.

The surrounding Torridon hills, rising almost vertically 3000 feet from the sea shore, contain many of the most dramatic landscapes in the Highlands. A hill walkers' paradise but plenty of gentler routes too. Nearby Applecross, over the 2000 feet pass of Benlach na Bo, has breathtaking views of Skye and the Outer Hebrides.

The hotel has private fishing (salmon/sea trout) in the River Balgy. In the hill lochs brown trout abound.

LOCATION

Take the A832 from Inverness to Kinlochewe. Turn onto A896 to Torridon and Shieldaig.

Shieldaig by Strathcarrow, Ross-shire IV54 8XN

Telephone 01520 755251
Fax 01520 755321

SCOTLAND

PROPRIETORS
Calum and Elizabeth Stewart

ROOM RATES

3 Singles	*£41.50*
8 Doubles/Twins	*£45.50*

Includes full breakfast and VAT

CHARGE/CREDIT CARDS

• MC • VI

ACCOLADES
S.T.B. ♛♛♛ Highly Commended
R.A.C. ★ + Merit Awards H C & R
A.A. ★★ ❀ 71%
The Good Hotel Guide

FACILITIES
Fishing
Hill walking nearby

RESTRICTIONS
No facilities for disabled guests
Dogs only, but not in public rooms

ATTRACTIONS
Applecross Peninsula, Inverewe Gardens, Ben Eighe Nature Reserve, Loch Torridon, Isle of Skye

AFFILIATIONS
Independent

NEAREST
MAJOR CITY:
Inverness - 71 miles/1¾ hrs

MAJOR AIRPORT:
Glasgow - 223 miles/4¼ hrs
Dalcross - 78 miles/2 hrs

RAILWAY STATION:
Strathcarron - 17 miles/30 mins

RESERVATIONS
Direct with hotel

ACCESS CODES
Not applicable

“ The Udny Arms is a small, family-run inn where the warmth of the welcome was such that some clients were reluctant to leave ”

Hamill Travel Service Newsletter

UDNY ARMS HOTEL

Country hotel

Main Street,
Newburgh,
Aberdeen AB41 0BL

Telephone 01358 789444
Fax 01358 789012

PROPRIETORS

Denis and Jennifer Craig

ROOM RATES

7 Singles £63
19 Doubles £82
Includes full breakfast and VAT

CHARGE/CREDIT CARDS

• DC • MC • VI

ACCOLADES

S.T.B. ♛♛♛♛ Commended
A.A. ★★ ❀ 68%
Taste of Scotland

FACILITIES

Garden, petanque
2 meeting rooms/max 60 people
Fishing nearby

RESTRICTIONS

No facilities for disabled guests

ATTRACTIONS

Balmoral and Slains Castles, Forvie Nature Reserve, Pennan (Local Hero), whisky and castle trails

AFFILIATIONS

Tartan Collection

NEAREST

MAJOR CITY:
Aberdeen - 12 miles/15 mins

MAJOR AIRPORT:
Aberdeen - 15 miles/20 mins

RAILWAY STATION:
Aberdeen - 15 miles/20 mins

RESERVATIONS

Direct with hotel

ACCESS CODES

Not applicable

Hospitality at its best for anglers, golfers and nature lovers alike

Genuine hospitality and exceptional award-winning cuisine are the hallmarks of this friendly hotel, owned and run by the Craig Family. Locals and guests mingle in the lively bar with its wide range of malt whiskies and real ales while a choice of restaurants attracts lovers of good food. Speciality seafood dishes are a feature of the constantly changing menus which also offer the best locally-produced beef, lamb, pork and venison. A varied and imaginative selection of vegetarian dishes is always available.

Overlooking the peaceful Ythan Estuary and the local golf course, the hotel is well situated for those following the whisky and castle trails in Grampian. It is just minutes from Slains Castle, inspiration for Bram Stoker's Dracula. Golfers have the pick of three championship courses within a 10-minute drive – Royal Aberdeen, Murcar and Cruden Bay. Anglers can take advantage of the hotel's location beside the peaceful Ythan Estuary while walkers and nature lovers can explore miles of deserted beaches and the renowned Sands of Forvie Nature Reserve. The hotel also has its own petanque rinks.

The bustling port and oil capital of Aberdeen – also the floral capital of Scotland – is just 15 minutes away and offers theatre, music, art galleries and museums.

LOCATION

Newburgh is 15 minutes north of Aberdeen, on the A92 Ellon Road.

North Country

Rievaulx Abbey, near Helmsley, North Yorkshire. Founded by Lord Helmsley in 1151, it was the first Cistercian abbey in the north of England. Most of the building is Early English (13th century) and there are some Roman remnants.

Heritage sites

The following heritage sites can be found on the map overleaf. The key numbers show where they are located.

CHESHIRE

Chester Castle	1
Roman Amphitheatre	2

CUMBRIA

Arthur's Round Table	3
Brough Castle	4
Brougham Castle	5
Carlisle Castle	6
Furness Abbey	7
Hardknott Roman Fort	8
Lanercost Priory	9
Penrith Castle	10
Ravenglass: Roman Bath House	11
Stott Park Bobbin Mill	12

DURHAM

Barnard Castle	13

HUMBERSIDE

Thornton Abbey	14

LANCASHIRE

Goodshaw Chapel	15
Salley Abbey	16
Warton Old Rectory	17
Whalley Abbey Gatehouse	18

NORTHUMBERLAND

Aydon Castle	19
Belsay Hall, Castle and Gardens	20
Berwick-upon-Tweed Barracks	21
Prudhoe Castle	22
Warkworth Castle and Hermitage	23

TYNE AND WEAR

St Paul's Monastery and Bede Monastery Museum	24
Tynemouth Castle and Priory	25

YORKSHIRE

Easby Abbey	26
Mount Grace Priory	27
Richmond Castle	28
Spofforth Castle	29
Whitby Abbey	30
York: Clifford's Tower	31
Conisbrough Castle	32
Roche Abbey	33

KEY

- Motorways
- 'A' Roads
- Railways
- Airports
- National Boundaries
- County Boundaries
- Heritage Sites
- English Heritage Sites
- Ferry Routes
- Urban Areas
- National Parks and Areas of Outstanding Natural Beauty

Each grid square equals 30 miles (approx. 50 km)

0 Miles 30
0 Kilometres 50

Scotland see pages 14, 15

TAYSIDE
FIFE
CENTRAL
DUNFERMLINE
LOTHIAN
BORDERS
DUMFRIES AND GALLOWAY
NORTHUMBERLAND
NORTHUMBERLAND NATIONAL PARK
THE BORDERS FOREST PARK
CUMBRIA
LAKE DISTRICT NATIONAL PARK
DURHAM
TYNE & WEAR
CLEVELAND
NORTH YORKS MOORS NATIONAL PARK

Berwick-upon-Tweed
Ancroft
Cornhill-on-Tweed
Bamburgh
Belford
Waren Mill
Wooler
Alnwick
Amble
Rothbury
Otterburn
ASHINGTON
Morpeth
Bedlington
Blyth
Whitley Bay
Bellingham
Newcastle
NEWCASTLE UPON TYNE
Jarrow
SOUTH SHIELDS
GATESHEAD
SUNDERLAND
Longtown
Carlisle
Low Crosby
CARLISLE
Brampton
Haltwhistle
Corbridge
Hallbankgate
Shotley Bridge
Stanley
Consett
CHESTER LE STREET
Seaham
Houghton le Spring
Peterlee
Silloth
Wigton
Southwaite
Alston
DURHAM
Stanhope
Wear Head
HARTLEPOOL
Maryport
Cockermouth
Workington
Bassenthwaite
Applethwaite
Pooley Bridge
PENRITH
Temple Sowerby
Spennymoor
Bishop Auckland
Redworth
Newton Aycliffe
Billingham
Redcar
Newlands
Keswick
Howtown
Appleby-in-Westmorland
Barnard Castle
STOCKTON-ON-TEES
Saltburn-by-the-Sea
WHITEHAVEN
BEES HEAD
Grange-in-Borrowdale
Glenridding
Bowes
DARLINGTON
Guisborough
MIDDLESBROUGH
Egremont
Grasmere
Brough
Tees-side
Whitby
Ambleside
Kirkby Stephen
Tebay
Scotch Corner
Richmond
Ravenglass
Windermere
Coniston
Bowness-on-Windermere
Reeth
Kendal
Sedbergh
Leyburn

From Bergen
From Stavanger
From Göteborg, Umlaut (Summer Only)
From Esbjerg (Summer Only)
From Hamburg (Summer Only)
From Amsterdam (Summer Only)

PAGE	HOTEL
96	Alderley Edge Hotel, The
97	Aldwark Manor Golf Club
98	Appleton Hall Hotel
99	Armathwaite Hall Hotel
100	Aynsome Manor
101	Borrowdale Gates
102	Broxton Hall
103	Burgoyne Hotel, The
104	Crabwall Manor
105	Crosby Lodge
106	Dale Head Hall
107	Devonshire, The
108	Dower House
109	Farlam Hall Hotel
110	Feversham Arms Hotel, The
111	Frogg Manor
112	Gilpin Lodge Hotel
113	Grange Hotel, The
114	Grants Hotel
115	Graythwaite Manor Hotel
116	Hipping Hall
117	Holbeck Ghyll Hotel
118	King's Arms Hotel
119	Lakeside Hotel
120	Linthwaite House
121	Manor House, The
122	Michaels Nook
123	Middlethorpe Hall
124	Miller Howe Hotel
125	Monk Fryston Hall
126	Mount Royale
127	Nanny Brow Hotel
128	Nidd Hall
129	Northcote Manor

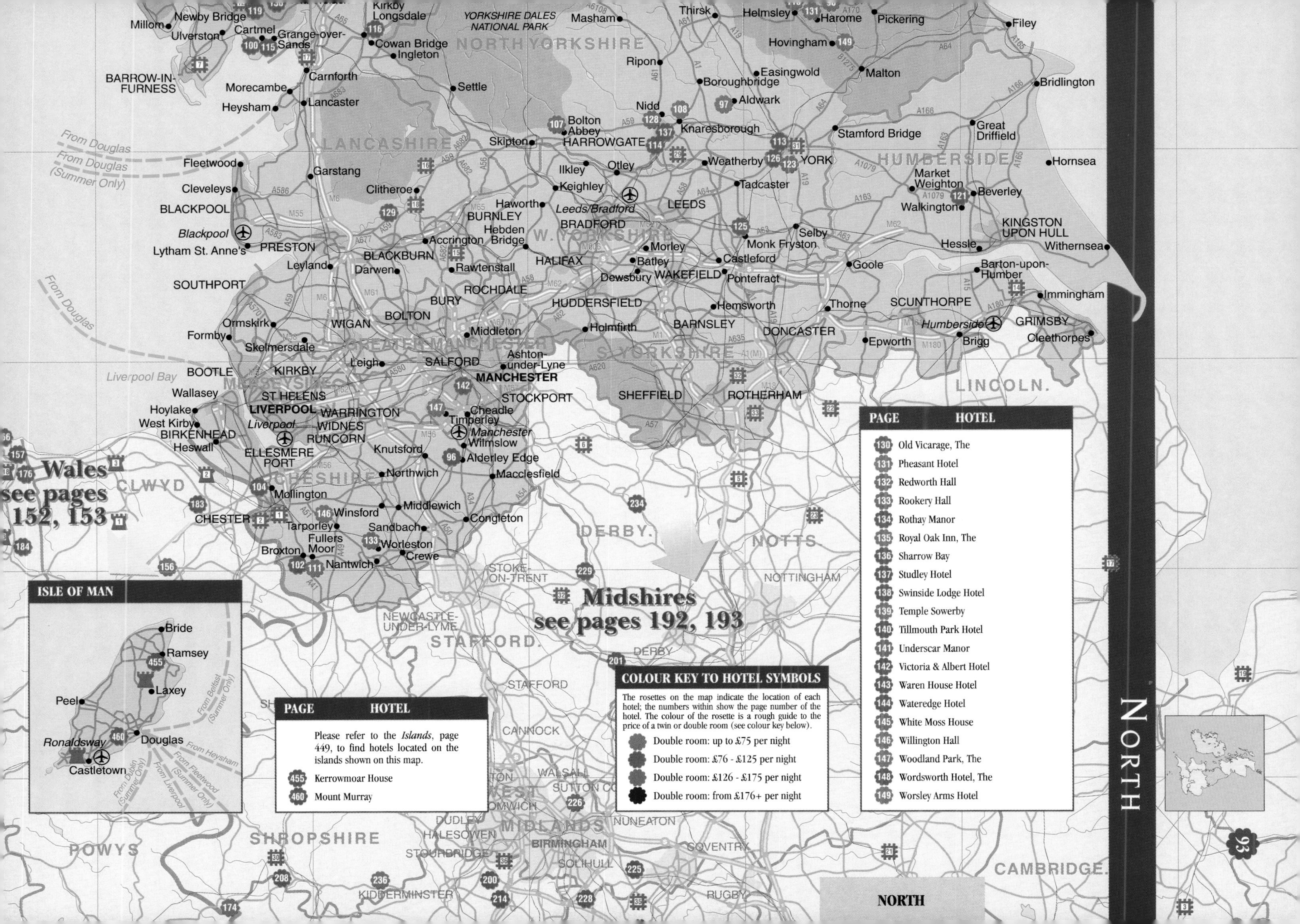

PAGE	HOTEL
130	Old Vicarage, The
131	Pheasant Hotel
132	Redworth Hall
133	Rookery Hall
134	Rothay Manor
135	Royal Oak Inn, The
136	Sharrow Bay
137	Studley Hotel
138	Swinside Lodge Hotel
139	Temple Sowerby
140	Tillmouth Park Hotel
141	Underscar Manor
142	Victoria & Albert Hotel
143	Waren House Hotel
144	Wateredge Hotel
145	White Moss House
146	Willington Hall
147	Woodland Park, The
148	Wordsworth Hotel, The
149	Worsley Arms Hotel

COLOUR KEY TO HOTEL SYMBOLS

The rosettes on the map indicate the location of each hotel; the numbers within show the page number of the hotel. The colour of the rosette is a rough guide to the price of a twin or double room (see colour key below).

- Double room: up to £75 per night
- Double room: £76 - £125 per night
- Double room: £126 - £175 per night
- Double room: from £176+ per night

PAGE	HOTEL
	Please refer to the *Islands*, page 449, to find hotels located on the islands shown on this map.
455	Kerrowmoar House
460	Mount Murray

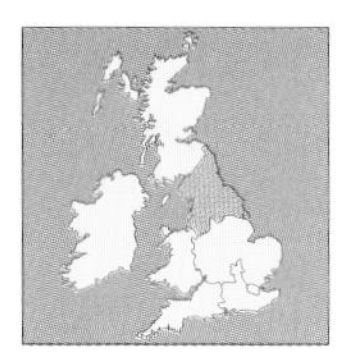

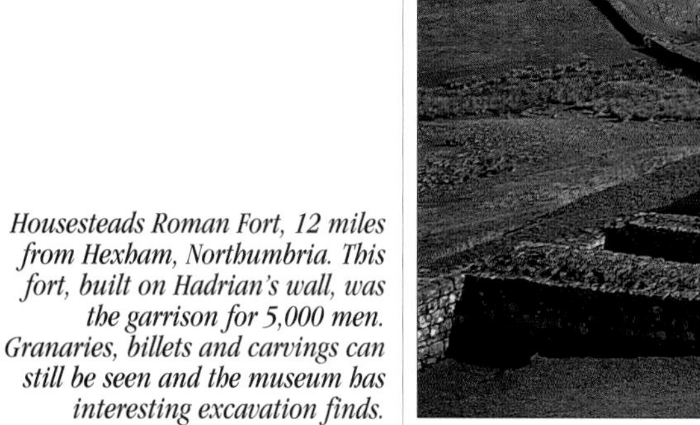

Housesteads Roman Fort, 12 miles from Hexham, Northumbria. This fort, built on Hadrian's wall, was the garrison for 5,000 men. Granaries, billets and carvings can still be seen and the museum has interesting excavation finds.

COUNTIES

Cheshire
Cleveland
Cumbria
Durham
Greater Manchester
Humberside
Lancashire
Merseyside
Northumbria
Northumberland
Yorkshire

In the North of England you will find sounds and songs and images and delights that live in the centre of your heart. You can walk in the Lakeland valley where William Wordsworth spied his host of daffodils and on the farm where Beatrix Potter created Peter Rabbit. Shelter in Haworth Parsonage, home of Jane Eyre and the Brontë sisters. Hear echoes of the great Northern music festivals in Leeds and Huddersfield, the Hallé Orchestra in Manchester, the brass band trumpets in the gritty Yorkshire mining villages, the beat of Alan Price on Tyneside – and of John Lennon and Paul McCartney on Merseyside. See Bradford with the eye of a David Hockney, and Salford where L.S. Lowry found his matchstick cats and dogs. On the Isle of Man there are cats with no tail at all – and that is a tale in itself.

Fast rail and motorway networks take you through spectacular scenery, yet natural panoramas are carefully preserved. You could fly in an hour across Lakeland, the Pennines, the Yorkshire moors, the Cheviot Hills and craggy Holy Island, the vanishing Humberside cliffs where the North Sea bites in at a rate of six feet or more each year, or you could spend six months walking across these natural phenomena and be refreshed every day by their ever-changing beauty.

Northerners are proud of their traditions. These may be simple things, such as the finest sausage in Cumberland, the best pint of beer in the West Riding, or the tastiest fish and chips served in a newspaper. They love their towns and villages; they like to show them to visitors. If you have an ear for the English language you will delight in listening as they speak. They in turn will welcome you. Their friendships are warm and true and loyal.

Castles, Stately Homes, Historic Houses

Alnwick Castle, Alnwick, Northumberland. Home of the Dukes of Northumberland (the Percy family) since 1309.

Bramhall Hall, Bramhall, Cheshire. Fine black and white half-timbered Elizabethan manor house. Landscaped grounds.

Brantwood, Coniston, Cumbria. John Ruskin's home. Ruskin's works and memorabilia.

Brontë Parsonage, Haworth, West Yorkshire. Manuscripts and personal effects of the Brontë sisters.

Burton Agnes Hall, Burton Agnes, North Humberside. Elizabethan house (1598). Fine furniture and china.

Castle Howard, North Yorkshire. Designed by Sir John Vanbrugh, superbly built 1699-1726. Lake, parkland, long gallery.

Gawsworth Hall, Gawsworth, Cheshire. Fully furnished Tudor house. Open air theatre June/July.

Grasmere, Cumbria. Dove Cottage, Wordsworth Museum. He lived and wrote here from 1799-1808.

House of Keys, Douglas, Isle of Man. Home of the Manx Tynwald, a Parliament that is older that the one at Westminster!

Hill Top, Hawkshead, Cumbria. Beatrix Potter wrote most of her stories in this 17th c farmhouse.

Richmond Castle, Richmond, North Yorkshire. 11th c Norman walls tower 100 ft high. Original 14th c dining hall.

Sizergh Castle, Kendal, Cumbria. 14th c pele tower. 15th c Great Hall. Splendid rock and rose gardens.

Skipton Castle, Skipton, North Yorkshire. A well preserved medieval castle. Conduit Court and ancient yew tree.

Museums, Galleries & Modern Highspots

Beatles Story, Albert Dock, Liverpool 3. Walk-through experience. Trip to Hamburg, Cavern Beat. Test yourself against the Beatles Brain computer.

Cars of the Stars Motor Museum, Keswick, Cumbria. James Bond's car and Chitty Chitty Bang Bang.

Coronation Street set, Manchester. Walk round the Rovers Return where Britain's best loved soap takes place.

Housesteads Roman Fort, Hadrian's Wall, Northumberland. Vercovicium is a well preserved 5-acre 2nd c fort.

Jorvik Viking Centre, York. Travel back in a timecar to visit York in the days of the Vikings.

National Museum of Photography, Film and Television, Bradford, West Yorkshire. Includes the Kodak Museum.

TOURIST OFFICE INFORMATION

Further information about the North will be gladly supplied by:

Northumbria Tourist Board,
Aykley Heads, Durham DH1 5UX
Tel: 0191 375 3000

North West Tourist Board,
Swan House, Swan Meadow Road,
Wigan Pier, Wigan WN3 5BB
Tel: 01942 821222

Yorkshire and Humberside Tourist Board, 312 Tadcaster Road,
York YO2 2HF ***Tel***: 01904 707961

For international offices, please turn to page 480

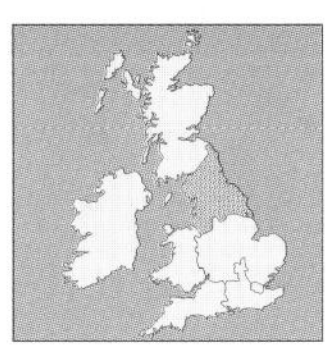

Dunstanburgh Castle, near Alnwick, Northumbria. This stronghold, built by the Earl of Lancaster in 1313, was further fortified by John of Gaunt in about 1380. It was captured by both the Lancastrians and Yorkists in the Wars of the Roses

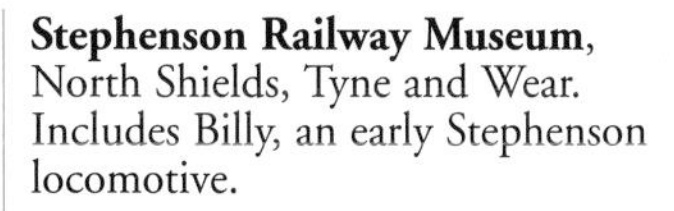

Stephenson Railway Museum, North Shields, Tyne and Wear. Includes Billy, an early Stephenson locomotive.

Walker Art Gallery, Liverpool. This gallery is particularly strong on the 19th c, and the pre-Raphaelites.

Churches & Cathedrals

Beverley Minster, Beverley, North Humberside. 1220-1420 Gothic architecture; Saxon sanctuary chair.

Carlisle Cathedral, Carlisle, Cumbria. Norman origin, medieval paintings, fine 14th c glass and tracery.

Chester Cathedral, Chester. 14/15th c with 12th c monastic buildings. Carved choir stalls. Audiovisual programme.

Durham Cathedral, Durham. Superb Norman church architecture. Tombs of St Cuthbert and the Venerable Bede.

Escomb Church, Bishop Auckland, County Durham. Saxon church dating back to 6th century, with Roman stonework.

Liverpool Cathedral. Britain's largest. See also the modern Catholic Metropolitan Cathedral in nearby Mount Pleasant.

Manchester Cathedral, Manchester. 15th c perpendicular building, widest nave in Britain.

Ripon Cathedral, Ripon, North Yorkshire. Complete crypt dating from 672. Superb 13th c west front.

St Mary, Nantwich, Cheshire. 13th c parish church of cathedral-like quality and size. Medieval carvings.

York Minster, York. Largest Gothic cathedral in England. Museum of Saxon and Norman remains.

Gardens

Chomondley Castle Gardens, Malpas, Cheshire. Ornamental gardens with lakeside picnic area and zoo.

LEFT: *Betty Surtees House, Newcastle-on-Tyne. This merchant's house was built in the Jacobean style and contains furnishings of the 17th Century.*

RIGHT: *Roche Abbey, near Maltby, South Yorkshire. These are the surviving transept walls built in the 1170's for the Cistercians. The Abbey gets its name from the steep rock beside it.*

Fletcher Moss Botanical Gardens, Didsbury, Manchester. Interesting rock garden with many rare alpines.

Japanese Garden, Horsforth. Authentic Japanese features.

Sheffield Botanical Gardens. Gardens with over 5,000 species of plant. Disabled persons garden.

Sport & Outdoors

Aintree, nr Liverpool. The Grand National, the world's greatest steeplechase.

Blackpool Beach and Promenade, Lancashire. Six mile sandy beach, 518 ft Blackpool Tower, lights Sep/Oct.

Southport. Nearby is Royal Birkdale, frequent venue for the Open Championship, one of the North's many fine golf courses.

Yorkshire Dales National Park. Golden plovers, red grouse, shaggy Swaledale sheep. Climb peaks to 2000 ft.

League Cricket. Spectacular one-day action in many of Lancashire and Yorkshire's industrial towns.

Manchester United FC, Old Trafford, Manchester. Museum and ground tours.

Rugby League. Unique, hard-tackling game. Wigan, Widnes, Castleford and many other Lancashire and Yorkshire towns.

Wetherby, Ripon, York are just three of the top-class flat horse racing courses in the region.

Yorkshire Dales National Park. Golden plovers, red grouse, shaggy Swaledale sheep. Brontë country. Climb peaks reaching 2000 ft or plumb the depths of the famous potholes.

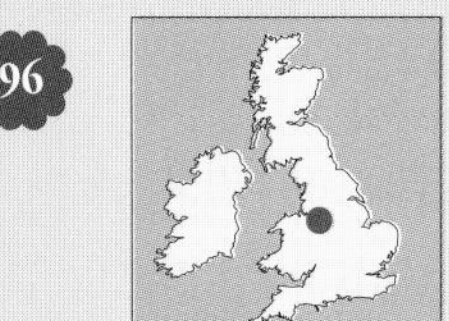

"Your staff are always top of the Premier League for me, and I always look forward to the warm welcome that you extend to all your visitors"

Alex Ferguson, Manager, Manchester United Football Club

THE ALDERLEY EDGE HOTEL

Country house

Macclesfield Road,
Alderley Edge,
Cheshire SK9 7BJ

Telephone 01625 583033
Fax 01625 586343

GENERAL MANAGER
Ahmet Kurcer

ROOM RATES

Single occupancy	*£36 - £87*
30 Doubles	*£67 - £99.50*
2 Four-posters	*£67 - £125*

Includes VAT

CHARGE/CREDIT CARDS

• *DC* • *MC* • *VI*

ACCOLADES
E.T.B. ♛♛♛♛ *Highly Commended*
R.A.C. ★★★ + *Merit Award H*
A.A. ★★★ ❀❀ *73%*

FACILITIES
Garden
3 meeting rooms/max 150 people
Golf nearby

RESTRICTIONS
No pets

ATTRACTIONS
Chester,
Tatton Park,
Styal Mill,
Granada Studios

AFFILIATIONS
Independent

NEAREST
MAJOR CITY:
Manchester - 14 miles/25 mins

MAJOR AIRPORT:
Manchester - 10 miles/15 mins

RAILWAY STATION:
Macclesfield - 6 miles/20 mins

RESERVATIONS
Direct with hotel

ACCESS CODES
Not applicable

A fistful of awards

Standing in its own grounds, The Alderley Edge Hotel could be miles from anywhere, hidden from the road by a screen of foliage.

Originally a wealthy mill owner's private residence, this attractive sandstone building became a hotel after the Second World War and was more recently bought and extensively refurbished by the family-owned Lees Brewery.

As well as 21 bedrooms, all beautifully appointed, there are 11 deluxe rooms four of which are charming cottage-style bedrooms. The deluxe rooms have the added luxury of whirlpool tubs and mini bars.

The hotel has an international reputation with a fistful of awards for its food. The restaurant has a selection of menus including one which features fresh fish delivered daily. Diners are sorely tempted by the choice of breads, cakes, pastries and decadent hot puddings baked each day in the hotel's own bakery.

Within a short drive are seven National Trust properties; Manchester and the historic city of Chester are within an hour's drive and Wordsworth's Lake District is an easy day trip.

LOCATION

From the M6, take Junction 18 (A54) to Holmes Chapel and A535 to Alderley Edge. Turn left onto B5087 (Macclesfield Road). From the M56, take the A538 at Junction 6. Follow the signs for Wilmslow and Alderley Edge.

"Hope places like this go on forever"

Mr & Mrs Siter, Merseyside

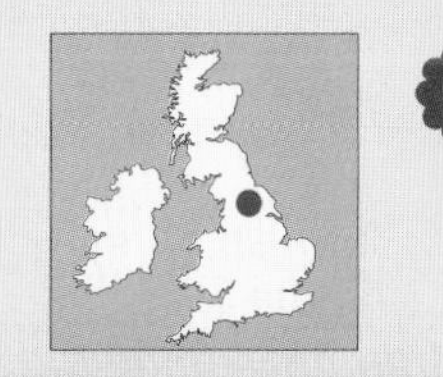

Stately home

ALDWARK MANOR GOLF HOTEL

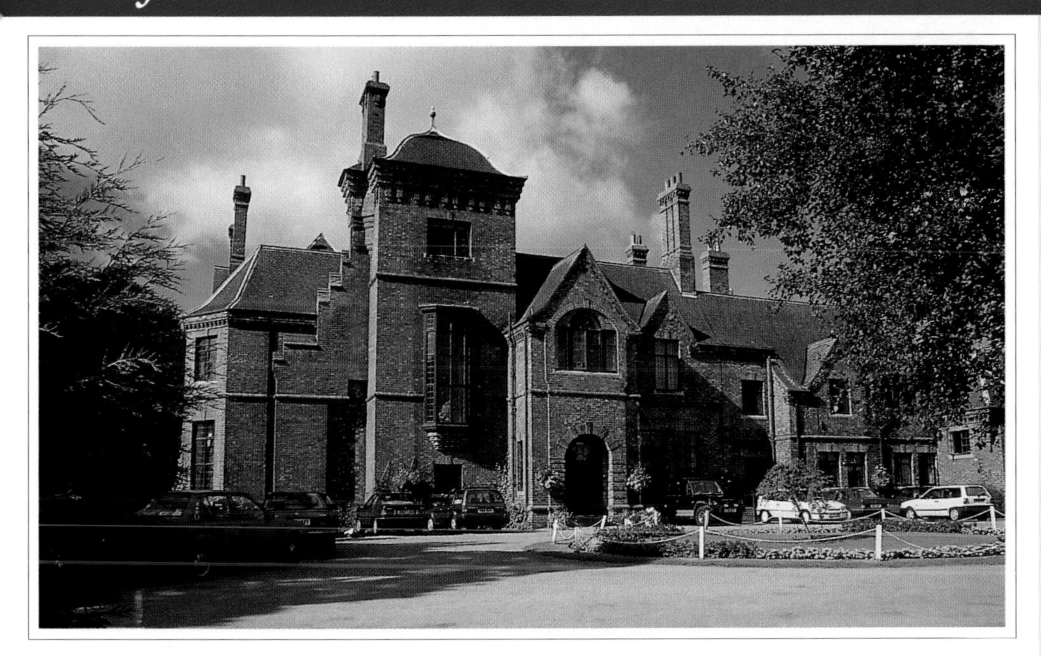

Parkland, your own golf course and the beautiful Yorkshire Dales

Aldwark Manor is a splendid 19th century country house hotel set in beautiful Yorkshire parkland and with its own 18 hole par 71 golf course. This magnificent residence was commissioned in 1865 by Lord Walsingham as a wedding present for his eldest daughter. The finest craftsmen of the day devoted five years to its completion, the plasterwork and beams being particularly noteworthy.

Elegant surroundings in the hotel's Rendelsham Restaurant complement fine food and friendly service, with an excellent wine list to complement the meal. The 19th Hole offers snacks, wines and ales all day, and also the lounge bar for a before or after dinner drink.

All 20 bedrooms are beautifully furnished and have en suite facilities, TV, radio, tea and coffee-making facilities, hair dryer, trouser press and direct-dial telephone.

The hotel is one of only two in Yorkshire with its own golf course. The easy walking parkland course is 6171 yards long, par 71. Hotel guests enjoy reduced green fees and priority tee times. Aldwark Manor is an ideal base for touring the Yorkshire Dales and Moors, which contain some of England's finest abbeys, stately homes and beauty spots. Historic York with its magnificent Minster and Jorvik Viking Centre is a delight. Castle Howard is within easy driving distance, as are six of Britain's top horse racecourses. Riding, fishing, hot air ballooning and theatre bookings at York, Harrogate or Leeds can be arranged at Reception.

LOCATION

15 miles north west of York, and close to both the A1 and A19, Aldwark is exactly halfway between London and Edinburgh.

Aldwark, North Yorkshire, YO6 2NF

Telephone 01347 838146
Fax 01347 838867

PROPRIETOR
R Harrison

ROOM RATES

2 Singles	*£45 - £55*
14 Doubles/Twins	*£55 - £80*
2 Four-posters	*£90*
2 Family rooms	*£55 - £80*

Includes full breakfast and VAT

CHARGE/CREDIT CARDS

• DC • JCB • MC • VI

ACCOLADES
E.T.B. ♛♛♛♛ *Highly Commended*
R.A.C. ★★★★
A.A. ★★★ *70%*

FACILITIES
Garden, fishing, golf
Riding nearby

RESTRICTIONS
No facilities for disabled guests

ATTRACTIONS
York, Harrogate, Yorkshire Dales, Fountains Abbey, Studley Royal, Beningborough Hall

AFFILIATIONS
Independent

NEAREST
MAJOR CITY:
York - 10 miles

MAJOR AIRPORT:
Leeds - 44 miles/1 hr

RAILWAY STATION:
York - 10 miles/25 mins

RESERVATIONS
Direct with hotel

ACCESS CODES
Not applicable

"A perfect place for a short break/holiday in the relaxing North Yorkshire countryside – we vow to return"

J Webster, Surrey

APPLETON HALL

Country house hotel

Appleton-le-Moors,
North Yorkshire YO6 6TF

Telephone 01751 417227
Fax 01751 417540

PROPRIETORS
Norma and Graham Davies

RATES PER PERSON
3 Singles £50 - £60
7 Doubles/Twins £50 - £60
Includes full breakfast, dinner and VAT

CHARGE/CREDIT CARDS

• *JCB* • *MC* • *VI*

ACCOLADES
E.T.B. ♛♛♛ Commended
R.A.C. ★★
A.A. ★★ ❀ 71%
Winner of Yorkshire in Bloom Award 1995

FACILITIES
Garden, croquet
Golf, fishing and riding nearby

RESTRICTIONS
No children under 12 years
No facilities for disabled guests

ATTRACTIONS
North York Moors National Park,
North York Moors Railway,
Castle Howard,
Rievaulx Abbey,
Spofforth Castle

AFFILIATIONS
Independent

NEAREST
MAJOR CITY:
York - 30 miles/45 mins

MAJOR AIRPORT:
Leeds/Bradford - 55 miles/1½ hrs

RAILWAY STATION:
York - 30 miles/45 mins

RESERVATIONS
Direct with hotel

ACCESS CODES
Not applicable

NORTH

Stylish decor and glorious garden amongst the moors

Situated in the unspoilt moorland village of Appleton-le-Moors on the edge of the North York Moors National Park, Appleton Hall was originally the home of a retired sea captain built in the mid-1800s. It is set in 2 acres of lawned gardens with magnificent specimen trees and award-winning floral displays in borders, beds, baskets and tubs.

Norma and Graham Davies have created a delightful hotel with a warm friendly atmosphere which is reflected in the number of guests who make return visits. Guests may enjoy the comfortable lounge or elegant dining room, both retaining the original marble fireplaces and ornate plasterwork ceiling. Alternatively, enjoy a pre-dinner aperitif in the small but well stocked bar.

The recently refurbished bedrooms with views over the gardens enjoy all the modern facilities.

The menu, under the personal supervision of Norma Davies, changes daily and offers a wide choice using fresh seasonal ingredients and local produce. There is an interesting and extensive wine list to complement your dinner.

LOCATION

Leave Kirkbymoorside A170 direction Scarborough. After 1½ miles turn left for Appleton-le-Moors. The hotel is at the far end of the village.

"A house of perfect and irresistible atmosphere"

Hugh Walpole

17th century hall

ARMATHWAITE HALL HOTEL

A stately home that will appeal to sportsman and connoisseur alike

Armathwaite Hall is set in a magnificent private estate encompassing park and woodlands and lake frontage. The present hall, part of which dates from 1650, stands on the site of an ancient manor owned by Sir Adam de Bassenthwaite in the reign of Edward II.

The Hall is run personally by the owners who pursue the continuing development of their hotel, its leisure and conference facilities with painstaking regard for the warm, elegant nature of this genuine English stately home.

Connoisseurs of fine cuisine will find much to appreciate at Armathwaite Hall. Master Chef Kevin Dowling takes full advantage of a wealth of local seasonal produce and Cumbrian specialities to create a variety of gastronomic delights.

Management training, personnel motivation courses and corporate hospitality days are popular with overseas vistiors making full use of the extensive sports and leisure facilities available on the estate.

An interesting feature is a safari on Quad bikes in an area famed for its spectacular views. This is the perfect centre for either business or pleasure to explore the Lake District.

LOCATION

Turn off the M6 at Junction 40 and follow the A66 to the Keswick roundabout. Then take the A591 to Carlisle for 8 miles and turn left at Castle Inn. The hotel is 300 yards ahead.

Bassenthwaite Lake, Keswick, Cumbria CA12 4RE

Telephone 017687 76551
Fax 017687 76220

PROPRIETORS

The Graves family

ROOM RATES

3 Singles	*£50 - £117*
36 Doubles/Twins	*£100 - £164*
1 Four-poster	*£190*
3 Studio Suites	*£190*

Includes full breakfast and VAT

CHARGE/CREDIT CARDS

• DC • MC • VI

ACCOLADES

A.A. ★★★★ 61%

FACILITIES

Indoor swimming pool, croquet, gardens, tennis, gymnasium, sauna, spa pool, steam cabinet, beauty therapists, snooker, equestrian centre, fishing, rare breeds animal farm, heli-pad, archery/clay shooting/quad bike safaris – by prior arrangement
5 meeting rooms/max 100 people
Golf nearby

RESTRICTIONS

£5 charge per dog per night

ATTRACTIONS

Beatrix Potter Museum & House, Muncaster Castle, Hadrian's Wall, Roman wall and forts

AFFILIATIONS

Independent

NEAREST

MAJOR CITY:
Carlisle - 20 miles/40 mins
Newcastle - 70 miles/1 ½ hrs

MAJOR AIRPORT:
Manchester - 120 miles/2 ½ hrs

RAILWAY STATION:
Carlisle - 20 miles/40 mins

RESERVATIONS

Direct with hotel

ACCESS CODES

Not applicable

"We have never enjoyed anything in all our travels to compare with the pleasure we experienced with you"

Bruce & Kathlyn Hotek, Chicago

AYNSOME MANOR

17th century residence

Cartmel,
Cumbria LA11 6HH

Telephone 015395 36653
Fax 015395 36016

PROPRIETORS
Tony and Margaret Varley

MANAGERS
Chris and Andrea Varley

ROOM RATES

Single occupancy	*£50 - £58*
11 Doubles/Twins	*£84 - £104*
1 Four-poster	*£84 - £104*

Includes dinner, full breakfast and VAT

CHARGE/CREDIT CARDS

• *MC* • *VI*

ACCOLADES
E.T.B. ♛♛♛ Highly Commended
A.A. ★★ ❀ 70%
The Good Hotel Guide

FACILITIES
Garden
Golf, fishing, riding, clay pigeon shooting, sailing and wind surfing nearby

RESTRICTIONS
No children under 5 years in dining room for dinner
No facilities for disabled guests
Pets not allowed in public areas

ATTRACTIONS
Holker Hall, Cartmel Priory, Levens Hall, Sizergh Castle, The Lake District National Park

AFFILIATIONS
Independent

NEAREST
MAJOR CITY:
Lancaster - 32 miles/40 mins

MAJOR AIRPORT:
Manchester 90 miles/1½ hrs

RAILWAY STATION:
Grange Over Sands - 3 miles/5 miles

RESERVATIONS
Direct with hotel

ACCESS CODES
Not applicable

Ancient residence with a feast of historical features

The descendents of William Marshall, Earl of Pembroke, founder in 1188 of Cartmel Priory, lived in this lovely manor house. Aynsome Manor looks southward to the priory, beyond which lies the quaint old village of Cartmel, untouched by time with its 14th-century gatehouse.

This elegant, yet comfortable hotel has 12 bedrooms with private bathroom. All have colour TV, radio alarm, direct dial telephone and tea and coffee making facilities.

The cosy, intimate candle-lit restaurant is a "must" for lovers of good food. The five-course dinner menu changes nightly, and is based on home cooking with delicious soups and main dishes with a sweets trolley to tempt even the most determined slimmer.

Commanding unspoiled views of woodland, fell and rich meadowland, Aynsome Manor is the ideal base for exploring the Lake District and coastline. Newby Bridge at the foot of Lake Windermere is four miles away; it is two miles to the unspoiled resort of Grange-over-Sands. Holker and Levens Halls, Sizergh Castle with its Elizabethan furniture display and Haverthwaite Steam Railway are all nearby. Above all, this was the heartland of great writers and artists. You can visit William Wordsworth's Dove Cottage, the Brantwood home of John Ruskin, and Beatrix Potter's home at Sawrey.

LOCATION

Leave M6 at Junction 36. Take A590 signposted to Barrow-in Furness. At top of long steep hill at Lindale, turn left at signposted junction for Cartmel. Aynsome is on the right, about ¼ mile before village.

" Our most favourite place – the perfect balance between peacefulness, efficient service, friendly staff and outstanding food "

T A Knowlton, Chairman, The Kellogg Company of Great Britain

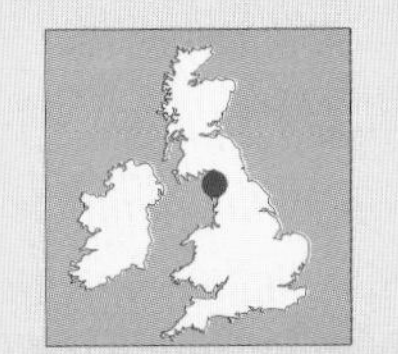

Victorian house BORROWDALE GATES COUNTRY HOUSE HOTEL

Grange in Borrowdale,
Keswick,
Cumbria CA12 5UQ

Telephone 017687 77204
Fax 017687 77254

PROPRIETORS

Terry and Christine Parkinson

ROOM RATES

2 Singles £54 - £68.50
18 Doubles/Twins £100 - £130
Includes dinner, full breakfast and VAT

CHARGE/CREDIT CARDS

• MC • VI

ACCOLADES

E.T.B. ♛♛♛♛ Highly Commended
R.A.C. ★★★ + Merit Award R
A.A. ★★★ ❀ 74%
The Good Hotel Guide

FACILITIES

Garden
Fishing and riding nearby

RESTRICTIONS

No pets

ATTRACTIONS

Borrowdale Valley,
Cockermouth, Grasmere,
Wordsworth's birthplace and Dove Cottage,
Carlisle Castle and Cathedral,
Muncaster Castle,
Hadrian's Wall

AFFILIATIONS

Fine Individual Hotels

NEAREST

MAJOR CITY:
Carlisle - 30 miles/45 mins

MAJOR AIRPORT:
Manchester - 120 miles/2½ hrs

RAILWAY STATION:
Penrith - 22 miles/30 mins

RESERVATIONS

Toll free in US 800-437-2687

ACCESS CODES

Not applicable

A rich stroke of fortune amongst the majestic Lakeland mountains

Baddeley's Guide to the English Lakes says: "... there can be no doubt that Borrowdale holds the first position amongst its (the Lake District's) valleys". In the north of the valley is Derwentwater, 'The Queen of the Lakes' and all around are the majestic Lakeland mountains, changing colour with the weather and the seasons. Settling easily into this idyllic picture is Borrowdale Gates secluded within its own two-acres of wooded gardens.

The house was built in 1860 as a private residence and its air of comfortable informality continues; this is a wonderful place to shed one's cares and release the tensions.

Throughout the house, the choice of furniture and fabrics contribute to the feeling of luxury and mellow good living. Antiques and fresh flowers add a personal touch that can only come from the owners Christine and Terry Parkinson. The bedrooms (six are on the ground floor) are generous and well-appointed with every modern facility and make the most of the breathtaking views from the house, as does the dining room with its picture windows.

This is the domain of Chef Patron, Terry Parkinson. His love of good food and fine wines accounts for the excellence of the cuisine inspired by the finest local produce and an ever-increasing host of appreciative bon vivants.

To find such hospitality in a place of such splendour is, indeed, a rich stroke of fortune.

LOCATION

From the M6, leave at Junction 40 and follow the A66 to Keswick. From there take the B5289 and after 4 miles, turn right at the double humpback bridge into Grange. The hotel is about a quarter of a mile past the village on the right.

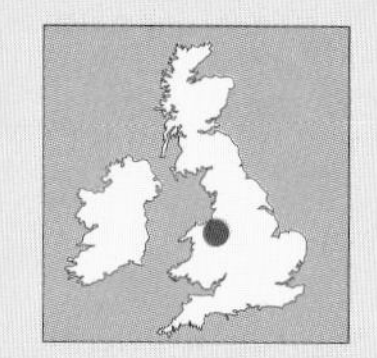

"Beyond the best! Nicest staff we've ever met!"

Jim & Melody Whitworth, Houston, Texas

BROXTON HALL

17th century Tudor house

**Whitchurch Road,
Broxton,
Chester CH3 9JS**

**Telephone 01829 782321
Fax 01829 782330**

PROPRIETORS

George and Rosemary Hadley

ROOM RATES

2 Singles	£60 - £65
12 Doubles/Twins	£70 - £80
1 Four-poster	£105

Includes full breakfast and VAT

CHARGE/CREDIT CARDS

• DC • MC • VI

ACCOLADES

R.A.C. ★★★ + Merit Awards H C & R
A.A. ★★★ 66%

FACILITIES

Garden, heli-pad
1 meeting room/max 20 people
Golf, riding and fishing nearby

RESTRICTIONS

Pets by arrangement

ATTRACTIONS

Peckfortod and Beeston Castles,
Snowdonia National Park,
Chester, Erdigg Hall,
Staveley Water Gardens,
Chester & Bangor-on-Dee Racecourses

AFFILIATIONS

Independent

NEAREST

MAJOR CITY:
Chester - 10 miles/15 mins

MAJOR AIRPORT:
Manchester - 30 miles/40 mins
Liverpool - 25 miles/35 mins

RAILWAY STATION:
Chester - 10 miles/15 mins
Crewe - 12 miles/15 mins

RESERVATIONS

Direct with hotel

ACCESS CODES

Not applicable

An historic house of character a league or so from Roman Chester

Built in 1671, Broxton Hall is a black-and-white half-timbered Tudor house set in five acres of grounds and extensive gardens. The historical walled city of Chester, famed for its Roman and medieval remains and buildings, is eight miles away. Broxton Hall is a perfect venue for anyone interested in fine buildings, English and Welsh history and the British countryside.

The hotel provides every modern comfort yet retains the ambience of a bygone age. The reception area reflects the character of the entire hotel – the furnishings, oak pannelled walls, carved mahogany staircase and a massive Jacobean fireplace, where a welcoming log fire burns most evenings.

All 15 bedrooms are beautifully furnished with antiques and offer every facility for your comfort. Each bedroom has a bathroom en-suite, tea and coffee making facilities, radio clock alarm, telephone and full central heating.

Overlooking the gardens, the restaurant receives consistent praise from regular diners. French and English cuisine is served, using local game in season and freshly caught fish. You can breakfast in the sunny conservatory beside the lawns.

Broxton Hall is ideally placed for visiting the delightful North Wales seaside and the dramatic scenery of Snowdonia. There are excellent golf courses locally and for the racing enthusiast, Chester and Bangor-on-Dee races are nearby.

LOCATION

From Chester, take the A41, signposted to Whitchurch. After 9 miles, you cross the A534. Broxton Hall is shortly after the A534 junction, on the left.

“ Just keeps getting better ”

D and K Cowham, Romford

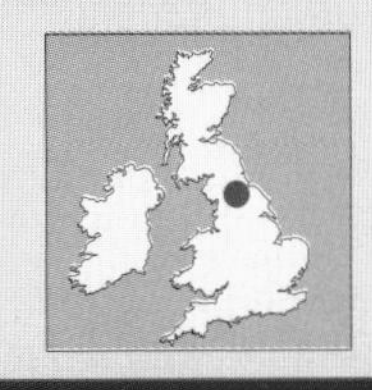

THE BURGOYNE HOTEL

The perfect resting place twixt London and Edinburgh

The house, a listed building and once a private home, is now transformed into a peaceful and relaxing small hotel where service is of paramount importance to those seeking that extra special holiday location.

It contains beautifully appointed bedrooms, all with private facilities and most having panoramic views of Swaledale.

The Burgoyne Hotel stands in the centre of Reeth on the village green. Owner operated, the hotel makes the ideal centre for grouse shooting, trout fishing and touring the Northern Dales of Yorkshire. Personalised walking tours can be arranged throughout Swaledale and Arkengarthdale, upon request.

The dining room serves English home-cooking of the highest quality using locally produced ingredients whenever possible. The menus give ample choice and all diets are catered for by prior arrangement. A comprehensive wine list has been personally selected by the proprietors.

This unique blend of English hospitality and lovely setting makes the Burgoyne Hotel a very special experience for guests from all over.

LOCATION

A1 north towards Scotch Corner. Take A6136 Richmond road, then west on A6108. Turn right onto B6270 to Reeth.

On the Green, Reeth, Richmond, North Yorkshire DL11 6SN

Telephone 01748 884292
Fax 01748 884292

PROPRIETORS

Derek Hickson and Peter Carwardine

ROOM RATES

Single occupancy £45 - £65
9 Doubles/Twins £55 - £80
Includes full breakfast and VAT

CHARGE/CREDIT CARDS

MC • VI

ACCOLADES

E.T.B. ♛♛♛ De Luxe
The Good Hotel Guide

FACILITIES

Gardens
1 meeting room/max 20 people
Fishing nearby

RESTRICTIONS

Pets and children at owners' discretion

ATTRACTIONS

Castle Bolton, Aysgarth Falls, Bowes Museum, Beamish Museum, Roman Roads

AFFILIATIONS

Independent

NEAREST

MAJOR CITY:
York - 45 miles/1½ hrs

MAJOR AIRPORT:
Manchester - 75 miles/3 hrs
Teesside/Newcastle - 18 miles/50 mins

RAILWAY STATION:
Darlington - 16 miles/40 mins

RESERVATIONS

Direct with hotel

ACCESS CODES

Not applicable

" Our evening at Crabwall Manor remains a highlight of our trip. The Manor is a winning bet, one I will not forget "

Jeri Dearden, Manhatten Beach, California

CRABWALL MANOR

Manor house

Parkgate Road, Mollington, Chester, Cheshire CH1 6NE

Telephone 01244 851666
Fax 01244 851400

PROPRIETOR
Carl Lewis

MANAGER
Julian Hook

ROOM RATES

Single occupancy	£78 - £98.50
42 Doubles/Twins	£104 - £130
5 Suites	£146 - £175
1 Four-poster	£200

Includes VAT

CHARGE/CREDIT CARDS

• DC • JCB • MC • VI

ACCOLADES
R.A.C. ★★★★ + Merit Awards H C & R
A.A. ★★★ ❀❀❀ 79%
Hotel & Restaurant of the Year 1993/94 - Cheshire Life

FACILITIES
Snooker, croquet, gardens, heli-pad
3 meeting rooms/max 100 people
Golf, riding and fishing nearby

RESTRICTIONS
No pets - guide dogs allowed

ATTRACTIONS
Chester, Chester Castle, Roman Amphitheatre, North Wales and Snowdonia, Styal Country Park, Tatton Park, River Dee, Welsh Castles, Chester Racecourse

AFFILIATIONS
Small Luxury Hotels

NEAREST
MAJOR CITY:
Chester - 2 miles/3 mins
MAJOR AIRPORT:
Manchester - 30 miles/40 mins
RAILWAY STATION:
Chester - 2 miles/3 mins

RESERVATIONS
Toll free in US/Canada: 800-525-4800

ACCESS CODES
AMADEUS/SYSTEM 1 LX CEGCWM
AXESS LX 5564
APOLLO LX 32334
WORLDSPAN LX CEGCM
SAHARA LX CEGCWM
SABRE LX 6042

Set beside historic Chester, gateway to the north of England and Wales

Crabwall Manor is a true embodiment of a 'town and country hotel' set in rolling Cheshire countryside, yet only a brief three miles trip from the centre of Chester, this ancient and atmospheric city lures travellers from all over the world. The old Rows with their wonderful mix of goldsmiths, silversmiths and antique shops are peppered with the most prestigious merchandise to be found in old English market towns.

At Crabwall Manor, all of the 48 elegant, individually decorated rooms, including six suites, have spacious en suite bathrooms with every conceivable facility to make your stay enjoyable. Lots of thoughtful little touches to make you feel at home. In short, the luxury you would expect from a first class hotel.

Enjoy the delights of the the highly acclaimed restaurant and wine cellar in the comfort and tranquillity of this charming country manor.

Relax in this peaceful and secluded haven, the gardens and woodlands extending to 17 acres seem to spill into every room, the sweet flowers leading you through with a country freshness. There is a croquet lawn at the front of the manor and a snooker room for the use of guests. Nowhere else will you experience the combination of ancient and modern so cleverly interwoven to offer possibly the most impressive accommodation in the country.

LOCATION

Go to the end of the M56, ignore signs to Chester. Follow signs to Queensferry and North Wales, taking A5117 to the next roundabout turning left onto the A540. After 2 miles, Crabwall is on the right set back from the road.

" What a treasure "

Colin McKenzie, "The Great British Experience"

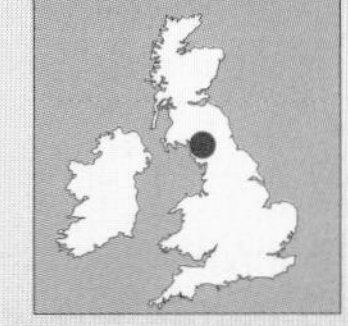

Georgian house

CROSBY LODGE

The splendours of good living in the neighbourhood of the Scottish border

This romantic and splendid Georgian house, is the home of the Sedgwick family. The lodge stands high above the village of Low Crosby, with a marvellous view of the River Eden and surrounded by wooded areas and parkland.

The house, built in 1802 and altered some years later to the castellated appearance of today, is beautifully furnished with family antiques, complemented by stunning flower arrangements. The crackling log fires in the winter add to the homely feeling of a bygone era.

Chef Patron Michael Sedgwick is an absolute perfectionist. The deliciously exciting menus feature authentic continental cuisine and the very best of traditional British fare which change daily. The Crosby Lodge sweet trolley, along with their home-made bread and preserves, are renowned far and wide.

Patricia looks after front of house and will greet you personally or you will catch her flower arranging in the afternoon. Son James works with Michael in the kitchen, and plays a large part in the efficient running of the hotel. The wine list, written and supplied by daughter Philippa, is exceptional, offering the very best of house wines through to the hidden cellar for the Connoisseur.

The house has eleven en suite bedrooms, all individual, and tastefully designed by Patricia. The friendly and efficient staff make this the ideal venue for that peaceful holiday, short break, shooting party, golfing holiday, or that important business meeting.

LOCATION

Situated just off the A689, 5 miles east of Carlisle. 3½ miles from Junction 44 on M6, on right, just through Low Crosby.

High Crosby, Crosby-on-Eden, Carlisle, Cumbria CA6 4QZ

Telephone 01228 573618
Fax 01228 573428

OWNER/PROPRIETOR

Patricia and Michael Sedgwick

ROOM RATES

5 Doubles/Twins	*£90*
2 Four-posters	*£98 - £110*
3 Family rooms	*£110 - £135*

Includes full breakfast and VAT

CHARGE/CREDIT CARDS

• JCB • MC • VI

ACCOLADES

E.T.B. ♛♛♛♛ Highly Commended
A.A. ★★★ ❀ 71%

FACILITIES

Garden
2 meeting rooms/max 20 people
Golf nearby

RESTRICTIONS

No facilities for disabled guests
Pets by arrangement

ATTRACTIONS

Hadrian's Wall, Wetheral Woods, Carlisle Castle and Cathedral, Gardens, Lake District, Lanercost Priory, Brougham Castle, Penrith Castle,

AFFILIATIONS

Independent

NEAREST

MAJOR CITY:
Carlisle - 5 miles/8 mins

MAJOR AIRPORT:
Newcastle - 58 miles/1 hr
Glasgow - 100 miles/1½ hrs

RAILWAY STATION:
Carlisle - 5 miles/15 mins

RESERVATIONS

Direct with hotel

ACCESS CODES

Not applicable

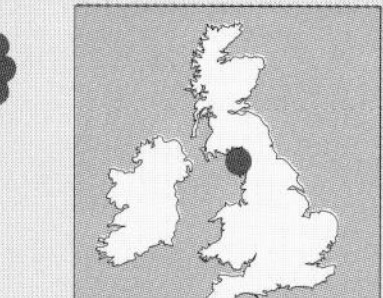

"Thank you so much for many wonderful vacations"

Laura Clark, New York

DALE HEAD HALL

Elizabethan manor house

Lake Thirlmere,
Keswick,
Cumbria CA12 4TN

Telephone 017687 72478
Fax 017687 71070

PROPRIETORS

Alan and Shirley Lowe

ROOM RATES

Single occupancy	*£72 - £104*
5 Doubles/Twins	*£94 - £138*
3 Superior Doubles/Twins	*£104 - £148*
1 Four-poster	*£114 - £158*

Includes dinner, full breakfast and VAT

CHARGE/CREDIT CARDS

• *MC* • *VI*

ACCOLADES

E.T.B. ♛♛♛♛ Highly Commended
R.A.C. ★★ + Merit Awards H & R
A.A. ★★ ❀ 75%

FACILITIES

Garden, croquet, fishing
Golf, sailing, canoeing
and riding nearby

RESTRICTIONS

No facilities for disabled guests
No pets

ATTRACTIONS

Dove Cottage,
Hill Top,
Brantwood,
Cumbrian fells

AFFILIATIONS

Independent

NEAREST

MAJOR CITY:
Carlisle - 40 miles/45 mins

MAJOR AIRPORT:
Manchester - 100 miles/2 hrs

RAILWAY STATION:
Penrith - 10 miles/20 mins

RESERVATIONS

Direct with hotel

ACCESS CODES

Not applicable

The bliss of solitude in a 16th century Lake District mansion

Beside Lake Thirlmere, surrounded by lush woodland, stands this glorious 16th century house. Rich green lawns sweep towards the water. The tranquillity of the location cannot be surpassed, since the house stands alone on the shores of the 3¼ mile lake.

The Leathes family came to Dale Head Hall in 1577; in 1877 lake and hall were purchased by Manchester to provide the city with clean drinking water and successive Lord Mayors with an idyllic summer retreat.

Today Alan and Shirley Lowe and their family offer exceptional accommodation and service. In restoring the hall, they set high priority on recreating its 16th century authenticity. The bar and lounge are delightful.

The 5-course dinner table d'hôte dinner is served in the oak-beamed Elizabethan dining room, which has an inglenook fireplace. The food is fresh and imaginatively prepared. It is complemented with a good choice of fine wines.

All the splendours of the Lake District are adjacent. Helvellyn is on the doorstep and Borrowdale is close by. Fishing, sailing and canoeing can all be enjoyed; please be sure to bring your own equipment as this cannot be supplied by the hotel.There are countless beautiful tree-lined walks beside the lakes or more intrepidly, you can pick your way up to (or towards) boldly austere rocky crags.

LOCATION

On the A591, halfway between Keswick and Grasmere. The hotel is situated along ¼ mile of private driveway overlooking Lake Thirlmere.

“ Thank you for being so special ”

Christopher Timothy (TV's James Herriot)

18th century country house

THE DEVONSHIRE

The dazzling Dales, the Devonshire family history and indulging service

Set in breathtaking scenery, a regular haunt of the Brontë sisters, Turner, and, more recently made famous by James Herriot, the Devonshire's magnificent Yorkshire Dales setting is without parallel.

Set in 12 acre grounds, the hotel is owned by the Duke and Duchess of Devonshire and has been in the same family since 1753. Most of the furniture and antiques come from the family home, Chatsworth, and all the interior design is personally supervised by the Duchess. Open log fires, handsome lounges and extravagant floral displays express the comfort and elegance which is at the heart of the hotel's philosophy.

The Burlington Restaurant, named after a celebrated family ancestor, displays some of the Earl's greatest architectural works and has built a fine reputation for the outstanding quality of its food and wine list.

Whilst features of historical interest abound, the present day has also been embraced by the recent addition of the 'Devonshire Club'. Here, guests can enjoy a heated indoor swimming pool, spa bath, Turkish steam room, Scandinavian sauna, cold-water plunge pool, high-powered sunbed, all-weather, floodlit tennis court and the very latest in health, beauty and fitness facilities.

Currently the Yorkshire and Humberside Tourist Board's Hotel of the Year, the Devonshire's 40 well-equipped bedrooms include eight individually-themed four-poster rooms.

LOCATION

On the B6160 to Bolton Abbey, 250 yards north from its roundabout junction with the A59 Skipton to Harrogate Road.

Bolton Abbey, Nr Skipton, North Yorkshire BD23 6AJ

Telephone 01756 710441
Fax 01756 710564

PROPRIETORS

Duke and Duchess of Devonshire

MANAGING DIRECTOR

Martin Harris

ROOM RATES

Single occupancy	*£95 - £115*
30 Doubles/Twins	*£130 - £165*
8 Four-posters	*£155 - £175*
3 Suites	*£200*

Includes full breakfast and VAT

CHARGE/CREDIT CARDS

• *DC* • *MC* • *VI*

ACCOLADES

E.T.B. ♛♛♛♛♛ De Luxe
R.A.C. ★★★★ + Merit Awards H C & R
A.A. ★★★ ❀❀ 79%
Yorkshire & Humberside Tourist Board 'Hotel of the Year' 1992, 1993, 1994

FACILITIES

Indoor swimming pool, croquet, tennis, gardens, sauna, solarium, spa, gym, beauty therapy rooms, steam room, fishing, heli-pad
5 meeting rooms/max 150 people
Golf nearby

RESTRICTIONS

Non-smoking restaurant

ATTRACTIONS

Bronte Parsonage, Bolton Priory, Skipton Castle, Castle Howard

AFFILIATIONS

Small Luxury Hotels

NEAREST

MAJOR CITY:
Leeds - 17 miles/30 mins

MAJOR AIRPORT:
Manchester - 60 miles/1¼ hrs

RAILWAY STATION:
Ilkley - 5 miles/10 mins

RESERVATIONS

Toll free in US/Canada: 800-525-4800

ACCESS CODES

SABRE LX 11172
APOLLO LX 44518
SAHARA LX MANDC
SYSTEM 1 LX LBA100
AXESS LX 5522
AMADEUS LX MRUPCH

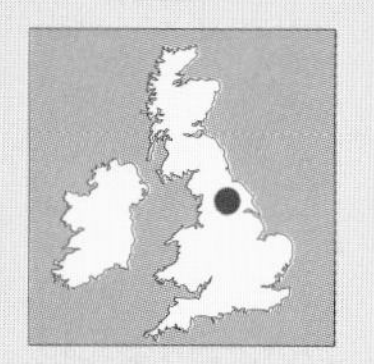

" The friendliness, service and food were out of this world – a rare combination in this day and age, together with your own generosity "

Peter Duggan, Birmingham

THE DOWER HOUSE

Jacobean country house

Bond End,
Knaresborough,
Yorkshire HG5 9AL

Telephone 01423 863302
Fax 01423 867665

PROPRIETOR

N R Davies

ROOM RATES

5 Singles	£55 - £60
26 Doubles/Twins	£70 - £85
1 Suite	£98

Includes full breakfast and VAT

CHARGE/CREDIT CARDS

• DC • MC • VI

ACCOLADES

E.T.B. ♛♛♛♛ Commended
R.A.C. ★★★
A.A. ★★★ ❀ 69%

FACILITIES

Garden, indoor pool, gym, sauna, jacuzzi, steam room
4 meeting room/max 65 people
Golf and riding nearby

RESTRICTIONS

No dogs in hotel

ATTRACTIONS

Yorkshire Dales, Yorkshire moors, Castle Howard, Harewood House, York, Newby Hall, Harrogate, Harlow Carr

AFFILIATIONS

Best Western

NEAREST

MAJOR CITY:
Leeds - 15 miles/20 mins

MAJOR AIRPORT:
Leeds/Bradford - 15 miles/20 mins

RAILWAY STATION:
Knaresborough - ½ mile/3 mins

RESERVATIONS

Direct with hotel

ACCESS CODES

SABRE BW 04806

Health and leisure amid the tranquil beauty of Yorkshire

Since Jacobean times The Dower House has maintained a tradition of fine hospitality. A typical English country house style hotel, the 32 tastefully furnished rooms, all with en-suite facilities, have been thoughtfully planned to provide every home-from-home comfort.

The hotel is owned by the Davies Family, who are second-generation professional hoteliers. Their hallmark is excellence so the warmth of your welcome is guaranteed. Many of the guests come back to stay again and again. It is said the reason for this is not only to experience the unrivalled treasures of Yorkshire and the outstanding cuisine, but because the staff ensure your pleasure is of paramount importance.

Dining at The Dower House is to enjoy the best of modern British cuisine. The menu offers a wide range of refreshing ideas and innovative tastes to suit every occasion. Carefully chosen wines from both the Old and New World will complement your meal.

You are invited to make full use of the luxurious Corniche Health and Leisure Club during your stay.

The historic and picturesque town of Knaresborough is perfectly situated at the heart of Yorkshire. The grandeur of historic houses and the tranquil beauty of the countryside are all within easy reach of The Dower House.

LOCATION

From the A1 turn right onto the A59 Harrogate/York road going toward Knaresborough and Harrogate. Follow the road down Knaresborough High Street towards Harrogate. At the bottom turn left and the hotel is on the right.

" Member of family to guest: 'Is everything all right for you Sir?' Guest's reply: 'Hell boy, we're on automatic happy!' "

J A Haslam III, Tennessee

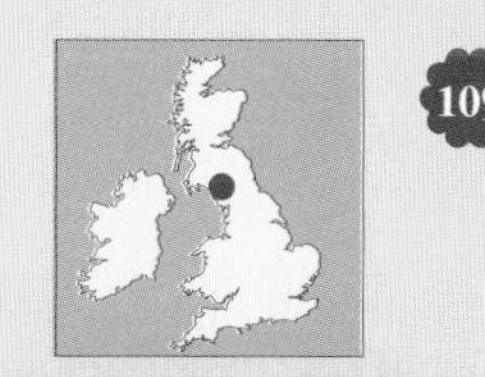

Country house

FARLAM HALL HOTEL

On the border, just a stone's throw from Hadrian's Wall

Farlam Hall was opened in 1975 by the Quinion and Stevenson families who, over the years, have managed to achieve and maintain consistently high standards of food, service and comfort.

This old border house, dating back to the 17th century, was extended in Victorian times and is now set in mature landscaped gardens which can be seen from the elegant lounges and dining room. Here, the fine silver, crystal and starched white linen combine to create the feeling of a more genteel era, complementing the quality of English country house style of cuisine produced by Barry Quinion and his chefs. Attentive service from family and local staff add the finishing touches.

There are only 12 bedrooms in this large house, some on a grand scale and others of a more conventional size, permitting a wide range of prices. Whatever the size, the same care and quality has been applied as it has throughout the house where antique and fine furnishings have been used wherever possible.

Starting from only four miles away, Hadrian's Wall stretches for miles, mainly through glorious unspoilt countryside, with a choice of exhibitions, museums and archaeological sites and digs.

LOCATION

From A69, Carlisle-Newcastle Road, take the A689 Alston Road at Brampton. The hotel is 2 miles from Brampton not in Farlam Village.

Hallbankgate,
Brampton,
Cumbria CA8 2NG

Telephone 016977 46234
Fax 016977 46683

PROPRIETORS

Quinion and Stevenson Families

ROOM RATES

11 Doubles/Twins £180 - £220
1 Four-poster £210
Includes full breakfast, dinner & VAT

CHARGE/CREDIT CARDS

• MC • VI

ACCOLADES

R.A.C. Blue Ribbon Award ★★★
A.A. ★★★ ❀❀
The Good Hotel Guide

FACILITIES

Gardens, heli-pad
1 meeting room/max 12 people
Golf and riding nearby

RESTRICTIONS

No children under the age of five
No facilities for disabled guests
Dogs not to be left alone in bedrooms

ATTRACTIONS

Carlisle Castle and Cathedral,
Hadrian's Wall,
Lake District,
Lanercost Priory

AFFILIATIONS

Relais & Châteaux

NEAREST

MAJOR CITY:
Carlisle - 12 miles /20 mins

MAJOR AIRPORT:
Manchester - 100 miles/2½ hrs
Newcastle - 40 miles/1 hr

RAILWAY STATION:
Carlisle - 12 miles /20 mins

RESERVATIONS

Direct with hotel

ACCESS CODES

Not applicable

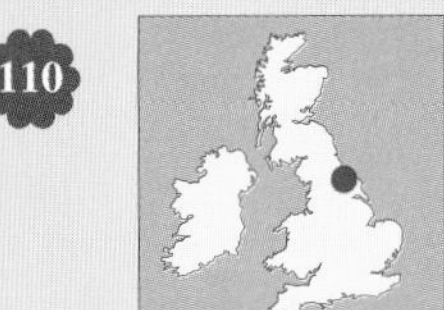

"I felt like a long lost uncle being welcomed home"

Gus Moerel, Holland

THE FEVERSHAM ARMS HOTEL

Coaching inn

1/8 High Street,
Helmsley, York,
North Yorkshire YO6 5AG

Telephone 01439 770766
Fax 01439 770346

MANAGING DIRECTOR

Gonzalo Aragües y Gaston

ROOM RATES

Single occupancy £55 - £65
12 Doubles/Twins £70
5 Four-posters £80
1 Suite £80
Includes full breakfast and VAT

CHARGE/CREDIT CARDS

• DC • MC • VI

ACCOLADES

E.T.B. ♛♛♛♛ Highly Commended
R.A.C. ★★★ + Merit Award R
A.A. ★★★ ❀ 70%
Les Routiers UK Cheeseboard of the Year

FACILITIES

Heated outdoor swimming pool, tennis, patio & gardens
1 meeting room/max 30 people
Riding and shooting nearby

RESTRICTIONS

No smoking in dining room

ATTRACTIONS

Helmsley Castle,
Duncombe Park,
Rievaulx Terraces & Abbey,
Castle Howard,
Jorvik Viking Centre

AFFILIATIONS

Independent

NEAREST

MAJOR CITY:
York - 22 miles/30 mins

MAJOR AIRPORT:
Teesside - 35 miles/40 mins

RAILWAY STATION:
York - 22 miles/30 mins

RESERVATIONS

Direct with hotel

ACCESS CODES

Not applicable

Probably the most revisited inn in the UK

In the "History of Helmsley" it is said that at one time there were 26 ale houses in the town – "The weavers were thirsty souls". One of these ale houses was The Feversham Arms, rebuilt and renamed in 1855 by the Earl of Feversham having been noted previously as Public House and earlier as Board Inn where ales and candles were made and sold.

In 1967, the Aragües family bought the Feversham Arms and later the three adjacent cottages. Today the four buildings are one unit, forming the actual hotel, which has been modernised to high standards while preserving the character and charm of the older coaching inn, with open fires and dinner by candlelight.

The 18 en suite bedrooms, intimate rather than large, are individually decorated with all modern facilities including safe. Six of them are on the ground floor, being very convenient for guests with walking difficulties.

The awarded Goya Restaurant, renowned for its good food, specialises in shellfish and game in season. The extensive wine list includes a good selection of French Grand Cru Classés and Spanish Gran Reservas.

The hotel is ideally placed in an exhilarating environment where the tourist, sports enthusiast and the businessman will find common ground for enjoyment. Bonanza Breaks are available from £45 per person per night, inclusive of dinner, bed and full English breakfast.

LOCATION

Set in the unique North York Moors National Park, 22 miles north of York, 30 miles west of Scarborough and the sea.

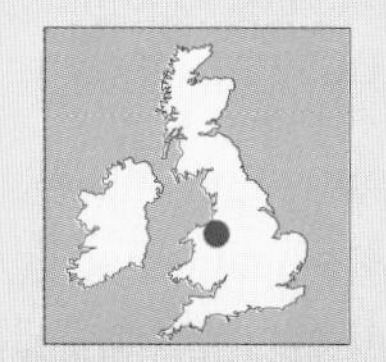

"What with the background music, soft lighting and the floodlit garden beyond dominated by a marble aphrodite, the effect is pure romance"

Paddy Burt, travel writer, Daily Telegraph

Georgian manor house

FROGG MANOR

Plush surroundings, old time music and frogs at the alternative Toad Hall

Frogg Manor is a graceful white Georgian house within ten miles of the centre of historic Chester. Grade II listed it stands in nine acres of woods and carefully tended gardens, watched over by a marble Aphrodite. Throughout, the furnishings are lavish, the furniture Georgian and Victorian. The large sitting room at the top of the stairs is the picture of gentility, with Regency armchairs, sturdy sofas, classy glass and china, and rich curtains and carpet.

It may seem like a classic English country house hotel. It is not. The first clues are a sign reading "Drive carefully, frogs crossing" and a human-sized frog in polka dot tie pointing the way. Owner John E Sykes named Frogg Manor partly in honour of frogs living in a big pond in the grounds and partly in tribute to his former girlfriend "Froggy". A little eccentricity has not stopped John from building a devoted clientele in the past few years. It may indeed have helped. A key factor is the hotel's determination to make sure that everything about Frogg Manor revives the spirits of its guests.

Lunches and dinners are unfussy, modern and delicious. Freshly made soups, savoury garlic mushrooms, rack of local lamb, steak and kidney pie, local beef fillet in various guises are the norm. Fat free, vegetarian, and any dislike or dietary restriction is no problem. Please let the hotel know, and advise time of arrival in advance. If your journey is delayed, dinner or a light supper can be served at any time.

LOCATION

From M6 join M54 at Junction 10A, leave M54 at Junction 3, go north on A41 to junction with A534. Turn right, direction Nantwich. ¾ mile to Frogg Manor on the right hand side.

Nantwich Road,
Fullers Moor, Broxton,
Chester CH3 9JH

Telephone 01829 782629
Fax 01829 782238

OWNER
John E Sykes

RATES PER PERSON
Single occupancy £40 - £95
6 Doubles £25 - £57.50
Includes VAT

CHARGE/CREDIT CARDS

• DC • MC • VI

ACCOLADES
Independent

FACILITIES
Garden, tennis, heli-pad
2 meeting rooms/max 25 people
Golf, fishing and riding nearby

RESTRICTIONS
No children under 4 years
No facilities for disabled guests
Pets allowed only in bedrooms

ATTRACTIONS
Chester,
Chester Castle,
Tatton Park,
Roman Amphitheatre,
Snowdonia,
Flint Castle

AFFILIATIONS
Independent

NEAREST
MAJOR CITY:
Chester - 10 miles/10 mins

MAJOR AIRPORT:
Manchester - 45 miles/45 mins

RAILWAY STATION:
Chester - 12 miles/10 mins

RESERVATIONS
Direct with hotel

ACCESS CODES
Not applicable

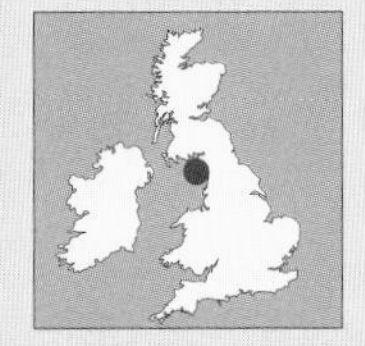

"Our second home – in Windermere"

Farida & Effendi Norwawi, Malaysia

GILPIN LODGE HOTEL

Country house

Crook Road, Nr Windermere, Cumbria LA23 3NE

Telephone 015394 88818
Fax 015394 88058

PROPRIETORS

John and Christine Cunliffe

RATES PER PERSON

Single occupancy £50 - £80
8 Doubles/Twins £80 - £130
5 Four-posters £100 - £130
Includes full breakfast and VAT

CHARGE/CREDIT CARDS

• DC • JCB • MC • VI

ACCOLADES

E.T.B. ♛♛♛♛ De Luxe
R.A.C. ★★★ + Merit Awards H C & R
A.A. ★★★ ❀❀ 77%
The Good Hotel Guide

FACILITIES

Croquet, gardens, heli-pad
2 meeting rooms/max 20 people
Golf, riding, tennis and fishing nearby

RESTRICTIONS

No children under 7 years
No facilities for disabled guests
No pets

ATTRACTIONS

Dove Cottage (Wordsworth's home),
World of Beatrix Potter,
Lake Windermere ,
Holker Hall,
Levens Hall

AFFILIATIONS

Selected British Hotels
Fine Individual Hotels

NEAREST

MAJOR CITY:
Manchester - 80 miles/1¼ hrs

MAJOR AIRPORT:
Manchester - 90 miles/1¾ hrs

RAILWAY STATION:
Windermere - 2 miles/10 mins

RESERVATIONS:

Toll free in US/Canada: 800-323-5463
Toll free in UK: 0800 269460

ACCESS CODES

Not applicable

Idyllic scenery, poetical history and a highly acclaimed dining room

Gilpin Lodge is a small, family-run country house hotel and restaurant in 20 acres of woodlands, moors and country gardens, two miles from Lake Windermere. The original Victorian building dates from the turn of the century – tastefully extended 90 years later.

A profusion of flower arrangements, picture-lined walls, antique furniture and log fires in the colder weather are all part of John and Christine Cunliffe's perception of hospitality. Their aim is to inspire relaxation in charming surroundings. The bedrooms all have en suite bathrooms and every comfort. Some have four-poster beds and whirlpool baths.

The food earned two Rosettes from the AA – which speaks for itself. Service in the elegant dining room is attentive but unpretentious. There is an extensive wine list to suit all tastes and pockets.

The beautiful gardens are the perfect place in which to muse while savouring the lakeland scenery. Windermere golf course is a half mile away. There's almost every kind of outdoor activity imaginable, and guests have free use of a nearby private leisure club. This is Wordsworth and Beatrix Potter country and nearby there are several stately homes, gardens and castles.

Gilpin Lodge is listed in all major guides. Dinner-inclusive rates and special terms for visits of three nights or more are available throughout the year. Christmas and New Year programmes on request.

LOCATION

Leave Motorway M6 at Junction 36. Take A590/591 to roundabout north of Kendal. Take B5284 for 5 miles.

"A charming place, I hope you didn't mind me bringing my own wine, your food complements it perfectly"

Baron Eric de Rothchild, Chateau Lafite

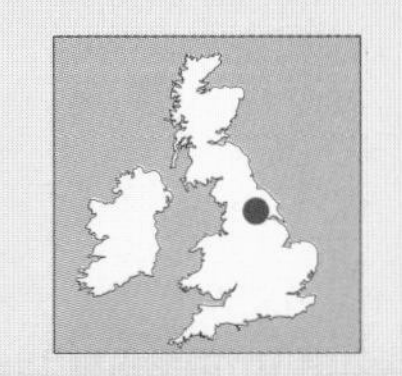

Regency townhouse THE GRANGE HOTEL

Luxury and fine cuisine in the grand Roman city of York

The Grange is a classical Regency townhouse within five minutes' walk of the City Walls and Great Minster. It was built in 1834 and has been carefully restored to create a luxurious 30 bedroom hotel.

Beautiful York stone flagged floors lead from the hall into the classically styled Morning Room with deep sofas and club-like atmosphere. This boasts flowers during the summer months and a blazing fire on cold wintery afternoons and evenings.

Light streams down the original vine leaf cast iron staircase, which leads to the individually decorated bedrooms. All have the brightest of bathrooms and are superbly equipped with direct dial telephone, remote control satellite TV and mini bars. Some contain original four-posters, antiques and many half-testers using deep coloured chintz and interesting choices of wallpaper.

The food has received many accolades and The Grange offers guests a choice of two restaurants. The Ivy is the more formal of the two with the emphasis on elegant surroundings and wonderful food. The menus are compiled to encompass local produce from moorland and sea.

The Brasserie on the other hand is very informal and is situated in the brick vaulted cellars. It has a relaxed cosy atmosphere, combining high quality food with the flexibility of eating early before theatre, or just popping in for a plate of pasta mid-evening.

LOCATION

From the A64, take the A1237 for 5 miles following signs to York North and Thirsk (A19) towards York centre. Turn right at A19. The Grange is 2 miles down on right.

Clifton, York, North Yorkshire YO3 6AA

Telephone 01904 644744
Fax 01904 612453

GENERAL MANAGER
Jonathan Tatton

ROOM RATES

3 Singles	*£78 - £95*
24 Doubles/Twins	*£98 - £118*
2 Four-posters	*£130 - £155*
1 Suite	*£170 - £185*

Includes full breakfast and VAT

CHARGE/CREDIT CARDS

• DC • MC • VI

ACCOLADES
E.T.B. ♛♛♛♛ *Highly Commended*
R.A.C. ★★★ *+ Merit Awards H C & R*
A.A. ★★★ ❀
The Good Hotel Guide

FACILITIES
3 meeting rooms/max 50 people
Golf and clay pigeon shooting nearby

RESTRICTIONS
None

ATTRACTIONS
York Minster, Yorkshire Museum, Castle Howard, Castle Museum, National Railway Museum, Yorkshire Dales and Moors

AFFILIATIONS
Selected British Hotels

NEAREST
MAJOR CITY:
In York centre

MAJOR AIRPORT:
Manchester - 45 miles/1½ hrs

RAILWAY STATION:
York - 1 mile/5 mins

RESERVATIONS
Toll free in US/Canada: 800-323-5463

ACCESS CODES
AMADEUS/SYSTEM 1 HK LBAGRA
SABRE HK 26908
WORLDSPAN HK GRANG
SAHARA HT 25926

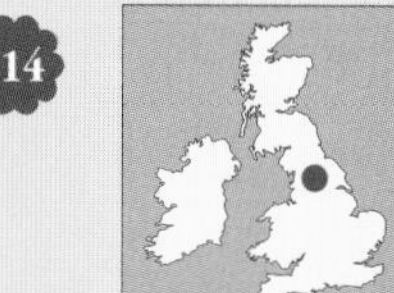

“ The best of Yorkshire and a great deal besides ”

Gina Lazenby

GRANTS HOTEL

Victorian hotel

**Swan Road, Harrogate,
North Yorkshire HG1 2SS**

**Telephone 01423 560666
Fax 01423 502550**

GENERAL MANAGER
Pam Grant

ROOM RATES

13 Singles	£50 - £99
26 Doubles/Twins	£70 - £137
2 Four-posters	£85 - £139
1 Suite	£90 - £149

Includes full breakfast and VAT

CHARGE/CREDIT CARDS

• DC • JCB • MC • VI

ACCOLADES
E.T.B. ♛♛♛♛ Highly Commended
R.A.C. ★★★ + Merit Award H
A.A. ★★★ 68%

FACILITIES
Patio gardens
5 meeting rooms/max 100 people
Golf, leisure club, riding and fishing nearby

RESTRICTIONS
Pets accepted at the discretion of the management

ATTRACTIONS
Fountains Abbey,
Herriot country,
Yorkshire Dales,
York, Harrogate

AFFILIATIONS
Fine Individual Hotels

NEAREST
MAJOR CITY:
Leeds - 15 miles /25 mins
MAJOR AIRPORT:
Leeds/Bradford - 12 miles/20 mins
RAILWAY STATION:
Harrogate - ½ mile/5 mins walk

RESERVATIONS
Toll free in US 800-437-2687

ACCESS CODES
GALILEO RM48485
SABRE RN04297

NORTH

Elegant and individual hospitality in the heart of historic England

Harrogate is a beautiful spa and award winning floral town set in the heart of an area rich in English history. James Herriot, the world's most celebrated vet, was a regular weekly visitor for many years, finding a convivial refuge from the nearby Yorkshire Dales, scene of all his adventures.

Within a short distance is the Roman city of York with its Jorvik Viking Centre or alternatively, Fountains Abbey, England's largest Cistercian Monastery, disestablished by Henry VIII and preserved to become a World Heritage Site.

Why not explore Middleham Castle, home of Richard III, immortalised by William Shakespeare and visit Bolton Castle where Mary Queen of Scots was imprisoned. Would you like to see Haworth, home of the Bronte Family and scene of Heathcliffe's tragic romance in 'Wuthering Heights'?

Grants is a family-run hotel with a reputation for quality of service that is the envy of its competitors, combining modern standards of efficiency with old fashioned hospitality. Each of the tastefully decorated bedrooms offers a full range of facilities including private bathroom and a lift serves all floors.

Chimney Pots Restaurant provides an imaginative menu in an elegant air-conditioned atmosphere and is a firm favourite with local gourmets.

LOCATION

From M1 or M62 at Leeds, take A61 to Harrogate, then 2nd left after The Royal Hall traffic lights into Swan Road.

" I'm fussy but I can't fault it. For the money its superb value, right down to the Imperial Leather "

J A O'Brien, Berkshire

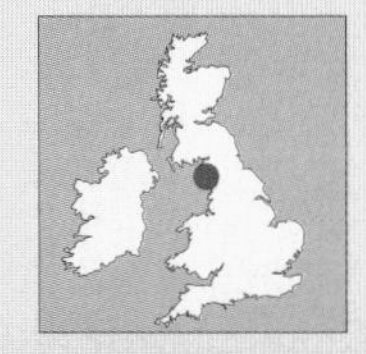

Victorian country house GRAYTHWAITE MANOR HOTEL

A beautiful country manor noted for its cuisine

There are many excellent reasons for choosing Grange-over-Sands as your weekend or holiday venue, at any time of the year, Graythwaite Manor is one of them. Started by the Blakemore family in 1937, the hotel is now under the supervision of the third generation of the same family. A warm welcome and personal care and attention is their constant aim as much today as it was then.

This beautifully furnished country house provides an exclusive, comfortable and tranquil setting in which to relax. It is set in eight acres of landscaped gardens and woodland, on the hillside looking out over Morecambe Bay.

Elegant, spacious lounges with fresh flowers and antiques are part of the atmosphere. Here you will find room to relax, to chat or read and whilst the hotel is always warm, log fires add extra cheer on chillier nights.

Each bedroom is tastefully furnished, and has private bathroom, colour television, telephone and tea/coffee-making facilities. Many provide superb views across the gardens and bay to the Pennines beyond.

The hotel is noted for its superb cuisine, the head chef working closely with the proprietors to ensure the highest standards.

However you spend your day you can look forward to a six-course dinner, a choice of carefully prepared dishes and the right wine from their extensive cellar. They use fresh local produce as much as possible. A traditional English roast, with all the proper trimmings is a regular feature on the menu.

LOCATION

Take left at top of main street, then 4th road to right (almost opposite Fire Station).

Fernhill Road,
Grange-over-Sands,
Cumbria LA11 7JE

Telephone 015395 32001
Fax 015395 35549

NORTH

PROPRIETORS
The Blakemore Family

MANAGER
Iain C Blakemore

ROOM RATES

5 Singles	*£40 - £62*
14 Doubles/Twins	*£80 - £120*

Includes full breakfast, dinner and VAT

CHARGE/CREDIT CARDS

• JCB • MC • VI

ACCOLADES
E.T.B. ♛♛♛♛ *Highly Commended*
R.A.C. ★★★ *+ Merit Award R*
A.A. ★★★ *66%*

FACILITIES
Tennis, gardens, putting, snooker
2 meeting rooms/max 50 people
Golf, riding and fishing nearby

RESTRICTIONS
Children at discretion of management
No pets

ATTRACTIONS
Halker Hall,
Cartmel Priory and Village,
Beatrix Potter's House – 'Hill Top',
Wordsworth's House – Dove Cottage

AFFILIATIONS
Independent

NEAREST
MAJOR CITY:
Manchester - 80 miles/1 1/2 hrs
MAJOR AIRPORT:
Manchester - 90 miles/1 1/2 hrs
RAILWAY STATION:
Grange-over-Sands - 1 mile/5 mins

RESERVATIONS
Direct with hotel

ACCESS CODES
Not applicable

" Still the best food, the best value and the best company I have ever found in England "

M Crumpler, North Carolina

HIPPING HALL

17th century country house

Cowan Bridge,
Kirkby Lonsdale,
Cumbria LA6 2JJ

Telephone 015242 71187
Fax 015242 72452

PROPRIETORS

Ian Bryant and Jocelyn Ruffle

ROOM RATES

Single occupancy	*£63*
5 Doubles/Twins	*£79*
2 Suites	*£89*

Includes full breakfast and VAT

CHARGE/CREDIT CARDS

• MC • VI

ACCOLADES

A.A. QQQQQ Premier Selected
The Good Hotel Guide

FACILITIES

Croquet and gardens
1 meeting room/max 20 people
Golf, riding and fishing nearby

RESTRICTIONS

Children over 12 years
No facilities for disabled guests
No dogs allowed in public rooms

ATTRACTIONS

Yorkshire Dales National Park,
Lake District National Park,
Warton Old Rectory

AFFILIATIONS

Independent

NEAREST

MAJOR CITY:
Lancaster - 18 miles/25 mins

MAJOR AIRPORT:
Manchester - 70 miles/1½ hrs

RAILWAY STATION:
Oxenholme - 12 miles/20 mins

RESERVATIONS

Direct with hotel

ACCESS CODES

Not applicable

Enjoy this friendly country house party style

Cowan Bridge, where the Brontë sisters attended their clergy daughters' school, is conveniently situated for both the Lakes and Dales. It lies on the Cumbrian/Yorkshire borders, two miles from the pretty market town of Kirkby Lonsdale in the Lune Valley, the view Ruskin described as ". . . one of the loveliest scenes in England – therefore in the world".

Hipping Hall is a 17th century country house set in four acres of walled gardens. A private home as well as an hotel, you'll find your stay very different to that in a more conventional English country house hotel.

For example, after helping yourself to a drink from the sideboard in the conservatory, you'll dine informally with other guests at one large table beneath the Minstrels' Gallery in the Great Hall. Jocelyn prepares a new five course menu each night; everything is fresh, mainly using home and local produce. During the meal, Ian serves three wines (optional) which he has chosen to suit that particular menu.

Hipping Hall is informal – but not slapdash. The bedrooms – mostly furnished with antiques – are well-equipped. There are two cottage suites and each has a kitchen and sitting room with a Victorian spiral staircase leading to the bedroom and bathroom.

Whether you spend several days here and make Hipping Hall your base from which to tour both the Cumbrian Lakes and the Yorkshire Dales (special rates for two nights) or just a night en route to Scotland, you will be sure to remember your stay at Hipping Hall with great affection.

LOCATION

On A65 2½ miles east of Kirkby Lonsdale, 8½ miles from M6, Junction 36.

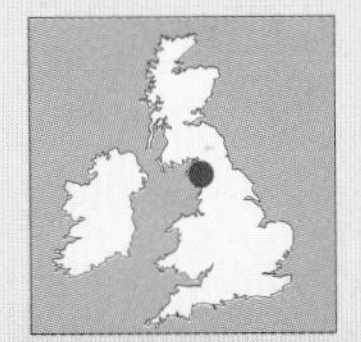

"Not only was the view unbelievable, it was quite easily the best and friendliest service we have ever experienced"

Will Carling, Captain, England Rugby Football team

19th century hunting lodge

HOLBECK GHYLL HOTEL

A dream of a country house hotel set in breathtaking English Lakeland

Holbeck Ghyll is an hotel of outstanding character and charm, situated in landscaped gardens and acres of natural woodland (see right). The views across Lake Windermere and the Langdale Fells are breathtaking.

Built in the early 19th century, the house was bought in 1888 by Lord Lonsdale for use as his Hunting Lodge. The 'Yellow Earl', as he was known, was the first president of the Automobile Association and bequeathed the famous Lonsdale Belt to boxing. The Lord led a colourful life and made a lasting impression on the style and appearance of Holbeck Ghyll.

Public rooms are elegant and comfortable, some with log fires, and throughout there is an abundance of magnificent features in the style of Charles Rennie Mackintosh with a wealth of oak panelling and stained glass. The bedrooms are individually designed and refurbished to the highest of standards.

Dining is an integral part of one's stay at Holbeck Ghyll and provides for a memorable experience. The interesting and extensive menu features dishes which are classically prepared and artistically presented, much in the English style yet with a French influence. Exciting and unusual vegetarian items are included in every course.

David and Patricia Nicholson look forward to welcoming you to Holbeck Ghyll.

LOCATION

M6 Junction 36. To Windermere, pass Brockhole Visitors' Centre, then after ½ mile turn right into Holbeck Lane (signed Troutbeck). Hotel is ½ mile on left.

Holbeck Lane, Windermere, Cumbria LA23 1LU

Telephone 015394 32375
Fax 015394 34743

PROPRIETORS

David and Patricia Nicholson

MANAGER

Elizabeth Cherry

ROOM RATES

10 Doubles/Twins £120 - £220
1 Four-poster £140 - £220
3 Suites £160 - £240
Includes full breakfast, 5-course dinner and VAT

CHARGE/CREDIT CARDS

• DC • JCB • MC • VI

ACCOLADES

E.T.B. ♛♛♛♛ De Luxe
R.A.C. Blue Ribbon Award ★★
A.A. ★★ ❀❀
The Good Hotel Guide

FACILITIES

Croquet, billiard room, putting green, gardens, woodland walks, tennis court
2 meeting rooms/max 45 people
Golf, riding, fishing and complimentary leisure facilities nearby

RESTRICTIONS

No children under 8 years in restaurant
No facilities for disabled guests
No dogs in public rooms

ATTRACTIONS

William Wordsworth's Dove Cottage, Beatrix Potter's home, lake cruises, spectacular mountain scenery, walking, cycling and golf

AFFILIATIONS

Small Luxury Hotels

NEAREST

MAJOR CITY:
Manchester - 90 miles/1½ hrs

MAJOR AIRPORT:
Manchester - 90 miles/1½ hrs

RAILWAY STATION:
Windermere - 3 miles/5 mins

RESERVATIONS

Toll free in US/Canada 800-525-4800

ACCESS CODES

SABRE LX 31195
APOLLO LX 21650
WORLDSPAN/SAHARA LX BWFHG
SYSTEM 1/AMADEUS LX VEMHGC
AXESS LX 5646

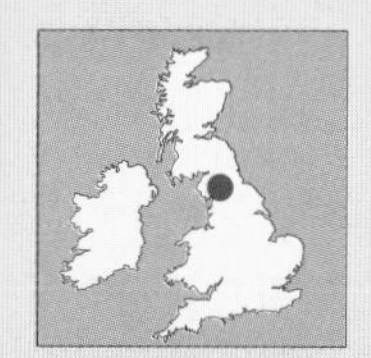

"Marvellous evenings. Bounteous hospitality and gastronomical feasts"

Katy Cropper, Sedbusk, only lady winner of BBC TV's sheepdog competition, "One Man and His Dog"

KING'S ARMS HOTEL

Georgian manor house

Askrigg, Wensleydale, North Yorkshire DL8 3HQ

Telephone 01969 650258
Fax 01969 650635

PROPRIETORS
Elizabeth and Raymond Hopwood

ROOM RATES

Single occupancy	*£50 - £70*
8 Doubles/Twins	*£75 - £85*
1 Four-poster	*£85*
2 Suites	*£105*

Includes full breakfast and VAT

CHARGE/CREDIT CARDS

• *JCB* • *MC* • *VI*

ACCOLADES
R.A.C. ★★ + Merit Awards H & R
A.A. ★★ ❀❀ 68%

FACILITIES
Courtyard gardens
2 meeting rooms/max 60 people
Fishing and shooting nearby

RESTRICTIONS
No children under 7 years
No facilities for disabled guests
Pets by prior arrangement

ATTRACTIONS
Bolton Castle,
York, Durham,
Middleham Castle,
Lake District

AFFILIATIONS
Logis of Great Britain

NEAREST
MAJOR CITY:
York - 60 miles/1¼ hrs

MAJOR AIRPORT:
Manchester - 80 miles/1¾ hrs

RAILWAY STATION:
Darlington - 30 miles/40 mins

RESERVATIONS
Direct with hotel

ACCESS CODES
Not applicable

NORTH

"There is nothing so fine created by man as an English pub"

So wrote Samuel Johnson, and it could have been written of the King's Arms at Askrigg. This special place is the distillation of a 200-year history as a coaching inn, the centre of Dales life, a Friendly Society meeting place and its origin as a Georgian manor house and race-horse stables. Each has left its indelible mark, creating the unique atmosphere and character so aptly captured as the "Drovers Arms" pub of Darrowby in the BBC TV series of James Herriot's All Creatures Great and Small.

In the heart of the ancient Yorkshire Dales village of Askrigg, the King's Arms is surrounded by pastoral scenery set against the backdrop of the northern Pennine Hills. Its beauty was inspirational to two famous guests – the English landscape painter Turner and the poet Wordsworth.

Food at the King's Arms has received accolades from seven national guides – whether it be savouring a local Yorkshire dish in the busy bars, stylish Silks Grill or a gourmet dish in the panelled Clubroom Restaurant. Cask ales, fine wines and a selection of single malt whiskies augment the food. The long-established innkeeping tradition for good food, comfort and company is continued with pride today by Liz and Ray Hopwood.

The King's Arms at Askrigg is the ideal centre for visiting the abounding heritage of England's North Country and is a place to relax and unwind in the country house style, en suite rooms or enjoy the bustle of Yorkshire rural life beside the pub's roaring log fires and savouring good food.

LOCATION

Askrigg is a ½ mile off A684 road at Bainbridge between A1 (Leeming Bar) and M6 (Junction 37) Sedbergh.

“ Once again you have exceeded all our expectations ”

Stephen Beresford & Lesley Haynes, Toshiba, Surrey

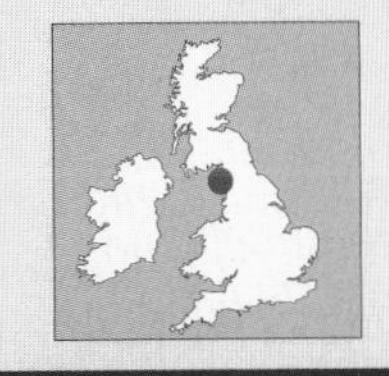

17th century coaching inn

LAKESIDE HOTEL

They overlook nothing but the lake

Lakeside Hotel offers you a unique location on the water's edge of Lake Windermere. Lakeside has long been a favourite for those who know the Lakes well. It is a classic, traditional Lakeland hotel offering all the comforts and facilities you would expect.

All the bedrooms are en suite and enjoy individually designed fabrics and colours; many of the rooms offer breathtaking views of the lake.

Guests may dine in either the award-winning Lakeview Restaurant or John Ruskin's Brasserie, where extensive menus offer a wide selection of dishes including Cumbrian specialities. The Lakeside Conservatory serves drinks and light meals throughout the day – once there you are sure to fall under the spell of this peaceful location.

Their location next to the Lake Cruisers allows you to discover the lake from the water, while the scope for watersports, climbing and walking is boundless. Guests also enjoy free use of the Cascades Leisure Club at Newby Bridge. The hotel offers a fully equipped conference centre and many syndicate suites, allowing plenty of scope and flexibility.

Most of all you are assured of a stay in an unrivalled setting of genuine character. The original panelling and beams of the old coaching inn create an excellent ambience, whilst you are sure to enjoy the quality and friendly service to which the Lakeside team are committed.

LOCATION

From Junction 36 of M6 join A590 to Barrow and follow signs to Newby Bridge. Turn right over the bridge and the hotel is 1 mile on the right.

Newby Bridge, Cumbria LA12 8AT

Telephone 015395 31207
Fax 015395 31699

GENERAL MANAGER

Clive Wilson

ROOM RATES

7 Singles	*£80 - £100*
34 Doubles	*£100 - £130*
24 Twins	*£100 - £130*
2 Four-posters	*£150*
2 Suites	*£160*

Includes full breakfast and VAT

CHARGE/CREDIT CARDS

• *DC* • *MC* • *VI*

ACCOLADES

E.T.B. ♛♛♛♛ *Highly Commended*
R.A.C. ★★★ + *Merit Awards H & C*
A.A. ★★★ ❀ *73%*

FACILITIES

Garden, croquet, fishing
7 meeting rooms/max 140 people
Riding and complimentary use of leisure club nearby

RESTRICTIONS

None

ATTRACTIONS

Lake District National Park,
Beatrix Potter's home,
Wordsworth's home,
Ruskin's Brantwood

AFFILIATIONS

Independent

NEAREST

MAJOR CITY:
Manchester - 80 miles/1½ hrs

MAJOR AIRPORT:
Manchester - 90 miles/1½ hrs
Barrow - 15 miles/30 mins

RAILWAY STATION:
Grange - 6 miles/10 mins

RESERVATIONS

Toll free in US: 800-437-2687

ACCESS CODES

Not applicable

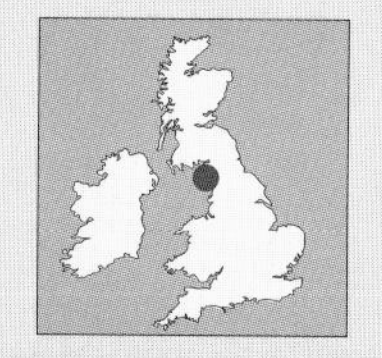

"The welcoming atmosphere, good food and magnificent views will mean you'll readily return to Linthwaite . . ."

Los Angeles Times

LINTHWAITE HOUSE

Victorian country house

**Crook Road,
Bowness-on-Windermere,
Lake District,
Cumbria LA23 3JA**

**Telephone 015394 88600
Fax 015394 88601**

PROPRIETOR
Mike Bevans

ROOM RATES

1 Single	£90
13 Doubles/Twins	£110 - £155
3 Four-posters	£130 - £155
1 Suite	£150 - £180

Includes full breakfast and VAT

CHARGE/CREDIT CARDS

• JCB • MC • VI

ACCOLADES
E.T.B. De Luxe
R.A.C. ★★★ + Merit Awards H C & R
A.A. ★★★ 76%
E.T.B Hotel of the Year 1994
A.A. Courtesy & Care Award 1994
The Good Hotel Guide

FACILITIES
Croquet, gardens, fly fishing
1 meeting room/max 47 people
Golf, riding, fishing and leisure spa nearby

RESTRICTIONS
No children under 7 years in restaurant
No pets in the hotel

ATTRACTIONS
Beatrix Potter's Home & Museum,
Wordsworth's Dove Cottage,
Lake Windermere, Sizergh Castle,
Levens Hall & Topiary Gardens

AFFILIATIONS
Fine Individual Hotels

NEAREST
MAJOR CITY:
Manchester - 95 miles/1 3/4 hrs

MAJOR AIRPORT:
Manchester - 95 miles/1 3/4 hrs

RAILWAY STATION:
Windermere - 3 miles/10 mins

RESERVATIONS
Toll free in US: 800-544-9993
Toll free in US: 800-437-2687

ACCESS CODES
AMADEUS GH MANCHH
APOLLO GH 48735
AXESS GH 1003
WORLDSPAN GH 1001
SABRE GH 35752
SYSTEM1 GH MANLHH

A relaxing break among the hills and valleys of the Lake District

Situated in 14 acres of glorious hilltop gardens overlooking Lake Windermere and 'Coniston Old Man', Linthwaite House is a haven for those with distinctive tastes who appreciate the finer things in life.

Breathtaking sunsets, superb scenery and a multitude of places of special interest within easy reach, including the home of William Wordsworth, Beatrix Potter's home, museum and gallery, historic houses, theatre and cinema. Sweeping fells and Lakeland villages have been the source of inspiration for poets and writers alike since time began.

Good food and fine wine served in a relaxed, unstuffy atmosphere and unpretentious surroundings combine to give you a rewarding break in the heart of the Lake District.

Eighteen rooms, some with lakeview, and garden suite with separate lounge. Each has en suite bath/shower, bathrobes, seven channel satellite TV, direct-dial telephone, radio, trouser press, hairdryer and tea/coffee making facility.

Whatever the occasion, whatever the season, Linthwaite House will be here to pamper you.

LOCATION

From the M6 Junction 36 follow Kendal by-pass (A591) for 8 miles. Take B5284 Crook Road for 6 miles. The drive to Linthwaite House is situated on the left, 1 mile beyond Windermere Golf Club.

" Food worth driving 100 miles for "

Derek Cooper, radio presenter

19th century retreat

THE MANOR HOUSE

Catering to people of taste and discernment in historic East Riding

Overlooking horse paddocks and parkland, and set in three acres of tree-lined grounds, The Manor House occupies a tranquil position on the rolling Yorkshire Wolds. This 19th-century retreat is perfect for those seeking relaxation and luxury. Lee and Derek Baugh maintain a high standard in all aspects of entertaining.

The bedrooms, with their open, attractive views, are individually furnished and decorated; guests will find themselves pampered with unexpected and useful personal comforts. Relax in the drawing room with an aperitif as you anticipate the delights being prepared for you by Chef-patron Derek Baugh, formerly of The Dorchester Hotel.

Through his inspired culinary approach, there has evolved a distinctive, creative style of cuisine and the connoisseur will find Lee Baugh's confections irresistible. To accompany your meal, the wine list reflects an informed interest in the best European wines. As an alternative to the restaurant, the conservatory is an ideal place to wine and dine on a summer evening. Overlooking the south terrace and lawns, it is also the perfect place for meetings of company executives or private functions.

A wealth of activities lies on the doorstep – the vastness of the North Yorkshire Moors, the rugged grandeur of the coastline from Bridlington to the old whaling port of Whitby and the many stately homes and villages.

LOCATION

Leave M62 at Junction 38 direction Gilberdyke and North Cave. Take the B1230 towards Beverley. At Walkington pass straight through the village and turn left at traffic lights. At first minor cross-raods, turn left again. the Manor House is 400 yards down the road on the left.

Northlands, Walkington, Beverley, East Yorkshire HU17 8RT

Telephone 01482 881645
Fax 01482 866501

NORTH

PROPRIETORS
Derek and Lee Baugh

ROOM RATES
Single occupancy £70 - £80
7 Doubles/Twins £80 - £100
Includes VAT

CHARGE/CREDIT CARDS

• MC • VI

ACCOLADES
R.A.C. Highly acclaimed
A.A. ★★ ❀❀ 70%
R.A.C. Best Small Hotel for the North 1995
R.A.C. Restaurant Award 1994/1995

FACILITIES
Garden
1 meeting room/max 20 people
Golf, riding and clay pigeon shooting nearby

RESTRICTIONS
No children under 12 years
Small dogs only allowed

ATTRACTIONS
Beverley Minster, Museum of Army Transport, Lincoln Cathedral, York, Thornton Abbey

AFFILIATIONS
Independent

NEAREST
MAJOR CITY:
Hull - 9 miles/12 mins

MAJOR AIRPORT:
Humberside - 20 miles/30 mins

RAILWAY STATION:
Hull - 9 miles/12 mins

RESERVATIONS
Direct with hotel

ACCESS CODES
Not applicable

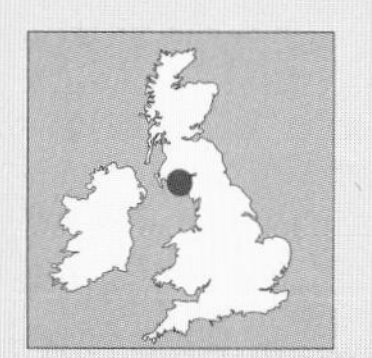

"How do we say thank you? You were all terrific! A joy to get to know"

Joan Rivers

MICHAELS NOOK

Victorian house

Grasmere, Ambleside,
Cumbria LA22 9RP

Telephone 015394 35496
Fax 015394 35645

PROPRIETOR
Reg Gifford

ROOM RATES

Single occupancy	*£124*
11 Doubles	*£188 - £272*
1 Four-poster	*£272*
2 Suites	*£330 - £380*

Includes full breakfast,
5-course dinner and VAT

CHARGE/CREDIT CARDS

• DC • MC • VI

ACCOLADES
A.A. ★★★ ❀❀❀
The Good Hotel Guide

FACILITIES
Garden, croquet, heli-pad
1 meeting room/max 30 people
Indoor swimming pool, sauna,
solarium, jacuzzi in nearby sister hotel
riding and fishing nearby

RESTRICTIONS
Children by arrangement
No facilities for disabled guests
No Pets

ATTRACTIONS
Wordsworth's Dove Cottage
and Rydal Mount,
Beatrix Potter's Hill Top,
John Ruskin's Brantwood,
Coniston, Sawrey,

AFFILIATIONS
Pride of Britain
The Celebrated Hotels Collection

NEAREST
MAJOR CITY:
Carlisle - 45 miles/50 mins

MAJOR AIRPORT:
Manchester - 100 miles/2 hrs

RAILWAY STATION:
Windermere - 9 miles/15 mins

RESERVATIONS
Toll free in US: 800-544-9941
or 800-98-PRIDE

ACCESS CODES
SABRE HK 35650
APOLLO HT 41204
WORLDSPAN HK MICHA

NORTH

At the heart of English lakeland, an hotel cherished worldwide

Michaels Nook is a fine, early Victorian Lakeland house, with a wealth of mahogany panelling and elegant plasterwork. It derives its name from William Wordsworth's poem "Michael", about a humble shepherd who spent his long life in the immediate vicinity.

It was opened as an hotel in 1969 by Reg Gifford, a former antique dealer, who has personally brought together the predominantly English embellishments, and it enjoys an international reputation for the excellence of its furnishings, food and service. There are two suites and 12 very comfortable bedrooms, varying in size, aspect and decor, but all exhibiting the same luxurious touches and meticulous care.

Dishes which combine artistry with flavour are created for the restaurant from the finest fresh produce, and the extensive and outstanding wine list reflects another of Reg Gifford's special interests.

With open fires, an abundance of flowers and plants, Great Danes and some exotic cats, Michaels Nook remains a home, with an atmosphere of intimacy and warmth – and just a hint of eccentricity.

Magnificent walks start from the doorstep, as do spectacular drives through some of Britain's most impressive scenery. Dove Cottage, Wordsworth's home, is nearby, and Beatrix Potter's home at Sawrey is only a short drive.

LOCATION

Turn uphill off the A591 just north of Grasmere at The Swan Hotel, and bear left with the lane for 400 yards.

"Stunningly well done and a marvellous place to escape the bustle of York"

Lord Lichfield

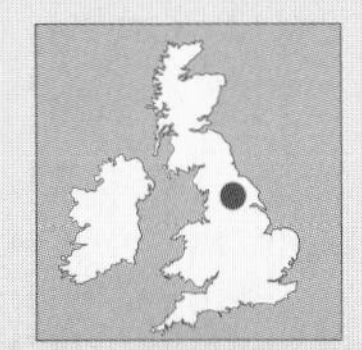

Queen Anne country house

MIDDLETHORPE HALL

A country house hotel close to the heart of the city

This beautiful Queen Anne building – built in 1699 – lies within the city boundary of York and is only 1½ miles from the centre, yet it is surrounded by 26 acres of gardens and parkland. Dominating the lawn at the back of the house is a magnificent Cedar of Lebanon and the beautifully tended gardens include a lake, a white garden and some original ha has.

Middlethorpe was rescued from decay by Historic House Hotels and after extensive restoration it opened as an hotel in 1984, beautifully decorated and furnished to reflect the elegance of its eighteenth century origins.

One of the finest rooms is the drawing room, once a small ballroom now comfortably furnished with soft armchairs, ticking clocks, a large open fire and an abundance of fresh flowers and orchids from the greenhouse. The oak panelled dining room is an admirable setting for the excellent food produced by head chef and his brigade. There are beautifully designed bedrooms and suites in the main house and the adjacent classical courtyard.

Middlethorpe is an ideal centre for exploring York, also known as Britain's living museum, the dramatic scenery of the Yorkshire dales and moors and for visiting stately homes like Castle Howard and Harewood House and the ruined abbeys at Fountains and Rievaulx.

LOCATION

From the A64 follow signs to York West (A1036) then follow signs to York Racecourse and Bishopthorpe. Middlethorpe Hall is on the right just before the racecourse.

Bishopthorpe Road, York, North Yorkshire YO2 1QB

Telephone 01904 641241
Fax 01904 620176

GENERAL MANAGER
Stephen J Browning

ROOM RATES

4 Singles	from £97
17 Doubles/Twins	£141 - £156
2 Four-posters	£196
7 Suites	£181 - £220

Includes full breakfast, service and VAT

CHARGE/CREDIT CARDS

• MC • VI

ACCOLADES
E.T.B. ♛♛♛♛ De Luxe
R.A.C. Blue Ribbon Award ★★★★
A.A. ★★★ ❀❀
The Good Hotel Guide

FACILITIES
Garden, croquet, heli-pad
2 meeting rooms/max 35 people
Golf and riding nearby

RESTRICTIONS
No children under 8 years
No facilities for disabled guests
No pets

ATTRACTIONS
Castle Howard, York, Harewood House, Newby Hall, Yorkshire moors and dales

AFFILIATIONS
Small Luxury Hotels

NEAREST
MAJOR CITY:
York - 1½ miles/5 mins

MAJOR AIRPORT:
Manchester - 84 miles/1½ hrs
Leeds/Bradford - 34 miles/45 mins

RAILWAY STATION:
York - 1½ miles/5 mins

RESERVATIONS
Toll free fax in US: 800-260-8338 (quote Middlethorpe Hall)
In Japan: 03-3434-7159

ACCESS CODES
AMADEUS/SYSTEM 1 LX LBAMHH
APOLLO LX 4510
AXESS LX 5566
SABRE LX 4540
WORLDSPAN/SAHARA LX HRTMH

" At Miller Howe you are welcomed, lapped in luxury and fed – almost overfed – with dedication "

Diana Petry, The Observer

MILLER HOWE HOTEL

Hotel & restaurant

Rayrigg Road, Windermere, Cumbria LA23 1EY

Telephone 015394 42536
Fax 015394 45664

NORTH

PROPRIETOR
John J Tovey

RATES PER PERSON
Single occupancy £95
12 Doubles/Twins £80 - £130
Includes full breakfast, dinner and VAT

CHARGE/CREDIT CARDS

• *DC* • *MC* • *VI*

ACCOLADES
A.A. ★★ ❀❀
The Good Hotel Guide

FACILITIES
Gardens
Golf and riding nearby

RESTRICTIONS
No children under 8 years
No facilities for disabled guests
No smoking in restaurant
Pets in bedrooms only

ATTRACTIONS
Lake District National Park,
Beatrix Potter's home and museum,
Steamboat Museum,
Dove Cottage,
Holebird Gardens,

AFFILIATIONS
Independent

NEAREST
MAJOR CITY:
Manchester - 90 miles/1½ hrs

MAJOR AIRPORT:
Manchester - 100 miles/1½ hrs

RAILWAY STATION:
Windermere - 1 mile/5 mins

RESERVATIONS
Direct with hotel

ACCESS CODES
Not applicable

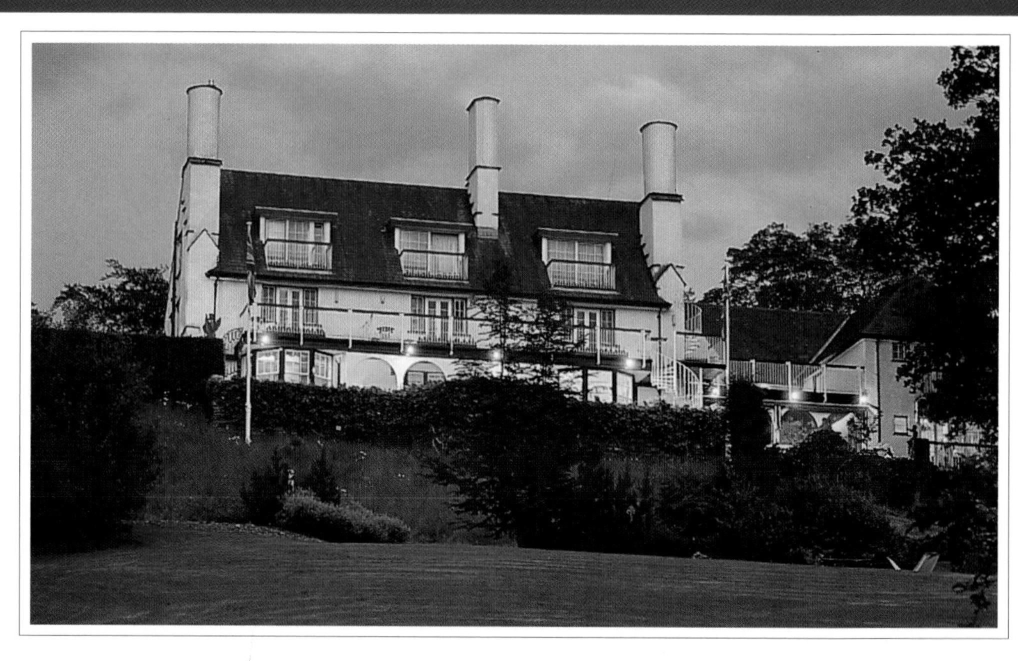

Exquisite cooking, magnificent scenery – sheer perfection!

Miller Howe is situated on the shores of Lake Windermere standing in four and a half acres of well-kept gardens. Guests may doubt if there is a finer view anywhere to compare with the one from the Conservatory and Terrace.

The accent is on friendly personal service with a high standard of English cooking – using mainly local produce – and the highlight of each day is the light textured, highly flavoured, four-course dinner served at seven thirty for eight.

Some recent press acclaims...

"The unfailing excellence of the food has never flagged – John Tovey has many imitators but no rivals" - Homes and Gardens

"You'll find that rain occurs in the Lake District and you'll also find that there are few better places to ride it out than in the ambience and warmth of John Tovey's elegant retreat" - Bon Appetit

"John Tovey's Miller Howe sets the standards for the region" - New York Times

LOCATION

A592 between Windermere and Bowness.

"The old place has lost none of its charm, the food quite marvellous and my accommodation extremely comfortable"

J Hunter, Walsham, Norfolk

16th century manor house

MONK FRYSTON HALL

A memorable combination of period elegance and the best modern facilities

Monk Fryston Hall is a 16th century manor house set in its own spacious grounds in the quiet, but accessible, village of Monk Fryston. The site of the hotel dates back to the time of William the Conqueror when monks lived at Monk Fryston during the building of Selby Abbey (1320).

With its grey stone walls, mullioned windows and the family coat of arms above the doorway, the Hall still has the appearance of a gracious manor house. It continued to be a private house up to the late 1940's. The Duke of Rutland purchased the Hall in 1954 and whilst creating a luxury hotel he also preserved the traditions and the mellow architectural heritage of this fine old house.

Monk Fryston Hall offers the visitor a memorable combination of period elegance and the best in modern facilities. The gardens and lakes of the park provide a wonderfully relaxed environment with old-fashioned comfort in the oak panelled bars and lounges.

The emphasis is on traditional hospitality. The food is traditionally English, with a 'hint' of French!

LOCATION

North Yorkshire just off A1 on to A63, 7 miles west of Selby.

Monk Fryston, Nr Leeds, North Yorkshire LS25 5DU

Telephone 01977 682369
Fax 01977 683544

GENERAL MANAGER

Jean Dodd

ROOM RATES

5 Singles £68.50 - £80
23 Doubles £95 - £112
Includes full breakfast and VAT

CHARGE/CREDIT CARDS

• MC • VI

ACCOLADES

E.T.B. ♛♛♛♛
R.A.C. ★★★ *+ Merit Awards H C & R*
A.A. ★★★ *68%*

FACILITIES

Gardens
3 meeting rooms/max 50 people
Golf nearby

RESTRICTIONS

None

ATTRACTIONS

York,
Harewood House,
Castle Howard,
Yorkshire Dales

AFFILIATIONS

Rutland Hotels Ltd

NEAREST

MAJOR CITY:
York -15 miles/30 mins
Leeds -14 miles/30 mins

MAJOR AIRPORT:
Leeds/Bradford - 18 miles/40 mins
Manchester -75 miles/1 1/2 hours

RAILWAY STATION:
Selby - 7 miles/15 mins
Leeds - 14 miles/30 mins

RESERVATIONS

Direct with hotel

ACCESS CODES

Not applicable

" The trouble with the Mount Royale is that the towels are too thick to put in your case "

Russ Abbott, TV personality

MOUNT ROYALE

Early 19th century town houses

The Mount, York,
Yorkshire YO2 2DA

Telephone 01904 628856
Fax 01904 611171

PROPRIETORS
The Oxtoby Family

MANAGER
Stuart Oxtoby

ROOM RATES

2 Singles	£65 - £90
13 Doubles/Twins	£85 - £110
3 Four-posters	£85 - £110
5 Suites	£110 - £140

Includes full breakfast and VAT

CHARGE/CREDIT CARDS

• DC • MC • VI

ACCOLADES
E.T.B. ♛♛♛♛ Highly Commended
A.A. ★★★ ❀ 72%
The Good Hotel Guide

FACILITIES
Outdoor swimming pool, gardens, trimnasium, sauna, steam room, sun-bed, jacuzzi, snooker room, 2 meeting rooms/max 18 people
Golf, riding and fishing nearby

RESTRICTIONS
No facilities for disabled guests
Small pets by arrangement

ATTRACTIONS
York, Castle Howard, Yorkshire Dales and Moors, James Herriot Country

AFFILIATIONS
Independent

NEAREST
MAJOR CITY:
In York centre

MAJOR AIRPORT:
Manchester - 45 miles/1½ hrs
Leeds/Bradford - 22 miles/40 mins

RAILWAY STATION:
York - 1 mile/5 mins

RESERVATIONS
Direct with hotel

ACCESS CODES
Not applicable

A refined taste of history at the gates of the Viking city of York

The Mount Royale is an unusual and highly personal small hotel comprising two elegant William IV houses lovingly restored with considerable flair and imagination by the owners, Richard and Christine Oxtoby.

The tranquil setting of the hotel, with its picturesque old English garden surrounding a heated swimming pool (summer only), belies the fact that it is so close to the ancient gates leading to the noble city of York.

The 23 bedrooms are luxurious and have been individually decorated – many furnished with beautiful antiques. The public rooms are extremely comfortable, not least being the impressive restaurant, overlooking the gardens, in which only the finest cuisine is presented, always under the supervision of a member of the Oxtoby family, thus ensuring discreet and courteous service.

The world-renowned historical city of York with its mediaeval streets, fine museums and, of course, the imposing York Minster is minutes away from the Mount Royale.

For followers of the horses, guests can enjoy flat racing at the famous York Racecourse from May to October. For country lovers, the Yorkshire Dales and the North Yorkshire Moors are close at hand with their profusion of majestic country mansions, hence York's description as the social capital of the North.

David Garson

LOCATION

On the west side of the city near race course. Main route into York from A64 taking green sign York West.

"As close to perfection as you can get"

Ross Compton, London

Edwardian country house

NANNY BROW HOTEL

Gracious living and woodland walks in the heart of Cumbria

This elegant country house hotel sits peacefully under Loughrigg in five acres of formal gardens and woodland with a stream running through the grounds. The hotel has its own access direct onto Loughrigg Fell and enjoys spectacular views of the River Brathay and the Langdale Pikes.

The hotel which is noted for its award-winning restaurant serves a five-course dinner which changes nightly; the candlelit restaurant is cosy and intimate and has views over the Brathay Valley. All dishes which are imaginatively concocted with style and flourish are individually created by the head chef and his team.

There are log fires on chilly evenings in the elegant lounge and hall. Fresh flowers are attended to daily.

All suites and rooms are individually designed and furnished in a traditional style. The hotel has in its own grounds, fishing and croquet together with a spa bath and solarium. Guests also have free use of the local private leisure club.

The hotel is personally managed by the resident owners Michael and Carol Fletcher who are proud of their achievements and their caring and attentive staff under the leadership of hotel Manager Rachel Gennard.

LOCATION

1½ miles outside Ambleside on the A593.

Clappersgate,
Ambleside,
Cumbria LA22 9NF

Telephone 015394 32036
Fax 015394 32450

PROPRIETOR

Michael and Carol Fletcher

GENERAL MANAGER

Rachel Gennard

ROOM RATES

7 Doubles/Twins	*£70 - £90*
2 Four-posters	*£80 - £100*
9 Suites	*£75 - £95*

Includes full breakfast, dinner and VAT

CHARGE/CREDIT CARDS

• DC • JCB • MC • VI

ACCOLADES

E.T.B. ♛♛♛♛ Highly Commended
R.A.C. ★★ + Merit Awards H C & R
A.A. ★★ ❀ 70%

FACILITIES

Croquet, gardens, jacuzzi, fishing, free use of local private leisure club
Riding and watersports nearby

RESTRICTIONS

No facilities for disabled guests
Dogs by prior arrangement

ATTRACTIONS

Brathay Valley, Wrynose Pass, Coniston, Tarn Howes

AFFILIATIONS

Independent

NEAREST

MAJOR CITY:
Manchester - 90 miles/1½ hrs

MAJOR AIRPORT:
Manchester - 100 miles/1¾ hrs

RAILWAY STATION:
Windermere - 5 miles/10 mins

RESERVATIONS

Direct with hotel

ACCESS CODES

Not applicable

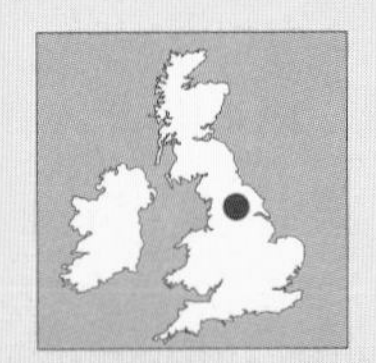

" Club Chairmen are a very demanding group and it is pretty unusual to find so many of them happy "

Rick Parry, Chief Executive – The FA Premier League

NIDD HALL

Georgian country manor house

Nidd, Harrogate,
North Yorkshire HG3 3BN

Telephone 01423 771598
Fax 01423 770931

GENERAL MANAGER

Stephen Watson

ROOM RATES

3 Singles	from £95
49 Doubles	£120 - £150
3 Four-posters	£175 - £200
4 Suites	£195 - £230

Includes complimentary use of leisure club, full breakfast, newspaper and VAT

CHARGE/CREDIT CARDS

• DC • JCB • MC • VI

ACCOLADES

R.A.C. ★★★★ + Merit Awards H C & R
A.A. ★★★★ ❀ 69%

FACILITIES

Garden, croquet, tennis, squash, gym, indoor swimming pool, sauna, sunbeds, health & beauty, table tennis, snooker, children's nursery and farm yard, boating and punting, fishing, heli-pad
7 meeting rooms/max 250 people
Golf and riding nearby

RESTRICTIONS

Pets by prior arrangement

ATTRACTIONS

Harrogate, York, Knaresborough, Yorkshire Dales and Moors, Ripon, Bronte parsonage

AFFILIATIONS

Independent

NEAREST

MAJOR CITY:
York - 20 miles/35 mins

MAJOR AIRPORT:
Manchester - 70 miles/1 hr 20 mins
Leeds/Bradford - 13 miles/20 mins

RAILWAY STATION:
Harrogate - 5 miles/10 mins

RESERVATIONS

Toll free in US/Canada: 800-323-5463

ACCESS CODES

Not applicable

A majestic manor house in the heart of beautiful Yorkshire

The hall is set in 45 acres of exquisitely landscaped grounds, and the splendour of its former days has been recaptured through painstaking restoration. Yet there is none of the pretentiousness or pomposity one might expect of such a grand, rural retreat. In their stead is a warmth, a welcome and certainty that your time spent at Nidd Hall will be relaxing, rejuvenating and utterly enjoyable.

Whether visiting Nidd Hall for business or for pleasure, the peaceful rural environment pervading is most conducive to a successful meeting or to unwinding after the frenetic life of the city. Withdraw to the comfort of a private suite or bedroom, each luxuriously appointed with fine period pieces chosen to enhance the unique Georgian ambience.

Nidd Hall welcomes all ages, for the young there is a professionally run childrens day nursery, a farm where you can stroll amongst deer, goats and pigs, and a secluded woodland playground. For the not so young the Leisure Club offers squash, snooker, gym, sauna, solarium, beauty salon and a small heated swimming pool. For those preferring outdoor pursuits there is tennis, croquet or trout fishing on the lake – something for everyone!

Nidd Hall's cuisine is a delightful melange of English and modern French classics. The wine list is comprehensive and if you should decide to visit our 14th century wine cellars to make the selection yourself you would be most welcome.

LOCATION

Take A61 north from Harrogate towards Ripon. At the roundabout after Killinghall turn right onto the B6165. Nidd Hall is situated approx 1 mile on the left hand side.

"The food was so fantastic that the Palace would have approved and the atmosphere so relaxed I kicked off my shoes"

Carol Chester, travel writer

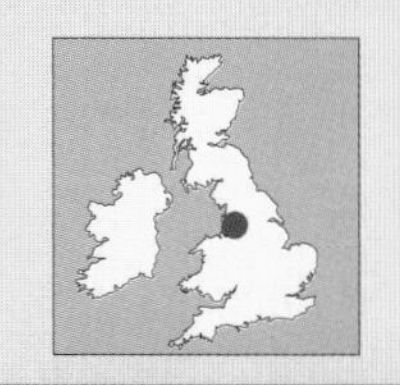

Victorian manor house

NORTHCOTE MANOR

*Northcote Road,
Langho, Nr Blackburn,
Lancashire BB6 8BE*

*Telephone 01254 240555
Fax 01254 246568*

NORTH

Where lovers of fine food and wine may want to stay forever

Northcote Manor is owned and run, with great talent and flair, by partners Craig Bancroft and Nigel Haworth. Together they have built up this small hotel in ten years to become one of the most successful in the country.

Northcote Manor is best known for its outstanding food and award winning restaurant and Nigel Haworth, is holder of the 1995 Egon Ronay Chef of the Year Award. His special love is traditional Lancashire cooking and he has recreated many of those dishes in a very different style, and delicious desserts, which include a sticky toffee pudding that has been voted one of the best in the country.

While Nigel cooks and presides over the kitchen, Craig looks after the guests' needs in the restaurant and rooms. His special love is fine wine, and he has created an excellent wine cellar and list and delights in personally matching food and wine for the guests.

When guests retire to their rooms, they will find them all decorated and furnished individually in keeping with the house. There are 14 bedrooms, all en suite, and one four-poster. Games, books, interesting ornaments, tea and coffee making facilities add to the home from home atmosphere. The very comfortable beds have created such comment that many visitors have asked where they can buy them.

Situated in the Ribble Valley, Northcote Manor lies in one of Lancashire's beauty spots, little known yet by many overseas visitors.

LOCATION

M6 Junction 31. Take A59 towards Clitheroe. Langho is close to junction with A666.

PROPRIETORS

Craig Bancroft and Nigel Haworth

ROOM RATES

Single occupancy	*£75 - £95*
13 Doubles/Twins	*£95 - £115*
1 Four-poster	*£115*

Includes full breakfast and VAT

CHARGE/CREDIT CARDS

• *DC* • *MC* • *VI*

ACCOLADES

E.T.B. ♛♛♛♛ Highly Commended
A.A. ★★★ ❀❀ 71%
Chef of the Year 1995
County Hotel of the Year 1995
White Leaf Clover Award 1995
The Good Hotel Guide

FACILITIES

Garden, heli-pad
1 meeting room/max 38 people
Golf and fishing nearby

RESTRICTIONS

No pets

ATTRACTIONS

Ribble Valley, Clitheroe, Stonyhurst College, Whalley Abbey, Pendle Witches, Ribchester

AFFILIATIONS

Fine Individual Hotels

NEAREST

MAJOR CITY:
Manchester - 28 miles/40 mins

MAJOR AIRPORT:
Manchester - 40 miles/45 mins
Blackpool - 29 miles/35 mins

RAILWAY STATION:
Preston - 11 miles/20 mins

RESERVATIONS

Direct with hotel

ACCESS CODES

Not applicable

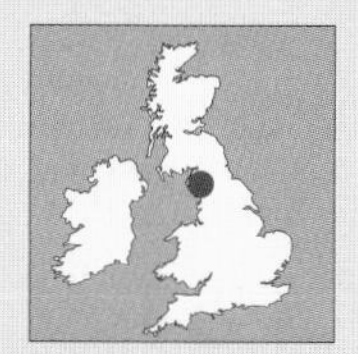

“ This lovely old house in its beautiful historic setting is surely God’s little acre ”

Derek Johansen

The Old Vicarage

Georgian country house

Church Road, Witherslack, Nr Kendal, Cumbria LA11 6RS

Telephone 015395 52381
Fax 015395 52373

NORTH

PROPRIETORS
Jill and Roger Burrington-Brown
Irene and Stanley Reeve

MANAGER
Andrew Ward

ROOM RATES

1 Single	£59 - £79
13 Doubles	£98 - £138
1 Four-poster	£158
1 Triple	£207

Includes full breakfast and VAT

CHARGE/CREDIT CARDS

• DC • JCB • MC • VI

ACCOLADES
E.T.B. ♛♛♛♛ Highly Commended
A.A. ★ ❀❀
Restaurant of the Year - Life Magazines
The Good Hotel Guide

FACILITIES
Garden, tennis
Golf, game shooting, riding and fishing nearby

RESTRICTIONS
No smoking in the dining room
No facilities for disabled guests
Pets by prior arrangement

ATTRACTIONS
Levens Hall and Gardens,
Lake Windermere,
Lake District National Park,
Beatrix Potter's home
Wordsworth's Dove Cottage

AFFILIATIONS
Fine Individual Hotels

NEAREST
MAJOR CITY:
Kendal - 6 miles/10 mins
MAJOR AIRPORT:
Manchester - 70 miles/1 hrs
RAILWAY STATION:
Oxenholm -10 miles/15 mins

RESERVATIONS
Toll free fax in US: 800-290-9319

ACCESS CODES
SABRE 17643
AMADEUS/SYSTEM 1 BWFOLD
WORLDSPAN/SAHARA OLDVW

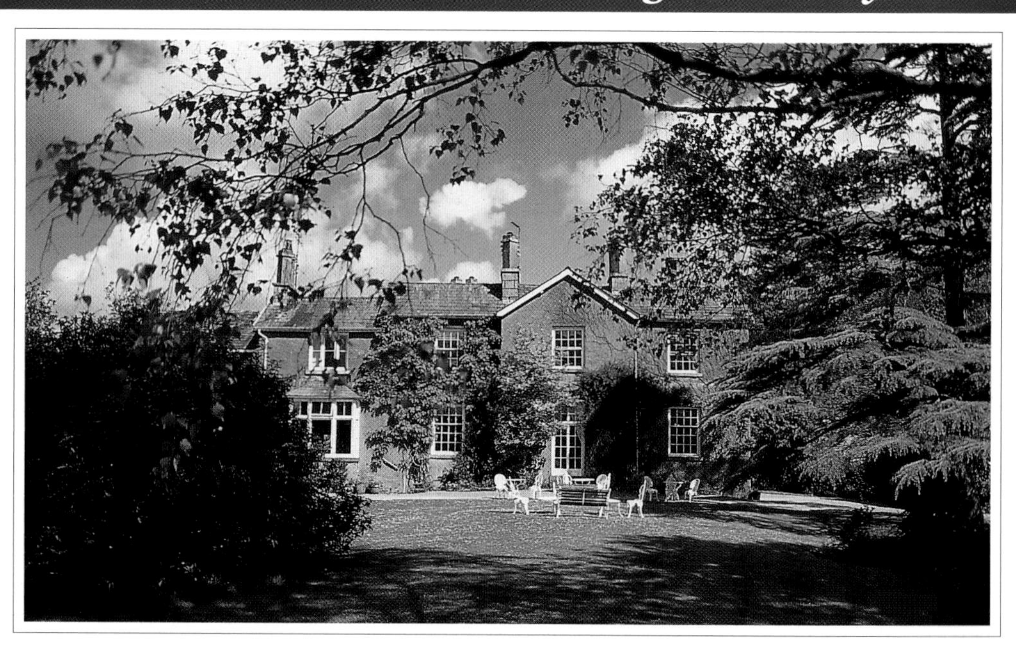

Near to the Lakes – far from the crowds

The traditional values of an English vicarage where comfort and refuge were sought and a warm welcome was always given, are well preserved at the family-run Old Vicarage, Witherslack.

The house, built in 1803, retains many original features. Interesting bric-a-brac includes a fascinating collection of antique pots and bottles unearthed in the surrounding woodland.

The delightful, mature garden is stocked with many interesting plants and part of it is left to develop naturally, to encourage the abundant wild flowers, unusual orchids, butterflies, dragonflies and birds.

In the old house, each of the comfortable en suite bedrooms has its own character, yet with all the modern facilities.

The Orchard House has particularly well equipped, spacious rooms, each with direct access onto its own beautiful woodland terrace.

The Old Vicarage has built a reputation for its award-winning food and wines. The well-planned menus are supported by fresh, mainly local ingredients.

Through this sleepy valley you have ‘back door access’ to all the magnificent splendour of the Lakes and fells of the National Park.

LOCATION

From M6 Junction 36 (6 miles/10 minutes), follow signs to Barrow, A590 to Witherslack village.

“ The skies were grey, the wind blew cold, but the warmth and comfort of the Pheasant's welcome shined on us throughout our short stay ”

J & M Wix, Hessle

17th century blacksmith's forge

PHEASANT HOTEL

A picturesque hotel by the mill stream and village pond

The hotel, established from what was at one time the village blacksmith's two cottages and the shop, has been renovated and extended to make a very comfortable country hotel with 12 bedrooms, all with private bathroom, central heating, tea and coffee making facilities, colour television, direct-dial telephone, and radio.

All the bedrooms face either south or south-west, some overlooking the village pond and mill stream, the remainder looking over the courtyard and walled garden.

There is a small oak-beamed bar with log fire, a large drawing room which, together with the dining room, open onto the stone flagged terrace overlooking the mill stream.

A large garden and paddock provide fresh eggs, vegetables and fruit to the hotel kitchen where the best of English food is produced under the supervision of Mrs 'Tricia Binks.

Ample car parking is provided.

Harome is a small village less than three miles from the attractive market town of Helmsley and the North York Moors National Park; it is unspoilt, still retaining six thatched cottages (probably more than any village in North Yorkshire). There are seven farms, an inn and both a church and chapel.

LOCATION

Leave Helmsley A170 direction Scarborough, after ¼ mile turn right for Harome. The hotel is near church in centre of village.

Harome, Helmsley, North Yorkshire YO6 5JG

Telephone 01439 771241

PROPRIETORS

The Binks family

ROOM RATES

2 Singles	*£52 - £59.50*
8 Doubles/Twins	*£52 - £59.50*
1 Thatched Cottage	*£52 - £62*

Includes full breakfast, dinner and VAT

CHARGE/CREDIT CARDS

ACCOLADES

R.A.C. ★★★ + Merit Award C

A.A. ★★ 72%

FACILITIES

Indoor swimming pool, gardens
Golf, riding, swimming and fishing nearby

RESTRICTIONS

No children under 12 years
Dogs by prior arrangement

ATTRACTIONS

Castle Howard,
Rievaulx Abbey,
Byland Abbey,
North York Moors National Park

AFFILIATIONS

Independent

NEAREST

MAJOR CITY:
York - 22 miles/40 mins

MAJOR AIRPORT:
Manchester - 90 miles/2½ hrs
Leeds/Bradford - 55 miles/1½ hrs

RAILWAY STATION:
York - 22 miles/40 mins

RESERVATIONS

Direct with hotel

ACCESS CODES

Not applicable

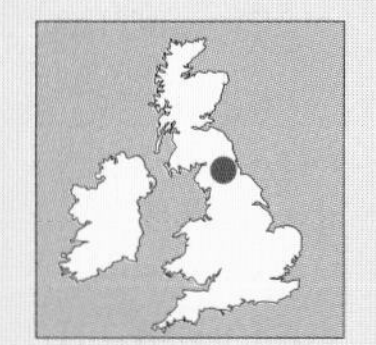

“Excellent – comparable with the best internationally”

T J Powell, Port Elizabeth, South Africa

REDWORTH HALL HOTEL

Country club

Redworth, Nr Newton Aycliffe, Co Durham DL5 6NL

Telephone 01388 772442
Fax 01388 775112

RESIDENT MANAGER
Pam Henderson

ROOM RATES

3 Singles	£103 - £112
90 Doubles/Twins	£120 - £140
3 Four-posters	£155
4 Suites	£140

Includes full breakfast and VAT

CHARGE/CREDIT CARDS

• DC • MC • VI

ACCOLADES
E.T.B. ♛♛♛♛♛ Highly Commended
R.A.C. ★★★★ + Merit Awards H C & R
A.A. ★★★★ ❀❀ 72%

FACILITIES
Garden, croquet, squash, tennis, indoor pool, snooker jacuzzi, sauna, health & beauty, gym, heli-pad
16 meeting rooms/max 300 people
Golf, riding and fishing nearby

RESTRICTIONS
No pets in public areas

ATTRACTIONS
Beamish Museum, Raby Castle, Durham, High Force Falls

AFFILIATIONS
Grand Heritage
Fine Individual Hotels

NEAREST
MAJOR CITY:
Darlington - 7 miles/15 mins

MAJOR AIRPORT:
Teesside - 10 miles/20 mins

RAILWAY STATION:
Darlington - 7 miles/15 mins

RESERVATIONS
Direct with hotel

ACCESS CODES
AMADEUS/SYSTEM 1 GH MMERHH
SAHARA GH 55418

Everything one could ever wish for under one historic roof

Redworth Hall is an imposing 17th century manor house which has been tastefully restored and converted into a 100 bedroom hotel with extensive leisure and conference facilities. It offers the discerning traveller that unique combination of the historic and the modern.

Each of the en suite bedrooms has colour TV with additional satellite stations, direct-dial telephone, hairdryer, trouser press, tea and coffee making facilities and a personal fax point. The executive bedrooms also have a minibar, bathrobe and air conditioning. In addition, there are several rooms suitable for disabled guests.

The hotel's Health Club has a heated indoor pool, spa bath, sunbeds, sauna, steam room, squash courts, all-weather tennis courts, a separate snooker room, a fully equipped gymnasium and a full time beauty therapist.

There are 16 meeting rooms, covering any number from three to 300 delegates.

Ideal for weddings, conferences and training courses, Redworth Hall also features an extensive 'Corporate/Leisure Pursuits' package which includes motorised vehicle rallies, clay pigeon shooting and paintball skirmishes. In addition, Medieval Banquets are held in the hotel's Great Hall throughout the year.

There are two restaurants for guests to choose from, each with an ambience all of its own: The Blue Room, for innovative cuisine in a sophisticated and intimate atmosphere and the light and airy Conservatory which offers a traditional as well as contemporary menu selection.

LOCATION

Exit 58 off the A1(M) onto the A68 towards Corbridge. At first roundabout take A6072 to Bishop Auckland. At second roundabout continue straight over. Hotel entrance is ½ mile on the left.

"We have stayed in many four and five star establishments but can honestly say none have compared to Rookery Hall"

Mrs P Thompson, Cheshire

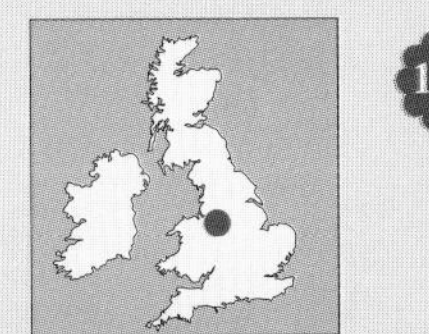

Georgian mansion

ROOKERY HALL

Ancestral splendour graced with a hint of Bavaria

Rookery Hall was built in 1816 and later modified by Baron Von Schroder, the merchant banker, who added a magnificent German Schloss-like tower. Inside, the reception rooms are beautifully proportioned. Highly polished oak panels adorn the splendid main staircase and the dining room. Guest rooms, many of which overlook the gardens, are all en suite and opulently furnished with generous sized beds.

General Manager, Jeremy Rata, encourages individuality amongst his dedicated staff: Receptionist Rachel was responsible for the ducks that roam around the 200-acre grounds and Eileen in Housekeeping thought of providing wellingtons by the front door for guests to use on walks over the delightful countryside!

Rookery has always had a reputation for hospitality, a tradition that flourishes today. There is always a personal greeting at the front door. But the core of Rookery is its restaurant. Head Chef David Alton, formerly of The Chester Grosvenor, leads a team with skill and innovation. First class local provisions ensure the highest standards of cuisine, including the home-made breads, sorbets and ices. There are fixed-price lunch and dinner menus and the opportunity of venturing into the cellar to select your own choice of wine. The cellar is also available for private candlelit dining parties.

LOCATION

From the south, turn off M6 at Junction 16 and follow the A500 towards Chester. Take the B5074 off the fourth roundabout on the Nantwich by-pass.

Worleston, Nantwich, Cheshire CW5 6DQ

Telephone 01270 610016
Fax 01270 626027

GENERAL MANAGER
Jeremy Rata

ROOM RATES

Single occupancy	£98.50
35 Doubles/Twins	£150
1 Four-poster	£250
9 Suites	£138.50 - £250

Includes full breakfast and VAT

CHARGE/CREDIT CARDS

• DC • MC • VI

ACCOLADES
E.T.B. ♛♛♛♛♛ De Luxe
R.A.C. Blue Ribbon Award ★★★
A.A. ★★★ ❀❀❀
NW Tourist Board Hotel of the Year 1994
The Good Hotel Guide

FACILITIES
Garden, croquet, tennis, clay shooting, falconry, heli-pad
5 meeting rooms/max 90 people
Fishing nearby

RESTRICTIONS
Pets by prior arrangement

ATTRACTIONS
Chester, The Potteries, Bridgemere Garden World, Little Moreton Hall

AFFILIATIONS
The Celebrated Hotels Collection
Fine Individual Hotels

NEAREST
MAJOR CITY:
Chester - 20 miles/30 mins

MAJOR AIRPORT:
Manchester - 35 miles/40 mins

RAILWAY STATION:
Crewe - 6 miles/15 mins

RESERVATIONS
Toll free in US: 800-322-2403

ACCESS CODES
Not applicable

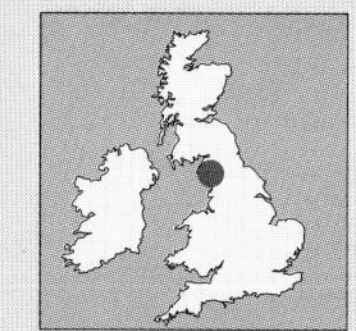

"In theory, you should be just like other hotels with high standards, but you're not. You must be doing something different, I just like it here"

J J Hammond, Winchester

ROTHAY MANOR

Regency manor house

Rothay Bridge, Ambleside, Cumbria LA22 0EH

Telephone 015394 33605
Fax 015394 33607

PROPRIETORS

Nigel and Stephen Nixon

ROOM RATES

2 Singles £72 - £78
13 Doubles/Twins £112 - £125
3 Suites £158
Includes full breakfast and VAT

CHARGE/CREDIT CARDS

• DC • MC • VI

ACCOLADES

E.T.B. ♛♛♛♛ Highly Commended
R.A.C. ★★★ + Merit Awards H C & R
A.A. ★★★ ❀ 74%
The Good Hotel Guide

FACILITIES

Croquet and gardens
1 meeting room/max 25 people
Golf, fishing and free use of leisure club nearby

RESTRICTIONS

No pets

ATTRACTIONS

Wordsworth's Homes – Rydal Mount & Dove Cottage, Beatrix Potter's House & Exhibition, The Lake District

AFFILIATIONS

Selected British Hotels
Fine Individual Hotels

NEAREST

MAJOR CITY:
Carlisle - 50 miles/1 hr

MAJOR AIRPORT:
Manchester - 95 miles/1 ½ hrs

RAILWAY STATION:
Windermere - 4 miles/10 mins

RESERVATIONS

Toll free in US: 800-323-5463

ACCESS CODES

Not applicable

NORTH

There are so many ways to relax – you'll find most of them here

Rothay Manor, an elegant Regency house built in 1825 as a private residence, stands in its own grounds a quarter mile from the head of Lake Windermere. The drawing rooms and candlelit dining room still retain the relaxed atmosphere of a private house, and the Nixon family have run the hotel for over 25 years.

Care, consideration and comfort are evident throughout. The dining room offers a varied menu and the food, served with flair and imagination, is complemented by a comprehensive wine list. Two bedrooms have been specially adapted for disabled persons. The hotel also offers family suites.

Residents have free use of a nearby leisure centre with a swimming pool, sauna, steam room and jacuzzi. Free fishing permits are also available.

During the winter months, there is a full programme of events, which include special French regional dinners, courses such as silver and antiques, painting, gardening and music appreciation. In Spring, walking holidays are offered.

William Wordsworth described the Lake District as "the loveliest spot that man has ever known", and it is still difficult to disagree with those sentiments. The area, Britain's first National Park, contains England's highest mountains and some of its most picturesque lakes, villages and valleys.

LOCATION

½ mile from Ambleside on the road to Coniston.

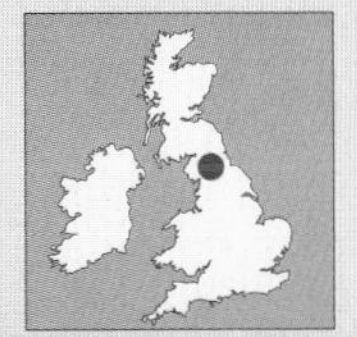

" The Royal Oak Inn is one of the very few pubs which manage to be held in equally high regard by its regulars and its many visitors "

Cumberland & Westmorland Herald

THE ROYAL OAK INN

Pride in the best traditional innkeeping on the trans-Pennine route 66

The Royal Oak Inn is a mediaeval coaching inn which nestles comfortably in Bongate, the oldest part of Appleby-in-Westmorland. Having been sensitively renovated, the Inn now offers excellent accommodation in pretty bedrooms with all the convenience required by today's travellers – and an excellent overnight stop on the way to or from Scotland.

Good food from fresh ingredients is available in the restaurant, the non-smoking dining room or either of the bars. One can also sample one of the extensive range of traditional ales, choose from many interesting wines or try a dram from the comprehensive range of malt whiskies.

Appleby is situated between the Lake District and the Pennines and is blessed by a good climate which is considerably drier than that of its neighbours. The Inn's location makes it an excellent touring centre with the Lake District, the Yorkshire Dales and the Scottish Borders being only a short drive away. Appleby is one of the stations on the famous Settle to Carlisle railway which passes through the high moors before descending into the gentler green Eden Valley and on to Carlisle.

The Royal Oak Inn is proud to continue the British tradition of coaching inns where you will always be warmly welcomed and cared for in historical surroundings.

LOCATION

Appleby is on the trans-Pennine route A66, 13 miles south east of Penrith (M6 Junction 40), 38 miles north west of Scotch Corner (A1). The Royal Oak Inn is on the southeast approach to the town.

Bongate, Appleby-in-Westmorland, Cumbria CA16 6UN

Telephone 017683 51463
Fax 017683 52300

PROPRIETORS
Colin and Hilary Cheyne

ROOM RATES
Single occupancy £39 - £45
7 Doubles £57 - £75
Includes full breakfast and VAT

CHARGE/CREDIT CARDS

• DC • JCB • MC • VI

ACCOLADES
E.T.B. ♛♛♛ Highly Commended
A.A. ★★ 68%

FACILITIES
Residents Lounge
1 meeting room/max 20 people
Golf, riding and fishing nearby

RESTRICTIONS
No pets in public rooms
Well-behaved children welcome
No facilities for disabled guests

ATTRACTIONS
Appleby Castle,
Beatrix Potter & Wordsworth heritage,
The Lake District,
Hadrian's Wall

AFFILIATIONS
Logis of Great Britain

NEAREST
MAJOR CITY:
Carlisle - 35 miles/1 hr

MAJOR AIRPORT:
Manchester - 105 miles/1¾ hrs
Newcastle - 74 miles/1¾ hrs

RAILWAY STATION:
Appleby - ½ mile/5 mins

RESERVATIONS
Direct with hotel

ACCESS CODES
Not applicable

“ Everything at Sharrow is done with love ”

N C Pooke, South Africa

SHARROW BAY COUNTRY HOUSE HOTEL

Country house

Lake Ullswater, Howtown, Cumbria CA10 2LZ

Telephone 017684 86301
Fax 017684 86349

PROPRIETORS
Francis Coulson MBE and Brian Sack MBE

DIRECTORS
Nigel Lawrence and Nigel Lightburn

RATES PER PERSON

4 Singles	*£95 - £190*
20 Doubles/Twins	*£85 - £160*
4 Suites	*£110 - £160*

Includes full breakfast, dinner and VAT

CHARGE/CREDIT CARDS
Cash or cheque only

ACCOLADES
R.A.C. Blue Ribbon Award ★★★
9th consecutive year
A.A. ★★★ ❀❀❀
Hosts of the Year 1994
The Good Hotel Guide
Life Magazines Lake District Hotel of the Year 1995

FACILITIES
Gardens, fishing
1 meeting room/max 12 people
Fell walking, pony trekking, yachting and wind surfing nearby

RESTRICTIONS
No children under 13
No facilities for disabled guests
No pets
Closed Dec-Jan

ATTRACTIONS
Beatrix Potter's home, William Wordsworth's Dove Cottage, Castlerigg Stone Circle, Levens Hall and Gardens

AFFILIATIONS
Relais et Châteaux

NEAREST
MAJOR CITY:
Manchester -100 miles/2 hrs

MAJOR AIRPORT:
Manchester - 120 miles/2 hrs

RAILWAY STATION:
Penrith - 7 miles/20 mins

RESERVATIONS
Direct with hotel

ACCESS CODES
Not applicable

NORTH

The world's first country house hotel – and still setting standards

Sharrow Bay was created by Francis Coulson in 1949 and in 1952 he was joined by Brian Sack and this gave birth to a wonderful partnership which has lasted forty-five years.

In 1956 they decided to change the title of Sharrow to Sharrow Bay Country House Hotel, and unwittingly gave birth to a new breed of hotels which are now prevalent all over Great Britain, and even in other countries.

The special nature of Sharrow ensures that all clients feel a great sense of well-being, and of being nurtured, nourished, and cosseted. A guest once said that it is like an oasis and that they felt cocooned from the world and its troubles! To create this rather special atmosphere there has to be a genuine concern for people.

Francis and Brian are blessed with fifty wonderful staff, some of whom have been with them for over twenty years, and they have been trained to develop this warmth of feeling for all their clients. They all really care for people and hope guests leave Sharrow Bay refreshed, and better able to cope with the pressures of the outside world.

LOCATION

M6 Junction 40. On eastern shore of Ullswater, 2 miles south of Pooley Bridge. Turn by small church in Pooley Bridge and take Howtown Lane.

"Whether for business or pleasure a stay at the Studley is like visiting old friends"

L Ackerman, London

Contemporary hotel — STUDLEY HOTEL

Stylish comfort and good food on the doorstep of Yorkshire's greatest sights

This privately owned 36-bedroomed hotel and French restaurant has been operated and run by 'the girls' Pat and Mary since 1975. Their personalities, personal service and attention to detail has made The Studley one of the most welcoming in the Harrogate area.

For the weary traveller, the hotel offers tastefully decorated and comfortable lounges and a choice of two bars. The attractive and individually designed en suite bedrooms all have the necessary and thoughtful extras required to ensure a memorable stay.

'Le Breton' restaurant has a genuine charcoal grill which is a unique feature in this busy dining room where the service is efficient and friendly. Head Chef, Michel, produces a table d'hôte and à la carte menu which offer a tempting variety of French and seasonal dishes. The extensive and value-for-money wine list complements the food. The 'Studley Special' for breakfast will leave any guest prepared for the day ahead.

The Studley is only a few minutes walk from the beautiful valley gardens, town centre and conference facilities. Yorkshire offers many places of interest such as abbeys, stately homes, golf courses and race meetings. Whether for business or pleasure, the courteous and enthusiastic staff will make your stay at the Studley unforgettable.

LOCATION

30 minutes from York, Leeds, the M1 and M62, and 20 minutes from the A1 (main north/south route).

Swan Road, Harrogate, North Yorkshire HG1 2SE

Telephone 01423 560425
Fax 01423 530967

OWNER
Guy Dilasser

MANAGER
Pat Wharldall

ROOM RATES

15 Singles	*£68 - £85*
19 Doubles/Twins	*£85 - £110*
2 Suites	*£100 - £120*

Includes full breakfast and VAT

CHARGE/CREDIT CARDS

• DC • MC • VI

ACCOLADES
E.T.B. ♛♛♛♛ *Commended*
A.A. ★★★ ❀ *64%*

FACILITIES
Le Breton Restaurant
1 meeting room/max 15 people
Golf and swimming nearby

RESTRICTIONS
No facilities for disabled guests

ATTRACTIONS
Fountains Abbey,
Harewood House,
Ripley Castle, Horse racing

AFFILIATIONS
Independent

NEAREST
MAJOR CITY:
Leeds - 16 miles/30 mins

MAJOR AIRPORT:
Manchester - 78 miles/1½ hrs
Leeds - 15 miles/30 mins

RAILWAY STATION:
Harrogate - 3 miles/5 mins

RESERVATIONS
Direct with hotel

ACCESS CODES
Not applicable

" Superb. Only regret it has taken so long to discover you "

Annette & Gerald Robson, Scarborough

SWINSIDE LODGE HOTEL

Victorian house

**Grange Road, Newlands,
Keswick, Cumbria CA12 5UE**

**Telephone 017687 72948
Fax 017687 72948**

PROPRIETOR
Graham Taylor

ROOM RATES
Single occupancy £60 - £76
7 Doubles/Twins £105 - £135
Includes full breakfast, dinner and VAT

CHARGE/CREDIT CARDS
Cash or cheque only

ACCOLADES
E.T.B. ♛♛♛ De Luxe
A.A. ★ ✿✿
The Good Hotel Guide - César Award 1996

FACILITIES
Garden
Golf, riding and fishing nearby

RESTRICTIONS
No facilities for disabled guests
Guests provide their own wine
No smoking
No pets

ATTRACTIONS
Lake District, Brough Castle, Beatrix Potter's House, Dove Cottage, Rydal Mount, Arthur's Round Table, Castlerigg Stone Circle

AFFILIATIONS
Independent

NEAREST
MAJOR CITY:
Carlisle - 38 miles/45 mins

MAJOR AIRPORT:
Newcastle - 100 miles/2 hrs
Carlisle - 38 miles/45 mins

RAILWAY STATION:
Penrith - 17 miles/20 mins

RESERVATIONS
Direct with hotel

ACCESS CODES
Not applicable

NORTH

At the foot of Cat Bells a stroll away from the "Queen of the Lakes"

Swinside Lodge is a delightful Victorian house within one of the most beautiful and tranquil corners of the English Lakes. It stands in its own grounds at the foot of 'Cat Bells', one of many favourite mountain walks and is a mere five minutes stroll from the shores of Derwentwater – 'Queen of the Lakes'. A regular launch service operates on the lake, providing a leisurely mode of travel to the nearby bustling market town of Keswick and many other local beauty spots.

Wild life abounds and the area is a paradise for birdwatchers and for walkers of all ages and abilities. Others will find it an ideal base from which to explore and enjoy the natural beauty of the countryside by car.

Swinside Lodge is fast gaining a reputation for its very comfortable and well-appointed accommodation and, in particular, for its award-winning cuisine served in the intimate ambience of the candlelit dining room by friendly and attentive staff.

For your added comfort the hotel has a no smoking policy and as it is unlicensed you are invited to bring your own favourite wines to be served without corkage charge.

You are invited to come and share in the relaxing and hospitable atmosphere of Swinside Lodge where caring staff will help to make your stay a happy and memorable experience. A warm welcome awaits you.

LOCATION

M6 Junction 40. Take A66 bypassing Keswick. Over main roundabout take 2nd left. Go through Portinscale, towards Grange. Hotel is 2 miles further on the right.

“ You treated us royally and we can’t wait to return ”

Craig Hunt, Cheshire

Country house

TEMPLE SOWERBY HOUSE

Sheer escapism beneath the highest peak in the Pennines

Temple Sowerby House overlooks Cross Fell, the highest peak in the Pennines, noted for its spectacular ridge walk. This old Cumbrian farmhouse, formerly the principal residence of the village, is set in two acres of gardens. Owners Cécile and Geoffrey Temple offer a warm, hospitable and friendly family service upon which the hotel prides itself.

There are two dining rooms – the cosy panelled room and the Rose Room which overlooks the garden. A five-course dinner is served each evening, using fresh local produce. The menu of delicious home-cooked dishes might include a starter of asparagus cheese tart with lemon cream, followed by venison steak in kumquat and orange liqueur, rounded off with a pudding of apricot and mango profiteroles in caramel sauce.

There are 12 comfortable, individually and tastefully furnished bedrooms, four of which are in the Coach House, which is situated a few steps away from the farmhouse and overlooks the cobbled yard and the fine garden.

Whilst you are here you can explore the Eden Valley where the average rainfall is half that of Windermere or Keswick. As the River Eden meanders gently northwards, you will find a welcoming land of red sandstone bridges, churches and castles and unspoilt foothill settlements nestling against the great eastern barrier of the Pennines.

LOCATION

Temple Sowerby is on the A66, 7 miles from Junction 40 on the M6 and 42 miles from Scotch Corner on the A1.

Temple Sowerby,
Nr Penrith,
Cumbria CA10 1RZ

Telephone 017683 61578
Fax 017683 61958

PROPRIETORS

Cécile and Geoffrey Temple

RATES PER PERSON

Single occupancy	*£50*
11 Doubles/Twins	*£35*
1 Four-poster	*£35*

Includes full breakfast and VAT

CHARGE/CREDIT CARDS

• MC • VI

ACCOLADES

R.A.C. ★★★ + Merit Awards H C & R
The Good Hotel Guide

FACILITIES

Garden, croquet
3 meeting rooms/max 25 people
Fishing nearby

RESTRICTIONS

None

ATTRACTIONS

Acorn National Trust Gardens,
Windermere,
Brougham Castle,
Arthur's Round Table,
Penrith Castle,
Lanercost Priory

AFFILIATIONS

Independent

NEAREST

MAJOR CITY:
Carlisle - 25 miles/30 mins

MAJOR AIRPORT:
Manchester - 120 miles/1 hr 50 mins
Carlisle - 25 miles/30 mins

RAILWAY STATION:
Penrith - 7 miles/10 mins

RESERVATIONS

Direct with hotel

ACCESS CODES

Not applicable

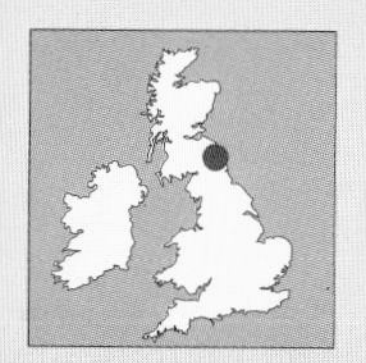

" A superb, baronial country house "

D Mackenzie, RAC Inspector

TILLMOUTH PARK HOTEL

Victorian mansion

Cornhill-on-Tweed, Northumberland TD12 4UU

Telephone 01890 882255
Fax 01890 882540

GENERAL MANAGER
Charles Carroll

ROOM RATES

1 Single	*£70 - £90*
7 Doubles/Twins	*£105*
3 Deluxe Doubles/Twins	*£115*
3 Staterooms	*£125*

Includes full breakfast and VAT

CHARGE/CREDIT CARDS

• DC • MC • VI

ACCOLADES
E.T.B. ♛♛♛♛ Highly Commended
R.A.C. ★★★ + Merit Awards H & C
A.A. ★★★ ❀ 69%

FACILITIES
Garden, croquet, heli-pad
2 meeting rooms/max 50 people
Golf, riding and fishing nearby

RESTRICTIONS
Limited facilities for disabled guests

ATTRACTIONS
Bamburgh Castle,
Holy Island and Lindisfarne Priory,
Flodden Field Abbey,
Farne Islands, Paxton House,
Northumberland National Park

AFFILIATIONS
Independent

NEAREST
MAJOR CITY:
Edinburgh - 54 miles/1 hr 20 mins

MAJOR AIRPORT:
Edinburgh - 58 miles/1 hr 20 mins
Newcastle - 60 miles/1 hr 20 mins

RAILWAY STATION:
Berwick-upon-Tweed - 12 miles/20 mins

RESERVATIONS
Toll free in US: 800-437-2687

ACCESS CODES
Not applicable

Galleried elegance of a bygone era

Tillmouth Park was built by renowned architect Charles Barry in 1882, using stones from nearby Twizel Castle. Sit in its galleried lounge and you'll feel yourself relax into a more leisured bygone age. Admire the spring daffodils and rhododendrons or fine autumnal colours in the gardens and the hustle of modern life slips away. Tillmouth Park continues to offer the same warm welcome today as it did when it was a private house.

All 14 bedrooms are generous in size and have recently been refurbished in a distinctive old fashioned style with period furniture. Most rooms have lovely views of the surrounding countryside.

The kitchen prides itself on traditional country fare. The chef takes fresh local produce, prepares it to a high standard, and presents it imaginatively. There is a well chosen wine list, and a vast selection of malt whiskies.

Tillmouth Park is an ideal centre for country pursuits, field sports, fishing, hillwalking, riding, birdwatching and golf. There are many stately homes such as Floors, Manderston and Paxton to visit. Ruined abbeys, Flodden Field, Lindisfarne and Holy Island are nearby – the coast is only 15 minutes away. You can shop for high quality knitwear and craftwork. Both Edinburgh and Newcastle are near enough for a day's outing.

LOCATION

From Cornhill-on-Tweed, take the A698 to Berwick-upon-Tweed. Hotel is 3 miles along the road on the right side.

“We were staying in a real English home in another more peaceful and serene century”

Janet & George Railey, New York

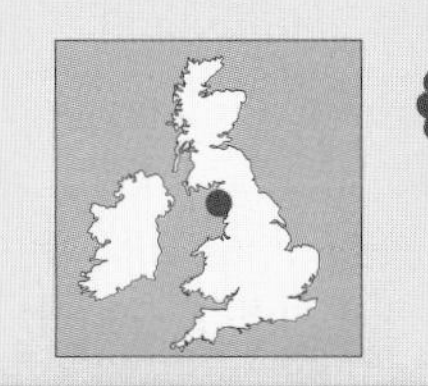

Country house

UNDERSCAR MANOR

The jewel of the Lakes

“Today my companion and I took tea with the Oxleys at their exquisite house, Underscar. The house has been constructed on one of the most breathtaking locations that I have ever seen; set against the slopes of Skiddaw, and overlooking the tranquil Derwentwater. A lush garden surrounds the house filled with flowers and shrubs; with places to sit and admire the view. As I sipped my tea in the drawing room, a gem with its ornate plaster-work ceiling, I gazed down towards the lake and watched the sun setting on the water; it was a moment of rare, joyous beauty and I wish I could have stayed at Underscar forever.”

‘The Diary of a Victorian Country Gentlewoman’ – 11th May 1860

Today, 136 years on, Underscar Manor is a family owned and operated country house in the experienced and caring hands of Pauline and Derek Harrison. The breathtaking location and panoramic views witnessed by that ‘Victorian Gentlewoman’ are still preserved in, what is now the Lake District National Park, designated an Area of Outstanding Natural Beauty.

The house stands in a tranquil, elevated situation surrounded by forty acres of gardens and woodland walks, by a cascading stream. Come home to award-winning fine cuisine in the beautiful Victorian restaurant.

LOCATION

M6 Junction 40 towards Workington on A66 for 17 miles. At large roundabout, take 3rd exit and turn immediately right up lane signposted ‘Underscar’. Entrance to drive ¾ mile on right.

Applethwaite, Nr Keswick, Lake District National Park, Cumbria CA12 4PH

Telephone 017687 75000
Fax 017687 74904

PROPRIETORS

Pauline and Derek Harrison
Gordon Evans

ROOM RATES

Single occupancy £90 - £125
11 Doubles/Twins £150 - £250
Includes full breakfast, dinner and VAT

CHARGE/CREDIT CARDS

• *MC* • *VI*

ACCOLADES

The Good Hotel Guide

FACILITIES

Gardens, direct access from house to major walking trails
1 meeting room/max 16 people
Golf, riding and fishing nearby

RESTRICTIONS

No children under 12 years
No pets

ATTRACTIONS

Lake District National Park,
Castlerigg Stone Circle,
Beatrix Potter's House,
Wordsworth's Dove Cottage,
Brougham Castle, Penrith Castle

AFFILIATIONS

Independent

NEAREST

MAJOR CITY:
Manchester - 120 miles/2 hrs

MAJOR AIRPORT:
Manchester - 120 miles/2 hrs

RAILWAY STATION:
Penrith - 17 miles/20 mins

RESERVATIONS

Direct with hotel

ACCESS CODES

Not applicable

" The rooms, food and facilities are all superb, but the staff really make a difference as they are invariably friendly, helpful and show initiative

Mark Hodson, Retail Development Executive, British Airways

VICTORIA & ALBERT HOTEL

Cotton warehouse

Water Street, Manchester M60 9EA

Telephone 0161 832 1188
Fax 0161 834 2484

GENERAL MANAGER
Jim Diamond

ROOM RATES
14 Singles £80 - £130
97 Doubles/Twins £90 - £130
17 Sovereign Rooms £120 - £160
4 Suites from £300
Includes VAT

CHARGE/CREDIT CARDS

• DC • MC • VI

ACCOLADES
E.T.B. ♛♛♛♛♛ Highly Commended
R.A.C. ★★★★ + Merit Awards H C & R
A.A. ★★★★ ❀❀ 74%
The Good Hotel Guide

FACILITIES
Garden, gym, sauna
10 meeting rooms/max 400 people
Complimentary use of leisure club swimming pool nearby

RESTRICTIONS
No pets (except guide dogs)

ATTRACTIONS
Granada Studios,
Museum of Science and Industry,
Manchester Town Hall,
Central Library

AFFILIATIONS
Summit International Hotels
Utell International

NEAREST
MAJOR CITY:
Manchester

MAJOR AIRPORT:
Manchester - 10 miles/15 mins

RAILWAY STATION:
Piccadilly - 1 mile/3 mins

RESERVATIONS
Direct with hotel

ACCESS CODES
AMADEUS/SYSTEM 1 UI MANVIC
AXESS UI 11484
SABRE UI 35607
APOLLO UI 40225
WORLDSPAN UI 19870
SAHARA UI MAN19052IG

In the centre of Manchester in a ragout of realism and fantasy

Blast off into space; or stroll down the streets of New York; listen, live, to the Hallé Orchestra; or feast on the pleasures of the Orient.

This is no fantasy – it's central Manchester where you will discover the hi-tech world of entertainment in Granada Studios, the performing arts in the G-Mex Centre and the exotic markets of Chinatown.

In the heart of this vibrant, cosmopolitan city is the V & A Hotel reflecting all these attributes. It's theatrical. It's graceful. And, behind the rich fabric of its design, is a state-of-the-art technology which, as they say, 'answers your needs more quickly than humanly possible'. The performance of the staff is professional and offered with such polish it has to have been well-rehearsed.

This is a showbiz hotel and you are not allowed to forget it! The Sherlock Holmes Restaurant, Cafe Maigret, Watson's Bar to conjure up a few famous sleuths of fiction. Your bedroom is named after a TV programme you have almost certainly heard of.

To maintain these realms of fanatasy, Chef John Benson-Smith obliges with panache! The scene is set: romantic lighting, soft music, the clink of crystal, silver-set tables . . . then the food makes its entrance, an entertainment all in itself.

But beware the Icarus factor: coming down to earth can be painful!

LOCATION

Leave the M6 at Junction 19 and follow signs for Manchester M56. Carry on to Manchester, picking up signs for 'Granada Studios Tour' which is adjacent.

“To visit the North East and not stay here would be foolish indeed”

R & R Sunley, Beaconsfield

Country house

WAREN HOUSE HOTEL

A gem of a country house amongst the treasures of the North East

One of England's most northerly Best Loved Hotels might well be summed up, “we kept the best till last”. Waren House is the home of Anita and Peter Laverack who, during the last eight years, have renovated and restored this lovely old house into an elegant “Country Inn”. Set in six acres of mature grounds and walled garden, the hotel looks out over Budle Bay towards the Holy Island of Lindisfarne, only reached by causeway at low water.

This is the least populated part of the county and even at the height of summer you can walk on miles of deserted golden beaches; visit ancient castles including Bamburgh, Alnwick, Lindisfarne and the ruins at Dunstanburgh; clamber over battlements including Hadrian's Wall; or have a round of golf on one of the numerous nearby courses before returning to Waren House, where a warm welcome, elegant accommodation, excellent food and a choice of over 250 wines awaits. For an extended stay there are two suites and one, the Edwardian, looks out over the walled garden and Cheviot Hills.

Waren House is within five miles of the three attractions you must visit in Northumberland (Farne Islands, Bamburgh Castle and Holy Island). A professionally run hotel offering true peace and quiet to the discerning traveller.

LOCATION

2 miles east of A1 on coast just south of Holy Island. There are advance signs from both north and south. Take B1342 to Waren Mill. The hotel (floodlit at night) is 2 miles from Bamburgh.

Waren Mill, Belford, Northumberland NE70 7EE

Telephone 01668 214581
Fax 01668 214484

PROPRIETORS

Anita and Peter Laverack

ROOM RATES

5 Doubles/Twins	*£104 - £124*
1 Four-poster	*£134 - £154*
2 Suites	*£134 - £154*

Includes full breakfast and VAT

CHARGE/CREDIT CARDS

• DC • JCB • MC • VI

ACCOLADES

E.T.B. Highly Commended
R.A.C. ★★★ + Merit Awards H & C
A.A. ★★ 75%
Favourite 'Best of Northumberland' Hotel 1993

FACILITIES

Gardens
Golf and riding nearby

RESTRICTIONS

No children under 14 years
Pets by arrangement

ATTRACTIONS

Bamburgh Castle, Holy Island, Alnwick Castle, Farne Islands

AFFILIATIONS

Independent

NEAREST

MAJOR CITY:
Edinburgh - 70 miles/1 ½ hrs
Newcastle-upon-Tyne - 45 miles/1 hr

MAJOR AIRPORT:
Newcastle - 45 miles/45 mins

RAILWAY STATION:
Berwick-upon-Tweed - 15 miles/20 mins

RESERVATIONS

Direct with hotel

ACCESS CODES

Not applicable

“ From the lovely room and friendly staff, to the beautiful setting and the excellent food, everything has been perfect ”

Alan & Hayley Henshall, Toddington

WATEREDGE HOTEL

17th century waterside hotel

NORTH

Waterhead Bay, Ambleside, Cumbria LA22 0EP

Telephone 015394 32332
Fax 015394 31878

PROPRIETORS

Derek and Pamela Cowap

ROOM RATES

3 Singles £59 - £73
10 Doubles/Twins £102 - £150
9 Superior £138 - £166
Includes full breakfast, dinner and VAT

CHARGE/CREDIT CARDS

• MC • VI

ACCOLADES

E.T.B. ♛♛♛♛ Highly Commended
R.A.C. ★★★ + Merit Awards H & C
A.A.★★ ❀ 77%
A.A. Courtesy and Care Award 1995
The Good Hotel Guide

FACILITIES

Garden to lake edge
Fishing, riding and complimentary use of leisure club nearby

RESTRICTIONS

No children under 7 years
No facilities for disabled guests
Dogs by prior arrangement

ATTRACTIONS

Lake District National Park, Beatrix Potter's home, Windermere steamer trips, Hardknott Roman Fort, Stott Park Bobbin Mill

AFFILIATIONS

Independent

NEAREST

MAJOR CITY:
Manchester - 100 miles/1¾ hrs

MAJOR AIRPORT:
Manchester - 100 miles/1¾ hrs

RAILWAY STATION:
Windermere - 4 miles/10 mins

RESERVATIONS

Direct with hotel

ACCESS CODES

Not applicable

At the water's edge – eat well, relax and melt into Ambleside's beauty

Wateredge is a delightfully situated, family-run hotel nestling on the shores of Windermere. The building was originally two 17th-century fishermen's cottages, which have been warmly converted and extended.

The well maintained gardens with spectacular views of the lake and hills run down to the water's edge; alongside is a pleasant promenade leading to the 'Steamer Pier', the embarkation for cruising around the lake. Adjacent is Borrans Park and within strolling distance the tranquillity of the nearby fells.

Guests can relax in the comfortable lounges overlooking the lake or on the lawn, where light lunches, afternoon teas or drinks are served or, perhaps, go for a row from the private jetty.

Dining at Wateredge is an occasion in itself. The dining area, set within the original cottages creates, its own particular ambience under oak-beamed ceilings. The six course dinners are prepared with flair and imagination by six chefs, using only fresh produce of the highest quality. Bread, pastries and jams are all home-made. A carefully chosen wine list complements the cuisine.

Pretty en suite bedrooms offer the best of lakeland comfort and hospitality, many with lake views. All these pleasures await you at Wateredge.

LOCATION

Travelling northwards on the A591, fork left just after the Ambleside sign, skirt the lake for a few hundred yards and look for Wateredge on your left.

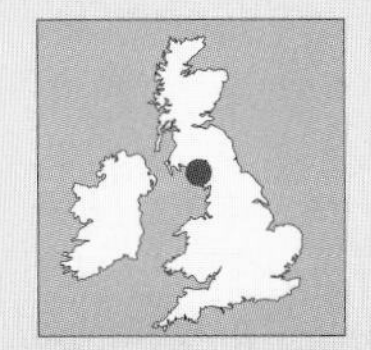

" I don't know how you people manage it, but that which has always seemed perfect just keeps on getting better "

Edward B Catton, Michigan

18th century country house

WHITE MOSS HOUSE

Rydal Water, Grasmere, Cumbria LA22 9SE

Telephone 015394 35295
Fax 015394 35516

Imagine, gourmet food and wine with a view that inspired the poets

White Moss House was bought by William Wordsworth for his son, and the poet often rested and wrote poetry there. Built in 1730, it overlooks Rydal Water in the heart of the Lake District. Many famous walks and drives, by lakes and over hills, begin from the front door.

Proprietors Sue and Peter Dixon have created an intimate family atmosphere. Personal care for the guests, and attention to detail are hallmarks of this charming hotel. There are five rooms in the main house and two situated in Brockstone Cottage Suite, whose isolated beauty makes it a truly romantic spot. All are individually furnished with many thoughtful touches, including a large selection of books and antiques.

The wine list of over 300 bins offers distinguished bottles from around the world, and is exceptional value for money.

Some recent comments:

Peter Dixon is a maestro of British cooking – *The Sunday Times*

Peter Dixon is an intuitive cook, with a deep understanding of ingredients and flavours. He uses wonderful local produce for his five course dinners – *Bon Appetit*

Nature and man combine harmoniously at White Moss House – *Binns Best of Britain*

Lovers of good food and wine, who appreciate the beautiful scenery immortalised by the romantic poets, will love White Moss House.

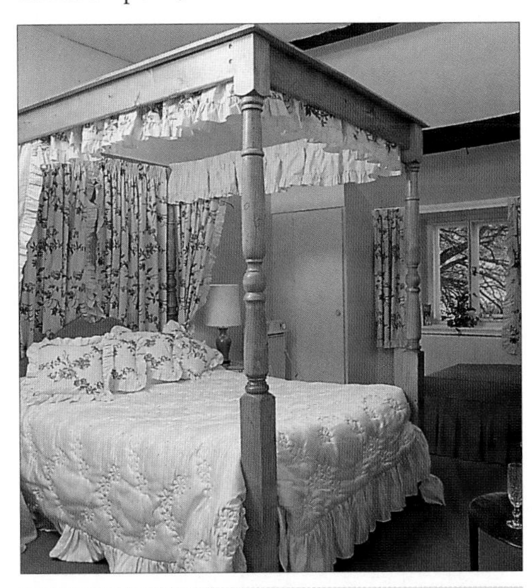

LOCATION

On A591 at north end of Rydal Water, one mile south of Grasmere.

PROPRIETORS

Sue and Peter Dixon

ROOM RATES

Single occupancy £64 - £87
5 Doubles £128 - £174
1 Four-poster £128 - £174
Includes full breakfast, dinner and VAT

CHARGE/CREDIT CARDS

MC • VI

ACCOLADES

E.T.B. ♛♛♛ Highly Commended
A.A. ★ ❀❀
The Good Hotel Guide

FACILITIES

Garden, fishing
Fell walking, riding and use of leisure club nearby

RESTRICTIONS

No children under 8 years
No facilities for disabled guests
No pets

ATTRACTIONS

Wordsworth's home - Dove Cottage; Beatrix Potter's home - Hilltop, Sawrey; Ruskin's home - Brantwood, Coniston; Hardknott Roman Fort, Ravenglass Roman Bath House

AFFILIATIONS

Independent Innkeepers Association

NEAREST

MAJOR CITY:
Carlisle - 40 miles/1 hr

MAJOR AIRPORT:
Manchester - 80 miles/2 hrs

RAILWAY STATION:
Windermere - 8 miles/15 mins

RESERVATIONS

Direct with hotel

ACCESS CODES

Not applicable

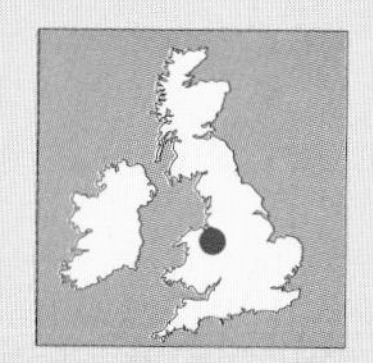

"The owners and staff strike an enviable balance between elegance and homely hospitality"

E G Parish, Sevenoaks, Kent

WILLINGTON HALL

Elizabethan-style manor house

Willington, Tarporley, Cheshire CW6 0NB

Telephone 01829 752321
Fax 01829 752596

NORTH

OWNERS
Ross Pigot and Richard Tomkinson

ROOM RATES

2 Singles	£38 - £48
8 Doubles/Twins	£68

Includes VAT

CHARGE/CREDIT CARDS

• DC • MC • VI

ACCOLADES
E.T.B. ♛♛♛♛ Commended
R.A.C. ★★★
A.A. ★★★ 62%

FACILITIES
Garden, tennis, riding
3 meeting rooms/max 16 people
Golf nearby

RESTRICTIONS
No facilities for disabled guests

ATTRACTIONS
Chester, Beeston Castle, Tatton Park, Pelamere Forest

AFFILIATIONS
Independent

NEAREST
MAJOR CITY:
Chester - 7 miles/15 mins

MAJOR AIRPORT:
Manchester - 18 miles/40 mins

RAILWAY STATION:
Chester - 7 miles/15 mins

RESERVATIONS
Direct with hotel

ACCESS CODES
Not applicable

Traditional style and service reminiscent of a bygone era

Willington Hall has the unmistakeable aura of a well-established home that echoes the whims and fancies of generations. The paintings tell the story of the Tomkinsons, a family with close military connections.

The house was built in 1829 by the great grandfather of the present owner. The style is Elizabethan, the manner grand and the welcome as warm and hospitable as you could wish.

The bedrooms have a quiet old world charm but comfort, however, takes precedence over the obvious nostalgia for the good times gone by. Every bedroom has its own bathroom, colour TV, radio and telephone. And, for added comfort, the convenience of a tea and coffee tray.

The food is good, fresh and, in the owners own words, "simple". The bar food is excellent, not only in its imaginative variety but in its tastiness. Formal meals are taken in the dining room whose tables are prettily set with fresh linen and flowers. Meanwhile, young William Tomkinson, hero of the Peninsula Wars, surveys the scene from his picture on the wall. The portrait depicts a forebear and the story behind it is worth a visit to Willington for that alone!

There is a delightful, well-established garden and a hard tennis court within the wooded estate. The whole experience at Willington is quintessentially English.

LOCATION

Take the A51 from Tarporley to Chester and turn right at the Bull's Head at Clotton. Willington Hall is 1 mile ahead on the left.

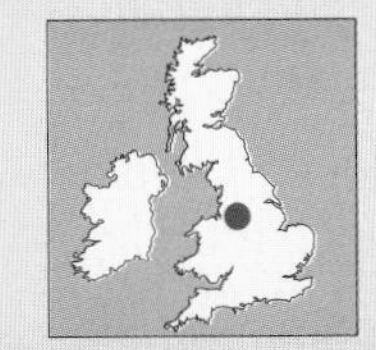

" The Hotel is superb and the rooms, restaurant, bars and the conservatory were all beautifully decorated and furnished

Lisa Valentine, Thomas Cook, London

Victorian private dwelling

WOODLAND PARK HOTEL

Happily situated between town and country

You are looking for somewhere convenient; close enough to Manchester but away from its restlessness; close to the International Airport but away from the flightpath; somewhere that's close to a motorway that will take you to the romance of the Peak District and the glories of some of the finest stately homes in England.

Above all, an hotel that is friendly and unpretentious – where you can get a decent drink, enjoy good food and cocoon yourself in a comfortable bedroom with all the accoutrements of modern living. Well, look no further, the Woodland Park Hotel is exactly what you are looking for.

Brian and Shirley Walker and their staff are professionals who know about hotelkeeping. Their manner is as unobtrusive and welcoming as you could wish from an old friend; they work to create an enthusiastic team who enjoy meeting people and pleasing them.

The decor and furnishings have the personal touch that chain hotels, however lavish, can never aspire to. The conservatory is the place to have a drink and meet your fellow guests (good fellowship is the hallmark of the locals). The food, served in the elegant Terrace Restaurant, is Brasserie in style or there is table d'hôte – whatever your choice it will be the right one!

For those with a predilection for indulgence, ask for a room with an aero spa bath.

LOCATION

Leave M56 at Junction 3 and take the A560 towards Altrincham. Turn right onto Wellington Road. The hotel is signposted from the A560.

Wellington Road,
Timperley, Nr Altrincham,
Cheshire WA15 7RG

Telephone 0161 928 8631
Fax 0161 941 2821

PROPRIETORS
Mr and Mrs B N Walker

MANAGER
Pat Grange

ROOM RATES

13 Singles	*£55.50 - £69.50*
14 Doubles/Twins	*£70 - £86*
1 Four-poster	*£70 - £86*
3 Family	*£82 - £98*
14 Executive	*£70 - £95*

Includes full breakfast and VAT

CHARGE/CREDIT CARDS

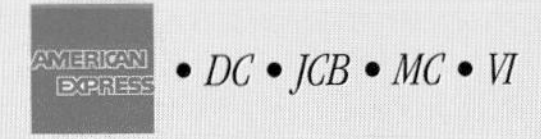

• DC • JCB • MC • VI

ACCOLADES
R.A.C. ★★★ + Merit Awards R & C
A.A. ★★★ 70%

FACILITIES
Conservatory, Terrace Restaurant
2 meeting rooms/max 200 people
Golf, riding and fishing nearby

RESTRICTIONS
No facilities for disabled guests
No pets

ATTRACTIONS
Granada Studios, Chester Castle, Chester, Tatton Hall, Roman Amphitheatre, Peveril Castle

AFFILIATIONS
Independent

NEAREST
MAJOR CITY:
Manchester - 8 miles/12 mins

MAJOR AIRPORT:
Manchester - 4 miles/8 mins

RAILWAY STATION:
Timperley - ¼ mile/3 mins

RESERVATIONS
Direct with hotel

ACCESS CODES
Not applicable

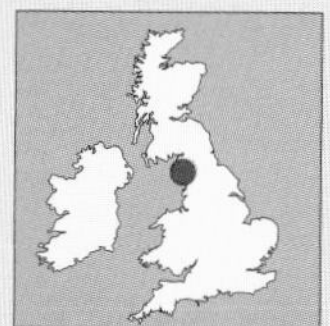

"Gracious service, courtesy, consideration and attention to detail"

P Heal

THE WORDSWORTH HOTEL

Village hotel

Grasmere,
Cumbria LA22 9SW

Telephone 015394 35592
Fax 015394 35765

GENERAL MANAGER
Robin M Lees

ROOM RATES

3 Singles	£58.50
29 Doubles/Twins	£118 - £145
3 Four-posters	£138 - £145
2 Suites	£185 - £195

Includes full breakfast and VAT

CHARGE/CREDIT CARDS

• DC • MC • VI

ACCOLADES
R.A.C. ★★★★ + Merit Awards H & R
A.A. ★★★★ ❀ 65%
The Good Hotel Guide

FACILITIES
Garden, croquet, indoor pool, gym, sauna, jacuzzi, pool, heli-pad
3 meeting rooms/max 120 people
Golf (complimentary), riding, sailing, walking and fishing nearby

RESTRICTIONS
No pets

ATTRACTIONS
Wordsworth's "Dove Cottage" and museum, John Ruskin's home, "Hilltop" Beatrix Potter's home, Levens Hall, Castlerigg Stone Circle - Keswick, Brougham, Penrith and Sizergh Castles

AFFILIATIONS
Independent

NEAREST
MAJOR CITY:
Manchester - 95miles/1½ hrs

MAJOR AIRPORT:
Manchester - 100 miles/2 hrs

RAILWAY STATION:
Windermere - 9 miles/20 mins

RESERVATIONS
Direct with hotel

ACCESS CODES
Not applicable

You'll wax poetic after staying at this lovely Lakeland beauty

In the very heart of English Lakeland, and the centre of one of its loveliest villages, The Wordsworth combines the sophistication of the first-class hotel with the magnificence of the surrounding countryside. Situated in two acres of landscaped grounds, next to the churchyard where William Wordsworth is buried, its name honours the memory of the area's most famous son. The scenery that so inspired the Lake Poets can be enjoyed from the peaceful lounges, furnished with fine antiques, or in the conservatory and cocktail bar, with the aid of a favourite aperitif or specially mixed drink.

The two suites and 35 bedrooms combine great character with comfort and all have well-equipped bathrooms, radio, television, direct-dial telephone and intercom. There is an attractive indoor pool with jacuzzi and mini-gym.

The Prelude Restaurant named after Wordsworth's well-known autobiographical poem, is the place to enjoy lighter or more substantial meals, skillfully prepared from a variety of fresh produce. 24-hour room service is available and the hotel has its own charming pub, The Dove and Olive Branch, a friendly meeting place for a traditional beer or tasty snacks.

The Wordsworth, known for its welcome, is very convenient for Lakeland's principal beauty spots and places of interest.

LOCATION

Leave M6 northbound, Junction 36 (A591). Follow A591 past Kendal, Windermere and Ambleside. 4 miles north of Ambleside, turn left into Grasmere the hotel is on the right next to the church.

"Superb food, relaxing atmosphere, excellent hospitality – a haven!"

Jane and Richard Wright, Surrey

Georgian coaching inn

WORSLEY ARMS

Country inn of renown in an Area of Outstanding Natural Beauty

The Worsley Arms is an attractive stone-built Georgian inn in the heart of Hovingham, near York, with a history stretching back to Roman times. The hotel was built in 1841 by Sir William Worsley, the first Baronet. Today the hotel still belongs to the Worsley family. Hovingham Hall, which stands on the edge of the village was designed around 1760 by Thomas Worsley, and is now the home of Sir Marcus Worsley, the fifth Baron. His sister, Her Royal Highness the Duchess of Kent, was born there.

The Worsley Arms has the welcoming and restful atmosphere of a pleasant country house. The spacious sitting rooms are ideal havens for morning coffee, full afternoon tea, or an aperitif. The restaurant, with its 18th century paintings, has a wide reputation for imaginative food prepared from local produce. Game from the estate is a speciality. The wines have been carefully selected to offer quality and variety.

The bedrooms, each with private bathroom, are individually and tastefully decorated, providing every comfort and modern facility.

The village is on the edge of a designated Area of Outstanding Natural Beauty; two national parks are on the doorstep; nearby are the dales and the moors. The area is rich in romantic and historic sites – the ruined abbeys of Rievaulx and Fountains, the castles of Helmsley and Pickering, the stately homes of Castle Howard, Duncombe Park and, of course, Hovingham Hall.

LOCATION

From the A1 take the A64 turnoff, by-passing York for Malton. Turn left at signpost to Slingsby and Hovingham. Take the B1257 and after 7 miles you reach Hovingham.

Hovingham,
Nr York,
North Yorkshire YO6 4LA

Telephone 01653 628234
Fax 01653 628130

GENERAL MANAGER

A Euan Rodger

ROOM RATES

2 Singles	*£55*
16 Doubles/Twins	*£75*
1 Four-poster	*£75*

Includes full breakfast and VAT

CHARGE/CREDIT CARDS

• MC • VI

ACCOLADES

E.T.B. ♛♛♛♛ Highly Commended
R.A.C. ★★★ + Merit Awards H C & R
A.A. ★★★ ❀❀ 70%
The Good Hotel Guide

FACILITIES

Garden, outdoor tennis, squash, shooting, cricket
2 meeting rooms/max 40 people
Championship golf and riding nearby

RESTRICTIONS

No facilities for disabled guests
Pets not allowed in public areas

ATTRACTIONS

North York Moors National Park, York, Castle Howard, Clifford's Tower, Rievaulx Abbey, Whitby Abbey, Duncombe Park

AFFILIATIONS

Great Estate Hotels
Fine Individual Hotels

NEAREST

MAJOR CITY:
York - 20 miles/30 mins

MAJOR AIRPORT:
Manchester - 107 miles/2 hrs

RAILWAY STATION:
Malton - 8 miles/15 mins

RESERVATIONS

Direct with hotel

ACCESS CODES

Not applicable

Pleasure & Leisure finder

A fun guide to Britain & Ireland

MAJOR CITIES

CATHEDRALS & CHURCHES

Top 10 Cathedrals and Churches

Westminster Abbey	***London***
York Minster	***North***
Canterbury Cathedral	***South***
St Paul's Cathedral	***London***
Chester Cathedral	***North***
Salisbury Cathedral	***South***
Norwich Cathedral	***Midshires***
Buckfast AbbeyDevon	***West***
Winchester Cathedral	***South***
Durham Cathedral	***North***

Source: British Tourist Authority

Some Other Cathedrals and Churches

Bath Abbey built 676 as a nunnery, King Edgar was crowned here in 973 ***West***

Rievaulx Magnificent monastic ruins on the North Yorkshire Moors ***North***

Ripon Cathedral Saxon crypt dates from 669 AD ***North***

Peterborough Cathedral Founded 656, destroyed by Danes 870, building dates from 1117 ***Midshires***

Ely Cathedral Norman Cathedral in the Fens, Cambridgeshire ***Midshires***

Fountains Abbey Founded by Benedictine monks in 1132. Vale of York ***North***

Tintern Abbey Founded 1131. Near Chepstow ***Wales***

Neath Abbey Founded 1130 ***Wales***

Christ Church Cathedral Protestant church, built 1038 by the Viking King Sigtryg, Dublin ***Ireland***

St David's Cathedral Built 1508. Britain's smallest cathedral. Dyfed ***Wales***

St Patrick's Cathedral Another Protestant church in Roman Catholic Dublin. Built 1213 ***Ireland***

Our Lady's Shrine Knock Co Mayo ***Ireland***

Worcester Cathedral Built 10th c site of miracles at the tomb of Bishop Wulfstan ***Midshires***

Hereford Cathedral Built over the tomb of St Ethelbert in 825 ***Midshires***

Exeter Cathedral Founded 932, built 1112 ***West***

St Mary Redcliffe Magnificent 13th - 15th c church. Bristol, Avon ***West***

St Giles's Kirk The High Kirk of Edinburgh ***Scotland***

St Mungo's Cathedral Glasgow. The only complete medieval cathedral on the Scottish mainland ***Scotland***

Beverley Minster Splendid Gothic church ***North***

MOST VISITED HISTORIC HOUSES, MONUMENTS & STATELY HOMES

The BTA's top 10 historic houses and monuments

Tower of London Roman fortress, Royal prison, now housing The Crown Jewels ***London***

Edinburgh Castle Strategic castle alternately held by the English and Scots since 1174 ***Scotland***

Roman Baths and Pump Room Originaly built in 54AD includes The Temple of Minerva ***West***

Windsor Castle State Apartments Royal home of British monarchs since William the Conqueror ***South***

Warwick Castle Founded circa 915, a fine medieval castle still lived in today ***Midshires***

Stonehenge Europe's most important Bronze age temple dating from 2100 BC ***West***

Shakespeare's Birthplace in picturesque Stratford -upon-Avon also home of Royal Shakespeare Theatre***Midshires***

Hampton Court Palace Built 1550 by Cardinal Wolsey became home to Henry VIII ***London***

Leeds Castle One of the most beautiful moated castles in the World. Dating from 12th c ***South***

Beaulieu Collection of vintage and veteran motor cars in a stately home setting ***South***

Other places well worth a visit

Avebury England's richest archaeological site includes 4000 year old stone circle built of 200 pairs of monoliths ***West***

Balmoral Castle Rebuilt by Victoria and Albert 1853 Near Braemar ***Scotland***

Beaulieu Home of the Montagu Motor Museum Fine collection of vintage and veteran vehicles. Hampshire***South***

Beaumaris Castle Built by Edward I, 1291, to guard the Menai Strait ***Wales***

Blair Castle 19th c castellated splendour. Nr Pitlochry***Scotland***

TOP 15 HISTORIC CITIES

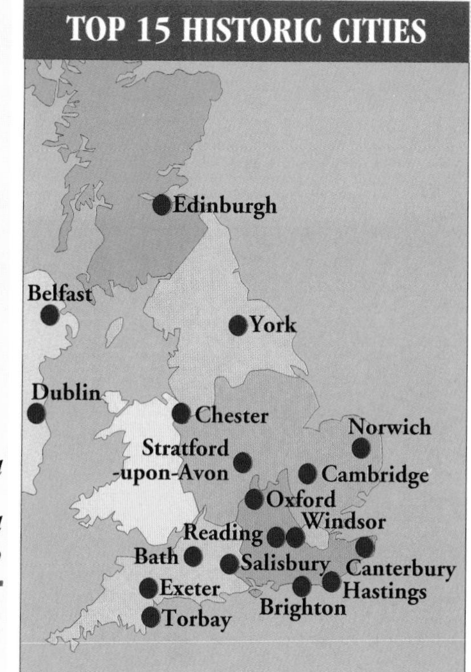

Blenheim Palace Churchill's birthplace. Oxfordshire***Midshires***

Caernarfon Castle Built 1283 - 1327. One of Europe's greatest medieval fortresses ***Wales***

Carisbrook Castle Charles I was imprisoned here. Isle of Wight ***Islands***

Castle Howard Near Malton. Built by Vanbrugh for the Earl of Carlisle ***North***

Chatsworth Classical mansion built 1707 for the Duke of Devonshire ***North***

Clonalis House Home of the O'Conors, Kings of Connaught. Castlerea ***Ireland***

Conwy Castle Impressive ruin, dating from 1283 ***Wales***

Corfe Castle Dorset. Here the 17-year-old King Edward was killed in 978 ***West***

Craigmillar Castle Ruined 14th c fortress on the outskirts of Edinburgh ***Scotland***

Eilean Dunnan Castle Once a Jacobite stronghold Near Kyle of Lochalsh, Highlands ***Scotland***

Erddig Magnificent country home. Near Wrexham ***Wales***

Harewood House 18th c mansion ornamented by Adam and Chippendale ***North***

Harlech Castle Built by Edward I, in 1283. ***Wales***

Hatfield House Historic Jacobean House, 1611 ***Midshires***

Holyrood House Home of Mary Queen of Scots and connected to Edinburgh Castle by The Royal Mile ***Scotland***

Longleat House Glorious Elizabethan Baroque mansion, in golden stone. Famous for its lions ***West***

Ludlow Castle Fine medieval castle, begun in 1085 as border fortress ***Midshires***

Richmond Castle Ruined Norman castle high above the Yorkshire Dales ***North***

Sizergh Castle Main tower built 1360 as defence against raiding Scots ***North***

Tantallon Castle14th c castle featured in Scott's "Marmion". North Berwick ***Scotland***

Woburn Abbey Home of the Dukes of Bedord for over 300 years. Bedfordshire ***Midshires***

More on pages 366 and 446

Wales

Rhuddlan Castle, which was begun in 1277, and where Edward I (1239-1307) is said to have proclaimed his infant son Prince of Wales. Kind Edward encouraged parliamentary institutions at the expense of feudalism and imposed the English system of government after subduing Wales.

Heritage sites

The following heritage sites can be found on the map overleaf. The key numbers show where they are located.

CLWYD

Denbigh Castle	1
Flint Castle	2
Rhuddlan Castle	3

DYFED

Carreg Gennen Castle	4
Dyfi Furnace	5
Kidwelly Castle	6
Lamphey Bishop's Palace	7
Llawhaden Castle	8
St Davids Bishop's Palace	9
Talley Abbey	10

GWENT

Caerleon Roman Fortress	11
Chepstow Castle	12
Raglan Castle	13
Tintern Abbey	14
White Castle	15

GWYNEDD

Beaumaris Castle	16
Caernarfon Castle	17
Conwy Castle	18
Criccieth Castle	19
Cymer Abbey	20
Dolbadarn Castle	21
Dolwyddelan Castle	22
Gwydir Uchaf Chapel	23
Harlech Castle	24

MID GLAMORGAN

Caerphilly Castle	25
Coity Castle	26
Tretower Castle	27
Tretower Court	28

SOUTH GLAMORGAN

Castell Coch	29

WEST GLAMORGAN

Neath Abbey	30
Weobly Castle	31

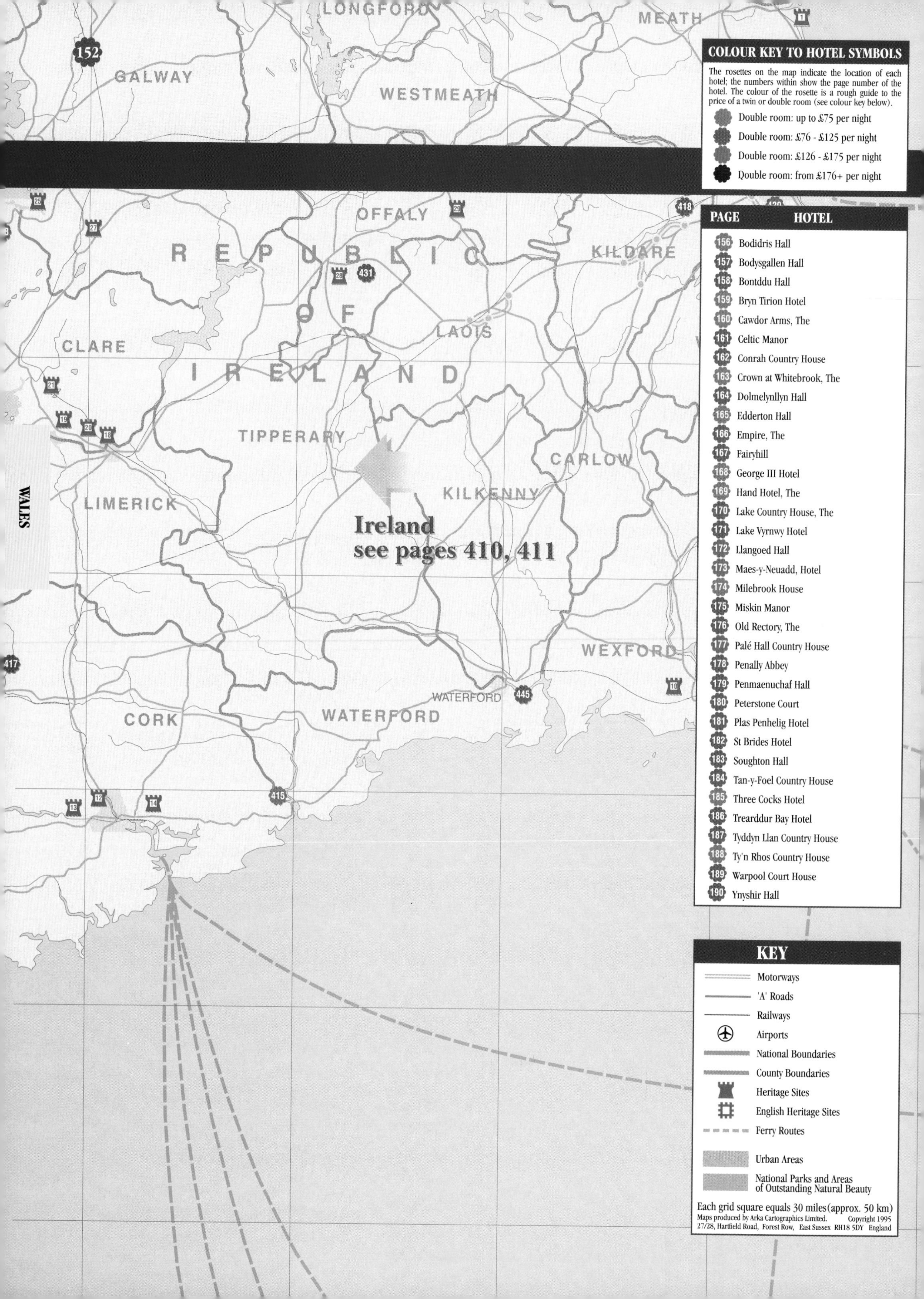
LONGFORD
MEATH
GALWAY
WESTMEATH
OFFALY
KILDARE
REPUBLIC OF IRELAND
LAOIS
CLARE
TIPPERARY
CARLOW
KILKENNY
LIMERICK
WALES
Ireland
see pages 410, 411
WEXFORD
WATERFORD
CORK
WATERFORD
COLOUR KEY TO HOTEL SYMBOLS
The rosettes on the map indicate the location of each hotel; the numbers within show the page number of the hotel. The colour of the rosette is a rough guide to the price of a twin or double room (see colour key below).
Double room: up to £75 per night
Double room: £76 - £125 per night
Double room: £126 - £175 per night
Double room: from £176+ per night
PAGE HOTEL
156 Bodidris Hall
157 Bodysgallen Hall
158 Bontddu Hall
159 Bryn Tirion Hotel
160 Cawdor Arms, The
161 Celtic Manor
162 Conrah Country House
163 Crown at Whitebrook, The
164 Dolmelynllyn Hall
165 Edderton Hall
166 Empire, The
167 Fairyhill
168 George III Hotel
169 Hand Hotel, The
170 Lake Country House, The
171 Lake Vyrnwy Hotel
172 Llangoed Hall
173 Maes-y-Neuadd, Hotel
174 Milebrook House
175 Miskin Manor
176 Old Rectory, The
177 Palé Hall Country House
178 Penally Abbey
179 Penmaenuchaf Hall
180 Peterstone Court
181 Plas Penhelig Hotel
182 St Brides Hotel
183 Soughton Hall
184 Tan-y-Foel Country House
185 Three Cocks Hotel
186 Trearddur Bay Hotel
187 Tyddyn Llan Country House
188 Ty'n Rhos Country House
189 Warpool Court House
190 Ynyshir Hall
KEY
Motorways
'A' Roads
Railways
Airports
National Boundaries
County Boundaries
Heritage Sites
English Heritage Sites
Ferry Routes
Urban Areas
National Parks and Areas of Outstanding Natural Beauty
Each grid square equals 30 miles(approx. 50 km)
Maps produced by Arka Cartographics Limited. Copyright 1995
27/28, Hartfield Road, Forest Row, East Sussex RH18 5DY England

WALES
North see pages 92, 93
Midshires see pages 192, 193
West Country see pages 256, 257
Anglesey
Holy Island
Holyhead
Trearddur Bay
Amlwch
Red Wharf Bay
Beaumaris
Llanfair P.G.
Menai Bridge
Bangor
Caernarfon
Llanddeiniolen
Llanberis
Penygroes
Beddgelert
Nefyn
Pwllheli
Criccieth
Porthmadog
Harlech
Bardsey Island
GT. ORMES HEAD
Llandudno
Conwy
Rhos-on-Sea
Colwyn Bay
Abergele
Llansanffraid Glan Conwy
Llanrwst
Betws-y-Coed
Capel Common
Dolwyddelan
Blaenau Ffestiniog
GWYNEDD
Trawsfynydd
SNOWDONIA NATIONAL PARK
Ganllwyd
Barmouth
Dolgellau
Prestatyn
Rhyl
St. Asaph
Holywell
Flint
Halkyn
Denbigh
Ruthin
Mold
Queensferry
Ewloe
CHESTER
CLWYD
Llandegla
Wrexham
CHESHIRE
Corwen
Llangollen
Bala
Llandderfel
Llandrillo
Llanarmon Dyffryn Ceiriog
SHROPSHIRE
SHREWSBURY
Llanfyllin
Llanwyddyn
Dinas Mawddwy
Llangadfan
Welshpool
Forden
Montgomery
Corris
Cemmaes Road
Machynlleth
Tywyn
Aberdovey
Eglwysfach
Borth
Talybont
Cardigan Bay
Caersws
Newtown
Llanidloes
Llangurig
Aberystwyth
Ponterwyd
Devil's Bridge
Chancery
POWYS
Knighton
Milebrook
Rhayader
Elan Village
Llanwrtyd Wells
Newbridge-on-Wye
Aberaeron
New Quay
Ystrad Aeron
Tregaron
Builth Wells
HEREFORD & WORCESTER
Cardigan
Lampeter
Llandrindod Wells
Llangammarch Wells
WALES
Newport
Fishguard
Newcastle Emlyn
Hay-on-Wye
Three Cocks
Talgarth
Talley
Llandovery
DYFED
Brecon
BRECON BEACONS NATIONAL PARK
Ramsey Island
St. David's
Wolf's Castle
PEMBROKESHIRE COAST NATIONAL PARK
Llawhaden
Whitland
Carmarthen
Llandeilo
Tretower
GWENT
Narberth
St. Clears
Skomer Island
Milford Haven
Skokholm Island
Kilgetty
Pendine
Saundersfoot
Pembroke
Lamphey
Tenby
ST. GOVEN'S HEAD
Kidwelly
Ammanford
Pen-y-Cae
Abercraf
Ystradgynlais
Pontardawe
Merthyr Tydfil
Brynmawr
Abergavenny
Tredegar
Blaenavon
Monmouth
Raglan
Whitebrook
Tintern Parva
Aberdare
Mountain Ash
Abertillery
Pontypool
Cwmbran
Bargoed
WEST GLAMORGAN
MID GLAMORGAN
Llanelli
SWANSEA
Neath
Killay
Swansea
The Mumbles
Rhossili
Port Talbot
Maesteg
Pontypridd
Caerphilly
NEWPORT
Chepstow
Miskin
Bridgend
Porthcawl
CARDIFF
Cowbridge
SOUTH GLAMORGAN
Penarth
Barry
Cardiff (Wales Airport)
Bristol Channel
AVON
BRISTOL
WESTON-SUPER-MARE
BATH
DEVON
SOMERSET
PRESTON
BLACKBURN
BOLTON
WIGAN
BIRKENHEAD
WIDNES
RUNCORN
0 Miles
30
0 Kilometres
50

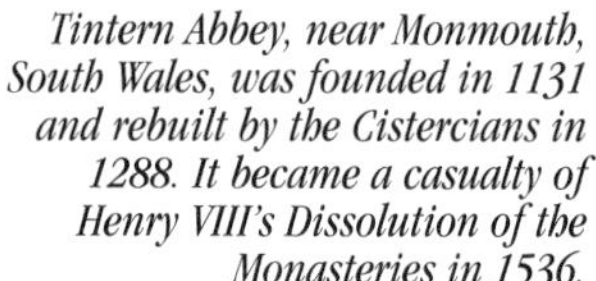

Tintern Abbey, near Monmouth, South Wales, was founded in 1131 and rebuilt by the Cistercians in 1288. It became a casualty of Henry VIII's Dissolution of the Monasteries in 1536.

COUNTIES

Clwyd

Dyfed

Gwent

Gwynedd

Mid Glamorgan

Powys

South Glamorgan

West Glamorgan

Wales is a land of natural unspoilt beauty and famed for its countryside, mountains and coastline. It has three National Parks, including Britain's only coastal park, and five other areas designated as being of Outstanding Natural Beauty. Wales has more castles per square mile than any country in Western Europe. Although part of Britain, Wales has its own language, history and heritage.

In the north you can marvel at Snowdon's magnificent mountain ranges whose rocky peaks rise to 3,560 ft. There's the timeless beauty of the Llyn peninsula, the enchanting Isle of Anglesey and the lush green Clwydian Range. There are World Heritage Listed Sites like Beaumaris and Harlech Castles, the elegant Victorian architecture of Llandudno with its sweeping promenade, picturesque Betws-y-Coed, the famous Swallow Falls, and Llangollen which hosts the annual international musical Eisteddfod. With mountain ranges, remote moorlands, ancient drovers' routes, deep dark forests, and lakes and waterfalls, the spectacular lakes and dams of the Elan Valley and the dramatic Abergwesyn Pass across the Roof of Wales, mid Wales is a tranquil area – though at Knighton you can see rising to 30 feet the famous Offa's Dyke, built by the King of Mercia in 784 to keep out the marauders.

South Wales too offers tremendous contrasts, encompassing the gentle, rolling hills and peaks of the Brecon Beacons, the wooded glory of the Wye Valley and the bays and beaches of Pembrokeshire and the Gower peninsula. Cosmopolitan Cardiff is Britain's newest capital city, and home of the acclaimed Welsh National Opera.

The distinctive Welsh cuisine uses the best of local produce – look out for the Taste of Wales/Blas ar Cymru symbol. Wales has a saying and a song: "We'll keep a welcome in the hillsides". The traditional warm welcome from Welsh people to their guests will make your visit a unique and memorable experience.

Areas of Outstanding Natural Beauty

Anglesey. 125 mile coastline with sandy coves and bays, wonderful beaches, rocky headlands, lovely little resorts and fishing villages.

Gower Peninsula. 14 miles from sandy Mumbles beach to Worms Head. Limestone cliffs, sandflats.

Snowdonia National Park. 840 square miles, with the highest mountain peak in Wales and England.

Wye Valley. The last 15 miles from Monmouth down to Chepstow. Superb scenery and walking country.

Castles, Stately Homes, Historic Houses

Bodrhyddan Hall, Rhuddlan, Clwyd. 17th c home of Lord Langford. Armour, pictures, period furniture and a 3,000-year-old mummy. Gardens and picnic area.

Caernarfon Castle, Gwynedd. 1283. A great medieval fortress. Built as a royal palace, seat of government and military stronghold.

Caerphilly Castle, Mid Glamorgan. A huge medieval fortress with water defences. Its tower leans even further off the vertical than Pisa!

Conwy Castle, Gwynedd. Built for King Edward I 1283-1287. An outstanding medieval castle.

Criccieth Castle, Gwynedd. A native castle of the Welsh princes, dating back to the 13th c.

Harlech Castle, Gwynedd. 13th c. Built on a concentric plan with a small impregnable inner Keep, and twin towered gatehouse.

Pembroke Castle, Dyfed. Its inner bailey was built in 1090. Oldest castle in Wales. Birthplace of Henry VII in 1457.

Tredegar House, Newport. Superb 17th c house. 90 acres of landscaped parks. Formal garden, carriage rides, boating lake.

Tretower Court, Crickhowell, Powys. Courtyard house dating to 14th c. Norman motte and bailey castle nearby.

Museums, Galleries & Modern Highspots

Bodelwyddan Castle, Clwyd. Magnificent Victorian house with major collection from the National Portrait Gallery.

Caerleon Roman Fortress, Gwent. Remains of the 50 acre legionary fortress of Isca.

Cardiff National Museum of Wales. Huge size and variety. Famed for its collection of Impressionist paintings.

Centre for Alternative Technology, nr Machynlleth. Village of the future, using wind and water turbines, wave power, solar energy.

Clive of India Museum, Powis Castle, Welshpool. Superb antiques, paintings and furniture. Britain's finest hanging gardens.

Great Little Trains of Wales. Narrow gauge steam trains running through wild mountain scenery.

TOURIST OFFICE INFORMATION

Further information about Wales will be gladly supplied by:

Wales Tourist Board,
Brunel House, 2 Fitzalan Road,
Cardiff CF2 1UY.
Tel: 01222 499909

For international offices, please turn to page 480

Devil's Bridge Falls. Part of the spectacular route taken by the River Mynach, where close by is Devil's Bridge erected in the 12th century.

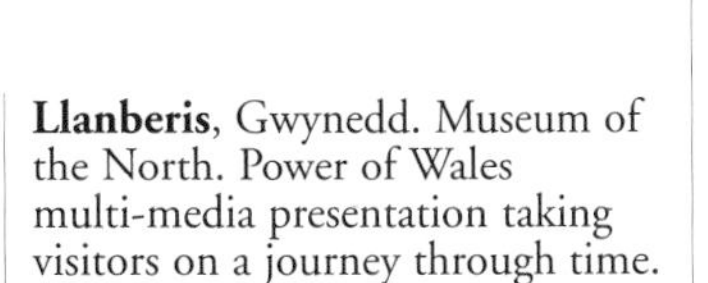

Llanberis, Gwynedd. Museum of the North. Power of Wales multi-media presentation taking visitors on a journey through time.

Llancaiach Fawr Living History Museum. Restored Elizabethan manor where actors in period costume recreate the time of the Civil War.

Lloyd George Museum, Llanystumdwy. The life and times of the statesman depicted in his boyhood home.

Portmeirion, nr Porthmadog, Gwynedd. Unique Italianate fantasy village by Sir Clough Williams-Ellis 1952-72. Setting of cult film The Prisoner.

Segontium Roman Fort, Caernarfon. Museum on the fort's site illustrates the Roman conquest of Wales.

Churches, Cathedrals, Abbeys, Monasteries

Bangor Cathedral. Founded by St Deinol in 6th c, 70 years before Canterbury was established. Claims to be Britain's oldest cathedral.

Brecon Cathedral. The best preserved set of medieval buildings in Wales.

Lamphey Bishop's Palace. Extensive remains of a lavish country retreat used by Bishops of St David's.

Llandaff Cathedral, South Glamorgan. Epstein's Christ in Majesty dominates this 12th c cathedral.

Penmon Priory, nr Beaumaris. Site of a 6th century monastery. Remains date back 1000 years.

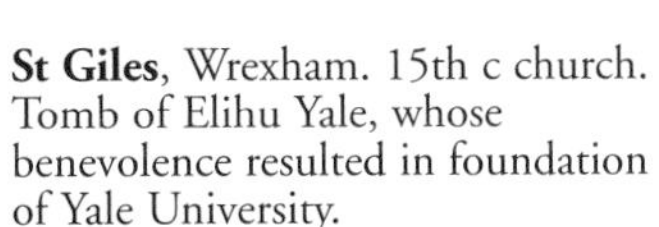

St Giles, Wrexham. 15th c church. Tomb of Elihu Yale, whose benevolence resulted in foundation of Yale University.

St David's Bishop's Palace. Imposing palace within the defended perimeter of the cathedral precincts.

St Asaph's Cathedral, Clwyd. Founded 537 AD, twice rebuilt. Museum contains the Welsh/Greek/Hebrew dictionary by Dic Aberdaron.

St Illtyd's Church, Llantwit Major. Collection of Celtic crosses and medieval inscribed stones.

Tintern Abbey, Gwent. Evocative ruined monastery founded in 1131 for Cistercian monks from the Norman Abbey of L'Aumone.

Gardens

Bryn Bras Castle Grounds, Llanrug, nr Llanberis. 32 acres of lawns, flowering trees, streams, woodland.

Welsh Mountain Zoo and Gardens, Colwyn Bay. Chimp Encounter, flying eagle display.

Ebbw Vale Festival Park. Created from the Garden Festival. Tropical plant house, wetlands, lake, nature trail.

Sport & Outdoors

Cardiff Arms Park. The home of the Welsh national soccer and rugby teams.

Fishing, sea and freshwater, in many coastal towns and rivers. Coracle fishing on the River Teifi.

Pony trekking in many centres, including Brecon, Builth Wells, Caerphilly, Crickhowell, Rhayader, Swansea.

Sheep dog trials at Vivod, nr Llangollen, Llanferris, the Dolgellau region and many other sheep farming centres.

Harlech Castle, built in 1283 by Edward I, stands on an even older celtic fortress. The spectacular views include the mountains of Snowdonia, the Lleyn Peninsula and Tremadoc Bay.

“In God’s own country, perhaps the closest place to heaven! What a wonderful stay we had!”

Graham & Sue Smith, Essex

BODIDRIS HALL

Tudor hunting lodge

Llandegla, Wrexham, Clwyd LL1 3AL

Telephone 01978 790434
Fax 01978 790335

PROPRIETOR
William J Farden

GENERAL MANAGER
Tudor Williams

ROOM RATES

1 Single	*£80*
7 Doubles/Twins	*£105*
3 Four-poster Suites	*£125*
1 Suite	*£125*

Includes full breakfast, newspaper and VAT

CHARGE/CREDIT CARDS

• DC • MC • VI

ACCOLADES
W.T.B. ♛♛♛♛ Highly Commended
A.A. ★★★ ❀❀ 69%
Taste of Wales

FACILITIES
Garden, fishing, heli-pad
2 meeting rooms/max 25 people
Golf, riding, walking, cycling, clay pigeon shooting and fishing nearby

RESTRICTIONS
No facilities for disabled guests
Charge made for pets

ATTRACTIONS
Roman City of Chester, Chirk Castle, Llangollen Railway, Loggerheads Country Park

AFFILIATIONS
Independent

NEAREST
MAJOR CITY:
Chester - 20 miles/30 mins

MAJOR AIRPORT:
Manchester - 45 miles/50 mins

RAILWAY STATION:
Wrexham - 10 miles/15 mins

RESERVATIONS
Direct with hotel

ACCESS CODES
Not applicable

Proud guardian of Celtic history with great food and wine

A visit to Bodidris Hall is a 900-year trip through history. It was built by two Crusaders, who were granted the estate by their Prince, Gryffydd ap Madoc, as a reward for valour. Rebuilt in Tudor times, the hall became the hunting lodge of Lord Robert Dudley, Earl of Leicester and controversial favourite of Queen Elizabeth I. His bear and ragged staff crest on the front gable is a reminder of the local legend that Elizabeth came to Bodidris to see the man she loved . . . but would never marry.

The tranquillity of the Welsh countryside and the unique history of the hall will make your trip to Bodidris an unforgettable experience. The accommodation is superb. All the bedrooms are en suite, and each is decorated in keeping with the hall and has its own tale to tell. There is a duelling staircase built in Tudor times so that unwelcome guests could be warded off. This facility is rarely used today!

In the evenings, you can relax beside the restaurant’s mighty fireplace that once roasted a whole lamb.

Driven shooting is available at Bodidris in the autumn. The spectacular Vale of Llangollen and the Horseshoe Pass are within easy reach. A 135-foot pinnacled steeple soars above St Giles’s Church in Wrexham. In the churchyard is the tomb of Elihu Yale, the Pilgrim Father after whom Yale University is named.

LOCATION

Llandegla is on the A525 Wrexham to Ruthin road. Bodidris is a mile up the A5104 road to Chester, on the left hand side.

“ Bodysgallen Hall deserves its reputation as one of our best country house hotels ”

Ian Irvine, Daily Telegraph

17th century country house

BODYSGALLEN HALL

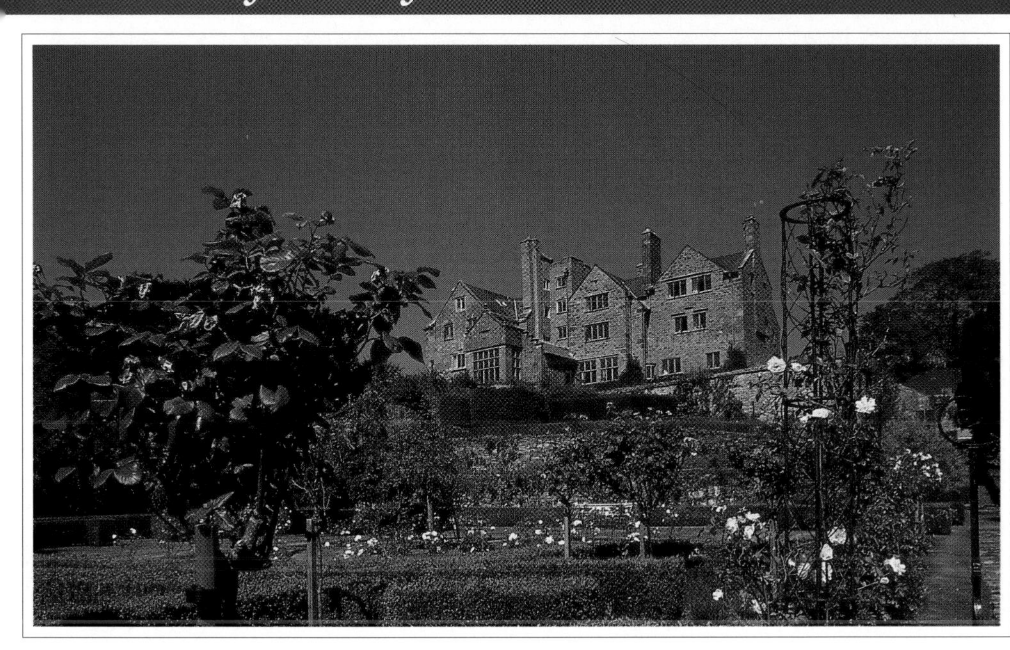

Whatever the season there is always something to admire

Bodysgallen Hall, near the seaside town of Llandudno, stands on a hillside in 200 acres of gardens and wooded parkland, looking down on to Conwy Bay with its medieval castle and across to the mountains of Snowdonia. The oldest part of the house is a 13th century tower reached by a winding stone staircase, once used as a lookout by soldiers serving the English kings of Conwy watching for Welsh marauders, now a safe place for guests to admire the breathtaking views.

The hotel, owned and restored by Historic House Hotels, has 19 bedrooms in the house and 16 cottage suites dotted around the grounds, many with their own private gardens. Two of the finest rooms in the house are the oak panelled entrance hall and the drawing room on the first floor with mullioned windows and a splendid fireplace. Imaginative food prepared by head chef Michael Penny, using the best local produce, is served in the two dining rooms which overlook the award-winning gardens.

New for 1996 is a health and leisure spa reached by a short stroll through the gardens, comprising a 54 foot indoor swimming pool, whirlpool spa bath, steam room, saunas, solaria, gym and beauty salon. The hotel has its own croquet lawn and tennis court and guests can sail in Conwy Bay and play golf at several courses nearby.

Bodysgallen Hall is an admirable place for a totally relaxed holiday with castles, stately homes and gardens, beaches and magnificent mountain scenery all within easy reach.

LOCATION

Take the A55 expressway from Chester to its intersection with the A470 then follow A470 towards Llandudno for 2 miles. The hotel is on the right.

Llandudno, Gwynedd LL30 1RS

Telephone 01492 584466
Fax 01492 582519

GENERAL MANAGER
R N Taylor

ROOM RATES

3 Singles	from £89
17 Doubles/Twins	from £128
16 Cottage Suites	from £150

Includes full breakfast and VAT

CHARGE/CREDIT CARDS

• MC • VI

WALES

ACCOLADES
W.T.B. Highly Commended
R.A.C. Blue Ribbon Award ★★★
A.A. ★★★
The Good Hotel Guide

FACILITIES
Garden, croquet, tennis, indoor pool, health & beauty, whirlpool spa bath, gym, sauna, heli-pad
2 meeting rooms/max 26 people
Sailing, water sports, riding, golf and fishing nearby

RESTRICTIONS
No children under 8 years
No facilities for disabled guests
Pets allowed in cottage suites only

ATTRACTIONS
Conwy Bay and Castle, Harlech, Caernarfon Castle, Swallow Falls, Betws-y-Coed, Plas Newydd, Anglesey, Penrhyn Castle, Bodnant Gardens

AFFILIATIONS
Small Luxury Hotels
Welsh Rarebits

NEAREST
MAJOR CITY:
Chester - 50 miles/55 mins
MAJOR AIRPORT:
Manchester - 85 miles/1 hr 20 mins
RAILWAY STATION:
Llandudno Junction - 1 mile/3 mins

RESERVATIONS
Toll free fax in US: 800-260-8338
(quote Bodysgallen Hall)
In Japan: 03-3434-7159

ACCESS CODES
AMADEUS/SYSTEM 1 XTPBGH
APOLLO LX 32324
AXESS LX 5562
SABRE LX 11426
SAHARA LX CEGBH
WORLDSPAN LX CEGBH

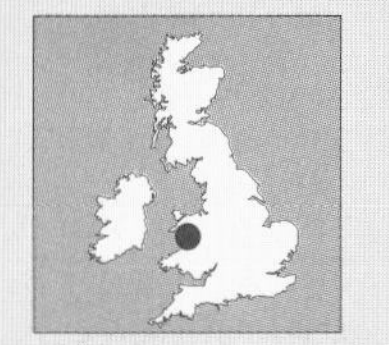

“ We look forward to future visits with eager anticipation ”

Tony & Judy Asbury, Buckinghamshire

BONTDDU HALL HOTEL

Victorian mansion

Bontddu, Nr Barmouth, Gwynedd LL40 2SU

Telephone 01341 430661
Fax 01341 430284

PROPRIETORS

Mike and Gretta Ball

ROOM RATES

2 Singles	£52.50 - £62.50
13 Doubles	£90 - £115
1 Four-poster	£150
3 Suites	£150

Includes full breakfast and VAT

CHARGE/CREDIT CARDS

• DC • JCB • MC • VI

ACCOLADES

W.T.B. De Luxe
R.A.C. ★★★ + Merit Awards C & R
A.A. ★★★ 68%

FACILITIES

Garden
Golf, riding, mountain walking, fishing and dry ski slope nearby

RESTRICTIONS

No children under 3 years
No facilities for disabled guests
Pets by arrangement

ATTRACTIONS

Snowdon Mountain Railway, Harlech Castle, Caernarfon Castle, Dinas Oleu

AFFILIATIONS

The Virgin Collection

NEAREST

MAJOR CITY:
Chester - 70 miles/1½ hrs

MAJOR AIRPORT:
Manchester - 120 miles/2 hrs

RAILWAY STATION:
Barmouth - 5 miles/10 mins

RESERVATIONS

Direct with hotel

ACCESS CODES

Not applicable

An historic home that has played host to three great Prime Ministers

This Victorian mansion is set in 14 acres of grounds with a profusion of azaleas, camellias, and rhododendrons against a backdrop of mountains and a river estuary. The magical views are amongst the finest in Wales.

The house was built by Charles Beale in 1873, father-in-law of Joseph Chamberlain, a prominent Victorian politician, whose son, Neville Chamberlain, became Prime Minister of Great Britain in the 1930's.

Bontddu Hall has a well-earned reputation for high standards and attention to detail. There are 19 bedrooms, individually designed and decorated, with three suites – Churchill, Chamberlain, and Lloyd George – named after previous guests. All bedrooms have bath, direct-dial telephone, colour TV, clock radio, hairdryer, and coffee/tea tray.

The cuisine is classic in style, using the best of fresh local produce – Welsh mountain lamb, Mawddach salmon, Cardigan Bay lobster. A fine wine cellar complements the food.

Bontddu Hall is situated in Snowdonia National Park only a few miles from the sandy beaches of the west coast. There are championship links golf courses at Harlech and Aberdyfi and historic castles in all directions. The locality provides for every interest, hill-walking, pony trekking, exploring slate and gold mines, bird watching, sea and river fishing and even narrow gauge steam railways.

LOCATION

Turn off A470 north of Dolgellau, on to A496 (direction Barmouth). 2 miles to village of Bontddu, hotel is on the right as you come into the village.

"We had a lovely, restful break. There is an atmosphere in your hotel that leads to relaxation. The food was superb!"

Pauline Patterson, Cheshire

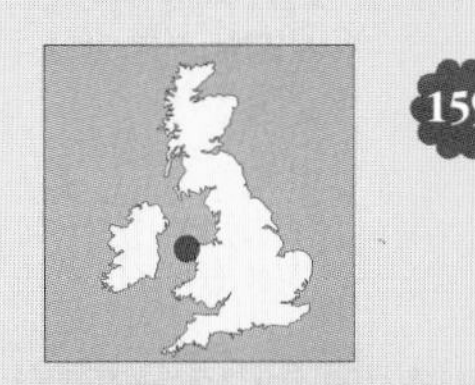

Country hotel

BRYN TIRION HOTEL

The Isle of Anglesey at your feet

Since 150 BC, Anglesey (from the Norse *Isle of the straits*) has been the centre of Celtic culture. The Druids had their fiercest battle against the Romans on the island which Thomas Telford joined to the mainland with his famous Menai Bridge in 1826. The Tudor Kings made their home at Plas Penmynydd only five miles from Bryn Tirion.

The hotel, with its with magnificent views of Red Wharf Bay, is owned by the Gilholm and Forster families who also run the hotel. Their love of the place shows in their hospitality, the decor, the food and wine - all have the same touch of care and consideration.

The bedrooms are individually designed with your comfort in mind. They are all en suite and thoughtfully appointed and provided with all the facilities to make your stay enjoyable.

The restaurant has a good reputation locally. The fare is characteristic of the region with daily changes to the menu reflecting the best produce available from the local markets. The wine list includes an excellent selection of wines from France, Italy and the New World.

Bryn Tirion is the perfect place from which to explore the pleasures of Anglesey. It is an island of outstanding natural beauty with its own individuality and fringed by 125 miles of the most beautiful coastline in Wales. The perfect ingredients for an unhurried, restful holiday.

LOCATION

Cross the Britannia Bridge A55. Take second exit A5025 to Benllech. When through village of Pentraeth, look for signs on right to Red Wharf Bay. The hotel is ¼ mile on the right.

Red Wharf Bay, Isle of Anglesey, Gwynedd LL75 8RZ

Telephone 01248 852366
Fax 01248 852013

PROPRIETORS

Christine and Jack Gilholm
Julie Forster

ROOM RATES

Single occupancy £40 - £50
17 Doubles/Twins £59 - £69
Includes full breakfast and VAT

CHARGE/CREDIT CARDS

• MC • VI

ACCOLADES

W.T.B. ♛♛♛♛ Highly Commended

FACILITIES

Garden with views of Red Wharf Bay
1 meeting room/max 100 people
Riding and fishing nearby

RESTRICTIONS

Children under 5 years by arrangement

ATTRACTIONS

Snowdonia National Park,
Anglesey Sea Zoo,
Beaumaris Castle,
5 golf courses nearby

AFFILIATIONS

Minotels
Welsh Connections

NEAREST

MAJOR CITY:
Bangor - 9 miles/15 mins

MAJOR AIRPORT:
Manchester - 80 miles/2 hrs

RAILWAY STATION:
Bangor - 9 miles/15 mins

RESERVATIONS

Direct with hotel

ACCESS CODES

Not applicable

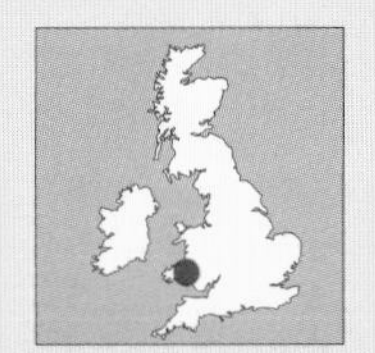

"One of the best in the West"

Patrick Bergin, actor

THE CAWDOR ARMS

18th century coaching inn

Llandeilo,
Carmarthenshire SA19 6EN

Telephone 01558 823500
Fax 01558 822399

PROPRIETORS

Peter Grey-Hughes
Paul and Delyth Wilson

ROOM RATES

2 Singles	*£55 - £70*
12 Doubles/Twins	*£70 - £100*
2 Four-posters	*£90 - £110*

Includes full breakfast and VAT

CHARGE/CREDIT CARDS

• *MC* • *VI*

ACCOLADES

W.T.B. ♛♛♛♛ *Highly Commended*
R.A.C. ★★★
A.A. ★★★ ❀ *64%*

FACILITIES

1 meeting room/max 30 people
Golf, fishing, hot air ballooning and riding nearby

RESTRICTIONS

None

ATTRACTIONS

Brecon Beacons National Park,
Talley Abbey,
Carreg Cennen Castle,
Kidwelly Castle,
Neath Abbey

AFFILIATIONS

Independent

NEAREST

MAJOR CITY:
Swansea - 20 miles/30 mins

MAJOR AIRPORT:
Cardiff - 55 miles/1 hr

RAILWAY STATION:
Llandeilo - ½ mile/3 mins

RESERVATIONS

Direct with hotel

ACCESS CODES

Not applicable

WALES

A fine tradition of hospitality – a place to seek out rather than happen upon

Monumental crumbling castles, rocky outcrops jutting out of the rolling hillsides, picturesque stone-built villages and broad valleys eroded by salmon-rich rivers are the tell-tale signs of an ancient kingdom whose treasures were worth fighting – and dying for.

In the middle of this pastoral settings is the Cawdor Arms, every bit a part of the history of this area. Now elegantly decorated with modern fabrics in a classic style, the aura is unmistakeably ancient; the well-worn stone flags in the foyer have yielded to the passing of time and a great many footsteps.

Continuing in this tradition of hospitality, The Cawdor Arms fulfils many a need: for the passer-by, a haven of comfort; for the sportsman, a base for some of the finest shooting and fishing in Britain; for the artist or poet, a centre for some of the most romantic scenery in the world; for the gourmet, an unexpected delight much coveted by the locals.

The prestige of the restaurant has lifted this humble inn into the realms of gastronomic excellence, thereby making this a place to seek and find rather than one to happen upon.

LOCATION

In the centre of Llandeilo on the A40 Swansea to Brecon road, 20 minutes from the end of the M4.

" The Celtic Manor is an hotel which I have used on many occasions. The service is wonderful and the food excellent. I highly recommend it "

Sir Anthony Hopkins, London

Victorian manor

CELTIC MANOR GOLF & COUNTRY CLUB

A timeless tradition of hospitality

Consistently acknowledged as one of the finest hotels in Wales, this refurbished Victorian Manor House is set in its own 1,000-acre estate of mature parkland and golf courses. Majestic trees adorn the lawns and surround the hotel. Spacious rooms are elegantly furnished with comfort in mind – a lounge for relaxation and two bars.

Two fine restaurants benefit from the superb culinary skills of Trefor Jones, twice winner of 'Welsh Chef of the Year' and prominent member of the Welsh culinary team. Hedleys is a fine oak-panelled Victorian dining room whilst Patio is an elegant conservatory-style brasserie.

The grand staircase leads to luxurious air-conditioned bedrooms individually designed with marble-clad private bathrooms, tea and coffee-making facilities, colour satellite television, radio and direct-dial telephone. Splendid four-poster beds adorn some of the rooms.

Golfers will enjoy the prestigious facilities of the golf club; an unforgettable round on one of two Robert Trent Jones courses, The Ian Woosnam Golf Academy and superb terraces where afternoon tea is served. All this is complemented by excellent recreational and leisure facilities. And for nature lovers there is an ancient woodland walk that winds its way through Coldra Wood, with its rare flora and fauna.

It is the staff at Celtic Manor who give the hotel character, leaving no doubt that their aim is to provide individual attention to every guest.

LOCATION

Junction 24 of the M4, then follow the signpost for Newport (A48). The hotel is 300 yards on right hand side.

Coldra Woods, Newport, Gwent NP6 2YA

Telephone 01633 413000
Fax 01633 412910

PROPRIETORS
Ray and Kay Dawes

MANAGER
David Morgan

ROOM RATES

1 Single	*£59 - £99*
64 Doubles/Twins	*£65 - £109*
2 Four-posters	*£90 - £125*
6 Suites	*£100 - £150*

Includes full breakfast and VAT

CHARGE/CREDIT CARDS

• DC • MC • VI

ACCOLADES
W.T.B. ♛♛♛♛♛ *Highly Commended*
R.A.C. ★★★★ *+ Merit Award R*
A.A. ★★★★ ❀❀ *65%*

FACILITIES
Gardens, 2 indoor swimming pools, sauna, solaria, steam room, aerobics, gym, health & beauty, 2 x18-hole golf courses, golf academy, riding, heli-pad
8 meeting rooms/max 450 people

RESTRICTIONS
No facilities for disabled guests
No pets

ATTRACTIONS
Tintern Abbey, Wye Valley, Tredegar House, Caerleon

AFFILIATIONS
Independent

NEAREST
MAJOR CITY:
Cardiff - 15 miles/20 mins
MAJOR AIRPORT:
London Heathrow - 120 miles/1¾ hrs
Cardiff - 35 miles/40 mins
RAILWAY STATION:
Newport - 3 miles/10 mins

RESERVATIONS
Toll free fax in US: 800-854-1986

ACCESS CODES
Not applicable

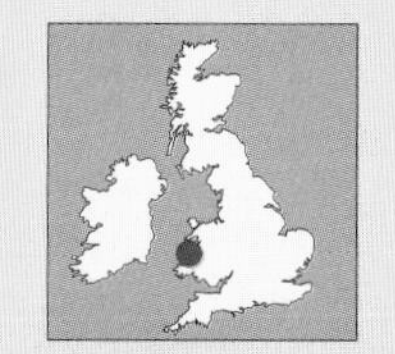

"A real find, the Conrah Country House Hotel is a haven of traditional courtesy, style and hospitality"

Janice Rice, Indianapolis

CONRAH COUNTRY HOUSE HOTEL *Edwardian manor house*

Chancery, Aberystwyth, Dyfed SY23 4DF

Telephone 01970 617941
Fax 01970 624546

PROPRIETORS
John and Patricia Heading

ROOM RATES
4 Singles £59 - £88
16 Doubles/Twins £88 - £110
Includes full breakfast and VAT

CHARGE/CREDIT CARDS

• DC • JCB • MC • VI

WALES

ACCOLADES
W.T.B. Highly Commended
R.A.C. ★★★
A.A. ★★★ 67%

FACILITIES
Indoor swimming pool, croquet, gardens, table tennis, sauna, heli-pad
1 meeting room/max 40 people
Golf, riding and fishing nearby

RESTRICTIONS
No children under 5 years
No facilities for disabled guests
No smoking in dining room
No pets

ATTRACTIONS
National Library of Wales, Vale of Rheidol Narrow Gauge Railway Devil's Bridge, Theatres, Silver/Lead Mining Museum, Snowdonia National Park

AFFILIATIONS
Welsh Rarebits

NEAREST
MAJOR CITY:
Cardiff - 115 miles/3 hrs

MAJOR AIRPORT:
Manchester - 130 miles/3 hrs

RAILWAY STATION:
Aberystwyth - 3½ miles/10 mins

RESERVATIONS
Direct with hotel

ACCESS CODES
Not applicable

A secluded setting, first class service, good old-fashioned values

The Conrah Country House Hotel is a long established favourite hotel for UK and overseas visitors alike. This elegant Edwardian manor house is set in 22 acres of private grounds and offers superb standards of accommodation, service and Celtic hospitality. Resident owners John and Patricia Heading extend a warm Welsh welcome to residential guests and patrons of the Conrah's exclusive restaurant.

The hotel's chefs use only the freshest of local ingredients and produce from the Conrah's kitchen garden for delicious 'Taste of Wales' menus. The food is complemented by a selection of fine wines and liqueurs.

Antique furnishings, log fires, books and flowers in the drawing room and writing room create a gracious elegance conducive to comfortable rest and relaxation. In addition, the heated indoor pool and sauna enjoy a beautiful garden setting.

Aberystwyth has been described as the "Athens of Wales" with its many cultural institutions, historical associations and attractions, including a fascinating museum, Edward I's castle and the National Library of Wales which contains many thousands of manuscripts, books and historic documents. Built in 1872, the university houses a public theatre, concert hall and important art collections.

LOCATION

3½ miles south of Aberystwyth on the main A487 coast road.

" The sort of place we hoped to find but thought we never would "

Dr Alan Scott, New York

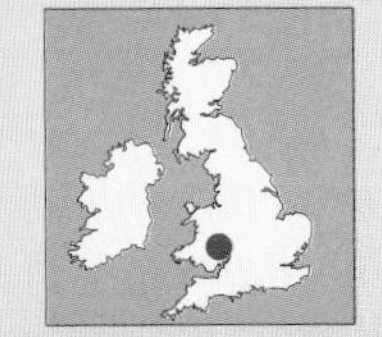

17th century inn

THE CROWN AT WHITEBROOK

A haven of tranquillity for those in search of peace and relaxation

Set in the idyllic Whitebrook Valley, one mile from the River Wye, The Crown at Whitebrook started life in 1679 and is now an award-winning restaurant with 12 comfortable en suite bedrooms all with modern facilities. The hotel features in all the independent guides. Your hosts are Sandra and Roger Bates, resident chef/ proprietors and their dog Portia.

The cuisine is French but not nouveau. Everything is cooked to order from the best of local ingredients. The wine list is extensive and carries something for every pocket. The house style is friendly with relaxed, informal yet very professional service.

The Wye Valley has a wealth of history from Roman times through the Welsh border battles to the end of the Industrial Revolution. It is now a haven of peace that is rightly designated as an Area of Outstanding Natural Beauty and probably contains the highest density of castles and historic sites in Britain.

Bristol and Cardiff with their theatres, museums and galleries are within easy reach. For a relaxing day out, the historic towns of Monmouth, Chepstow and Ross are well worth a visit.

For the golfer, there are eight excellent courses within 25 minutes. Fishing, cycling, horse riding, caving and canoeing are available nearby and footpaths from The Crown join The Offa's Dyke Path and Wye Valley Walk.

LOCATION

From Heathrow: Travel west on M4, take first exit after crossing Severn Bridge, follow signs for Monmouth (A466) through Tintern and Llandogo. At Bigsweir Bridge, bear left for Whitebrook. The Crown is 2 miles up a narrow country lane, on left.

Whitebrook, Monmouth, Gwent NP5 4TX

Telephone 01600 860254
Fax 01600 860607

PROPRIETORS

Roger and Sandra Bates

ROOM RATES

Single occupancy	*£45*
11 Doubles/Twins	*£62 - £70*
1 Four-poster	*£76 - £84*

Includes full breakfast and VAT

CHARGE/CREDIT CARDS

• DC • JCB • MC • VI

ACCOLADES

W.T.B. ♛♛♛ Highly Commended
A.A. ★★ ❀❀❀ 73%
Logis of Great Britain Regional Cuisine Competition Winner 1993
The Good Hotel Guide

FACILITIES

Gardens
1 meeting room/max 20 people
Golf, riding and fishing nearby

RESTRICTIONS

No facilities for disabled guests

ATTRACTIONS

Tintern Abbey, Chepstow Castle, Forest of Dean, Raglan Castle, Brecon Beacons, Wye Valley, Clearwell Caves

AFFILIATIONS

Welsh Rarebits
Logis of Great Britain

NEAREST

MAJOR CITY:
Cardiff - 20 miles/40 mins

MAJOR AIRPORT:
London Heathrow - 100 miles/1½ hrs

RAILWAY STATION:
Chepstow - 12 miles/15 mins

RESERVATIONS

Direct with hotel

ACCESS CODES

Not applicable

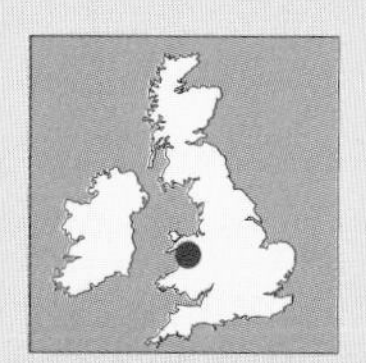

“ A veritable ‘box of delights’ ”

Amanda Drew, Portsmouth

DOLMELYNLLYN HALL

16th century manor house

Ganllwyd, Dolgellau, Gwynedd LL40 2HP

Telephone 01341 440273
Fax 01341 440273

PROPRIETORS
The Barkwith family

ROOM RATES

2 Singles	£42.50 - £55
6 Doubles	£80 - £95
1 Four-poster	£100 - £110
1 Suite	£100 - £110

Includes full breakfast, tea on arrival and VAT

CHARGE/CREDIT CARDS

• DC • MC • VI

ACCOLADES
W.T.B. ♛♛♛♛ Highly Commended
A.A. ★★★ ❀ 70%
Regional Cuisine Competition finalist 1994 – Logis of Great Britain

FACILITIES
Gardens, fishing on the river and lake
1 meeting room/max 18 people

RESTRICTIONS
No children under 10 years
No facilities for disabled guests
No smoking

ATTRACTIONS
Erddig House, Penrhyn Castle, Plas Newydd, Harlech Castle, Snowdonia National Park, narrow gauge railways, gold mines, slate caverns, The Alternative Technology Centre

AFFILIATIONS
Logis of Great Britain

NEAREST
MAJOR CITY:
Chester - 55 miles/1¾ hrs

MAJOR AIRPORT:
Manchester - 65 miles/2 hrs

RAILWAY STATION:
Barmouth - 10 miles/20 mins

RESERVATIONS
Direct with hotel

ACCESS CODES
Not applicable

WALES

In the land that time forgot

Dolmelynllyn, ‘The House by the Yellow Lake’, is a small manor dating from the 16th century nestling in the hills above the River Mawddach surrounded by its own terraced gardens with mountains and meadows beyond. It was enlarged during the last century to become a substantial country house which, today, is filled with family possessions and furniture creating the tranquil atmosphere and informal elegance of earlier times. The facilities are of the 20th century and blend unobtrusively into their mature surroundings.

This is the ideal place to explore the lesser-known attractions of Mid-Wales and South Snowdonia, an area of magnificent scenery and wildlife, of castles and stately homes as well as the enchantment of the ‘Great Little Trains of Wales’.

In the evening, returning guests can look forward to the culinary pleasures prepared by Joanna, the daughter of the house, who creates a daily changing menu wonderfully enhanced by contents of the extensive wine cellar. After dinner, guests may enjoy the disappearing art of conversation in one of the two sitting rooms or lose themselves in a good book in the library. The whole house is a non-smoking area.

Although no attempt is made to offer a formal hotel service, the comfort and care for guests is the prime concern of the family and its friendly staff.

Dolmelynllyn is altogether a delight and short stays with dinner included are available upon request.

LOCATION

The drive entrance is at the southern end of Ganllwyd, 5 miles north of Dolgellau on the A470.

" An evening of very special delights "

Jack Higgins, author

Georgian manor house

EDDERTON HALL

Forden, Nr Welshpool, Montgomeryshire SY21 8RZ

Telephone 01938 580339
Fax 01938 580452

PROPRIETORS

The Hon Warren Hawksley, MP and Evelyn Hawksley

ROOM RATES

2 Singles	*£22*
1 Superior Single	*£35*
3 Doubles/Twins	*£48*
1 Four-poster with Victorian bath	*£65*
1 Four-poster with jacuzzi	*£70*

Includes full breakfast and VAT

CHARGE/CREDIT CARDS

• *DC* • *MC* • *VI*

ACCOLADES

W.T.B. ♛♛♛♛ Commended
R.A.C. ★★ + Merit Award R
Logis Three Fireplaces

FACILITIES

Garden, chess, jigsaws, old books, heli-pad Quad trekking, shooting, riding and golf nearby

RESTRICTIONS

No children under 10 years
No facilities for disabled guests

ATTRACTIONS

Powis Castle and Gardens, Montgomery Castle, Celtica Museum, Machynlleth Centre for Alternative Technology, Brother Cadfael's home

AFFILIATIONS

Logis of Great Britain

NEAREST

MAJOR CITY:
Chester - 40 miles/50 mins

MAJOR AIRPORT:
Birmingham - 75 miles/1½ hr
Welshpool - 1 mile/3 mins

RAILWAY STATION:
Welshpool - 2 miles/5 mins

RESERVATIONS

Direct with hotel

ACCESS CODES

Not applicable

WALES

Comfortable home with a friendly ghost and ancestral portraits

Edderton Hall is a country house hotel in the true sense. The rooms are comfortable and the service unpretentious. There is a friendly ghost, the floorboards creak, you can bring the dog, leave your muddy wellingtons in the porch, and they do not ban you from smoking or insist that you dress for dinner.

There are no keep fit facilities except the stairs, but the outdoor activities more than compensate. Walking (Offas Dyke passes within 400 yards) shooting, riding and golf are all nearby. In an area rich in myth and legend, there are ruins to explore, castles, museums, chapels; gardens, lakes, waterfalls and narrow gauge railways to enjoy. You may also learn to fly, shoot or rally drive or go quad trekking.

What they have to offer at Edderton is a very warm welcome, beautiful views across the Severn Valley to Powis Castle, a well stocked cellar and excellent food. The nightly feast, with a small choice on most of four courses, features fresh local produce enhanced by home-grown herbs and vegetables. Welsh lamb is a particular speciality in the summer with mint and elderflower fritters; in autumn and winter it is studded with garlic and rosemary and finished over the wood fire in the dining room. Game from Mr Hawksley's shoot is served in a variety of guises. Home-made breads, soups and puddings and ice-creams all contribute to a memorable gastronomic experience. And don't be surprised if your drinks are served by a Member of Parliament when the House isn't sitting.

LOCATION

1½ miles from Welshpool on A490 Montgomery road. Leave Welshpool by-pass on A490. Pass airport and continue over bridge and up hill. Turn down drive opposite riding school.

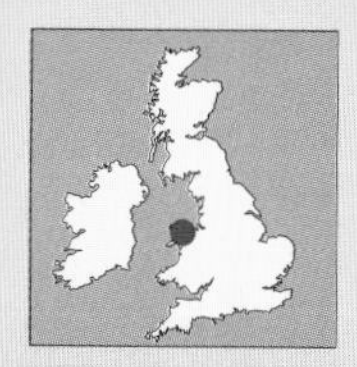

" Send me 10 postcards. We enjoyed our stay with you so much I want to send cards to all my friends and relatives. We hope to return very soon "

Val Ashcroft, Cheshire

THE EMPIRE

Victorian resort hotel

Church Walks, Llandudno, Gwynedd LL30 2HE

Telephone 01492 860555
Fax 01492 860791

PROPRIETORS
Len and Elizabeth Maddocks

MANAGERS
Elyse and Michael Waddy

ROOM RATES

4 Singles	£45 - £65
47 Doubles/Twins	£70 - £95
7 Suites	£85 - £100

Includes full breakfast and VAT

CHARGE/CREDIT CARDS

• DC • JCB • MC • VI

ACCOLADES
W.T.B. ♛♛♛♛♛ De Luxe
R.A.C. ★★★ + Merit Awards H C & R
A.A. ★★★ ❀ 75%

FACILITIES
Sauna, steamroom,
indoor/outdoor pools with whirlpools,
beauty therapist,
1 meeting room/max 40 people
Golf and riding nearby

RESTRICTIONS
No pets allowed
No facilities for disabled guests

ATTRACTIONS
Caernarfon and Conwy Castles,
Bodnant Gardens,
Snowdonia National Park,
Portmeirion Village

AFFILIATIONS
Independent

NEAREST
MAJOR CITY:
Chester - 45 miles/50 mins

MAJOR AIRPORT:
Manchester - 84 miles/1½ hrs

RAILWAY STATION:
Llandudno Junction - 4 miles/15 mins

RESERVATIONS
Direct with hotel

ACCESS CODES
Not applicable

Luxury accommodation at affordable prices for that special occasion

The Empire has been owned by the Maddocks family since 1946 and now has a third generation of the family in charge. Conveniently located, the hotel is situated in Wales's most stylish resort remaining unspoilt with the passing of time, an ideal centre for touring Snowdonia, medieval castles and the world-famous Bodnant Gardens.

The hotel is furnished throughout with antiques and silk drapes. A special feature is the largest private collection of artist's proofs by Sir William Russell Flint outside the Flint estate. Impeccably appointed, the bedroooms and suites have original cast iron beds clad in French linen, goose down duvets and pillows, satellite TV/video. The Italian marble bathrooms have jacuzzi baths and all modern amenities.

The award-winning Watkins Restaurant serves fresh local produce and locally caught fish prepared by son-in-law, Michael Waddy, and his team of enthusiastic chefs. The daily changing menu is complemented by an extensive wine list. The poolside Coffee Shop is available for lighter meals.

Amongst the hotel's facilities are indoor and outdoor heated swimming pools, sauna, steam room and whirlpool, roof terraces and patio. A beauty therapist is also in residence. And there is a fully equipped conference room. Mini breaks and discounted rates for dinner, bed and breakfast are offered throughout the year.

LOCATION

Take A55 to the turn off with A470. Follow signs to Llandudno then Promenade. At pier, turn left into Church Walks. Hotel 56 metres on the right.

“ Peace, beauty and wonderful food and a great welcome ”

P D James

Georgian manor house

FAIRYHILL

'Midst woods and valleys there's a kitchen of delightful surprises

Fairyhill is a haven of peace and tranquillity, nestling in the heart of the beautiful Gower peninsular. A delightful mansion built in 1720 and still the epitome of relaxed country living. Here, in 24 acres of park and woodland alongside the beautiful valley through which the little Burry trout stream meanders, you can be at peace!

The pleasantly furnished bedrooms offer all the essentials for an enjoyable stay. Each is equipped with remote controlled TV and CD stereo systems and you will be welcome to enjoy the music from an extensive CD library.

In the public rooms there is every service, and if the day keeps you indoors there is lunch in the dining room or afternoon tea in the drawing room.

Chef, Paul Davies has achieved recognition in several major food guides. The menus are designed around the seasons and the locality with regular use of sewin (a local fish), lobster and, if the fancy takes you, famous laverbread.

The surrounding scenery will be an added pleasure to your stay. The famous beaches and spectacular Worms Head are a few minutes away. For the golfing enthusiast there is a choice from five golf courses (parkland and links) within eight miles.

LOCATION

Take Junction 47 off M4 and follow signs to Gowerton/Gower. At Gowerton turn right at lights – B4295 through Penclawdd Crofty and Oldwalls. Fairyhill is 1 mile past Greyhound Inn on left.

Reynoldston, Gower, Swansea, West Glamorgan SA3 1BS

Telephone 01792 390139
Fax 01792 391358

PROPRIETORS

Andrew Hetherington, Peter Camm, Jane Camm and Paul Davies

ROOM RATES

Single occupancy	*£65 - £110*
8 Doubles	*£85 - £120*

Includes early morning tea, newspaper, full breakfast and VAT

CHARGE/CREDIT CARDS

• *JCB* • *MC* • *VI*

ACCOLADES

W.T.B. ♛♛♛ *Highly Commended*
A.A. ★★ ❀❀ *74%*
A.A. Courtesy and Care Award 1995

FACILITIES

Croquet, gardens, heli-pad
1 meeting room/max 24 people
Riding and fishing nearby

RESTRICTIONS

No children under 8 years

ATTRACTIONS

The Gower Peninsula, Swansea, Weobley Castle, Aberdulais Falls, Brangwyn Hall

AFFILIATIONS

Welsh Rarebits

NEAREST

MAJOR CITY:
Swansea - 12 miles/25 mins

MAJOR AIRPORT:
London Heathrow - 170 miles/2½ hrs
Cardiff - 50 miles/1 hr

RAILWAY STATION:
Swansea - 12 miles/25 mins

RESERVATIONS

Direct with hotel

ACCESS CODES

Not applicable

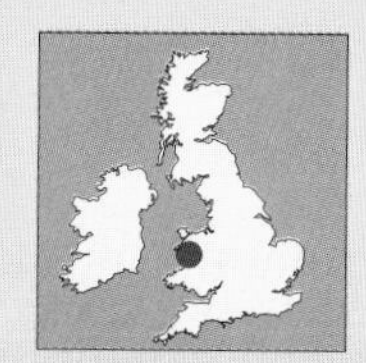

“ The atmosphere is friendly and relaxed, while the service is impeccable. The Cartwrights have got it exactly right ”

Allan James, Location Manager, First Knight Productions, London

GEORGE III HOTEL

17th century inn

Penmaenpool, Dolgellau, Gwynedd LL40 1YD

Telephone 01341 422525
Fax 01341 423565

OWNERS
John and Julia Cartwright

ROOM RATES
Single occupancy £37.50 - £45
12 Doubles/Twins £70 - £88
Includes full breakfast and VAT

CREDIT CARDS
JCB • MC • VI

ACCOLADES
W.T.B. ♛♛♛♛ Highly Commended
R.A.C. ★★
A.A. ★★ 66%

FACILITIES
Gardens, fishing, mountain bikes
1 meeting room/max 20 people
Golf, pony trekking, walking, clay pigeon shooting and riding nearby

RESTRICTIONS
No smoking in restaurant

ATTRACTIONS
Snowdonia National Park
Cymer Abbey, Harlech Castle, Ffestiniog Railway, Difi Furnace, Dinas Oleu, Cader Idris

AFFILIATIONS
Independent

NEAREST
MAJOR CITY:
Chester - 70 miles/1½ hrs

MAJOR AIRPORT:
Manchester - 90 miles/2 hrs

RAILWAY STATION:
Barmouth - 8 miles/15 mins

RESERVATIONS
Direct with hotel

ACCESS CODES
Not applicable

Wonderful location for the energetic or not so energetic

The George III Hotel is situated on the edge of the magnificent Mawddach Estuary, said to be one of the most beautiful in Europe. The main hotel was built circa 1650 and was once two separate buildings, pub and ship chandlers, which were united over a century ago to form the gracious George III. The adjacent Lodge is a Victorian building built as a Waiting Room, Ticket Office and Station Master's house for the adjacent railway station, now closed. The building was then acquired by the hotel in 1977 and extended and renovated to form six bedrooms with private bathrooms.

Guests may choose between accommodation in the hotel or in the lodge; whatever the choice their comfort is assured. Each bedroom is individually furnished and decorated, with wonderful estuary views. Ancient wooden beams and a huge inglenook fireplace all create an atmosphere of warmth and welcome.

The hotel is owned and personally run by John and Julia Cartwright and their family. Great emphasis is placed on the food with Welsh lamb and seafood a speciality. On fine days, Welsh cream teas and bar lunches are served on the balcony overlooking the estuary. The cellar bar is ideal for families with children's menu, no smoking and seating outside overlooking the estuary.

Energetic guests can enjoy the use of the hotel's mountain bikes or fish over 12 miles of river and lake for salmon and trout. Clay pigeon shooting and power trekking make an exciting day out or perhaps a visit to a gold mine, castle or one of the many little railways in the area.

LOCATION

Turn left off A470 signposted Tywyn, approximately 2 miles, turn right for toll bridge, then first left for hotel.

"Everything was of an excellent standard with everything provided"

S E Woods, Shrewsbury

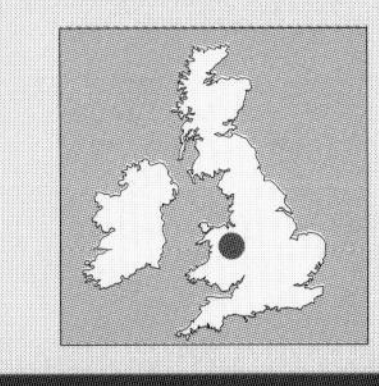

16th century farmhouse

THE HAND HOTEL

A cosy hideaway in the beautiful Ceiriog Valley

Standing in an acre of garden in a picturesque village amid mountain scenery, The Hand Hotel is an excellent base for those wishing to explore this region. Originally a 16th-century farmhouse, it retains its beams and, in the bar, an open fire.

There are 13 bedrooms all with private bathrooms, TV, radio and direct dial telephones.

The varied table d'hôte menu has something to satisfy most tastes, offering many fish dishes, Welsh lamb and to finish, a selection of Welsh cheeses. Given prior notice, the kitchen is happy to cater for special diets. They also have a wide selection of wines to accompany your meal.

Take advantage of the hotel for nearby fishing, shooting and golf. The Hand is also perfectly situated for many fine walks through the Ceiriog, Tanat and Vyrnwy Valleys. The setting for the film "The Englishman That Went Up the Hill And Came Down A Mountain" was located in this area. Erddig Hall, Chirk Castle and Powis Castle, Snowdonia, Caernarfon, Portmeirion and Bodnant Gardens are within easy travelling distance, while Chester and Shrewsbury are only 34 miles away.

LOCATION

Take the A5/A483 to Chirk then the B4500 to Glyn Ceiriog and Llanarmon DC. Follow the road for 13 miles. The Hand is immediately facing you as you enter the village.

Llanarmon DC, Ceiriog Valley,
Nr Llangollen,
Clwyd LL20 7LD

Telephone 01691 600666
Fax 01691 600262

PROPRIETOR
Lilian Brunton

ROOM RATES
Single occupancy £36 - £45
13 Doubles £58 - £68
Includes full breakfast and VAT

CHARGE/CREDIT CARDS

• DC • MC • VI

ACCOLADES
W.T.B. ♛♛♛♛ Highly Commended

FACILITIES
Garden, croquet, riding
1 meeting room/max 20 people
Walking, shooting and fishing nearby

RESTRICTIONS
Pets by prior arrangement
Closed in February

ATTRACTIONS
Caernarfon Castle, Chirk Castle, Powis Castle, Erddig Hall, Bodnant Gardens, Pistyll Rhaeadr (waterfall), Snowdonia National Park, Portmeirion,Ceiriog, Tanat and Vyrnwy Valleys

AFFILIATIONS
Independent

NEAREST
MAJOR CITY:
Manchester - 80 miles/1¾ hrs

MAJOR AIRPORT:
Manchester - 75 miles/1¼ hrs

RAILWAY STATION:
Chirk - 12 miles/20 mins

RESERVATIONS
Direct with hotel

ACCESS CODES
Not applicable

WALES

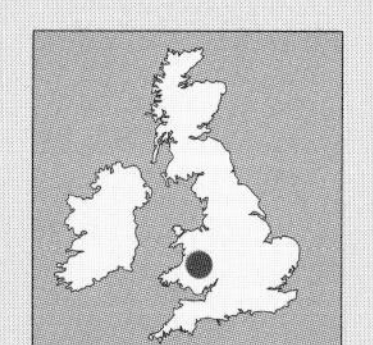

"You've bought a hotel and turned it into a home"

John J Howells, Cardiff

THE LAKE COUNTRY HOUSE

Victorian country house

Llangammarch Wells,
Powys LD4 4BS

Telephone 01591 620202
Fax 01591 620457

PROPRIETORS
Jean-Pierre and Janet Mifsud

ROOM RATES

Single occupancy	£70
2 Standard Doubles	£80
6 Luxury Doubles	£115
1 Four-poster	£110
10 Suites	£120 - £130

Includes full breakfast and VAT

CHARGE/CREDIT CARDS

• DC • JCB • MC • VI

ACCOLADES
W.T.B. ♛♛♛♛♛ De Luxe
R.A.C. Blue Ribbon Award ★★★
A.A. ★★★ ❀❀
A.A. Courtesy and Care Award
A.A. Inspectors Selected Hotel
The Good Hotel Guide – César Award

FACILITIES
Croquet, tennis, gardens, snooker, putting, heli-pad, clay pigeon shooting, salmon/trout fishing (river), trout fishing (lake)
1 meeting room/max 65 people

RESTRICTIONS
No children 7 years and under in dining room after 7 pm
Pets by prior arrangement

ATTRACTIONS
Powys Castle, The Elan Valley, Brecon Beacons, Hay-on-Wye's bookshops

AFFILIATIONS
Welsh Rarebits

NEAREST
MAJOR CITY:
Hereford - 40 miles/45 mins

MAJOR AIRPORT:
Cardiff - 60 miles/1 ¼ hrs

RAILWAY STATION:
Llangammarch Wells - 1 mile/5 mins

RESERVATIONS
Direct with hotel

ACCESS CODES
Not applicable

Retreat to the hills of Wales – to an idyllic haven

An air of elegance and calm informality pervades this exquisitely furnished Welsh country house. Warmly welcoming, this award-winning retreat stands serenely in 50 acres of parkland including a large trout lake, a haven for fascinating wildlife. In such a setting, guests may acquaint themselves with the true feeling of Wales.

One may enjoy a mouth-watering, traditional Welsh afternoon tea in front of log fires in the lounge or in the garden in summer. Dining by candlelight in the restaurant is a memorable experience; the cuisine has been winning prestigious awards for its excellence.

Suites and bedrooms are delightfully appointed, each having a private bathroom, television, direct-dial telephone, period furniture and fine pictures and books.

This is a sportsman's delight with excellent salmon and trout fishing available on both the rivers Wye and Irfon or on the hotel's own picturesque lake which regularly yields trout of five pounds and over and has no closed season. There is tennis, croquet, clay pigeon shooting and a six-hole golf course within the grounds. The hotel's billiards room is a popular evening venue. Golfing enthusiasts will find four 18-hole courses in the vicinity and pony trekking can be arranged.

LOCATION

Take the A40 to Abergavenny-Brecon, go through Brecon turning left onto the B4519 then turn left for Llangammarch Wells. Drive across Mount Eppynt (6 miles), at the foot of the hill, turn left and the hotel is one mile along on the right.

“ I will always remember my thoroughly enjoyable stay. The staff were incredibly nice and welcoming ”

Hugh Grant, actor

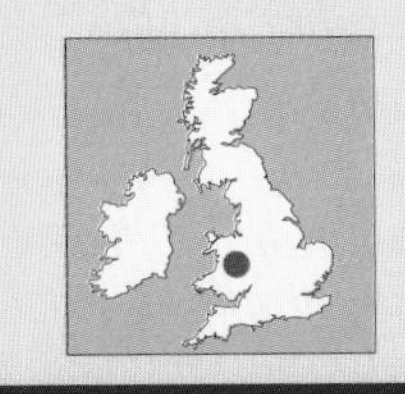

Victorian country house

LAKE VYRNWY HOTEL

A great estate for lovers of nature and bons vivants

This hotel is situated high on the hillsides within the 24,000 acres of the Vyrnwy Estate, commanding breathtaking views of mountains, lake and moorland. The hotel is surrounded by lawns and fringed with an abundance of rhododendrons, woods and meadowlands. Built in 1890, its heritage has been maintained for 100 years on as a retreat for all country lovers.

Each bedroom is individually furnished and decorated, many with antiques; some have jacuzzis, four-posters, suites or private balconies. The public rooms are all warm and welcoming with log fires. There is an elegant drawing room with cozy chintz sofas, a grand piano and oil paintings, whilst the cocktail bar has a club atmosphere, with deep leather chairs, sporting prints and pitch pine.

The award-winning restaurant has a menu which changes daily. Everything from the marmalade at breakfast to the bread rolls and petit-fours at dinner are created in the Vyrnwy kitchens.

The hotel owns sole sporting rights on the estate together with the fishing rights on the five-mile long lake. 16,000 acres are also a nature sanctuary providing a wealth of wildlife and beautiful walks. Other activities include tennis, cycling, boating and sailing. Peace and tranquillity reign. Special two-day breaks are available.

LOCATION

Follow brown tourist signs for Lake Vyrnwy from Shrewsbury A458 or from Oswesty A5.

Lake Vyrnwy, Llanwddyn, Montgomeryshire SY10 0LY

Telephone 01691 870692
Fax 01691 870259

MANAGER
Jim Talbot

ROOM RATES
33 Doubles/Twins £77.50 - £127.50
2 Suites £127.50
Includes full breakfast and VAT

CHARGE/CREDIT CARDS

• DC • MC • VI

ACCOLADES
W.T.B. ♛♛♛♛♛ De Luxe
R.A.C. ★★★ + Merit Awards C & R
A.A. ★★★ ❀❀ 72%
The Good Hotel Guide

FACILITIES
Garden, tennis, fly fishing, shooting, heli-pad
3 meeting rooms/max 130 people
Cycling, walking trails, RSPB Reserve, rowing, sailing, canoeing and clay pigeon shooting nearby

RESTRICTIONS
No facilities for disabled guests
No dogs in public areas

ATTRACTIONS
Powis Castle, Cymer Abbey, Great Little Trains of Wales, Vyrnwy Visitor Centre, Lake Vyrnwy

AFFILIATIONS
Independent

NEAREST
MAJOR CITY:
Shrewsbury - 32 miles/45 mins
Chester - 43 miles/1 hr

MAJOR AIRPORT:
Birmingham/Manchester - 90 miles/1½ hrs

RAILWAY STATION:
Welshpool - 22 miles/ 30 mins

RESERVATIONS
Direct with hotel

ACCESS CODES
Not applicable

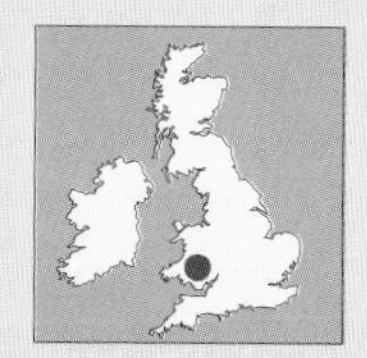

“I only knew I was not staying at a friend’s house when they gave me a bill”

Arthur Miller, 1990

LLANGOED HALL

Country house

Llyswen, Brecon, Powys LD3 0YP

Telephone 01874 754525
Fax 01874 754545

GENERAL MANAGERS
Gareth and Helen Pugh

ROOM RATES
2 Singles £95
10 Doubles/Twins £155 - £195
8 Four-posters £195
3 Suites £195 - £285
Includes tea and cake on arrival, full breakfast and VAT

CHARGE/CREDIT CARDS

• DC • JCB • MC • VI

ACCOLADES
W.T.B. De Luxe
R.A.C. ★★★★ + Merit Awards H C & R
A.A. ★★★★
Hotel of the Year 1994
The Good Hotel Guide

FACILITIES
Croquet, tennis, gardens, maze, snooker, fly fishing, heli-pad, heated kennels, 2 meeting rooms/max 50 people

RESTRICTIONS
No children under 8 years
No facilities for disabled guests
No pets in the house

ATTRACTIONS
Caerphilly and Raglan Castles, Brecon Beacons, Cardiff, Llanthony Priory, Hay-on-Wye

AFFILIATIONS
Welsh Rarebits
The Celebrated Hotels Collection
Small Luxury Hotels

NEAREST
MAJOR CITY:
Cardiff - 55 miles/1 hr

MAJOR AIRPORT:
London Heathrow - 160 miles/2½ hrs
Cardiff - 65 miles/1½ hrs

RAILWAY STATION:
Newport - 48 miles/1 hr

RESERVATIONS
Toll free in US/Canada: 800-322-2403
Toll free in Japan: 0120 4126220

ACCESS CODES
SABRE LX 30168
APOLLO LX 21658
AMADEUS/SYSTEM 1 LX CWLHHL
WORLDSPAN LX GLOLH
AXESS LX 5555

A magnificent country house hotel in Wales on the banks of the River Wye

Let me tell you about Llangoed Hall. When you arrive, there is no reception desk, no-one demanding a hostage credit card, just friendly staff to take your coats and carry your bags.

The dining room is handsome with yellows and cornflower blue. In Ben Davies, we are lucky to have one of the finest young chefs in Britain. His cooking is modern classical, prepared in a classic manner but with an emphasis on lightness. I like the way he insists on making the most of fresh local produce such as Welsh lamb, Wye salmon and traditional laverbread.

Upstairs, you will be greeted by warm Laura Ashley fabrics and every small comfort: fresh fruit, a decanter of sherry or mineral water ready to pour, plenty of books and, apart from the ubiquitous television, a radio. All of our spacious 23 bedrooms and suites are quite different from one another.

I think you'll find the Morning Room wonderfully restful. Here we will bring you a tray of our famous Welsh afternoon tea. The sort of tea Mrs Beeton would have applauded.

We hope you will think of Llangoed Hall as both a haven and a place for celebration. Gareth and Helen Pugh, our General Managers, and their charming, devoted staff will look forward to welcoming you to Llangoed Hall.

Sir Bernard Ashley

LOCATION

Situated 11 miles south east of Builth Wells and 11 miles north east of Brecon on the A470, the main road between Cardiff and Builth Wells. You can easily join the M4 motorway at Cardiff or Newport and the M50 at Ross-on-Wye.

"Comfortable rooms, beautiful gardens, delicious cuisine, and consummate hosts. We look forward to our return"

Norman & Kathryn Kinney, Michigan

600-year old manor house

HOTEL MAES-Y-NEUADD

Elegance and serenity in the midst of magnificent Snowdonia

Deep in Snowdonia, amongst some of the most beautiful scenery in Britain, the manor house of Maes-y-Neuadd has watched over this timeless, magnificent scene for more than 600 years.

For centuries the home of one family, the house is now owned by two couples, Olive and Malcolm Horsfall and June and Michael Slatter. Over the past twelve years, they have lovingly restored and refurbished the house, creating a warm and welcoming haven for travellers from all over the world. The rooms are furnished using the best of modern craftsmanship, filled with fine antiques and many paintings by local artists. The eight acres of grounds reflect the beauty of the seasons, nurtured by the mild Gulf Stream climate.

Chef Peter Jackson revels in the quality of the 'natural larder' on his doorstep. To complement the fine lamb, cheese, fish and game for which Wales is renowned, many of the vegetables, fruit and herbs are grown in their kitchen garden. Through the hotel's associate company, "Steam & Cuisine" all this can also be enjoyed on the famous Ffestiniog Railway.

The ancient language, culture and music, proudly preserved throughout the surrounding area, set this part of Wales apart from the rest of Britain. Above all the welcome, 'Croeso', for which Wales is so famous, is nowhere warmer than at Maes-y-Neuadd.

LOCATION

Located ½ mile off B4573, 3½ miles north of Harlech. Hotel sign on corner of lane.

Talsarnau, Nr Harlech, Gwynedd LL47 6YA

Telephone 01766 780200
Fax 01766 780211

PROPRIETORS

June and Michael Slatter
Olive and Malcolm Horsfall

ROOM RATES

1 Single	£40 - £70
12 Doubles/Twins	£95 - £162
1 Four-poster	£100 - £120
2 Suites	£120 - £190

Includes full breakfast and VAT

CHARGE/CREDIT CARDS

 • DC • JCB • MC • VI

ACCOLADES

W.T.B. ✿✿✿✿ De Luxe
R.A.C. Blue Ribbon Award ★★
A.A. ★★ ✿✿✿
The Good Hotel Guide

FACILITIES

Croquet, gardens, heli-pad
1 meeting room/max 20 people
Golf, riding, fishing, walking and shooting nearby

RESTRICTIONS

No children under 8 yrs at dinner after 7 pm
No facilities for disabled guests

ATTRACTIONS

Mount Snowdon, Caernarfon and Harlech Castles, Royal St David's Golf Course

AFFILIATIONS

Pride of Britain
Welsh Rarebits
The Celebrated Hotels Collection

NEAREST

MAJOR CITY:
Bangor - 35 miles/1 hr

MAJOR AIRPORT:
Manchester - 100 miles/2 hrs

RAILWAY STATION:
Harlech - 3 miles/10 mins

RESERVATIONS

Toll free fax in US: 800-635-3602

ACCESS CODES

Not applicable

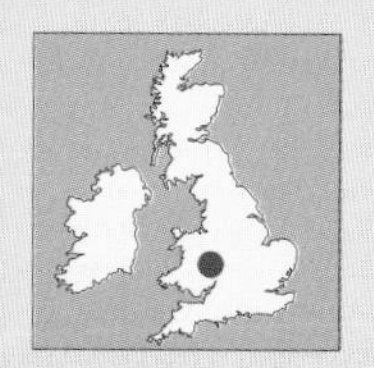

"Beautiful house, gracious hospitality"

Ken & Ellen Shipley, California

MILEBROOK HOUSE

Country house

**Milebrook, Knighton,
Powys LD7 1LT**

**Telephone 01547 528632
Fax 01547 520509**

PROPRIETORS
Mr and Mrs R T Marsden

ROOM RATES
Single occupancy £47
6 Doubles/Twins £67
Includes full breakfast and VAT

CHARGE/CREDIT CARDS

• DC • JCB • MC • VI

ACCOLADES
W.T.B. Highly Commended
A.A.★★ 72%
The Good Hotel Guide

FACILITIES
*Garden, croquet,
heli-pad, fishing
Golf, riding and walking nearby*

RESTRICTIONS
*No children under 8 years
No facilities for disabled guests
No pets allowed*

ATTRACTIONS
*Ludlow, Offas Dyke,
Powys Castle and Gardens,
Brecon Beacons*

AFFILIATIONS
*Wales, Great Little Places
Logis of Great Britain*

NEAREST
*MAJOR CITY:
Shrewsbury - 25 miles/40 mins*

*MAJOR AIRPORT:
Birmingham - 55 miles/1¾ hrs
Shobdon - 10 miles/15 mins*

*RAILWAY STATION:
Knighton - 2 miles/5 mins*

RESERVATIONS
Direct with hotel

ACCESS CODES
Not applicable

WALES

Centrally situated in one of the most attractive areas of the country

Milebrook House is set amidst wooded, rolling Marches landscape, much of which is designated an area of outstanding natural beauty. The house was once the home of Wilfred Thesiger the explorer and was visited by Emperor Haile Selassie. Now sensitively restored, there are six spacious bedrooms, a bar, sitting room and elegant dining room which is open to non-residents. The food is prepared with imagination and skill using fresh home-grown and local produce; the extensive wine list is chosen with care.

The three acres of gardens and grounds surrounding the house include formal gardens with croquet lawn, herbaceous gardens and a productive kitchen garden leading to the river Teme and riverside walks. Trout fly-fishing is available from the hotel.

Offas Dyke is superb for bird watching and walking. Driving is a pleasure on traffic-free roads. For golfers there are nearby courses at Knighton, Kington and Ludlow.

The turbulent history of the Marches has left numerous picturesque castles and towns within easy reach. The old Marcher capital, Ludlow, with its splendid Norman castle, narrow alleys and market square, can justly claim to be one of the most beautiful towns in Britain. Even closer to hand are the border townships of Clun, Bishops Castle, Presteigne and Kington.

LOCATION

Situated 2 miles to the east of Knighton on the A4113, Ludlow Road.

“ I cannot remember a more pleasant stay at any hotel in the world. I had no idea there was such a jewel in South Wales ”

Kenneth Wolstenholme, Surrey

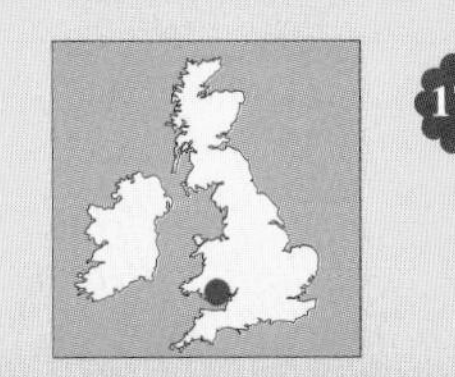

11th century manor house

MISKIN MANOR

It would be difficult to find a more beautiful building in Wales

Nestling in the lush rolling hills of Mid Glamorgan, South Wales, is the beautiful Miskin Manor Country House Hotel, whose history dates back to 1092 AD when a manor on this site was the home of the Prince of Glamorgan's daughter. The Grade II listed charming mellow stone-faced building, was constructed in its present form in 1858 on the banks of the River Ely.

With the oak panelled public and dining rooms, each with open fireplaces, a most comfortable haven is provided.

The surrounding 20 acres of private gardens, edged with topiary hedges and woodlands, offers a home to many rare and interesting species of flora and fauna, and ensures peace and tranquillity.

The 32 individually appointed en suite bedrooms include a suite which was once occupied by the Prince of Wales, latterly King Edward VII, and two four-poster rooms. All rooms are spacious and offer charm and every comfort. The conference suites are many and varied.

The Meisgyn à la carte restaurant is renowned for its Welsh produce: Welsh Black Beef, Llangollen lamb and Brecon venison, and presents a wide choice of dishes which includes several vegetarian selections. This is matched with a fine international wine list.

Fredericks, their sports and leisure club, extends excellent facilities for all guests.

LOCATION

South Wales, 1¾ miles from Junction 34 of the M4. 8 miles from Cardiff on the A4119.

Miskin, Pontyclun, Nr Cardiff, Mid Glamorgan CF7 8ND

Telephone 01443 224204
Fax 01443 237606

GENERAL MANAGER

John Millard

ROOM RATES

4 Singles	*£55 - £80*
25 Doubles/Twins	*£70 - £110*
2 Four-posters	*£95 - £110*
1 Suite	*£110 - £175*

Includes full breakfast and VAT

CHARGE/CREDIT CARDS

• *DC* • *MC* • *VI*

ACCOLADES

W.T.B. ♛♛♛♛♛ *Highly Commended*
R.A.C. ★★★ + *Merit Awards C & R*
A.A. ★★★★ ❀ *65%*

FACILITIES

Garden, croquet, indoor pool, squash, snooker, sauna, jacuzzi, health & beauty, gym, heli-pad
5 meeting rooms/max 200 people
Golf and riding nearby

RESTRICTIONS

No facilities for disabled guests
No pets

ATTRACTIONS

National Museum of Wales, St Fagan's, Cardiff Museum, Caerphilly Castle

AFFILIATIONS

Independent

NEAREST

MAJOR CITY:
Cardiff - 8 miles/15 mins

MAJOR AIRPORT:
London Heathrow - 110 miles/2 hrs
Cardiff - 8 miles/20 mins

RAILWAY STATION:
Cardiff - 10 miles/15 mins

RESERVATIONS

Toll free in US: 800-544-9993

ACCESS CODES

Not applicable

“ The torch for cooking on the North Wales coast is carried by Wendy Vaughan ”

Vogue Magazine

THE OLD RECTORY

Georgian country house

***Llansanffraid Glan Conwy,
Nr Conwy,
Gwynedd LL28 5LF***

***Telephone 01492 580611
Fax 01492 584555***

PROPRIETORS

Michael and Wendy Vaughan

ROOM RATES

Single occupancy	*£52 - £72*
5 Doubles/Twins	*£84 - £114*
1 Four-poster	*£84 - £114*

Includes full breakfast and VAT

CHARGE/CREDIT CARDS

• DC • JCB • MC • VI

ACCOLADES

W.T.B. ♛♛♛♛ *De Luxe*
R.A.C. Blue Ribbon Award ★
A.A. ★★ ❀❀❀
The Good Hotel Guide

FACILITIES

Gardens
Golf, riding and fishing nearby
Car hire arranged to meet train

RESTRICTIONS

No children under 5 years
No facilities for disabled guests
No pets in main house
No smoking in main house

ATTRACTIONS

Conwy Castle,
Bodnant Gardens,
Snowdonia National Park,
Llandudno

AFFILIATIONS

Welsh Rarebits
Selected British Hotels
Wolsey Lodges

NEAREST

MAJOR CITY:
Chester - 40 miles/45 mins

MAJOR AIRPORT:
Manchester - 70 miles/1 1/2 hrs

RAILWAY STATION:
Llandudno Junction - 1 1/2 miles/5 mins

RESERVATIONS

Toll free in US: 800-323-5463

ACCESS CODES

AMADEUS HK CEGOLD
SABRE HK 31998
APOLLO HT 25905
WORLDSPAN/SAHARA HK OLDRE

WALES

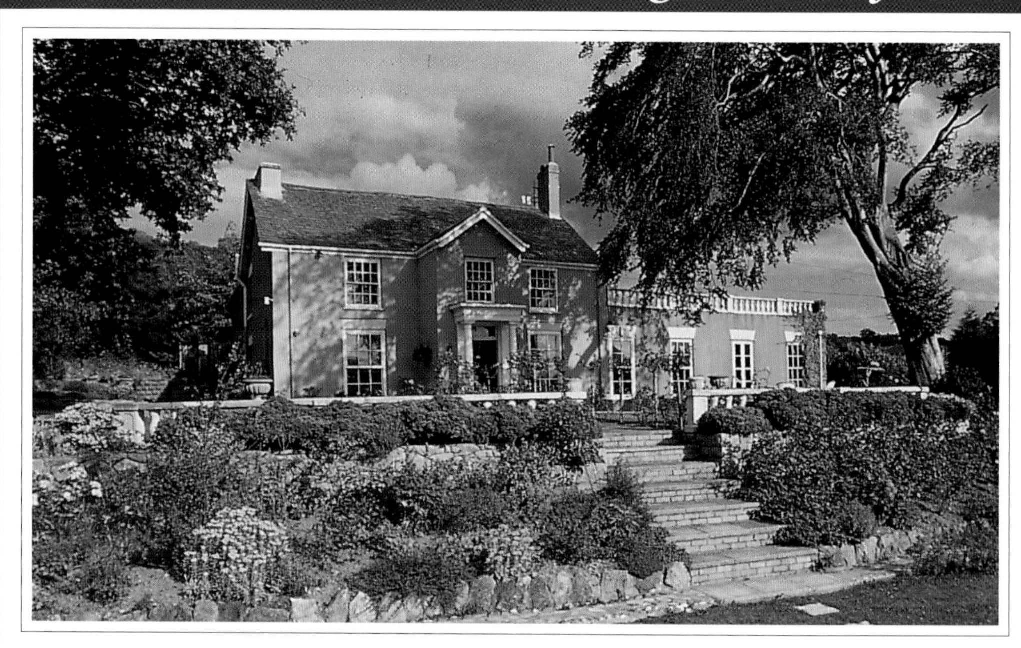

“Outstanding comfort, welcome, service and food” – lovely place, too!

The panoramic views from the gardens are reason enough for staying at this charming Old Rectory. Its hillside perch overlooks the grand sweep of Conwy estuary, historic Conwy Castle and the Snowdonia Mountains. There are many things to delight the eye in this elegant Georgian country house. Its highly polished rooms are decorated with old paintings, antiques and porcelain.

The Vaughans have created a calm, relaxing, unfussy atmosphere and have received an award for 'Welsh Hospitality at its Best'. They have also been granted Red Star status by the A.A. and a coveted Blue Ribbon by the R.A.C. for 'outstanding comfort, welcome, service and food'. This six-bedroom country house is deserving of its 'De Luxe' Tourist Board classification. Wendy Vaughan's acclaimed cuisine – she is Wales's highest-rated female chef in a major good food guide – is complemented by an award-winning wine cellar.

Situated midway between Chester and Caernarfon, it is an ideal centre for touring North Wales, Bodnant Gardens, historic Conwy, the Victorian seaside spa of Llandudno. Within three miles there are three championship golf courses. Michael's help with touring routes and his knowledge of all things Welsh, guarantee a memorable stay. You are assured of personal attention at this 'beautiful haven of peace'.

LOCATION

On the A470, ½ mile south of its junction with the A55.

“We found Palé Hall a haven of peace and tranquillity . . . Good food and accommodation”

Mr & Mrs Holmes, Derbyshire

PALÉ HALL COUNTRY HOUSE

A magnificent house once graced by the presence of Queen Victoria

Palé Hall, a luxurious Victorian mansion set in acres of parkland, was built in 1870 for a wealthy Scottish gentleman, his profession being that of an engineer. His brief to the architects was that “no expense should be spared” in building this family home.

This splendid house has stunning interiors including exquisite features like the magnificent entrance hall with its lofty vaulted ceiling and galleried oak staircase, the boudoir with its handpainted ceiling, the marble bar and fireplaces. Each of the bedrooms is individually and beautifully decorated and provide every comfort for a good night's rest. The public rooms express a quiet confidence reflecting the more leisured times in which they were built.

All bedrooms are individually decorated and en suite with television, direct dial telephone, luxury toiletries and hospitality tray. They all enjoy a commanding view of the gardens and surrounding panoramic scenery, including the entrance to the Queen's Walk named after a stay by Queen Victoria in 1889. The original bath and half tester bed used by Her Majesty during her stay are still available for the comfort of guests.

The restaurant is acclaimed for its good food, including vegetarian and other diets, the emphasis on the fresh and natural with a regular change of menu. The restaurant possesses a restful intimate atmosphere for that ‘by candlelight’ dinner.

Palé Hall is easily accessible by road and is an excellent base for touring.

LOCATION

The house is situated just off the B4401 Corwen to Bala road 4 to 5 miles from Llandrillo.

Llandderfel, Bala, Gwynedd LL23 7PS

Telephone 01678 530285
Fax 01678 530220

PROPRIETORS

Saul and Judith Nahed

ROOM RATES

1 Single £85 - £95
16 Doubles/Twins £160 - £175
Includes full breakfast, dinner and VAT

CHARGE/CREDIT CARDS

• DC • MC • VI

ACCOLADES

W.T.B ♛♛♛♛ Highly Commended
A.A.★★★ 70%

FACILITIES

Croquet, gardens, heli-pad, clay pigeon shooting, salmon and trout fishing.
2 meeting rooms/max 40 people
Game shooting arranged by appointment

RESTRICTIONS

None

ATTRACTIONS

Ffestiniog narrow gauge railway, Horseshoe Pass, Snowdonia National Park, Llangollen narrow gauge railway

AFFILIATIONS

Independent

NEAREST

MAJOR CITY:
Wrexham - 30 miles/40 mins

MAJOR AIRPORT:
Manchester - 70 miles/1¾ hrs

RAILWAY STATION:
Welshpool - 30 miles/40 mins

RESERVATIONS

Direct with hotel

ACCESS CODES

Not applicable

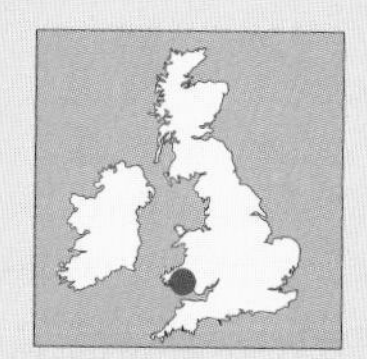

"We raise our wine glasses to toast the magnificent south Pembrokeshire coast. What better way to end a perfect day in this enchanting place, the Riviera of Wales"

P Wyman, Calgary Herald

PENALLY ABBEY

17th century abbey

Penally, Nr Tenby, Pembrokeshire SA70 7PY

Telephone 01834 843033
Fax 01834 844714

PROPRIETORS
Stephen and Elleen Warren

ROOM RATES

Single occupancy	£60
5 Doubles/Twins	£92
7 Four-posters	£104

Includes full breakfast, newspaper and VAT

WALES

CHARGE/CREDIT CARDS

• MC • VI

ACCOLADES
W.T.B. ♛♛♛♛ De Luxe
A.A. ★★ ❀❀ 81%

FACILITIES
Garden, croquet, indoor pool, snooker
1 meeting room/max 12 people
Golf, riding and fishing nearby

RESTRICTIONS
No children under 7 years allowed in restaurant in the evening
No facilities for disabled guests
No pets

ATTRACTIONS
Tenby,
Dillon Thomas Boathouse,
Pembroke Castle, Manorbear Castle

AFFILIATIONS
Welsh Rarebits

NEAREST
MAJOR CITY:
Cardiff - 90 miles/1¾ hrs

MAJOR AIRPORT:
London Heathrow - 150 miles/4 hrs
Cardiff - 90 miles/1¾ hrs

RAILWAY STATION:
Tenby - 1¼ miles/5 mins

RESERVATIONS
Direct with hotel

ACCESS CODES
Not applicable

Panache and a leisurely pace, high above an incomparable coastline

Penally Abbey is, quite simply, one of Pembrokeshire's loveliest listed country houses. Elegant but not imposing, its very name conjures up an air of tranquillity, where the emphasis is on relaxation.

The five acres of gardens and woodland, wishing well and a ruined chapel, the last surviving link with its monastic past.

The elegant lounge and dining room, overlooking the gardens and terrace, enjoy spectacular sea views across the golf course and Carmarthen Bay. Sympathetically furnished and decorated, the effect is romantic without being sentimental.

Dinner is a candlelit affair, with mouthwatering dishes of fresh seasonal delicacies, complemented by excellent wines from the cellar. Each meal is a celebration especially prepared for you.

The bedrooms are exquisitely furnished and decorated with antiques and period furniture. Many have four-poster beds and all have en suite bathrooms, tea and coffee making facilities, telephones, colour television and hairdryers. Whether in the main building or the adjoining converted coach-house you will be delighted with their old world charm.

After an exciting day, unwind in the warm indoor pool; play snooker, or just sip cocktails on the terrace before dinner.

LOCATION

Penally Abbey is situated adjacent to the 12th century church on the village green in the village of Penally, 1½ miles from Tenby. Off the A4139 Tenby-Pembroke coast road.

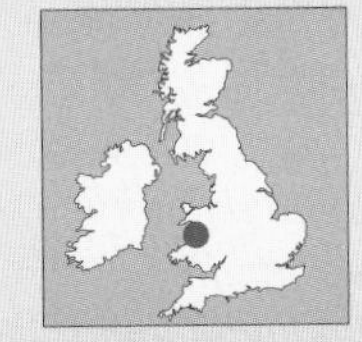

"Penmaenuchaf is a precisely cut gem in an artful setting"

Elizabeth King, travel and food writer, Australia

Victorian mansion

PENMAENUCHAF HALL

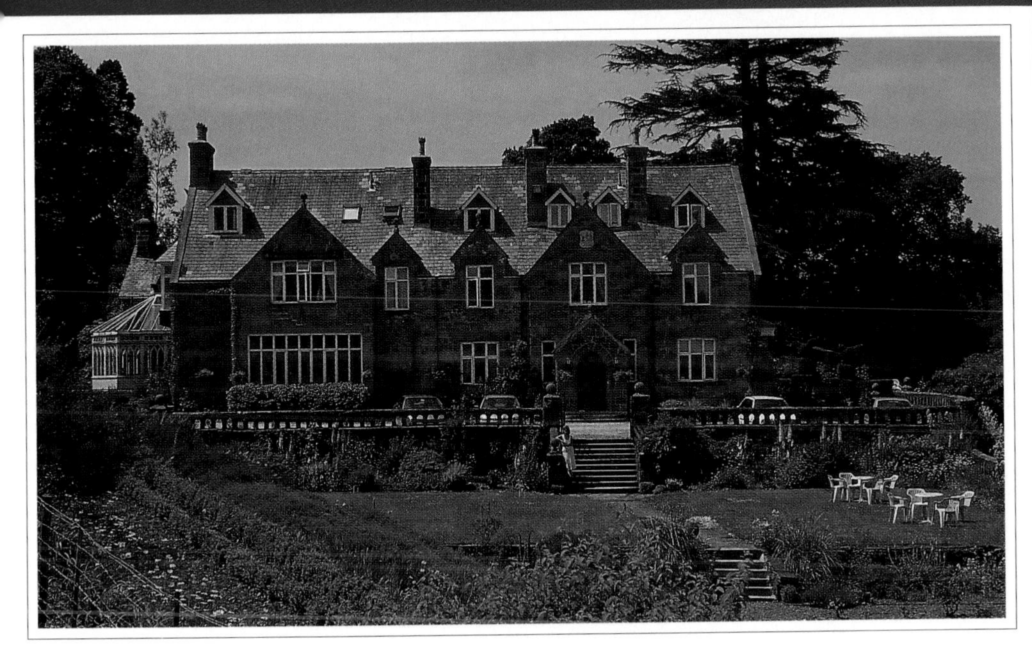

A secluded hideaway in the foothills of Cader Idris, Snowdonia

The splendour of the magnificent Cader Idris forms the backdrop to this handsome Victorian mansion. Set within the Snowdonia National Park amidst 21 acres of landscaped gardens and woodland, the views of the Mawddach Estuary and the mountains beyond are breathtaking.

Originally built in 1860 by a Bolton cotton magnate as a summer and sporting residence, Penmaenuchaf Hall is a relative newcomer to the Welsh luxury hotel scene and already ranks as one of the finest hotels in Wales. The beautiful interior features oak and mahogany panelling, stained glass windows, blazing log fires and an abundance of fresh cut flowers.

Guests are delighted with the superb food prepared by the talented, award-winning chefs. Fresh local produce and herbs from the gardens combine to create the exceptional cuisine. To complement the food there is an extensive selection of wines from various regions of the world.

Penmaenuchaf Hall is secluded and yet within easy reach of many attractions such as historic castles, 'Great Little Trains' and gold and slate mines. The hall boasts 13 miles of salmon and sea trout fishing; it is an ideal base for walking, horse riding and gold panning to name but a few activities. For the less energetic, there is a choice of snooker, cards, backgammon and a grand piano.

LOCATION

From Dolgellau by-pass (A470) take A493 towards Tywyn and Fairbourne. The entrance is ¾ mile on left.

Penmaenpool, Dolgellau, Gwynedd LL40 1YB

Telephone 01341 422129
Fax 01341 422129

PROPRIETORS

Mark Watson and Lorraine Fielding

ROOM RATES

14 Doubles/Twins £95 - £150
Includes full breakfast and VAT

CHARGE/CREDIT CARDS

• DC • JCB • MC • VI

ACCOLADES

W.T.B. ♛♛♛♛♛ *De Luxe*
A.A. ★★★ ❀❀ *74%*
The Good Hotel Guide

FACILITIES

Garden, croquet, snooker, fishing
2 meeting rooms/max 50 people
Riding nearby

RESTRICTIONS

No children under 8 years
(does not apply to babies)
No pets

ATTRACTIONS

Gwynfynydd Gold Mine,
Portmeirion,
Ffestiniog Railway,
Llechwedd Slate Caverns,
Harlech Castle

AFFILIATIONS

Welsh Rarebits

NEAREST

MAJOR CITY:
Chester - 69 miles/1¼ hrs

MAJOR AIRPORT:
Manchester - 100 miles/2 hrs

RAILWAY STATION:
Fairbourne - 6 miles/10 mins

RESERVATIONS

Direct with hotel

ACCESS CODES

Not applicable

“Excellence shows in the tiniest detail”

Edward Thomas, Chichester

PETERSTONE COURT

Georgian country house

**Llanhamlach, Brecon,
Powys LD3 7YB**

**Telephone 01874 665387
Fax 01874 665376**

PROPRIETORS
Michael and Barbara Taylor

ROOM RATES
10 Doubles/Twins £95
2 Four-posters £115
Includes full breakfast and VAT

CHARGE/CREDIT CARDS

• *DC* • *JCB* • *MC* • *VI*

WALES

ACCOLADES
W.T.B. ♛♛♛♛♛ *De Luxe*
R.A.C. ★★★ + *Merit Awards H C & R*
R.A.C. Restaurant Award

FACILITIES
Outdoor swimming pool, croquet, gardens, snooker, gymnasium, sauna, jacuzzi, fishing
2 meeting rooms/max 80 people
Golf, riding, walking/trekking, canoeing, land rover tours and ballooning nearby

RESTRICTIONS
No facilities for disabled guests

ATTRACTIONS
Brecon Beacons National Park
Hay-on-Wye (Antiquarian bookshops),
Caerphilly Castle, Llanthony Abbey,
Danyr Ogof Caves, Cardiff

AFFILIATIONS
Welsh Rarebits

NEAREST
MAJOR CITY:
Swansea - 40 miles/45 mins

MAJOR AIRPORT:
Birmingham - 130 miles/2½ hrs
Cardiff - 60 miles/1½ hrs

RAILWAY STATION:
Abergavenny - 16 miles/30 mins

RESERVATIONS
Direct with hotel

ACCESS CODES
AMADEUS HK CWLPET
SABRE HK 36210
SAHARA/WORLDSPAN HK PETER

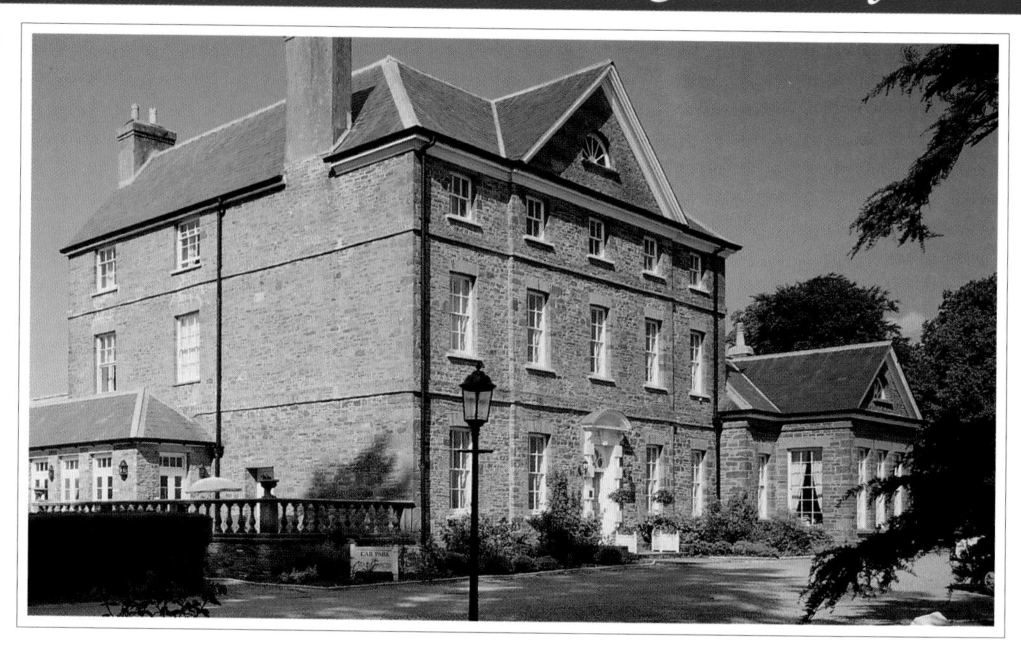

A haunting magic where problems melt away

“Peterstone is a place where problems melt away, as if by magic”, wrote journalist Roger Clark after his visit. Perhaps the magic encompasses the tale of a ghost of a former servant haunting the drive or a visit by King Charles I when recruiting forces in his struggle to regain power. One thing is certain, the setting has a magic all of its own on the banks of the Usk to the east of the Beacons National Park.

Guest rooms are spacious and restored to their Georgian splendour, and include two four-posters. A welcoming sherry awaits you, together with local mineral water. Satellite television, video players and tape recorders are just some of the extras for guest comfort. Bathrooms are huge and, of course, have telephones and thick bathrobes and towels.

The food at the Court is served either in the small Terrace Bistro or the dining room. Dinner can start with a tempting morsel from the chef and run to six courses. Naturally maximum use is made of local produce. A fine cellar has been established to complement the cuisine.

The latest addition is the bar in the old vaulted cellars, complete with a snooker table, and now offering a choice of real ales as well as wines and champagne by the glass and yes they still use pewter tankards.

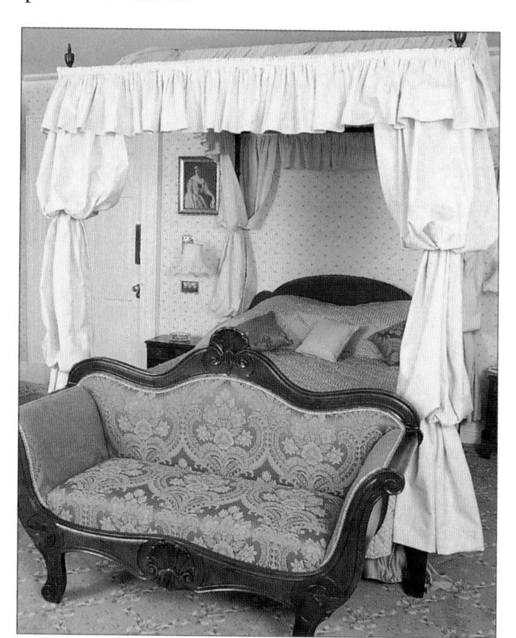

LOCATION

Peterstone is on the A40 in the tiny village of Llanhamlach 3 miles east of Brecon. 16 miles west of Abergavenny.

" Plas Penhelig is just what a country house hotel should be: unobtrusively personal, supremely comfortable and totally relaxing "

Dan Maskell, Sports Commentator

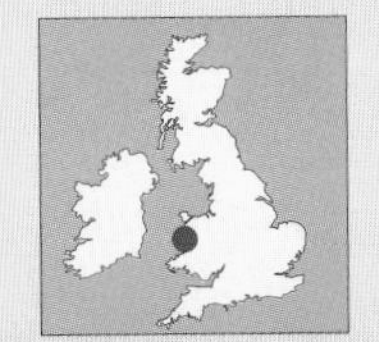

Country house

PLAS PENHELIG HOTEL

Award-winning gardens and glorious views across the Dovey Estuary

From the moment you leave the main road for the wooded driveway leading to Plas Penhelig, you will sense the atmosphere of an assured country house hotel: comfortable lounges, log fires and a special welcome from the resident proprietor and his dedicated staff.

The hotel stands in its own seven acres of secluded grounds and enjoys glorious views across the Dovey estuary.

The reputation of any hotel stems from the kitchen and French Chef Nicole Riot has been responsible for the high regard in which the hotel is held. Fresh fruit, seasonal vegetables and crisp salads are a speciality. The home produce is the perfect complement to the local fish, meat and game – all freshly supplied – that goes to make up the imaginative daily menus.

And when it comes to say 'good night', the hotel's comfortable bedrooms will not disappoint; all have en suite bath or shower, and each is furnished sympathetically to match the decor and style of the room. You can look forward to a good night's rest, lulled by the pure Welsh air and tranquil country surroundings.

Plas Penhelig is the ideal base for exploring Snowdonia National Park, its castles, beaches, countryside and the Great Little Trains of Wales. For the more energetic, there is also the famous Aberdovey Golf Course.

LOCATION

On the A493 from Machynlleth.

Aberdovey, Gwynedd LL35 0NA

Telephone 01654 767676
Fax 01654 767783

OWNER

David Richardson

ROOM RATES

Single occupancy	*£63*
11 Doubles	*£105*

Includes full breakfast, dinner and VAT

CHARGE/CREDIT CARDS

• JCB • MC • VI

WALES

ACCOLADES

W.T.B. ♛♛♛♛ Highly Commended
A.A. ★★★ 64%

FACILITIES

Gardens, croquet, heli-pad
2 meeting rooms/max 50 people
Golf and fishing nearby

RESTRICTIONS

No facilities for disabled guests

ATTRACTIONS

Harlech Castle,
Powys Castle,
Talyllyn narrow gauge railway,
Bodnant Gardens,
Portmeirion,
Snowdonia National Park

AFFILIATIONS

Welsh Rarebits

NEAREST

MAJOR CITY:
Birmingham - 120 miles/2½ hrs

MAJOR AIRPORT:
Birmingham - 120 miles/2½ hrs

RAILWAY STATION:
Penhelig Halt - ¼ mile/2 mins

RESERVATIONS

Direct with hotel

ACCESS CODES

Not applicable

"I liked your hotel! I consider it to be the most clean, most efficient and most organised accommodation I have ever encountered"

Irene Hill, Manchester

St Brides Hotel

Tudor-style hotel

St Bride's Hill, Saundersfoot
Pembrokeshire SA69 9NH

Telephone 01834 812304
Fax 01834 813303

OWNER
Ian Bell

ROOM RATES

3 Singles	*£57 - £80*
34 Doubles/Twins	*£80 - £95*
1 Four-poster	*£130*
5 Suites	*£130*

Includes full breakfast and VAT

CHARGE/CREDIT CARDS

• DC • MC • VI

WALES

ACCOLADES
W.T.B. ♛♛♛♛ Highly Commended
R.A.C. ★★★
A.A. ★★★ 67%

FACILITIES
Garden, outdoor swimming pool
5 meeting rooms/max 150 people
Golf, riding, fishing and squash nearby

RESTRICTIONS
No facilities for disabled guests
No dogs allowed in public rooms
Dogs allowed in limited number of bedrooms

ATTRACTIONS
Tenby, Pembroke Castle,
St David's Cathedral,
St Govan's Chapel,
Pembrokeshire Coast National Park

AFFILIATIONS
Countess Hotels
Logis of Great Britain
Les Routiers

NEAREST
MAJOR CITY:
Swansea - 54 miles/60 mins

MAJOR AIRPORT:
Cardiff - 90 miles/1½ hrs

RAILWAY STATION:
Tenby - 3 miles/15 mins

RESERVATIONS
Toll free fax in US/Canada: 800-646-1620
Toll free in UK: 0800-616825

ACCESS CODES
Not applicable

Gateway to the Pembrokeshire Coast National Park

St Brides Hotel stands in a superb position just 300 yards from the centre of Saundersfoot with sweeping and dramatic views from its Commodore Restaurant over Carmarthen Bay. The restaurant features locally caught fish and seafood in its varied menus. The selection of flambé dishes cooked at the table include the whisky based Chicken Balmoral and the famous Bananas Foster.

The 43 bedroom hotel has five elegant suites, named to reflect their maritime tradition – The Admiral's Quarters, The Captain's Quarters, The Bosuns's Cabin and The Stateroom, and as Lord Nelson travelled through on his way to Milford Haven the "Lady Hamilton Suite" has a romantic four-poster bed.

Afficionados of Dylan Thomas, who lived at nearby Laugharne, will appreciate the Kaptain Kat'z Drink Salon with its solid oak bar and leaded light windows. History surrounds the hotel – the ancient castles which defended Pembrokeshire, the nearby medieval walled town of Tenby, elegant and majestic churches and notorious inlets where the Vikings landed and smugglers plied their trade.

The outdoor heated swimming pool is open from mid-May to mid-September and there is parking for over 70 cars in the hotel car park – boats and trailers can be accepted when notice is given. The hotel is approved for the solemnisation of marriages.

LOCATION

From the M4 use the A40 and A477 to Kilgetty joining the A476 from Fishguard. Follow direction signs to Saundersfoot. The hotel is 300 yards from the centre on the Tenby road.

"Soughton Hall is superb! It exceeds all the rest! There are many that are good, but this is the best"

Mr & Mrs K Larry, Florida

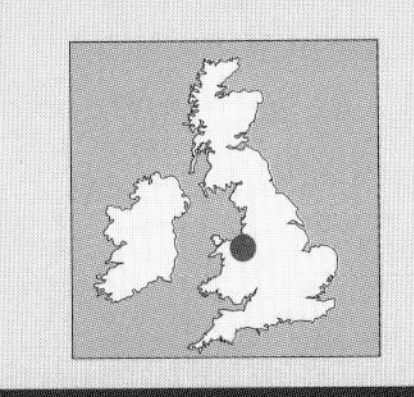

18th century Bishop's palace

SOUGHTON HALL

An elegant Welsh stately home only a few miles from Roman Chester

Soughton Hall, built as a bishop's palace in 1714, nestles in magnificent parkland and is approached via a spectacular half mile avenue of lime trees. It's leafy, rural setting in North Wales, belies its proximity to the historic walled city of Chester and its easy journey to Manchester Airport.

Beautiful antique furniture adorns a house of unique history and architecture. With just 14 authentic original bedroooms and the personal welcome of the Rodenhurst family, a memorable stay is assured.

1996 features the opening of a country inn within the old coach house and stables, a Grade I listed building of historical and architectural interest. A beer parlour will feature many real ales from local breweries, while within the original haylofts above, there will be a wine and steak bar.

This offers an opportunity to stay in one of Britain's grand houses and dine either formally within the acclaimed hotel dining room (past awards include Welsh Restaurant of the Year) or informally within the stables – a choice rarely offered.

There are many lovely drives nearby delightfully described in John Rodenhurst's exclusive full colour guide which will direct you to the many interesting places in North Wales and the surrounding area.

LOCATION

From the A55 North Wales expressway take A5119 to Northop, cross the traffic lights and the Hall is about one mile along the road on the left hand side.

Northop, Nr Chester, Clwyd CH7 6AB

Telephone 01352 840811
Fax 01352 840382

PROPRIETORS

John and Rosemary Rodenhurst

ROOM RATES

Single occupancy £70 - £80
14 Doubles £80 - £120
Includes full breakfast and VAT

CHARGE/CREDIT CARDS

• *MC* • *VI*

ACCOLADES

Independent

FACILITIES

Garden, croquet, outdoor tennis, golf and clay pigeon shooting in surrounding parkland, heli-pad
Boardroom facilities

RESTRICTIONS

Unsuitable for children 12 yrs
No facilities for disabled guests
Pets by arrangement

ATTRACTIONS

Roman City of Chester, Bodnant Gardens, The Castles of North Wales, Tatton Park, Erddis Hoore, Snowdonia National Park

AFFILIATIONS

Independent

NEAREST

MAJOR CITY:
Chester - 10 miles/15 mins

MAJOR AIRPORT:
Manchester - 30 miles/40 mins

RAILWAY STATION:
Chester - 10 miles/15 mins

RESERVATIONS

Direct with hotel

ACCESS CODES

Not applicable

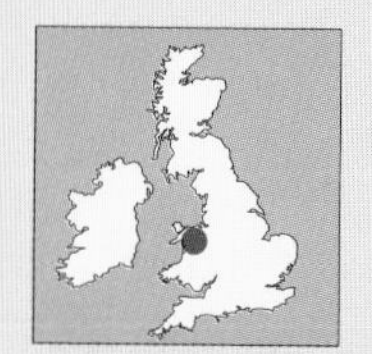

"It was difficult to find, it was even more difficult to leave"

Gabriel Pety, Belgium

TAN-Y-FOEL COUNTRY HOUSE

17th century house

Capel Garmon, Betws-y-Coed, Gwynedd LL26 0RE

Telephone 01690 710507
Fax 01690 710681

PROPRIETORS
Peter and Janet Pitman

ROOM RATES
6 Doubles/Twins £76 - £110
2 Four-posters £110
Includes full breakfast and VAT

CHARGE/CREDIT CARDS

• DC • JCB • MC • VI

WALES

ACCOLADES
W.T.B. ♛♛♛♛ De Luxe
R.A.C. Highly acclaimed
R.A.C. Best Small Hotel 1996
A.A. QQQQQ Premier Selected
A.A. Best Guest House in Wales Award 1995
The Good Hotel Guide

FACILITIES
Garden
Golf, riding, fishing and walking nearby

RESTRICTIONS
No children under 7 years
No facilities for disabled guests
No pets
Totally no smoking establishment

ATTRACTIONS
Snowdonia National Park, Caernarfon Castle, Conwy Castle, Chester

AFFILIATIONS
Welsh Rarebits
Taste of Wales

NEAREST
MAJOR CITY:
Manchester - 80 miles/1¾ hrs

MAJOR AIRPORT:
Manchester - 80 miles/1¾ hrs

RAILWAY STATION:
Llandudno Junction - 11 miles/25 mins

RESERVATIONS
Direct with hotel

ACCESS CODES
Not applicable

Life is too short for only one night here

This is one place where guests really feel as if they are being welcomed into someone's home. Tan-y-Foel "the little house under the hillside" is as its title spells out – a country house rather than a country house hotel. The characterful stone-built house dating from around the 16th century is set in eight acres, high in the hillside above Betws-y-Coed with mature gardens which overlook the Conwy Valley and the magnificent rugged peaks of Snowdonia.

Tan-y-Foel has been refurbished to accommodate just a few visiting couples "in search of a breather". No busy clamour here, simply beautiful scenery with an air of peacefulness and tranquillity. There is a variety of bedrooms from which to choose, four-posters, twins, king size and even super king size beds, all with en suite facilities. Furnishings are carefully chosen, colours and fabrics finely blended and fresh flowers are to be seen everywhere.

Janet is a fine cook, preparing interesting French style cuisine based on quality local produce, fish straight from the sea, local Welsh lamb and homemade bread. The food is served by Peter who may round off the meal with an informal lesson on the delights of Welsh cheeses.

The whole area is rich in historic sites and structures with mines, museums and mills adding interest. Two day special breaks including dinner are available on request.

LOCATION

Turn off A55 at Llandudno Junction onto A470. Travel 11 miles to Llanrwst. 2 miles outside of Llanrwst take left turn marked Capel Garmon/Nebo Travel. 1½ miles up hill, Tan-y-Foel is on the left.

"Once a traditional inn, the Three Cocks is now a famed eating place and ambassador of Belgian cooking"

Roger Thomas, travel writer

15th century inn

THREE COCKS HOTEL

Good old-fashioned hospitality with a Belgian flair

The Three Cocks Hotel is an old inn dating back to the 15th century with the unique distinction of being built around a tree which can still be seen. The hostelry is complete with coat of arms, cobbled forecourt, mounting block, ivy clad walls, crooked doorways, great oak beams, log fires and a warm welcome.

The restaurant offers continental cuisine with the accent on Belgian dishes. Chef/Proprietor Michael Winstone's efforts have been rewarded with two rosettes by the Automobile Association.

The hotel has an elegant panelled lounge where guests can relax by the fire. There are seven completely modernised bedrooms offering the convenience of private facilities but still retaining their original charm.

The hotel is in the Brecon Beacons National Park, an Area of Outstanding Beauty and is ideal for exploring the Elan Valley reservoirs, the Ystradfellte Waterfalls, Hay-on-Wye (the world's largest second-hand book centre), Hereford and the Mappa Mundi (1290). Cardiff, Gloucester, Worcester (and its porcelain museum) are all within one hour's drive.

Golfing, pony trekking, fishing, hang gliding, caving, climbing and hot air ballooning can be arranged for our guests.

LOCATION

In the centre of the small village of Three Cocks on the A438, Hereford to Brecon road.

Three Cocks, Nr Brecon, Powys LD3 0SL

Telephone 01497 847215
Fax 01497 847215

PROPRIETORS

Mr and Mrs M Winstone

ROOM RATES

Single occupancy £40 - £62
7 Doubles/Twins £62
Includes full breakfast and VAT

CHARGE/CREDIT CARDS

• MC • VI

ACCOLADES

AA ★★ ❀❀ 73%
The Good Hotel Guide

FACILITIES

Gardens and large car park
Riding and fishing nearby

RESTRICTIONS

No facilities for disabled guests
No pets except in freezing weather

ATTRACTIONS

Hay-on-Wye's bookshops, Black Mountains, Elan and Golden Valleys Brecon Beacons, Hereford, Hereford Cathedral and Mappa Mundi

AFFILIATIONS

Logis of Great Britain

NEAREST

MAJOR CITY:
Hereford - 27 miles/40 mins

MAJOR AIRPORT:
Cardiff - 60 miles/1½ hrs

RAILWAY STATION:
Hereford - 27 miles/40 mins

RESERVATIONS

Direct with hotel

ACCESS CODES

Not applicable

"Anglesey, Wales's Treasure Island at Trearddur Bay"

Ron Boole, Alderley Edge

TREARDDUR BAY HOTEL

Coastal hotel

Lon Isallit, Trearddur Bay,
Nr Holyhead,
Anglesey LL65 2UN

Telephone 01407 860301
Fax 01407 861181

MANAGERS

Mark and Noelle Gulesserian

ROOM RATES

5 Singles	£65 - £80
16 Doubles	£96 - £100
1 Four-poster	£120 - £130
8 Suites	£112 - £120

Includes full breakfast and VAT

CHARGE/CREDIT CARDS

• DC • JCB • MC • VI

ACCOLADES

W.T.B. Highly Commended
R.A.C. ★★★ + Merit Awards H C & R
A.A. ★★★ 73%
R.A.C. 'Welsh Consort Hotel of the Year' 1993

FACILITIES

Gardens, croquet, indoor pool, children's play room, fishing, heli-pad
2 meeting rooms/max 120 people
Golf, riding and bowling nearby

RESTRICTIONS

No facilities for disabled guests

ATTRACTIONS

Beaumaris Castle, Llanfairpwllgwyngyllgogerychwyrndrobwllllantysiliogogogoch Railway Station, South Stack Lighthouse and Bird Sanctuary

AFFILIATIONS

Consort Hotels
Welsh Rarebits
Logis of Great Britain

NEAREST

MAJOR CITY:
Manchester - 100 miles/2 hrs
Dublin - 65 miles/2 hrs (by seacat)

MAJOR AIRPORT:
Manchester - 100 miles/1¾ hrs

RAILWAY STATION:
Holyhead - 2 miles/10 mins

RESERVATIONS

Toll free in US: 800-55-CONSORT

ACCESS CODES

AMADEUS/SYSTEM 1 CN HLYTRE
SABRE CN 34833
WORLDSPAN CN TREAR
SAHARA CN 46880

Magnificent views and high standards at the gateway to Ireland

This hotel enjoys a magnificent location on the Anglesey coast, overlooking Trearddur Bay and close to a mediaeval chapel dedicated to the nun St Brigid.

An extensive refurbishment programme in recent years has given the hotel a completely new look. Many of the spacious bedrooms, all of which are en-suite, have panoramic views over the bay. All are furnished to a high standard. There are also nine studio suites, including one with four-poster bed.

The lounge is the perfect place to relax and read the papers over morning coffee or afternoon tea. The hotel restaurant enjoys a reputation for excellent food – including locally caught fish and seafood – complemented by fine wines. Table d'hôte and à la carte menus offer a good choice of dishes.

The beach is just a short walk away and there is a testing 18-hole golf course nearby. Anglesley is a haven for watersports enthusiasts and bird-watchers. Places of interest include Beaumaris Castle and the Celtic burial mound at Bryn Celi Ddu. The Trearddur Bay Hotel is also perfectly placed for those travelling to and from Ireland on the ferry from the nearby port of Holyhead.

LOCATION

From Holyhead Port take the B4545 for 2 miles. Turn right and hotel is further 200 yds. From Bangor turn left off A5 at Valley on B4545. Turn left at Shell petrol station. Hotel is a further 200 yds.

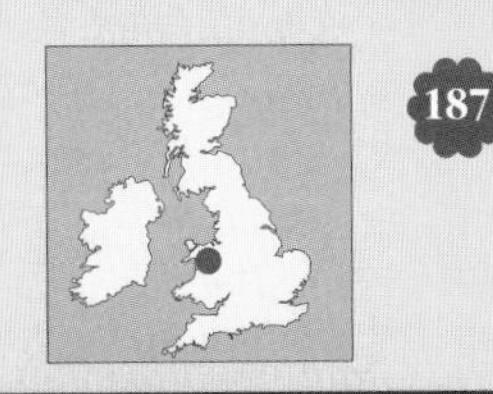

"Found on a stormy night we have returned again and again . . . it's a special treat at all times of the year"

Jill Tweedie & Alan Brien, Authors

Georgian country house TYDDYN LLAN COUNTRY HOUSE

A stylish oasis in the midst of this magical Welsh valley

Tyddyn Llan is simply a lovely Georgian country house surrounded by some of the most magnificent countryside in Wales. A one-time shooting lodge for the Dukes of Westminster, it was converted in 1983 by Peter and Bridget Kindred into an hotel that they, after much travelling, would like to stay in. Its pervasive atmosphere of peace and good taste is totally relaxing. Peter's career as a set designer in television and films has been used to advantage to create the elegant decor and Bridget's knowledge and love of food has established a much acclaimed restaurant.

Friendly and informal with antiques, interesting paintings, some by Peter himself, comfortable furniture and encircled by its own beautiful gardens, it is an oasis amidst the mountains, rivers and the great outdoors. This unspoilt valley of the River Dee provides excellent walking over the Berwyn Mountains, fishing (with a ghillie if required), horseriding and shooting in season.

The hotel is also well placed to explore the splendour of Snowdonia with its many castles and monuments and it is not far from the Roman City of Chester and the majestic Mawddach and Dyfi Estuaries with their fine sandy beaches and rocky coves. The Kindreds look forward to wishing you 'Croeso I Gymru' – 'Welcome to Wales'.

LOCATION

From A5 in Corwen, take 1st left turning to Llandrillo – B4401 for 4½ miles. Tyddyn Llan is on the right side on the way out of the village to Bala.

Llandrillo, Nr Corwen, Clwyd LL21 OST

Telephone 01490 440264
Fax 01490 440414

PROPRIETORS

Peter and Bridget Kindred

ROOM RATES

10 Doubles/Twins £92.50 - £102
Includes full breakfast and VAT

CHARGE/CREDIT CARDS

• DC • JCB • MC • VI

ACCOLADES

W.T.B. ♛♛♛♛ De Luxe
A.A. ★★ ❀❀
A.A. Care and Hospitality Award 1993
The Good Hotel Guide

FACILITIES

Croquet, gardens, 4 miles of private fishing on the river Dee,
2 meeting rooms/max 50 people
Riding and shooting nearby

RESTRICTIONS

Children preferred to take early supper
No facilities for disabled guests
Dogs by arrangement

ATTRACTIONS

Snowdonia National Park, Bodnant Gardens, Portmeirion Village, Harlech, Chirk and Caernarfon Castles, Erdigg Hall, Chester, Golf at Bala and Llangollen courses

AFFILIATIONS

Welsh Rarebits

NEAREST

MAJOR CITY:
Chester - 35 miles/50 mins

MAJOR AIRPORT:
Manchester - 65 miles/1¼ hrs

RAILWAY STATION:
Chester - 35 miles/50 mins
Wrexham - 28 miles/45 mins

RESERVATIONS

Direct with hotel

ACCESS CODES

Not applicable

“ Ty'n Rhos has set the standard that all other hotels will have to live up to ”

Woman and Home Magazine

TY'N RHOS COUNTRY HOUSE

17th century farm

Seion, Llanddeiniolen,
Caernarfon,
Gwynedd LL55 3AE

Telephone 01248 670489
Fax 01248 670079

PROPRIETORS

Nigel and Lynda Kettle

ROOM RATES

1 Single £35 - £40
9 Doubles/Twins £56 - £80
Includes full breakfast and VAT

CHARGE/CREDIT CARDS

• JCB • MC • VI

ACCOLADES

W.T.B. ♛♛♛♛ De Luxe
A.A. ★★ ❀ 73%
The Good Hotel Guide

FACILITIES

Gardens, croquet, heli-pad
Vegetarian dishes available
Golf, riding, fishing and leisure centre nearby

RESTRICTIONS

No children under 6 years
No pets

ATTRACTIONS

Caernarfon and Conwy Castles, Snowdonia National Park, Bodnant Gardens

AFFILIATIONS

Welsh Rarebits

NEAREST

MAJOR CITY:
Manchester - 90 miles/1 ½ hrs

MAJOR AIRPORT:
Manchester - 90 miles/1 ½ hrs

RAILWAY STATION:
Bangor - 4 ½ miles/15 mins

RESERVATIONS

Direct with hotel

ACCESS CODES

Not applicable

A taste of Wales in the land of legend, castles and mountains

Ty'n Rhos (the house on the heath) started life as a humble working farm. In 1695, it was described as a single storey cottage with a thatched roof. Over the years, it has changed considerably and is now a country house of distinction offering the finest accommodation to discerning travellers and lovers of good food.

All the bedrooms are en suite and are decorated and furnished to the highest standards. Each room is individual in character and all have tea/coffee making facilities, colour television and direct-dial telephone.

There is a lovely dining room with wonderful views across farmland to the Isle of Anglesey. Lynda is a talented chef who prepares high quality dishes using the finest fresh local ingredients to promote a Taste of Wales.

Situated in a land of legend, castles and mountains, Ty'n Rhos is an ideal touring base as it stands between Snowdonia and the sea. It lies close to the mighty castle of Caernarfon, the wonderful beaches of Anglesey and the beauty of the Llyn peninsula.

Quality allied to value for money are the keynotes at Ty'n Rhos.

LOCATION

Take the B4366 (signposted Bethel) from Caernarfon. Pass through Bethel and after passing the Gors Bach Inn take the first left signposted Seion. Ty'n Rhos is on the left.

"We found a historic but friendly country house which combines peace, unsurpassed views and excellence in every way"

T H Davies, LVO

Country house

WARPOOL COURT HOTEL

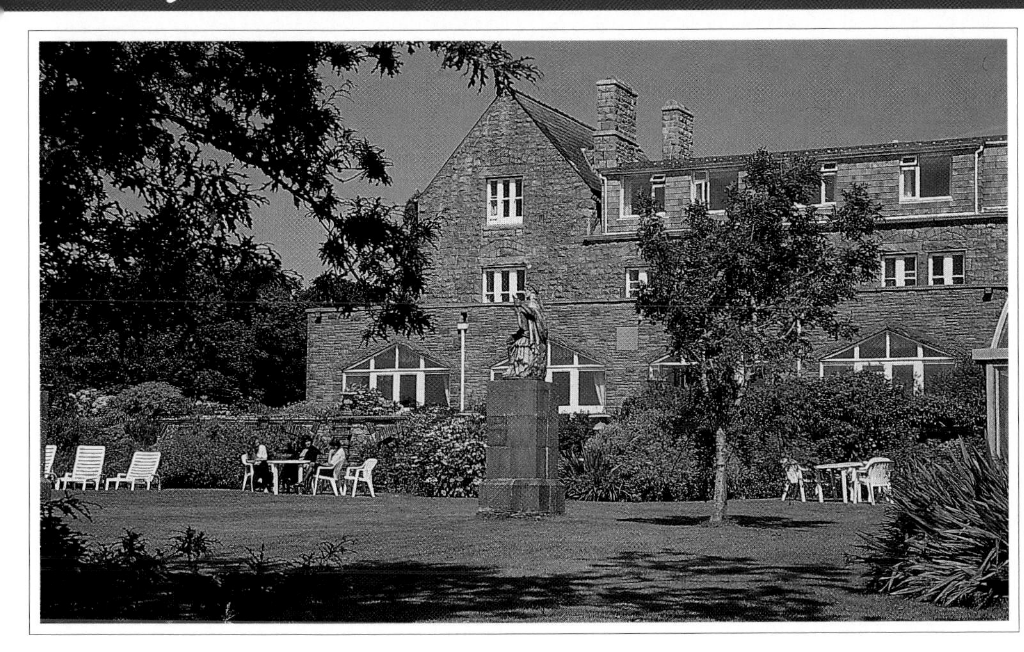

On the western-most point of Wales, a magical setting in St Davids

Originally built as St Davids Cathedral's choir school in the 1860's this privately owned hotel enjoys spectacular scenery at the heart of the Pembrokeshire National Park, with views over the coast and St Brides Bay to the islands beyond.

First converted to a hotel 30 years ago, the Court offers a unique antique tile collection and 25 comfortable and individually decorated bedrooms, many of which have glorious sea-views.

The dining room enjoys a splendid reputation offering imaginative menus and vegetarian dishes using local produce – crab, lobster, sewin and seabass are caught just off the coast and the hotel smokes its own salmon and mackerel.

Set in seven acres, the tranquil gardens offer pre-dinner drinks on the lawns or peaceful strolls. For those wishing for a more active pursuit, the covered heated pool (open April to October), exercise rooms, sauna or tennis court beckon – croquet, pool and table tennis are also available.

A five minute walk will take you either to the coastal path with its spectacular scenery or the Cathedral and Bishops Palace in St Davids. The area boasts of many sandy beaches, and offers a wealth of history and natural beauty.

LOCATION

From Cross Square in St Davids, bear left between Cartref Restaurant and Midland Bank. Go down Goat Street. At bottom, fork left and follow hotel signs.

**St Davids,
Pembrokeshire SA62 6BN**

**Telephone 01437 720300
Fax 01437 720676**

GENERAL MANAGER
Rupert Duffin

ROOM RATES
2 Singles £67 - £74
23 Doubles/Twins £92 - £138
Includes full breakfast and VAT

CHARGE/CREDIT CARDS

• DC • MC • VI

WALES

ACCOLADES
S.T.B. ♛♛♛♛ Highly Commended
R.A.C. ★★★ + Merit Award R
A.A.★★★ ❀❀ 68%
The Good Hotel Guide

FACILITIES
Garden, croquet, gym, sauna, indoor heated pool, putting green
2 meeting rooms/max 200 people
Riding, sea fishing, surfing and windsurfing nearby

RESTRICTIONS
No facilities for disabled guests

ATTRACTIONS
St Davids Cathedral, Pembroke Castle, Bishops Palace - St Davids, Pembrokeshire Coast National Park

AFFILIATIONS
Independent

NEAREST
MAJOR CITY:
Swansea - 75 miles/2 hrs

MAJOR AIRPORT:
Cardiff - 115 miles/2¾ hrs

RAILWAY STATION:
Fishguard - 15 miles/30 mins
Haverfordwest - 15 miles/30 mins

RESERVATIONS
Direct with hotel

ACCESS CODES
Not applicable

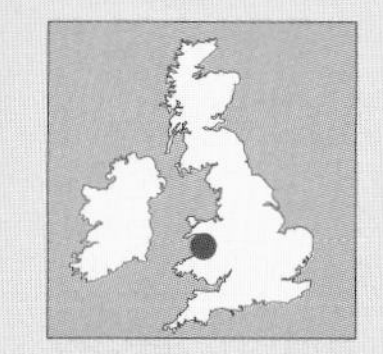

" I didn't think places like this existed in Wales "

Richard Gere, Actor

YNYSHIR HALL

Previous Royal residence

Eglwysfach, Machynlleth, Powys SY20 8TA

Telephone 01654 781209
Fax 01654 781366

PROPRIETORS
Joan and Rob Reen

ROOM RATES

Single occupancy	£75 - £95
6 Doubles	£100 - £130
3 Suites	£120 - £145

Includes full breakfast and VAT

CHARGE/CREDIT CARDS

• DC • JCB • MC • VI

WALES

ACCOLADES
W.T.B. De Luxe
R.A.C. Blue Ribbon Award ★★
A.A. ★★
A.A. Courtesy & Care Award 1994
The Good Hotel Guide

FACILITIES
Large landscaped gardens,
Ynyshir Bird Reserve
Riding, fishing and shooting nearby

RESTRICTIONS
No children under 9 years
Pets by arrangement in some rooms
No smoking in dining room and a number of bedrooms

ATTRACTIONS
Powys Castle,
Dyfi Estuary,
The Centre for Alternative Technology,
Snowdonia National Park

AFFILIATIONS
Pride of Britain
Welsh Rarebits

NEAREST
MAJOR CITY:
Birmingham - 120 miles/3 hrs

MAJOR AIRPORT:
London Heathrow - 180 miles/4 hrs
Birmingham - 120 miles/3 hrs

RAILWAY STATION:
Machynlleth - 6 miles/10 mins

RESERVATIONS
Toll free in US: 800-777-6536

ACCESS CODES
Not applicable

Grace and idyllic seclusion in the realm of Celtic princes

Ynyshir Hall is set amongst inspiring scenery in the secret heart of Wales. Surrounded by mountains that were once the refuge of Celtic princes and graced by valleys of infinite shades of green, it enjoys a perfect location.

Twelve acres of glorious gardens laid down over the centuries are aglow with seasonal colour. Sequoia and Wellingtonia trees flank the drive and one is immediately captivated by its charming amphitheatre setting.

The hotel shares the Dyfi Estuary with one of Britain's finest bird reserves. Here the buzzard, the curlew and the kingfisher and many others live in harmony with the unspoilt landscape of the marshes and dunes.

Cherished by a succession of eminent owners, including Queen Victoria, the house is now owned by artist Rob Reen and his wife Joan who, with flair and skill, have created one of Wales' finest privately owned hotels.

Relaxation is assured in the elegant lounges and beautifully appointed bedrooms where Rob's own bold paintings are on display.

The impeccable and innovative cuisine is a celebration of the true flavours of fine local produce. Cardigan Bay lobsters, wild Dyfi salmon, and farmhouse cheeses are stylishly presented and backed by a wine list of distinction. Guests are assured of a memorable occasion.

LOCATION

5 miles from Machynlleth and 11 miles from Aberystwyth on the A487

Midshires

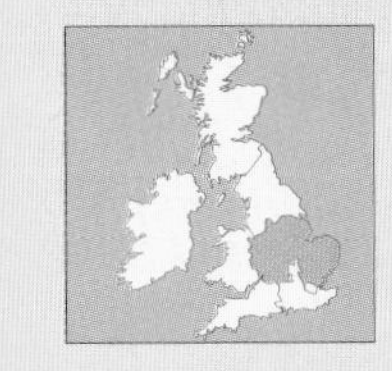

Bolsover Castle, Derbyshire. There was a castle here in the 11th century during the reign of William the Conqueror. Charles Cavendish transformed it in 1612 into a romantic dream of chivalry. It remains one of the great houses of the 17th century.

Heritage sites

The following heritage sites can be found on the map overleaf. The key numbers show where they are located.

BEDFORDSHIRE

Bushmead Priory	1
Wrest Park House and Gardens	2

CAMBRIDGESHIRE

Denny Abbey	3
Longthorpe Tower	4

DERBYSHIRE

Bolsover Castle	5
Peveril Castle	6

GLOUCESTERSHIRE

Cirencester Amphitheatre	7
Great Witcombe Roman Villa	8
Odda's Chapel, Deerhurst	9

HEREFORD & WORCESTER

Arthur's Stone, Dorstone	10
Goodrich Castle	11
Mortimer's Cross Water Mill	12

HERTFORDSHIRE

Berkhamsted Castle	13

LEICESTERSHIRE

Ashby de la Zouch Castle	14
Kirby Muxloe Castle	15

LINCOLNSHIRE

Bolingbroke Castle	16
Sibsey Trader Windmill	17

NORFOLK

Castle Acre Castle	18
Castle Rising Castle	19

NORTHAMPTONSHIRE

Kirby Hall	20
Rushton Lodge	21

NOTTINGHAMSHIRE

Mattersey Priory	22
Rufford Abbey	23

OXFORDSHIRE

Abingdon County Hall	24
Minster Lovell Hall and Dovecote	25
North Leigh Roman Villa	26
Rycote Chapel	27
Uffington Castle & White Horse	28

SHROPSHIRE

Boscobel House & The Royal Oak	29
Stokesay Castle	30
Wroxeter Roman City	31

STAFFORDSHIRE

Croxden Abbey	32

SUFFOLK

Framlingham Castle	33
Landguard Fort	34

WARWICKSHIRE

Kenilworth Castle	35

WEST MIDLANDS

Halesowen Abbey	36

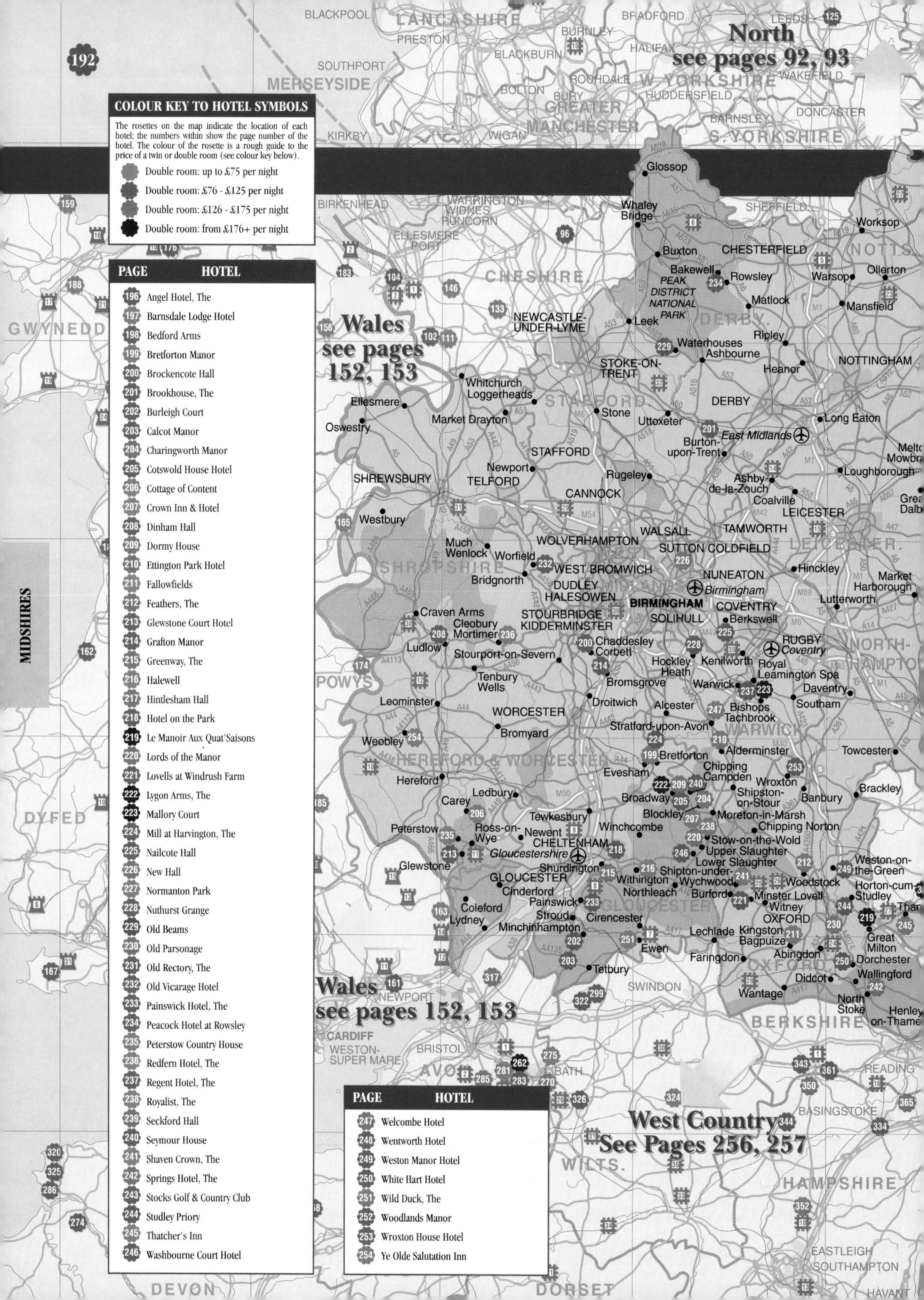
COLOUR KEY TO HOTEL SYMBOLS
The rosettes on the map indicate the location of each hotel; the numbers within show the page number of the hotel. The colour of the rosette is a rough guide to the price of a twin or double room (see colour key below).
Double room: up to £75 per night
Double room: £76 - £125 per night
Double room: £126 - £175 per night
Double room: from £176+ per night
PAGE HOTEL
196 Angel Hotel, The
197 Barnsdale Lodge Hotel
198 Bedford Arms
199 Bretforton Manor
200 Brockencote Hall
201 Brookhouse, The
202 Burleigh Court
203 Calcot Manor
204 Charingworth Manor
205 Cotswold House Hotel
206 Cottage of Content
207 Crown Inn & Hotel
208 Dinham Hall
209 Dormy House
210 Ettington Park Hotel
211 Fallowfields
212 Feathers, The
213 Glewstone Court Hotel
214 Grafton Manor
215 Greenway, The
216 Halewell
217 Hintlesham Hall
218 Hotel on the Park
219 Le Manoir Aux Quat'Saisons
220 Lords of the Manor
221 Lovells at Windrush Farm
222 Lygon Arms, The
223 Mallory Court
224 Mill at Harvington, The
225 Nailcote Hall
226 New Hall
227 Normanton Park
228 Nuthurst Grange
229 Old Beams
230 Old Parsonage
231 Old Rectory, The
232 Old Vicarage Hotel
233 Painswick Hotel, The
234 Peacock Hotel at Rowsley
235 Peterstow Country House
236 Redfern Hotel, The
237 Regent Hotel, The
238 Royalist, The
239 Seckford Hall
240 Seymour House
241 Shaven Crown, The
242 Springs Hotel, The
243 Stocks Golf & Country Club
244 Studley Priory
245 Thatcher's Inn
246 Washbourne Court Hotel
PAGE HOTEL
247 Welcombe Hotel
248 Wentworth Hotel
249 Weston Manor Hotel
250 White Hart Hotel
251 Wild Duck, The
252 Woodlands Manor
253 Wroxton House Hotel
254 Ye Olde Salutation Inn
North see pages 92, 93
Wales see pages 152, 153
Wales see pages 152, 153
West Country See Pages 256, 257
MIDSHIRES
LANCASHIRE
MERSEYSIDE
GREATER MANCHESTER
W. YORKSHIRE
S. YORKSHIRE
CHESHIRE
GWYNEDD
DYFED
POWYS
SHROPSHIRE
STAFFORD
DERBY
NOTTS
LEICESTER
WARWICK
HEREFORD & WORCESTER
GLOUCESTER
OXFORD
BERKSHIRE
AVON
WILTS
HAMPSHIRE
DORSET
DEVON
BIRMINGHAM
COVENTRY
WORCESTER
CHELTENHAM
GLOUCESTER
OXFORD
SHREWSBURY
TELFORD
STAFFORD
DERBY
NOTTINGHAM
LEICESTER
WOLVERHAMPTON
WALSALL
STOKE-ON-TRENT
CHESTERFIELD
SHEFFIELD
BRISTOL
CARDIFF
SWINDON
READING
BASINGSTOKE
SOUTHAMPTON

193
MIDSHIRES
HUMBERSIDE
KINGSTON UPON HULL
SCUNTHORPE
GRIMSBY
Caistor
Market Rasen
Louth
Gainsborough
Mablethorpe
Alford
LINCOLN
Horncastle
Spilsby
Skegness
Woodhall Spa
LINCOLN
Newark-on-Trent
Sleaford
Heckington
Boston
Bottesford
Grantham
The Wash
Hunstanton
Burnham Market
Wells-next-the-Sea
Sheringham
Cromer
Mundesey
Docking
Little Walsingham
Great Snoring
Fakenham
Aylsham
North Walsham
Holbeach
Spalding
Bourne
King's Lynn
East Dereham
Hoveton
Norwich
Hemsby
Ranworth
Market Deeping
Wisbech
Swaffham
NORWICH
Great Yarmouth
Stamford
PETERBOROUGH
Downham Market
Stoke Ferry
Wymondham
Loddon
March
NORFOLK
Attleborough
LOWESTOFT
Corby
Oundle
CAMBRIDGE
Brandon
Bungay
Beccles
Ramsey
Chatteris
Littleport
Thetford
Diss
Kettering
Thrapston
Ely
Mildenhall
Southwold
Eye
Irthlingborough
Huntingdon
St. Ives
Bury St. Edmunds
Wellingborough
Rushden
Newmarket
Saxmundham
NORTHAMPTON
St. Neots
Cambridge
Stowmarket
Wickham Market
Aldeburgh
Clapham
CAMBRIDGE
SUFFOLK
BEDFORD
Sandy
Haverhill
Long Melford
Lavenham
Woodbridge
Orford
MILTON KEYNES
BEDFORD
Biggleswade
Great Chesterford
Hintlesham
IPSWICH
Shefford
Royston
Sudbury
Hadleigh
Ampthill
Saffron Walden
Felixstowe
Baldock
Letchworth
ESSEX
Halstead
Manningtree
From Zeebrugge
Woburn
Hitchin
Harwich
HERTFORD.
Great Dunmow
Braintree
COLCHESTER
From Esbjerg, Hoek Van Holland
Göteborg, Hamburg
Luton
Stevenage
Stansted
Walton-on-the-Naze
Frinton
Dunstable
LUTON
Welwyn Garden City
Bishop's Stortford
Brightlingsea
Harpenden
Hertford
Witham
Clacton-on-Sea
Aldbury
CHELMSFORD
West Mersea
Hatfield
HARLOW
Maldon
Hoddesdon
HEMEL HEMPSTEAD
Cheshunt
Chipping Ongar
BUCKS.
Epping
Watford
Chenies
HIGH WYCOMBE
Brentwood
Burnham-on-Crouch
London see pages 368, 369
BASILDON
Rochford
Southend
SOUTHEND-ON-SEA
Grays
Tilbury
GRAVESEND
MARGATE
ROCHESTER
GILLINGHAM
CAMBERLEY
CHATHAM
WOKING
SURREY
REIGATE
MAIDSOTNE
GUILDFORD
KENT
South see pages 328, 329
WEST SUSSEX
EAST SUSSEX
BRIGHTON
HASTINGS
KEY
Motorways
'A' Roads
Railways
Airports
National Boundaries
County Boundaries
Heritage Sites
English Heritage Sites
Ferry Routes
Urban Areas
National Parks and Areas of Outstanding Natural Beauty
Each grid square equals 30 miles(approx. 50 km)
Maps produced by Arka Cartographics Limited. Copyright 1995
27/28, Hartfield Road, Forest Row, East Sussex RH18 5DY England
0 Miles 30
0 Kilometres 50
MIDSHIRES

Berney Arms Mill, near Great Yarmouth, Norfolk. A marsh mill that continued working until 1951. It has seven floors and serves as a landmark for many miles in this flat rural landscape.

COUNTIES

Bedfordshire
Cambridgeshire
Derbyshire
Essex
Gloucestershire
Hereford & Worcester
Hertfordshire
Leicestershire
Lincolnshire
Norfolk
Northamptonshire
Nottinghamshire
Oxfordshire
Shropshire
Staffordshire
Suffolk
Warwickshire
West Midlands

Castles, Stately Homes, Historic Houses

Audley End, nr Saffron Walden, Essex. Built in 1603 by Thomas Howard, 1st Earl of Suffolk, Lord High Treasurer.

Belvoir Castle, Lincolnshire. 4th castle on site, 1st built 11th c. Home of the Duke of Rutland. Art treasures by Holbein and Gainsborough.

Berkeley Castle, Gloucestershire. 850-year-old castle. 14th c great hall, keep, dungeon. Scene of the murder of Edward II.

Chatsworth House, Bakewell, Derbyshire. Built 1707 for 1st Duke of Devonshire. Fine pictures, books, furniture.

Framlingham Castle, Suffolk. Built for the Earls of Norfolk. Home of Mary Tudor in 1543. 12th c curtain walls.

Hardwick Hall, Near Chesterfield, Derbyshire. Built 1591 in the Tudor style with four corner towers and large windows across the entire front.

Kenilworth Castle, Warwickshire. Edward II abdicated here. John of Gaunt built the Banqueting Hall.

Ludlow Castle, Shropshire. Built by Earl of Shrewsbury in 1085. Milton's Comus first produced in Castle Hall 1634.

Tattershall Castle, Leicestershire. Fine survival of Fortified moated castle, built 1440 by Ralph Cromwell, Treasurer of England.

Warwick Castle. 14th c still inhabited by Earl of Warwick. State rooms, armoury, dungeon, torture chamber, clock tower.

The Midshires hold the key to English life and arts. Here decisive battles shaped the nation's history. At Bosworth Field, Henry Tudor slew Richard III and took the crown himself. In 1651 the Battle of Worcester confirmed Cromwell in power. The drama of the Gunpowder Plot took place here. Shakespeare was born at Stratford-upon-Avon. Edward Elgar came from Broadheath, near Worcester, and captured the sounds of the English countryside. The industrial heartlands of Birmingham and the Black Country mass-produced everything from chocolate to jewellery to cars.

There is much to see and enjoy today. Music lovers come to the concerts at Snape Maltings in Suffolk. Nearby are the Constable landscapes and Flatford Mill. Lincolnshire welcomes you with seaside resorts like Mablethorpe and bracing Skegness. Derbyshire has the rugged Peak District and Chesterfield's twisted spire. Leicestershire is famed for its broad hunting acres. There are new facilities and ideas for visitors – the National Exhibition Centre near Birmingham is a fine example. In Staffordshire you can visit the tradition of fine pottery. Westward is the peaceful scenery of the tranquil Malvern Hills, A.E. Houseman's Wrekin in Shropshire and the Black Mountains. At Oxford, the dreaming spires rise above an ancient university and a modern city. The Cotswolds in Gloucestershire colour the towns and villages and even the walls between the fields with their mellow grey Cotswold stone.

For active holidays, there is tremendous scope for walking, cycling, horseriding, fishing and shooting. There are golf courses, tennis courts, soccer and rugby. There is a profusion of fine art and antique collections, historic houses, stately homes, castles, gardens. You can cruise on a quiet canal or discover your own quaint pub in an old-world village. You will find the Midshires are counties rich in friendship.

Museums, Galleries & Highspots

Avoncroft Museum of Buildings, Stoke Heath, Worcestershire. Re-erected buildings include a working windmill and a 1946 prefab.

Banbury Museum, Oxfordshire. Beside Banbury Cross. Local history of Banbury and the Cherwell Valley.

Chatterley Whitfield Mining Museum, Tunstall, Staffordshire. A guided tour to pit ponies, winding engine, locomotives.

Dean Heritage Centre, Soudley, Gloucestershire. Forest of Dean iron mining history. Old corn mill in woodland setting.

Dyson Perrins Museum, Worcester. World's largest collection of Worcester Porcelain.

Imperial War Museum, Duxford, Cambridgeshire. Over 120 aircraft on display, with guns, tanks and other vehicles.

Jew's House, The Strait, Lincoln. Dates from c 1170, one of the oldest houses still in use in Britain today.

Lavenham Guildhall, Suffolk. Impressive 1520s timber framed building. Museum of medieval wool trade.

Nottingham Castle. Built by William the Conqueror in 1068. Burnt down in 1831, now the city's museum and art gallery.

Oxford Story, Broad Street, Oxford. Heritage Centre depicting 800 years of University life.

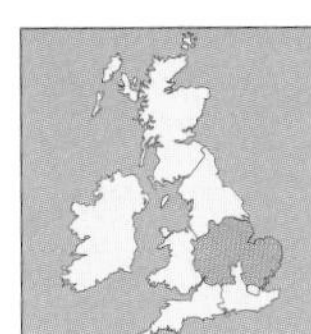

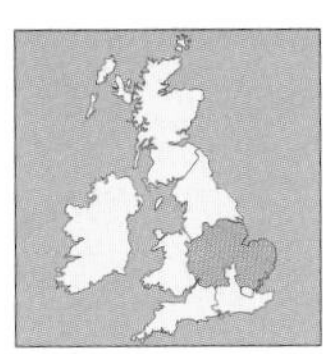

TOURIST OFFICE INFORMATION

Further information about the Midshires will be gladly supplied by:

Heart of England Tourist Board,
Woodside, Larkhill Road,
Worcester WR5 2EF
Tel: 01905 763436

East Anglia Tourist Board,
Toppesfield Hall, Hadleigh,
Suffolk IP7 5DN
Tel: 01473 822922

East Midlands Tourist Board,
Exchequergate, Lincoln LN2 1PZ
Tel: 01522 531521

For international offices, please turn to page 480

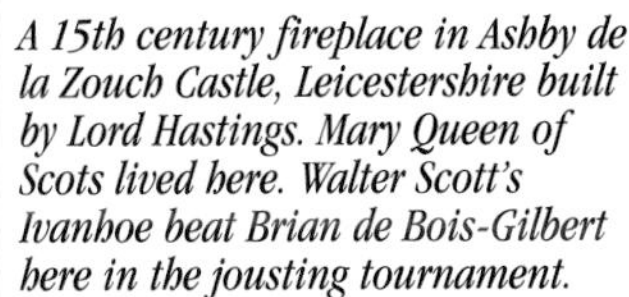

A 15th century fireplace in Ashby de la Zouch Castle, Leicestershire built by Lord Hastings. Mary Queen of Scots lived here. Walter Scott's Ivanhoe beat Brian de Bois-Gilbert here in the jousting tournament.

Churches, Crosses & Cathedrals

All Saints Church, Chesterfield, Derbyshire. Built 14th c. Twisted spire 238 ft high, nearly 8 ft out of true at its summit!

Coventry Cathedral, Warwickshire. 1962. Designed by Sir Basil Spence to replace medieval church bombed in 2nd World War.

Ely Cathedral, Cambridgeshire. Norman to Perpendicular. Very fine chapel. Superb choral acoustics.

Hereford Cathedral. Built on 7th century site. Norman, Early English, Perpendicular buildings. Chained library. Mappa Mundi.

Holy Trinity, Old Town, Stratford-upon-Avon, Warwickshire. One of England's most beautiful, on the River Avon. Shakespeare's christening font and grave.

Lichfield Cathedral, Staffordshire. Only English medieval cathedral with three spires. 8th c gospel manuscript.

Lincoln Cathedral. Built 12th - 14th c, after earthquake destroyed an earlier church. 365 ft high, with superb West Front.

Newstead Abbey, Nottingham. Built by Henry II in 1170 to atone for Becket's murder. In 1540 became home of Lord Byron's family.

Peterborough Cathedral, Cambridgeshire. Norman, with Early English West front. 13th c painted nave ceiling.

St Botolph's, Boston, Lincolnshire. 14th c, roof carvings. 272-ft 'Boston Stump' Perpendicular tower rises over Fenlands.

St Mary's Collegiate, Warwick. Incomparable 15th c Beauchamp Chapel. Superb glass and medieval/ Tudor tombs. Norman crypt.

St Mary the Virgin, High Street, Oxford. Historic University church. Bishop Cranmer's trial was held here.

Walsingham, Norfolk. 14th c Slipper Chapel. Catholic National Shrine. 15th c Parish Church.

Waltham Abbey, Essex. Built as a great abbey by Henry II to expiate the murder of Thomas a Becket. Vast Norman nave.

Parks & Gardens

Alton Towers, Staffordshire. Stupendous pleasure park in the grounds of 19th c Gothic mansion.

Cambridge University Botanic Garden, Bateman Street, Cambridge. Arboretum. Rock, scented and winter gardens.

Sherwood Forest, Nottinghamshire. Perhaps Robin Hood never really lived, but you can still explore his forest.

Tulip Fields, Spalding, Lincolnshire. Millions of blooms in April and May.

Westbury Court Garden, Westbury-on-Severn, Gloucestershire. 17th c formal water gardens with trees of unusual size. Yew hedges laid 1696 - 1705.

Sport & Outdoors

Canal Boat Cruising. Grand Union Canal and many others.

Cricket. Essex, Gloucestershire, Northamptonshire, Nottinghamshire, Warwickshire and Worcestershire play in the Championship.

Golf. Many public courses. Championship course at Sutton Coldfield, Warwickshire.

Motor Racing. Silverstone, Northamptonshire. Home of the British Grand Prix.

National Agricultural Centre, Stoneleigh, Warwickshire. Here the Royal Agricultural Show is held each summer.

Norfolk Broads. 30 open expanses of wide water, linked by rivers and man-made waterways. Sail or motor-boat.

Arthur's Stone near Dorstone, Hereford and Worcester. A massive burial chamber still exists beneath this Neolithic construction.

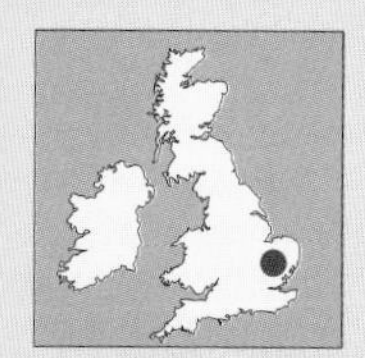

" . . . and stopped before a large inn situated in a wide open street, nearly facing the old abbey. 'And this,' said Mr Pickwick, looking up 'is The Angel' "

Charles Dickens – Pickwick Papers

THE ANGEL HOTEL

Historic market town hotel

Angel Hill,
Bury St Edmunds,
Suffolk IP33 1LT

Telephone 01284 753926
Fax 01284 750092

PROPRIETOR
Mary Gough

GENERAL MANAGER
Jolyon Gough

ROOM RATES

15 Singles	£65
16 Doubles	£85 - £125
11 Twins	£85 - £95

Includes full breakfast and VAT

CHARGE/CREDIT CARDS

 • DC • MC • VI

ACCOLADES
E.T.B. ♛♛♛♛ Highly Commended
R.A.C. ★★★ + Merit Awards H C & R
A.A. ★★★ ❀❀ 68%

FACILITIES
5 meeting rooms/max 120 people
Gardens, riding and golf nearby

RESTRICTIONS
No facilities for disabled guests

ATTRACTIONS
Newmarket, Norman Abbey, Cambridge, Clock Museum, Long Melford, Ixworth House, Lavenham

AFFILIATIONS
Independent

NEAREST
MAJOR CITY:
London - 70 miles/1¼ hrs

MAJOR AIRPORT:
Stansted - 50 miles/45 mins
Cambridge - 32 miles/40 mins

RAILWAY STATION:
Bury St Edmunds - 1 mile/15 mins

RESERVATIONS
Direct with hotel

ACCESS CODES
Not applicable

History preserved and first class service for over 500 years

Steeped in history and located in one of the finest Georgian squares in England, The Angel Hotel is renowned for its first-class service to travellers, continuing the tradition since first becoming an inn in 1452. Visitors have the immediate impression of a hotel that is loved and nurtured by its owners.

In the public rooms guests will appreciate the carefully chosen ornaments and pictures, fresh flowers and log fires. Bedrooms are individually furnished and decorated, and all have en suite bathrooms and those extra touches that add to the comfort and warm welcome you receive. The 'fine room' where Mr Pickwick stayed has been preserved today exactly as it was more than a century ago.

The elegant dining room has been awarded two rosettes by the AA for excellent food and service. Overlooking the ancient abbey, the dining room serves classic English cuisine, including local speciality dishes and succulent roasts.

The hotel is within an hour of east coast ferry ports and 45 minutes from Stansted Airport. Nearby there is racing at Newmarket and several golf courses within easy reach. Bury St Edmunds is an interesting and historic market town and an excellent centre for touring East Anglia.

LOCATION

Leave M11 at Junction 9 and take A11 to Newmarket. From the A14 take 2nd exit to Bury St Edmunds. At second roundabout veer left. At second set of lights turn right. The Angel is on the right.

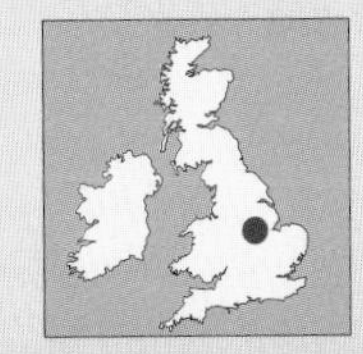

“ Wonderful hotel, wonderful atmosphere, wonderful staff – need I say more ”

Mr J F Kelly, Swindon

17th century farmhouse **BARNSDALE LODGE HOTEL**

By Europe's largest man-made lake in England's smallest county

Set in the ancient county of Rutland amid unspoilt countryside, Barnsdale Lodge Hotel overlooks Rutland Water, Europe's largest man-made lake. The hotel is a restored 17th century farmhouse with a distinctly Edwardian atmosphere and style, a theme that is evident from its high standards of service right through to the sumptuous furnishings.

Traditional English cuisine and fine wines are served in the three dining rooms. Prime roast beef from the trolley is always available. Buttery lunches, afternoon teas and suppers may be taken in the bar, conservatory or the courtyard.

The 17 bedrooms (four on the ground floor), are attractively furnished with en suite facilities, colour TV, direct-dial telephone, and self-contained beverage unit. A baby listening service and safe play area are available.

Conference facilities, with a full package of visual aids, are available for up to 200 delegates. The Barn Suite (furnished as a luxury marquee) is perfect for stylish receptions.

Nearby places of historic interest include churches and castles: 12th century Oakham Castle has a famous collection of horseshoes. Visitors to the area can enjoy Shakespeare performed outdoors, country walking, clay pigeon shooting, riding, watersports and cruises on Rutland Water. A 350 acre nature reserve offers good birdwatching facilities.

LOCATION

Situated on the A606 Oakham to Stamford road.

The Avenue,
Rutland Water North Shore,
Nr Oakham,
Rutland LE15 8AH

Telephone 01572 724678
Fax 01572 724961

PROPRIETORS

Robert Reid and The Hon Thomas Noel

ROOM RATES

4 Singles	*£49.50*
10 Doubles	*£69.50 - £79.50*
1 Four-poster	*£79.50*
2 Family rooms	*£79.50*

Includes full breakfast and VAT

CHARGE/CREDIT CARDS

• *MC* • *VI*

ACCOLADES

E.T.B. ♛♛♛♛ *Highly Commended*
A.A. ★★★ ❀ *70%*
County Hotel of the Year 1995 - a leading guide

FACILITIES

Gardens, heli-pad
3 meeting rooms/max 200 people
Golf, riding, fishing and watersports nearby

RESTRICTIONS

None

ATTRACTIONS

Rutland Water, Belvoir Castle, Tolethorpe Hall, Burghley House, Rockingham Castle

AFFILIATIONS

Independent

NEAREST

MAJOR CITY:
Leicester - 17 miles/30 mins

MAJOR AIRPORT:
East Midlands - 39 miles/1 hr

RAILWAY STATION:
Leicester - 17 miles/30 mins
Oakham - 2 miles/5 mins
Stamford - 9 miles/15 mins

RESERVATIONS

Direct with hotel

ACCESS CODES

Not applicable

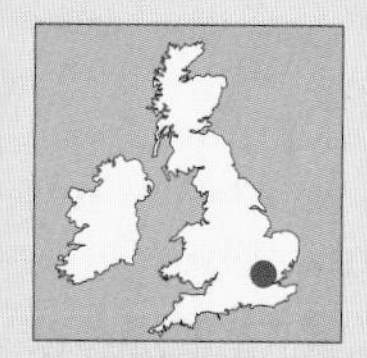

" One of the better places in England "

Mark Kalesh, Beverly Hills, California

BEDFORD ARMS

Village inn

Chenies, Nr Rickmansworth, Hertfordshire WD3 6EQ

Telephone 01923 283301
Fax 01923 284825

GENERAL MANAGER
Jean-Louis Jegard

ROOM RATES

3 Singles	£100
6 Doubles/Twins	£110
1 Four-poster	£135
1 Suite	£155

Includes VAT

CHARGE/CREDIT CARDS

• DC • JCB • MC • VI

ACCOLADES
E.T.B. Highly Commended
R.A.C. ★★★ + Merit Awards H C & R
A.A. ★★★ 72%

FACILITIES
Garden
1 meeting room/max 35 people
Golf, riding, fishing and clay-pigeon shooting nearby

RESTRICTIONS
No facilities for disabled guests
No pets

ATTRACTIONS
Chenies Manor, Windsor Castle, Windsor Safari Park

AFFILIATIONS
A Thistle Country House Hotel

NEAREST
MAJOR CITY:
London - 20 miles/45 mins

MAJOR AIRPORT:
London Heathrow - 15 miles/25 mins
Denham - 6 miles/10 mins

RAILWAY STATION:
Watford - 7 miles/15 mins

RESERVATIONS
Toll free in US/Canada: 800-847-4358
Toll free in Australia: 800-062-055

ACCESS CODES
Not applicable

French classic cuisine in the historic village of Chenies

Warmth, tranquillity, personal attention and superb cuisine in the style and surroundings of a classic English country house. These are the hallmarks of this small but immensely charming hotel on the outskirts of the attractive and historic village of Chenies.

The oak-panelled restaurant is considered to be one of the finest in the area, offering excellent french classic cuisine from an extensive à la carte menu. Adjacent to this is the intimate cocktail bar, while the lounge bar serves snacks in pleasant and informal surroundings.

The newly refurbished bedrooms enjoy views of the hotel's attractive gardens. Each has been individually decorated and includes every modern facility, including deluxe marble tiled bathrooms, teletext and satellite TV, direct dial telephone, trouser press, hairdryer and tea and coffee making facilities. Room service is also available 24 hours a day. Meeting and private dining facilities are also offered.

The hotel is within easy access of the west and midlands via the M40, the north by the M1, and the south and east on the M25, and is surrounded by some of the most picturesque countryside on the borders of Hertfordshire and Buckinghamshire. For corporate entertainment, clay-pigeon shooting at famous Holland & Holland; golfing and tennis can also be arranged. Also, 200 yards from the hotel, is Chenies Manor House dating back to the 16th century and open to visitors during the summer. Private parties can be arranged.

LOCATION

8 miles from M1 motorway, 2 miles from Junction 18 M25. Take A404 to Amersham. Hotel is in village of Chenies signposted.

“ At long last a beautiful stately home with gracious hosts – we'll come back ”

Dot Ashton, Naples, Florida

16th century manor house

BRETFORTON MANOR

Once owned by Queen Elizabeth I – now a sheltered retreat

Sheltering in the lee of The Cotswolds, Bretforton Manor welcomes you to a world of tranquillity, comfort and luxury from the moment you enter its carved Tudor oak-panelled hall, where log fires burn in the winter months.

While its ancient charm and Elizabethan artifacts remain undisturbed, the Manor has been beautifully appointed to high standards of luxury. The centrally heated, spacious bedrooms have a sherry decanter, colour TV, hairdryer, and tea and coffee-making facilities. All bedrooms have large en suite bathrooms with bidet, shower and bath. Your hosts pride themselves on their hospitality. Nothing is too much trouble.

The Manor is set in an unspoilt 8th century village, and the eight-acre grounds hold the old village stocks, a superb dovecote and a 17th century thatched barn. Private paths lead to the church and the Fleece Inn, preserved by the National Trust as an alehouse that also serves food. Nearby restaurants range from international cuisine to informal bar meals.

The Manor is ideally placed for touring. Stratford-upon-Avon, the fascinating hill villages of The Cotswolds, the medieval splendours of Warwick Castle and the Malvern Hills are all close by, as is a comprehensive activities centre.

LOCATION

From M5, leave at Junction 9 and follow signs for Evesham on A438, then A435. On Evesham by-pass, turn right on to B4035. Bretforton is signposted and is 2 miles down this road.

Bretforton,
Nr Broadway,
Worcestershire WR11 5JH

Telephone 01386 833111
Fax 01386 833111

PROPRIETOR
Janet Crittenden

ROOM RATES
3 Doubles/Twins £65 - £85
Includes full breakfast and VAT

CHARGE/CREDIT CARDS

ACCOLADES
A.A. QQQQ

FACILITIES
Garden
Golf and fishing nearby

RESTRICTIONS
No children under 15 years
No smoking

ATTRACTIONS
Stratford-upon-Avon, Warwick Castle, Broadway, Cotswolds and Malverns, Hidcote Gardens, Blenheim Palace, Royal Worcester Porcelain Factory

AFFILIATIONS
Independent

NEAREST
MAJOR CITY:
Birmingham - 30 miles/45 mins

MAJOR AIRPORT:
London Heathrow - 90 miles/1¾ hrs
Birmingham - 25 miles/40 mins

RAILWAY STATION:
Evesham - 3 miles/5 mins

RESERVATIONS
By appointment only – no callers please

ACCESS CODES
Not applicable

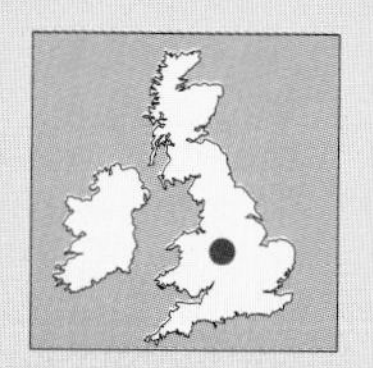

"Tranquillity and beauty only surpassed by the excellence of the food and service"

Henry Blofeld, cricket commentator

BROCKENCOTE HALL

Victorian country mansion

Chaddesley Corbett,
Nr Kidderminster,
Worcestershire DY10 4PY

Telephone 01562 777876
Fax 01562 777872

OWNERS
Alison and Joseph Petitjean

ROOM RATES

Single occupancy	*£80*
17 Doubles	*£110 - £135*
2 Four-posters	*£135*

Includes full breakfast and VAT

CHARGE/CREDIT CARDS

• DC • MC • VI

ACCOLADES
E.T.B. De Luxe
R.A.C. ★★★ + Merit Awards C & R
A.A. ★★★ 79%
The Good Hotel Guide

FACILITIES
Croquet and gardens,
2 meeting rooms/max 30 people
Golf, riding and fishing nearby

RESTRICTIONS
No pets

ATTRACTIONS
Warwick Castle,
Worcester,
Hereford Cathedral,
Stratford-upon-Avon,
Black Country Museum,
Cotswolds, Ironbridge

AFFILIATIONS
Independent

NEAREST
MAJOR CITY:
Birmingham - 18 miles/30 mins

MAJOR AIRPORT:
Birmingham - 20 miles/30 mins

RAILWAY STATION:
Kidderminster - 4 miles/10 mins

RESERVATIONS
Direct with hotel

ACCESS CODES
Not applicable

Authentic French enclave in the heart of the Worcestershire countryside

The builders of the original Victorian mansion that is now the beautiful Brockencote Hall Hotel, certainly knew a thing or two about finding a perfect place for relaxation.

Nestling in the heart of the Worcestershire countryside, Brockencote Hall is set in 70 acres of private parkland yet is close to the motorway network, just half an hour from Birmingham – the perfect location for touring the sites of an area rich in history and culture. From here, you are equally well-placed to visit Shakespeare's Stratford-upon-Avon, Warwick Castle, the idyllic Cotswolds and the wonders of Wales.

But guests at Brockencote Hall will experience something that is unique in the area: the hotel is renowned for its authentic French ambience. Proprietors Joseph and Alison Petitjean have created a charming Gallic oasis in the heart of England, combining traditional French comfort and friendliness with superb French cuisine.

The hotel offers a choice of 17 superb bedrooms, all with en suite facilities, including one that has been especially designed to make stays comfortable for disabled guests.

LOCATION

Exit 1 (M42) or Exit 4 (M5). Go into Bromsgrove and take the A448 towards Kidderminster. The hotel is 5 miles along on the left.

" I am sure that when you decide to stay at the Brookhouse you will find comfort and relaxation "

D Fotheringham-Kidd

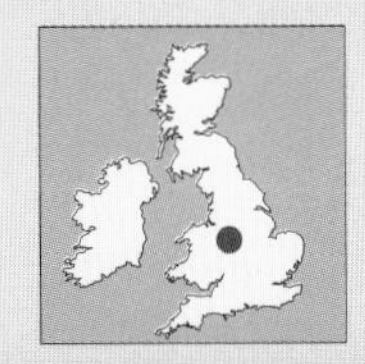

17th century farmhouse

THE BROOKHOUSE

Dine in antique splendour on cuisine with a worldwide reputation

Originally built as a farmhouse in 1694, this attractive, ivy-clad house is situated in a tranquil position beside a gently flowing brook and lush gardens. It was converted into an hotel in 1976, and since then it has earned a fine reputation for its friendly service and hospitality.

Attention to detail is to be found in the comfortable bedrooms. All 19 are individually styled with antique furniture, many with four-poster, half-tester or Victorian brass beds trimmed with Nottingham lace. Each has its own colour television, radio, direct-dial telephone, a tea and coffee tray and a luxurious en suite bathroom.

The restaurant has a worldwide reputation for superb food and wine. The atmosphere is set by soft lights and candlelight. The antique tables are laid with silver and crystal and decorated with fresh flowers.

Much effort is placed upon producing food of the highest standard using fresh fish, meats, poultry, game in season and vegetables. Everything is just a little different and freshly cooked to order. The wine list offers some imaginative, rare and unusual wines.

LOCATION

Rolleston is just outside Burton-upon-Trent between the A50 to Stoke-on-Trent and the A38 to Derby.

Brookside, Rolleston-on-Dove, Burton-upon-Trent, Staffordshire DE13 9AA

Telephone 01283 814188
Fax 01283 813644

PROPRIETOR

John S Westwood

ROOM RATES

7 Singles	*£65 - £73*
12 Doubles/Twins	*£85 - £95*

Includes full breakfast, complimentary newspaper and VAT

CHARGE/CREDIT CARDS

• DC • MC • VI

ACCOLADES

E.T.B. ♛♛♛♛ Commended

FACILITIES

Gardens
1 meeting room/max 18 people
Golf and riding nearby

RESTRICTIONS

No children under 12 yrs
Dogs by arrangement

ATTRACTIONS

Tutbury Castle,
Derbyshire Dales,
Calke Abbey,
Haddon and Keddleston Halls

AFFILIATIONS

Independent

NEAREST

MAJOR CITY:
Derby - 8 miles/15 mins

MAJOR AIRPORT:
Birmingham - 25 miles/40 mins
Manchester - 70 miles/1 ½ hrs

RAILWAY STATION:
Burton-upon-Trent - 3 miles/10 mins

RESERVATIONS

Direct with hotel

ACCESS CODES

Not applicable

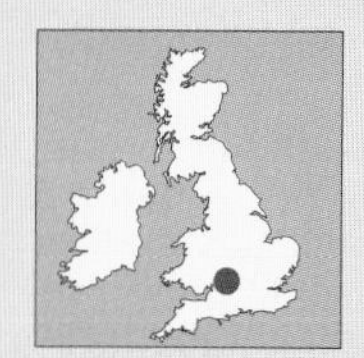

"Our seventh visit! Could be we think it's the best hotel in the British Isles!"

John & Barbara Bye, Cambridge

BURLEIGH COURT

18th century manor house

Minchinhampton,
Nr Stroud,
Gloucestershire GL5 2PF

Telephone 01453 883804
Fax 01453 886870

PROPRIETORS

Ian and Fiona Hall

ROOM RATES

Single occupancy £62.50 - £75
16 Doubles/Twins £80 - £105
1 Suite £145
Includes full breakfast and VAT

CHARGE/CREDIT CARDS

DC • MC • VI

ACCOLADES

A.A. ★★★ 65%

FACILITIES

Garden, croquet, outdoor pool, putting lawn, childrens play area

RESTRICTIONS

Pets allowed in coach house rooms only – not in public areas

ATTRACTIONS

Cheltenham,
Bath,
Berkeley Castle,
Cirencester Amphitheatre,
Great Witcombe Roman Villa,
Gatcombe,
Badminton

AFFILIATIONS

Grand Heritage Hotels

NEAREST

MAJOR CITY:
Cheltenham - 25 miles/35 mins

MAJOR AIRPORT:
London Heathrow - 100 miles/2 hrs
Bristol - 30 miles/45 mins

RAILWAY STATION:
Stroud - 2 miles/5 mins

RESERVATIONS

Direct with hotel

ACCESS CODES

Access codes applied for (GH)

A hidden gem at the heart of the undiscovered Cotswolds

Burleigh Court is an 18th century manor house originally built as a family home. All your requirements be it for holiday or business will be provided. You can enjoy logs fires and squashy chairs in winter, long country walks and cool drinks in summer. Set in 3½ acres of mature gardens and grounds, its Cotswold stone walls, spring fed fountain and heated Victorian plunge pool are delightful.

There are sweeping views across the Golden Valley. A notable feature of the estate is the trees, particularly the acers, a superb purple beech, Californian redwood, and several enormous cedars.

The 11 bedrooms of the main house and the six family rooms of the coach house, are all very different in their character, and are furnished with love and care. Each enjoys views over the valley or the mature gardens and landscape, and all rooms have full en suite bathrooms, direct dial telephone, colour TV and radio. They provide everything you need for a relaxing stay, yet preserve the feeling of being in a friend's home.

The menus offered in the elegant dining room is based on fresh local produce, cooked with skill and imagination with herbs and salad vegetables being grown in the hotel's own gardens. The menu changes frequently to take advantage of fresh asparagus or the finest wild salmon.

Situated in the centre of some notable places to visit, Burleigh Court is ideal for exploring the mellow Cotswold towns of Minchinhampton, Chipping Campden, Bourton on the Water, as are the Regency splendours of Cheltenham and Bath.

LOCATION

Take the A419 out of Stroud towards Cirencester. After approx 2.5 miles, take the right turn signposted Burleigh and Minchinhampton. Continue up the hill for 500 yards taking a left turn signposted Burleigh Court. The hotel is a further 300 yards on your right.

"We don't come on holiday to England . . . we come on holiday to Calcot"

Paul and Lynda Steggada, Phoenix

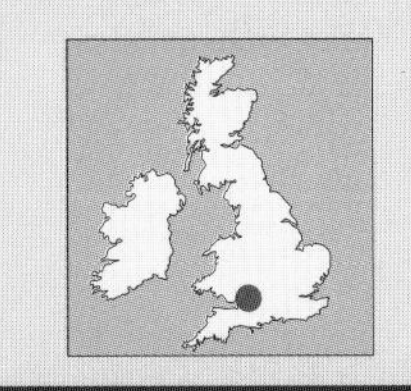

14th century manor house

CALCOT MANOR

Ancient and modern . . . an enduring family favourite

Calcot was originally converted in 1984 and is now run by Richard Ball and his wife Catherine. The hotel is located in an unspoilt part of the Cotswold Hills, well-placed for visiting the city of Bath and within reach of the country's finest antique centres.

There is a heated swimming pool, two tennis courts and a croquet lawn in the grounds and bicycles can be provided for touring the famous Cotswold villages.

This charming Cotswold manor house was originally a farmhouse dating back to the 15th century. Its beautiful stone barns and stables, now converted into further superb bedrooms, include a 14th century tithe barn that was built by Cistercian Monks in 1300 and is amongst the oldest in Britain.

The hotel is beautifully furnished and the service is friendly and unobtrusive. In the award-winning restaurant, guests can linger over delicious meals whilst enjoying wonderful views of the countryside.

Calcot welcomes families and has a number of suites with sofa beds, toys, child-listening facilities and a safe outdoor play area.

LOCATION

Ideally situated on the edge of the Cotswolds, Calcot is only 35 minutes north of Bath. Leaving the M4 at Junction 18, Calcot is 4 miles west of Tetbury at the junction of the A46 and A4135.

Nr Tetbury, Gloucestershire GL8 8YJ

Telephone 01666 890391
Fax 01666 890394

PROPRIETOR

Richard J G Ball

ROOM RATES

16 Doubles/Twins £87 - £105
4 Family Suites £125
Includes continental breakfast and VAT

CHARGE/CREDIT CARDS

• DC • MC • VI

ACCOLADES

E.T.B. ♛♛♛♛ Highly Commended
A.A. ★★★ ❀❀
The Good Hotel Guide

FACILITIES

Heated outdoor pool, 2 tennis courts, croquet, gardens, jacuzzi, heli-pad
4 meeting rooms/max 60 people
Golf and riding nearby

RESTRICTIONS

No pets

ATTRACTIONS

Westonbirt Arboretum, Bath, Cotswold villages, Berkeley Castle, Badminton

AFFILIATIONS

Pride of Britain
Relais du Silence

NEAREST

MAJOR CITY:
Bath - 22 miles/35 mins

MAJOR AIRPORT:
London Heathrow - 100 miles/1½ hrs
Bristol - 30 miles/45 mins

RAILWAY STATION:
Kemble - 15 miles/10 mins

RESERVATIONS

Toll free in US: 800-544-4970

ACCESS CODES

Not applicable

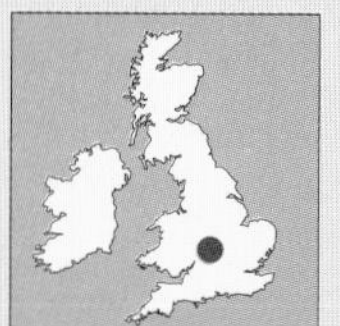

" Charingworth Manor stands for unadulterated pleasure and I am not ashamed to enjoy it "

Patrick Maclagan, Berkshire

CHARINGWORTH MANOR

14th century manor

Nr Chipping Campden, Gloucestershire GL55 6NS

Telephone 01386 593555
Fax 01386 593353

GENERAL MANAGER
Colin Heaney

ROOM RATES

Single occupancy	*£90*
19 Doubles/Twins	*£120 - £195*
2 Four-posters	*£205*
3 Suites	*£220*

Includes full breakfast and VAT

CHARGE/CREDIT CARDS

• *DC* • *MC* • *VI*

ACCOLADES
E.T.B. ♛♛♛♛ *De Luxe*
R.A.C. ★★★ + *Merit Awards H C & R*
A.A. ★★★ ❀❀

FACILITIES
Indoor swimming pool, croquet, gardens, sauna/steam room, solarium, billiards, heli-pad
2 meeting rooms/max 70 people
Clay shooting, archery and off road fun nearby

RESTRICTIONS
No children under 10 yrs in restaurant for dinner
No facilities for disabled guests

ATTRACTIONS
The Cotswolds, Broadway, Oxford
Chipping Campden, Stratford-upon-Avon

AFFILIATIONS
Small Luxury Hotels
English Rose Hotels

NEAREST
MAJOR CITY:
Birmingham - 40 miles/1 hr
MAJOR AIRPORT:
London Heathrow - 65 miles/2 hrs
Birmingham - 36 miles/1 hr
RAILWAY STATION:
Moreton-in-Marsh - 8 miles/10 mins

RESERVATIONS
Toll free in US/Canada: 800-525-4800

ACCESS CODES
AMADEUS/SYSTEM 1 LX BHXCWM
APOLLO LX 21651
AXESS LX 5648
WORLDSPAN LX GLOCM
SABRE/SAHARA LX 31194

The perfect retreat from the twentieth century

The ancient manor of Charingworth lies amidst the gently rolling Cotswold countryside, just three miles from the lovely town of Chipping Campden, described as having "the most beautiful High Street in the whole of England". The 14th century Manor House is set in its own gardens and grounds of fifty acres and offers peace, tranquillity and breathtaking views.

Inside Charingworth is an historic patchwork of intimate public rooms with log fires burning during the colder months. The atmosphere is warm and relaxed, the service friendly and attentive. There are 24 individually designed bedrooms, all furnished with antiques and fine fabrics. Outstanding cuisine is regarded as being of great importance and guests at Charingworth are assured of imaginative dishes where great emphasis is placed on the finest produce available. Recognition has come in the form of two rosettes from the A.A.

To enhance your stay there is an elegant romanesque leisure spa, entirely in keeping with the relaxed comfort found throughout Charingworth. It offers an indoor heated pool, sauna, steam room, solarium and billiards room, there is also a tennis court in the grounds.

One of the joys of visiting the Cotswolds is the wealth of things to do and see. The lovely Cotswold villages and famous gardens of Hidcote and Kiftsgate are very close by. Also easily reached are the historic towns of Stratford-upon-Avon and Oxford.

LOCATION

Charingworth is situated on the B4035 between Chipping Campden and Shipston-on-Stour. 2½ miles from the A429.

“ Something special for your money, THE place to stay in this delectable Cotswold town ”

Hilary Rubinstein, Editor, The Good Hotel Guide

Regency house

COTSWOLD HOUSE HOTEL

Wit, elegance and history in the heart of The Cotwolds

Situated in pride of place on Chipping Campden's historic High Street, the Cotswold House is a must for independent travellers in search of high standards of hospitality and comfort, discreet attentive service and an atmosphere that is informal and friendly.

Resident owners Christopher and Louise Forbes have decorated their Regency property with wit and taste and created a unique home from home. Bedrooms are both charming and individual with well appointed bathrooms whilst public rooms have a quietly understated elegance, with well chosen antique furniture and complementary modern fabrics.

Good food is synonymous with the Cotswold House. The restaurant, arguably the most beautiful dining room in the Cotswolds, enjoys delightful views of the gardens and offers interesting and delicious seasonal menus and a pianist who plays several times each week. For more informal dining, a separate brasserie is open throughout the day. Fresh local produce and specialities are featured, together with a comprehensive selection of wines from around the world.

Easily accessible by road or rail, Chipping Campden is excellent for Cotswold touring, with many world-famous attractions and gardens all within a short drive.

LOCATION

On B4081, 2 miles north of A44 between Moreton-in-Marsh and Broadway.

Chipping Campden, Gloucestershire GL55 6AN

Telephone 01386 840330
Fax 01386 840310

PROPRIETORS

Mr and Mrs C S Forbes

ROOM RATES

3 Singles	£70 - £85
11 Doubles/Twins	£100 - £140
1 Four-poster	£155

Includes full breakfast and VAT

CHARGE/CREDIT CARDS

• DC • MC • VI

ACCOLADES

E.T.B. ♛♛♛♛ Highly Commended
R.A.C. Blue Ribbon Award ★★★
A.A. ★★★ ❀❀
The Good Hotel Guide

FACILITIES

Croquet, garden
1 meeting room/max 20 people
Golf, riding, fishing, clay shooting, hot air ballooning and helicopter treasure hunt nearby

RESTRICTIONS

No children under 8 yrs
No facilities for disabled guests
No pets

ATTRACTIONS

Hidcote and Kiftsgate Gardens, Broadway, Stratford-upon-Avon, Snowshill Manor, Warwick Castle, Batsford Arboretum

AFFILIATIONS

The Cotswold Collection

NEAREST

MAJOR CITY:
Stratford - 12 miles/20 mins

MAJOR AIRPORT:
London Heathrow - 90 miles/$1\frac{3}{4}$ hrs
Birmingham - 30 miles/30 mins

RAILWAY STATION:
Moreton-in-Marsh - 7 miles/10 mins

RESERVATIONS

Direct with hotel

ACCESS CODES

AMADEUS HK BHXCOT
APOLLO/SABRE HK 30593
WORLDSPAN HK COTSW
SAHARA HX COTSW

" These people understand what a pub should be "

'The Quest for the Perfect Pub' by Nick and Charlie Hurt

COTTAGE OF CONTENT

15th century cottages

Carey,
Hereford,
Herefordshire HR2 6NG

Telephone 01432 840242
Fax 01432 840208

PROPRIETOR
Michael J Wainford

ROOM RATES
Single occupancy £30
4 Doubles £40 - £48
Includes full breakfast and VAT

CHARGE/CREDIT CARDS

• JCB • MC • VI

ACCOLADES
Independent

FACILITIES
Gardens
Riding and fishing nearby

RESTRICTIONS
No facilities for disabled guests

ATTRACTIONS
Wye Valley,
Symonds Yat,
Cotswolds,
Malvern Hills,
Tintern Abbey,
Hay on Wye,
Hereford Cathedral,
Black Mountains

AFFILIATIONS
Independent

NEAREST
MAJOR CITY:
Hereford - 8 miles/12 mins

MAJOR AIRPORT:
Birmingham - 50 miles/1 hr

RAILWAY STATION:
Hereford - 8 miles/12 mins

RESERVATIONS
Direct with hotel

ACCESS CODES
Not applicable

A lot more than just oak beams and flagstones!

The Cottage of Content was originally three workmens' cottages built around 1485 by the then landowner who arrived from France some 800 years ago and whose descendants still live in nearby Treago Castle.

Ale and cider have been served in one of the cottages since it was built some five hundred years ago, and over the intervening years the inn has been enlarged by the absorption of the other two cottages.

Modernisation has retained all the original features. The old beams and flagstones are still very much in evidence. From outside, the pub is approached through a tunnel of trees and over a bridge and stream and has a 1930's 'chocolate box' appearance with a cottage garden in the front and a large grass bank with tables at the rear.

There are four cottage bedrooms, three en-suite. Real ales and a good choice of food, including vegetarian dishes, are always available with a choice of some 60 different wines.

The Wye Valley is one of the most beautiful and unspoilt areas of Britain with many lovely walks and places of interest to visit. A warm welcome awaits at the Cottage of Content.

LOCATION

From the end of the M50 continue on A40 for 2 miles to the A49 to Hereford. After ½ mile turn right towards Hoarwithy. After 4 miles you will pass the Hoarwithy Public House. After 100 yards turn right and then left. Carey is 1½ miles further on.

" Superb food, good wine, even forgot the weather "

Patrick Dewitt

207

16th century coaching inn

THE CROWN INN & HOTEL

A comfortable and traditional inn with an award-winning restaurant

A charming mellow-stoned 16th century coaching inn set in a picturesque unspoilt village in the heart of the Cotswolds.

The hotel has a welcoming atmosphere and an efficient but friendly staff who provide that special personal touch. There are 21 well-equipped and tastefully furnished bedrooms all of which are en suite and include colour television and tea making facilities.

In the winter, many of the public areas have blazing log fires giving that homely feel. There are two restaurants to please every appetite. The Brasserie, which was runner-up 'Fish Pub of the Year', is smart but informal and has a superb and extensive menu, from fresh mussels to Cornish lobsters.

The second restaurant, The Coach House, is also relaxed with a restful intimate atmosphere for that special candlelit dinner. The à la carte menu has an interesting selection of fish and meat which Richard Smith, the head chef, takes upon himself to change very regularly. As he puts it: "to offer the best foods of the season. The pheasant is a must!"

The Crown Hotel reflects the tranquil nature of the Cotswolds with walks along tree-lined footpaths and horse riding from local stables. There is a golf club nearby.

LOCATION

2 miles off the A44 Evesham to Moreton-in-Marsh road.

High Street, Blockley, Nr Moreton-in-Marsh, Gloucestershire GL56 9EX

Telephone 01386 700245
Fax 01386 700247

PROPRIETORS

Messrs Champion

RATES PER PERSON

Single occupancy	*£53*
13 Doubles	*£39 - £44.50*
2 Four-posters	*£52 - £57*
4 Suites	*£57*

Includes full breakfast and VAT

CHARGE/CREDIT CARDS

• DC • MC • VI

ACCOLADES

E.T.B. ♛♛♛♛ Highly Commended
R.A.C.★★★
A.A.★★★ ❀ 65%
County Hotel of the Year 1996 - a leading guide

FACILITIES

Golf, leisure centre, riding, clay pigeon shooting, archery and quad-biking nearby

RESTRICTIONS

No facilities for disabled guests
Pets by arrangement

ATTRACTIONS

Broadway, Stratford-upon-Avon, Warwick Castle, Oxford, Cotswold villages

AFFILIATIONS

Independent

NEAREST

MAJOR CITY:
Oxford - 25 miles/30 mins

MAJOR AIRPORT:
Birmingham - 40 miles/1 hr

RAILWAY STATION:
Moreton-in-Marsh - 5 miles/10 mins

RESERVATIONS

Direct with hotel

ACCESS CODES

Not applicable

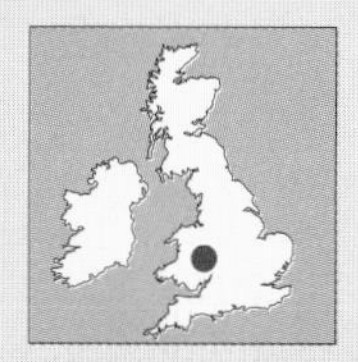

" A place where time for living has not been overtaken by the pace of life "

Mr J Harris, New York

DINHAM HALL

18th century town house

Dinham, Ludlow, Shropshire SY8 1EJ

Telephone 01584 876464
Fax 01584 876019

PROPRIETORS

J P and J E Mifsud

ROOM RATES

2 Singles	£65
8 Doubles/Twins	£93 - £104
2 Four-posters	£110

Includes full breakfast and VAT

CHARGE/CREDIT CARDS

• DC • JCB • MC • VI

ACCOLADES

E.T.B. ♛♛♛♛ *De Luxe*
R.A.C. ★★★
A.A. ★★★ ❀ *68%*

FACILITIES

Garden, sauna, gym
1 meeting room/max 28 people
Golf, riding, fishing and racecourse nearby

RESTRICTIONS

Limited facilities for disabled guests

ATTRACTIONS

Ludlow Castle, Stokesay Castle, Hereford, Ironbridge Museum, Shrewsbury, Burford House

AFFILIATIONS

Best Western

NEAREST

MAJOR CITY:
Hereford - 25 miles/30 mins

MAJOR AIRPORT:
Birmingham - 40 miles/1½ hrs

RAILWAY STATION:
Ludlow - ½ mile/2 mins

RESERVATIONS

Direct with hotel

ACCESS CODES

Not applicable

An enviable location in one of England's most beautiful country towns

Built in 1792 Dinham Hall is situated in the fascinating historic town of Ludlow. It lies only 40 metres from the Castle which, having played an important part in England's history, today hosts the Shakespearean productions which form the major part of the annual Ludlow Festival. Dinham's enviable location provides its guests with the combination of ready access to the town and picturesque views over the open Shropshire countryside.

The magnificent fireplace in the sitting room dates back to 1874 although part of the surround has been placed in the 14th century.

In the restaurant, pastel colours and attractive flowers help to provide a subtle atmosphere in which to enjoy the creative prize-winning cuisine while the Merchant Suite, with its 14th century timbers, is an ideal setting for private dinners and meetings.

The restaurant and many bedrooms command views over the gardens and Teme Valley to wooded hills. The decor of the bedrooms is a harmony of modern facilities and period design with luxurious appointments, a number of rooms having four poster beds.

Guests may also enjoy a visit to Ludlow Races or spend a few hours browsing in the town's numerous antique shops. South Shropshire is one of the most beautiful parts of the country with Ludlow amongst the finest of market towns.

LOCATION

On the A49, 25 miles north of Hereford and 28 miles south of Shrewsbury.

"I love it here! I always feel welcomed, relaxed and spoilt, not a bad combination!"

Carrie Rose, London

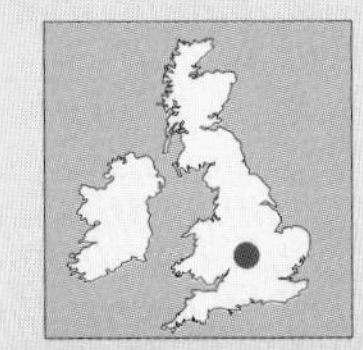

17th century farmhouse

DORMY HOUSE

A haven for Stratford-upon-Avon, The Cotswolds and Broadway itself

Dormy House is set high in the beautiful Cotswold countryside amid picturesque, medieval villages. Originally a 17th century farmhouse, the hotel manages to blend its historic past with all the facilities of the 20th century and personalized service. Each of the forty-nine bedrooms is individually and beautifully decorated and provides every comfort for a good night's rest.

A welcoming haven, its charming lounges, enhanced with bowls of fresh flowers, have deep armchairs in which to relax. Throughout the winter months roaring log fires provide a welcoming atmosphere. The candlelit Tapestries Restaurant offers diners the choice of cosy alcoves in the old farmhouse or the elegant new dining room, with views over the garden and putting green. The food is of a truly international standard; the freshest ingredients of the highest quality ensure an unforgettable gastronomic experience. In the oak-beamed Barn Owl bar, lunchtime and evening meals are served as well as drinks.

Surrounding the hotel on three sides are the greens of the Broadway Golf Club where guests can play by prior arrangement. Guests with time to explore soon find that Cheltenham's shops and Stratford's theatres are within easy reach and the friendly staff are a mine of information on myths, legends and the surrounding Cotswold villages, numerous sporting facilities, country homes and gardens.

LOCATION

From Broadway Village join the A44 signposted to Oxford. Turn at first left signposted "Dormy House" and "Broadway Golf Club". After ½ mile fork right. Dormy House is on the left.

Willersey Hill, Broadway, Worcestershire WR12 7LF

Telephone 01386 852711
Fax 01386 858636

PROPRIETOR

Ingrid Philip-Sorensen

ROOM RATES

7 Singles	*£60 - £80*
39 Doubles/Twins	*£120 - £145*
3 Suites	*£155 - £195*

Includes full breakfast and VAT

CHARGE/CREDIT CARDS

• DC • MC • VI

ACCOLADES

E.T.B. ♛♛♛♛ *Highly Commended*
R.A.C. ★★★ *+ Merit Awards H C & R*
A.A. ★★★ ❀❀ *68%*

FACILITIES

Croquet, gardens, putting green, sauna, gymnasium, billiards, nature and jogging trail
5 meeting rooms/max 200 people
Golf, riding, fishing, clay shooting and archery nearby

RESTRICTIONS

None

ATTRACTIONS

Stratford-upon-Avon, The Cotswolds, Broadway, Chipping Campden, Stow -on-the-Wold and The Slaughters

AFFILIATIONS

Selected British Hotels
J's Hotel Network
Thames Valley Hotels

NEAREST

MAJOR CITY:
Oxford - 40 miles/1 hr

MAJOR AIRPORT:
London Heathrow - 90 miles/2 hrs
Birmingham - 40 miles/1 hr

RAILWAY STATION:
Moreton-in-Marsh - 6 miles/10 mins

RESERVATIONS

Toll free in US: 800-323-5463

ACCESS CODES

Not applicable

"A beautiful place to relax, we loved it!"

Mr & Mrs Beckett, Hertfordshire

ETTINGTON PARK

900 year old manor

Alderminster,
Stratford-upon-Avon
Warwickshire CV37 8BS

Telephone 01789 450123
Fax 01789 450472

GENERAL MANAGER
Kevin Poulter

ROOM RATES

Single occupancy	*from £115*
39 Doubles/Twins	*from £152*
9 Suites	*from £200*

Includes full breakfast and VAT

CHARGE/CREDIT CARDS

• DC • MC • VI

ACCOLADES
E.T.B. Highly Commended
R.A.C. ★★★★
A.A. ★★★★ 75%

FACILITIES
Garden, croquet, tennis, sauna, jacuzzi, indoor pool, riding, fishing, heli-pad
5 meeting rooms/max 80 people

RESTRICTIONS
No facilities for disabled guests
No pets

ATTRACTIONS
Stratford-upon-Avon, The Cotswolds, Warwick Castle, Oxford, Blenheim Palace

AFFILIATIONS
Arcadian Hotels

NEAREST
MAJOR CITY:
Birmingham - 30 miles/1 hr

MAJOR AIRPORT:
London Heathrow - 70 miles/1½ hrs
Birmingham - 26 miles/45 mins

RAILWAY STATION:
Stratford-upon-Avon - 5 miles/10 mins

RESERVATIONS
Toll free in US/Canada: 800-637-7200

ACCESS CODES
AMADEUS WR BHXEPH
APOLLO WR 1288
SAHARA WR BHXET
SABRE WR 15003

Enjoy the finery of Shakespeare country in this 900 year old estate

For 900 years, the Manor of Ettington Park, known today as Ettington Park has belonged to the Shirleys, one of Warwickshire's oldest families and boasts an uninterrupted descent in the male line stretching back before the writing of the Domesday Book (1086).

Nestled in 40 acres of parkland, Ettington now offers 48 luxuriously appointed bedrooms in which to relax and be pampered.

Entering through the conservatory, a world of Victorian architecture unfolds and the restaurant, with its fine example of 19th century hand-carved family crests and 18th century Rococo ceiling, exudes an ambience for fine dining, offering English and French cuisine.

An elegant drawing room and library bar enables one to relax and browse through the morning papers or enjoy the selection of cognacs and liqueurs in front of burning log fires.

Leisure facilities include an indoor heated swimming pool, spa bath, solarium and sauna, whilst outside there are all-weather tennis courts, croquet and horse-riding through the estate.

A perfect setting to relax and experience the splendours of Shakespeare's county.

LOCATION

Located 5 miles south of Stratford-upon-Avon along the A3400, after the village of Alderminster on the left hand side.

" Outstanding! "

Cabell Bruce, New York

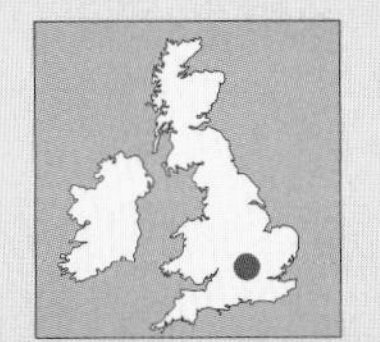

Oxfordshire country house

FALLOWFIELDS

Relax in comfort and enjoy the fruits of a prolific kitchen garden

Originally part of the Kingston Estate, Fallowfields was once the home of the Begum Aha Khan and dates back over 300 years. It has been in private hands for about a century and was extended during that time. Today, whilst its southern aspect is early Victorian Gothic, the northern elevation is a magnificent late Victorian facade.

Fallowfields is set in 12 acres of grounds, two of which are given over to formal gardens and prolific vegetable and herb gardens. Chef/ patron Peta Lloyd makes good use of the home-produce for her imaginative fare.

Personal attention is assured in this intimate establishment which has a small heated outdoor swimming pool plus a croquet lawn and tennis facilities.

Situated ten miles to the west of Oxford, Fallowfields is an ideal centre for touring. It is convenient for Stratford-upon-Avon, the Cotswolds, Blenheim Palace, Oxford University, Bath and Bristol. The surrounding Vale of the White Horse, named after the White Horse at Uffington which was carved out of the chalk downs in pre-Saxon times, is worth exploring too.

LOCATION

In Kingston Bagpuize with Southmoor. From Oxford take the A420 to Faringdon. At the roundabout where the A415 crosses the A420, turn left, and then first right. Fallowfields is only a short distance on.

Faringdon Road, Kingston Bagpuize, Nr Oxford, Oxfordshire OX13 5BH

Telephone 01865 820416
Fax 01865 821275

PROPRIETORS

Peta and Anthony Lloyd

ROOM RATES

Single occupancy	*£59 - £79*
1 Double	*£65 - £80*
2 Four-posters	*£70 - £90*

Includes full breakfast and VAT

CHARGE/CREDIT CARDS

• MC • VI

ACCOLADES

E.T.B. ♛♛♛ Highly Commended
A.A. QQQQQ Premier Selected

FACILITIES

Garden, outdoor pool, croquet, tennis, heli-pad
Riding, fishing, golf, windsurfing and water skiing nearby

RESTRICTIONS

Children under 8 years
No facilities for disabled guests
Pets by arrangement

ATTRACTIONS

Oxford, Cotswolds, Blenheim Palace, River Thames

AFFILIATIONS

Independent

NEAREST

MAJOR CITY:
Oxford - 10 miles/15 mins

MAJOR AIRPORT:
London Heathrow - 50 miles/1 hr

RAILWAY STATION:
Oxford - 8 miles/10 mins

RESERVATIONS

Toll free in US: 800-989-7676

ACCESS CODES

Not applicable

"Comfortable, charming and unpretentious . . . it is one of the places to which I keep coming back"

Elizabeth Ortiz, Gourmet Magazine

THE FEATHERS

17th century inn

Market Street, Woodstock, Oxfordshire OX20 1SX

Telephone 01993 812291
Fax 01993 813158

PROPRIETORS
Howard Malin, Simon Lowe and Andrew Leeman

MANAGER
Tom Lewis

ROOM RATES

1 Single	£75 - £120
13 Doubles	£99 - £150
3 Suites	£185 - £195

Includes tea on arrival, newspaper, continental breakfast and VAT

CHARGE/CREDIT CARDS

• DC • JCB • MC • VI

ACCOLADES
A.A. ★★★ ❀❀ 73%
The Good Hotel Guide

FACILITIES
Courtyard garden, mountain bikes
1 meeting room/max 60 people
Golf, riding and fishing nearby

RESTRICTIONS
No facilities for disabled guests
Dog's bedding and food must be provided by guest

ATTRACTIONS
Blenheim Palace, Broughton Castle, Oxford, Cotswolds, Silverstone Grand Prix circuit

AFFILIATIONS
Selected British Hotels
The Cotswold Collection

NEAREST
MAJOR CITY:
Oxford - 8 miles/15 mins
MAJOR AIRPORT:
London Heathrow - 40 miles/1 hr
RAILWAY STATION:
Oxford - 8 miles/15 mins

RESERVATIONS
Toll free in US: 800-323-5463

ACCESS CODES
APOLLO HK 25900
WORLDSPAN HK FEATH
SABRE HK 30576
SAHARA HK FEATH
AMADEUS HK OXFFEA

Warmth and charm next to Sir Winston Churchill's birthplace

This privately owned 17th century town hotel is located in the heart of picturesque Woodstock which nestles by the gates of Blenheim Palace, the home of the 11th Duke of Marlborough and birth place of Sir Winston Churchill. The Feathers offers the ideal base from which to explore the dreaming spires of the university city of Oxford and the beautiful Cotswolds, yet it is only 1½ hours from London.

The hotel has 14 individually designed rooms and three suites all with antiques, books and interesting pictures. All rooms have private bathrooms, colour televisions with satellite channels and direct dial telephones.

During the winter, log fires blaze in all the sitting rooms and the bar, whilst in warmer months, the courtyard garden provides the ideal location to relax and partake of a light meal or refreshment.

The well renowned restaurant has received much critical acclaim. The interesting dishes on the menu are carefully but simply created using only the finest ingredients. Guests may select from the constantly changing à la carte menu or choose a selection of dishes to create a fixed price menu.

The Feathers is a popular meeting place for locals who return to enjoy the relaxing and friendly atmosphere.

LOCATION

From the south, take the A44 to Woodstock. After Blenheim Palace gates take second turning on the left – the hotel is on left.

" Like stepping into another world with real values "

Russell Deane

Country house

GLEWSTONE COURT HOTEL

Relaxed elegance in an area of outstanding natural beauty

Glewstone Court is an award-winning 'Proper' Country House Hotel and Restaurant; unstuffy and relaxed in elegant but comfortable surroundings. Real log fires, squashy sofas, antique furnishings, decorative paint finishes – even an Edwardian doll's house on the galleried porticoed landing – are the background for their special form of hospitality.

The popular restaurant is acclaimed for its good food – offering the best of local produce from their own garden, neighbouring farms and orchards and the River Wye.

All the individually decorated bedrooms are en suite with television, telephone, radio and hospitality trays. They all enjoy views over Goodrich Castle, the surrounding fruit orchards towards Ross-on-Wye and the Royal Forest of Dean.

Glewstone is ideally situated – just five minutes from Ross-on-Wye. Within 30 minutes there is a host of beauty spots and places of interest: The Black Mountains, Golden Valley, Hereford Cathedral with the Mappa Mundi, Cheltenham and the Cotswolds. The Wye Valley is a designated 'Area of Outstanding Natural Beauty' and Bath is only an hour away.

Now in their ninth year, Bill and Christine Reeve-Tucker were flattered to receive the Automobile Association's 'Care and Courtesy Award for Central England' – one of only 15 out of 4,000 hotels in the UK.

LOCATION

From Ross market-place take A40/A49 towards Monmouth/Hereford, over Wilton Bridge to roundabout, turn left on to A40 dual carriageway to Monmouth/South Wales. After 1 mile turn right for Glewstone. The Court is about half a mile on your left.

Glewstone, Near Ross-on-Wye, Herefordshire HR9 6AW

Telephone 01989 770367
Fax 01989 770282

PROPRIETORS

Christine and William Reeve-Tucker

ROOM RATES

1 Single	*£40*
4 Doubles/Twins	*£80*
1 Four-poster	*£94*
1 Half Tester	*£94*

Includes full breakfast and VAT

CHARGE/CREDIT CARDS

 *• JCB • MC • VI*

ACCOLADES

E.T.B. ♛♛♛♛ Highly Commended
A.A. ★★ 73%
A.A. Courtesy and Care Award 1994/95

FACILITIES

Croquet, gardens, hot air ballooning
3 meeting rooms/max 42 people
Golf, riding & fishing nearby

RESTRICTIONS

No facilities for disabled guests

ATTRACTIONS

Wye Valley, Forest of Dean, Goodrich Castle, Rotherwas Chapel, Hereford Cathedral, Symonds Yat, Tintern Abbey, Malvern Hills, The Cotswolds, The Golden Valley

AFFILIATIONS

Independent

NEAREST

MAJOR CITY:
Birmingham - 55 miles/1 hr

MAJOR AIRPORT:
London Heathrow - 105 miles/2 hrs
Birmingham - 55 miles/1 hr

RAILWAY STATION:
Hereford - 12 miles/30 mins

RESERVATIONS

Direct with hotel

ACCESS CODES

Not applicable

"I'm hard pressed to name any family enterprise, in France or Britain, that can match the remarkable efforts of the Morris team"

Richard Binns, travel writer

GRAFTON MANOR

Manor house

Grafton Lane, Bromsgrove, Worcestershire B61 7HA

Telephone 01527 579007
Fax 01527 575221

PROPRIETOR
The Lord of Grafton

MANAGER
Stephen Morris

ROOM RATES

1 Single	*£85 - £95*
5 Doubles/Twins	*£105 - £125*
1 Four-poster	*£125*
2 Suites	*£150*

Includes full breakfast and VAT

CHARGE/CREDIT CARDS

• *DC* • *MC* • *VI*

ACCOLADES
A.A. ❀❀
Member of Master Chefs Institute
The Good Hotel Guide

FACILITIES
Croquet, gardens, special wedding marquee, fishing, heli-pad, license to perform marriages
2 meeting rooms/max 20 people
Golf and riding nearby

RESTRICTIONS
No facilities for disabled guests
No pets

ATTRACTIONS
Stratford-upon-Avon, Worcester, Cotswolds, Warwick Castle, Stourbridge Glass, Welsh Marches

AFFILIATIONS
Pride of Britain

NEAREST
MAJOR CITY:
Birmingham - 17 miles/30 mins

MAJOR AIRPORT:
Birmingham - 25 miles/25mins

RAILWAY STATION:
Bromsgrove - 2 miles/5 mins

RESERVATIONS
Toll free in US: 800-98-PRIDE

ACCESS CODES
AMADEUS HK BHXGRA
SABRE HK 36237
WORLDSPAN HK GRAFT

A great house with an illustrious past now the epitome of modern elegance

The Manor of Grafton has a long and illustrious history; from its foundation before the Norman Conquest to the present, Grafton has been recognised as one of Worcestershire's great historic houses.

This splendid house, for centuries the home of king makers, was opened as an hotel in 1980 by the present owners John (now The Lord of Grafton) and June Morris who, together with their family, ensure guests receive attentive and friendly service.

The elegant 17th century dining room is the focal point of a visit to Grafton, with imaginative menus created by Simon Morris who aims to produce only the best for guests, complemented by a fine wine list. Damask-rose petal and mulberry sorbets are indicative of the inspired style of cuisine.

The guest bedrooms have been painstakingly restored, introducing the comforts demanded today while retaining the grace and elegance of another age.

There is much to enjoy at Grafton: a superb formal Herb Garden in 26 acres of beautiful grounds, a two-acre lake, a 16th century fish stew (brick building in the stream), and a 15th century private chapel. Grafton Manor is an ideal base from which to explore the Worcestershire countryside.

LOCATION

From M5 Junction 5 proceed via A38 towards Bromsgrove. Bear left at first roundabout; Grafton Lane is first left after half a mile.

"It was a delight to be able to return to such a pleasant hotel"

The Rt Hon John Major, Prime Minister

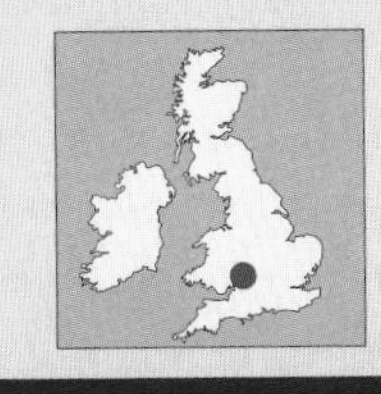

Elizabethan country manor

THE GREENWAY

A taste of excellence in the Cotswolds

Set amidst formal gardens, with the rolling Cotswold Hills beyond, The Greenway is an Elizabethan Country Manor House with a unique personal style of its own. Renowned for the warmth of its welcome, its friendly atmosphere and its personal service, The Greenway is the ideal place for total relaxation.

The public rooms with their antique furniture and fresh flowers are elegant, spacious and very comfortable, with crackling log fires in winter and access to the beautiful gardens in summer.

The 19 bedrooms all have private bathrooms and are individually decorated with co-ordinated colour schemes. Eleven of the rooms are situated in the main house whilst eight further large rooms are in the immediately adjacent Georgian coach house.

The Conservatory Dining Room overlooks the sunken garden and lily pond and provides the perfect backdrop to superb cuisine, complemented by an outstanding selection of wines.

Situated in one of Britain's most charming areas, The Greenway is ideally placed for visiting the many delightful Cotswold villages, the spa town of Cheltenham, Stratford-Upon-Avon and Shakespeare country. Personally run by owners, David and Valerie White, The Greenway offers the best in traditional hospitality and a lot more besides.

LOCATION

Leave M5 at Junction 11A and join A417 towards Cirencester. At A46 turn left direction Cheltenham. Hotel is 1 mile on the right.

Shurdington, Cheltenham, Gloucestershire GL51 5UG

Telephone 01242 862352
Fax 01242 862780

PROPRIETORS

David and Valerie White

ROOM RATES

2 Singles £87.50
17 Doubles/Twins £127.50 - £180
Includes full breakfast and VAT

CHARGE/CREDIT CARDS

• DC • MC • VI

ACCOLADES

R.A.C. Blue Ribbon Award ★★★
A.A. ★★★ ❀❀❀
The Good Hotel Guide

FACILITIES

Garden, croquet, heli-pad
2 meeting rooms/max 45 people
Golf, fishing, walking, clay pigeon shooting, tennis, swimming and riding nearby

RESTRICTIONS

No children under 7 years
No pets

ATTRACTIONS

The Cotswolds, Stratford-Upon-Avon, Cheltenham Spa, Painswick, Wye Valley, Sudeley Castle, Forest of Dean

AFFILIATIONS

Pride of Britain
Selected British Hotels

NEAREST

MAJOR CITY:
Cheltenham - 2½ miles/5 mins

MAJOR AIRPORT:
Birmingham - 60 miles/1 hr 10 mins
Bristol - 45 miles/50 mins

RAILWAY STATION:
Cheltenham - 2½ miles/5 mins

RESERVATIONS

Toll free in US: 800-543-4135

ACCESS CODES

Not applicable

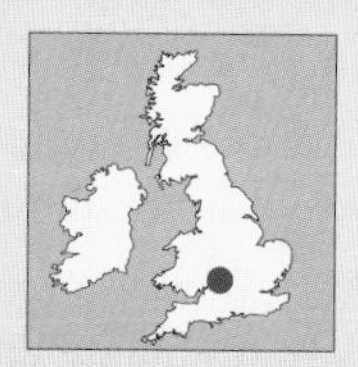

"To say that Jasmine and I felt really at home is, I know, a crashing cliché, but happens to be the simple and genuine truth"

John Canning, London

HALEWELL

15th century former monastery

Withington, Cheltenham, Gloucestershire GL54 4BN

Telephone 01242 890238
Fax 01242 890332

OWNER
Mrs Elizabeth Carey-Wilson

ROOM RATES
Single occupancy £49.50
6 Doubles/Twins £79 - £83
Includes full breakfast and VAT

CHARGE/CREDIT CARDS

• *MC* • *VI*

ACCOLADES
Independent

FACILITIES
Outdoor pool, gardens, parkland, trout fishing lake

RESTRICTIONS
Children by arrangement
Pets by arrangement

ATTRACTIONS
The Cotswolds, Oxford, Blenheim Palace, Bath, Warwick and Sudeley Castles, Stratford-upon-Avon, Chedworth Roman Villa

AFFILIATIONS
Wolsey Lodges

NEAREST
MAJOR CITY:
Cheltenham - 7 miles/20 mins

MAJOR AIRPORT:
London Heathrow - 80 miles/2 hrs
Bristol - 50 miles/1¼ hrs

RAILWAY STATION:
Cheltenham - 8 miles/30 mins

RESERVATIONS
Direct with hotel

ACCESS CODES
Not applicable

Once a monastery now every comfort

Halewell, a private home, is built round an internal courtyard. On the west side, originally a small monastery and dating from about 1400, are two magnificent reception rooms, downstairs the Jacobean oak-panelled dining room, and upstairs a cathedral-ceilinged two-storey drawing room.

The east side, probably built originally in the 18th century as barns has, in the last twelve years, been completely reorganised by the owner, Mrs Elizabeth Carey-Wilson, to contain six double bedrooms. These are all very large, individually decorated and furnished to a very high standard, with bathrooms (and mostly showers) en suite, and include two family suites (not family rooms where the children sleep with the parents), a suite for three adults and a purpose-built, twin room for disabled guests, listed by Radar.

Dinner is a set meal of traditional English food served en famille. Snacks are available in the evening, and there is a residential drinks licence.

The setting is extremely quiet on the edge of a pretty Cotswold village and the 50 acres of private grounds include terraces, formal and informal gardens and a five acre trout lake, and swimming pool.

The atmosphere at Halewell is of total peace, quiet and comfort, and when several guests are staying together, of a country house party.

LOCATION

7 miles east of Cheltenham, south of the A40 Oxford/London Road. Do not confuse with nearby village of Whittington.

"Surely one of the finest in England in all respects"

Diana Noronha

Elizabethan manor house

HINTLESHAM HALL

A great house with an international reputation for excellence

One of England's loveliest hotels, Hintlesham Hall is a Grade I listed Elizabethan manor house located in Suffolk, where 16th century towns and villages are still characterised by ancient timbered houses.

Behind Hintlesham's famous Georgian façade are 33 bedrooms and suites, each individually designed and finished with elegant fabrics, antiques and works of art. All rooms have modern bathrooms and are supplied with Penhaligon's toiletries, towelling robes and hairdryers as well as digital telephones, colour TVs and mini bars.

Very high ratings in all major guides, endorse the Hall's reputation for excellence which is enhanced by the superb restaurant. Hintlesham's cuisine goes from strength to strength, complemented by an award-winning wine list.

The leisure facilities include the Hall's own championship standard golf course which is screened by trees from the tranquil 40 acres of gardens and grounds. The new nationally-acclaimed Clubhouse offers golfers and non-golfers an alternative place for dining and relaxation. There are saunas, a steam room and spa bath. The Orangery Leisure Club features a work-out room with balconies, lovely views and a heated outdoor swimming pool. Guests may also enjoy clay shooting and trout fishing on the estate, or snooker in the Hall. The hotel's own Antiques Guide is a must for touring the area.

Friendliness and professionalism are the watchwords at Hintlesham Hall where the warmest of welcomes awaits.

LOCATION

Travelling north on the A12 go towards Ipswich town centre at the A12/A14 (formerly A45) interchange roundabout. Left on to A1071 (Hadleigh). Then straight on for 2 miles into Hintlesham village. Entrance to Hall is past church on the right.

Hintlesham, Nr Ipswich, Suffolk IP8 3NS

Telephone 01473 652334
Fax 01473 652463

PROPRIETOR
David Allan

GENERAL MANAGER
Timothy Sunderland

ROOM RATES

Single occupancy	£85 - £105
26 Doubles/Twins	£110 - £200
2 Four-posters	£200
4 Suites	£225 - £300

Includes full breakfast and VAT

CHARGE/CREDIT CARDS

• DC • MC • VI

ACCOLADES
E.T.B. De Luxe
R.A.C. Blue Ribbon Award ★★★★
A.A. ★★★★ ❀❀❀
The Good Hotel Guide
E.A.T.B. Hotel of the Year 1994

FACILITIES
Outdoor pool and tennis, croquet, gardens, steam room, spa bath, health & beauty, sauna, gym, snooker, clay pigeon shooting, golf, heli-pad
4 meeting rooms/max 120 people
Riding and fishing nearby

RESTRICTIONS
None

ATTRACTIONS
Cambridge, Suffolk, Norwich, Constable country, Heritage Coast

AFFILIATIONS
Small Luxury Hotels

NEAREST
MAJOR CITY:
Ipswich - 5 miles/10 mins

MAJOR AIRPORT:
London Heathrow - 85 miles/2 hrs
Stansted - 50 miles/50 mins

RAILWAY STATION:
Ipswich - 5 miles/10 mins

RESERVATIONS
Toll free in US: 800-525-4800

ACCESS CODES
AMADEUS/SYSTEM 1 LX LONHAN
APOLLO LX 32326
AXESS LX 5634
WORLDSPAN LX LTNHM
SABRE LX 31485

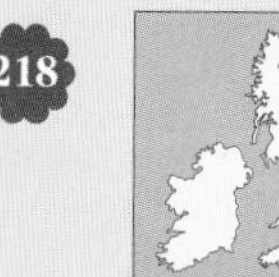

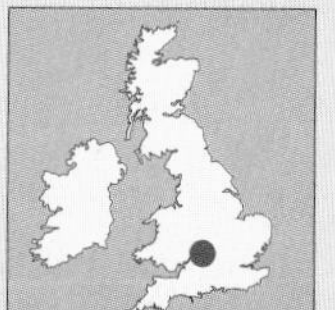

" Didn't want to leave, one night turned into three. Excellent all round "

Mr & Mrs Pearce, London

HOTEL ON THE PARK

Regency town house

Evesham Road,
Cheltenham,
Gloucestershire GL52 2AH

Telephone 01242 518898
Fax 01242 511526

PROPRIETOR
Darryl Gregory

ROOM RATES

Single occupancy	£70 - £110
9 Doubles/Twins	£85 - £95
1 Four-poster	£145
2 Superior Suites	£115

Includes VAT

CHARGE/CREDIT CARDS

• DC • MC • VI

ACCOLADES
E.T.B. ♕♕♕♕ De Luxe
R.A.C. ★★★ + Merit Awards H & C
A.A. ★★★ ❀❀❀
The Good Hotel Guide

FACILITIES
Garden, The Restaurant
1 meeting room/max 18 people
Golf, riding and fishing nearby

RESTRICTIONS
No children under 8 years
No facilities for disabled guests
Pets by arrangement
with own bedding and food

ATTRACTIONS
Pittville Pump Room,
Gustav Holst birthplace,
Cheltenham Races,
The Cotswolds

AFFILIATIONS
The Cotswold Collection
European Connection

NEAREST
MAJOR CITY:
Birmingham - 49 miles /1 hr

MAJOR AIRPORT:
Birmingham - 49 miles /1 hr

RAILWAY STATION:
Cheltenham - 2 miles /10 mins

RESERVATIONS
Direct with hotel

ACCESS CODES
Not applicable

Regency elegance in the centre for the Cotswolds

This beautifully restored Regency building is the finest town house hotel in the Cheltenham area and is perfectly located for touring the Cotswolds and surrounding towns of interest such as Stratford-upon-Avon and Bath.

The hotel is in a superb position overlooking Pittville Park yet is only a short walk from the town centre and the National Hunt Racecourse.

This exclusive privately-owned hotel offers the discerning traveller unparalleled comfort and luxury with friendly and courteous staff to assist with your every need.

The bedrooms are individually designed and dressed with traditional fabrics, crisp Egyptian cotton sheets, fine antiques and porcelain with original paintings adorning the walls.

All rooms feature en suite bathrooms, some with ball and claw baths. Facilities include Satellite TV, radio, direct-dial telephone and complimentary hot and cold drinks. There is an elegant, candlelit drawing room and bar or an intimate library with crackling log fire to read and relax in, and perhaps to contemplate the delights awaiting you for dinner.

The hotel is also privileged to have as its restaurant, "The Restaurant", with food prepared by Graham Mairs, cooking predominantly British food with modern European influence.

LOCATION

In the Regency spa town of Cheltenham. Take Evesham signpost from town centre. Hotel on left opposite Pittville Park.

"Le Manoir is one of the most sumptuous country house hotels in Great Britain and its restaurant the best in the nation"

Michael Balter, Bon Appetit

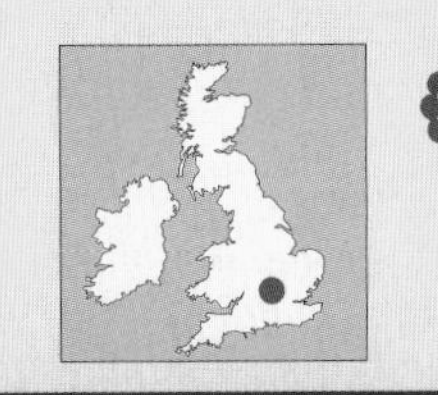

15th century manor LE MANOIR AUX QUAT' SAISONS

Discover the magic of Le Manoir

Situated in secluded and beautiful grounds a few miles south of the historic university town of Oxford in the rural Cotswolds, Le Manoir aux Quat' Saisons is one of Europe's finest restaurants and a lovely country house hotel.

Le Manoir is the inspired creation of chef, Raymond Blanc, whose extraordinary cooking has received the highest tributes from all international guides to culinary excellence. Uniquely, the London Times gives Blanc's cooking 10 out of 10 and rates it "the best in Britain".

The restaurant is the natural focus of this lovely 15th Century manor house which stands in landscaped gardens, its sweeping lawns set against a backdrop of fine trees. A feature of the estate is a carefully tended vegetable garden which supplies the kitchen with the finest and freshest organic produce.

The atmosphere throughout is one of understated elegance whilst all nineteen bedrooms and suites offer guests the highest standards of comfort and luxury. Every need is anticipated, for service is a way of life here, never intrusive but always present. "It is as if the entire staff has been touched by spirits beyond the reach of sordid commerce", writes the Daily Telegraph.

LOCATION

Leaving London, take the M40 Motorway to Oxford, leaving at Junction 7 signposted to Thame and Wallingford. Turn left at the junction onto the A329. Continue for 2 miles then turn right at the sign for Great Milton Manor. Le Manoir is located 200 yards on the right.

Church Road, Great Milton, Oxford, Oxfordshire OX44 7PD

Telephone 01844 278881
Fax 01844 278847

PROPRIETORS
Raymond Blanc and Richard Branson

GENERAL MANAGER
Simon Rhatigan

ROOM RATES
16 Doubles/Twins £185 - £345
3 Suites £395
Includes VAT

CHARGE/CREDIT CARDS

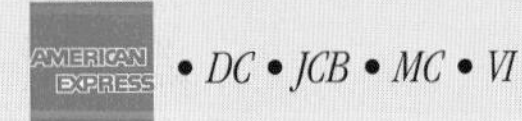

• DC • JCB • MC • VI

ACCOLADES
E.T.B. ♛♛♛♛♛ De Luxe
R.A.C. Blue Ribbon Award ★★★★
A.A. ★★★★ ✿✿✿✿✿
The Good Hotel Guide

FACILITIES
Outdoor swimming pool, croquet, tennis, gardens, cookery school, heli-pad
1 meeting room/max 40 people
Fishing nearby

RESTRICTIONS
No facilities for disabled guests
No dogs in hotel - kennels in grounds

ATTRACTIONS
Cotswolds, Blenheim Palace, Waddesden Manor, Oxford

AFFILIATIONS
Relais & Châteaux

NEAREST
MAJOR CITY:
Oxford - 7 miles/15 mins

MAJOR AIRPORT:
London Heathrow - 40 miles/45 mins

RAILWAY STATION:
Oxford - 7 miles/15 mins

RESERVATIONS
Toll free in US: 800-845-4274

ACCESS CODES
Not applicable

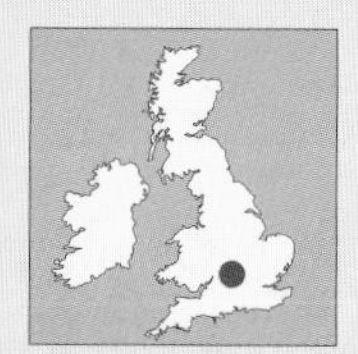

"A veritable haven of peace and tranquillity"

Anthony Donaldson, London

LORDS OF THE MANOR

17th century manor house

Upper Slaughter,
Nr Bourton-on-the-Water,
Gloucestershire GL54 2JD

Telephone 01451 820243
Fax 01451 820696

GENERAL MANAGER

Richard Young

ROOM RATES

2 Singles £90
22 Doubles/Twins £115 - £140
3 Old Rectory Rooms £190 - £225
Includes full breakfast and VAT

CHARGE/CREDIT CARDS

• *DC* • *JCB* • *MC* • *VI*

ACCOLADES

E.T.B. ♛♛♛♛ De Luxe
R.A.C. ★★★ + Merit Awards H C & R
A.A. ★★★ ❀❀❀ 77%
The Good Hotel Guide
County Restaurant of the Year 1994
- a major guide

FACILITIES

Croquet, gardens, fishing
2 meeting rooms/max 30 people
Clay pigeon shooting, archery, golf, riding, fishing and quad-biking nearby

RESTRICTIONS

No facilities for disabled guests
No pets

ATTRACTIONS

Blenheim Palace, Woodstock, Oxford, Stratford-upon-Avon, Cotswolds

AFFILIATIONS

Small Luxury Hotels
The Celebrated Hotels Collection

NEAREST

MAJOR CITY:
Oxford - 35 miles/40 mins

MAJOR AIRPORT:
Birmingham - 45 miles/1 1/4 hrs

RAILWAY STATION:
Moreton-in-Marsh - 8 miles/20 mins

RESERVATIONS

Toll free in US: 800-872-4564

ACCESS CODES

Not applicable

Paradise found in the heart of The Cotswolds

The Lords of the Manor is a 17th Century country house hotel situated in the heart of the Cotswolds. Built in 1650 this former rectory stands in eight acres of secluded gardens and parkland amidst the small historic village of Upper Slaughter, one of the Cotswolds' prettiest and most unspoilt villages.

Comfortable settees and big roaring fires, beautifully tended well-loved gardens and croquet on the lawn create an idyllic setting.

The dining room at the Lords of The Manor has a fine reputation for modern English cooking using the best of fresh local produce, and the cellars offer an outstanding wine list. The dining room itself looks on to the Rectory's original walled gardens.

All the 27 bedrooms with en suite bathrooms are individually decorated with period furniture and original oil paintings and watercolours.

For leisure activities guests can enjoy a game of croquet or coarse fishing on the lake. Other activities including riding, golf, game and clay pigeon shooting can be arranged locally.

Upper Slaughter is just eight miles from Moreton-in-Marsh which offers a train service to London Paddington, and is located in the centre of the Cotswold touring country.

LOCATION

2 miles off the A429 between Stow-on-the-Wold and Bourton-on-the-Water. Signed to 'The Slaughters'.

"When hospitality becomes an art and not only work . . . things like Lovells may happen"

G Basso, Italy

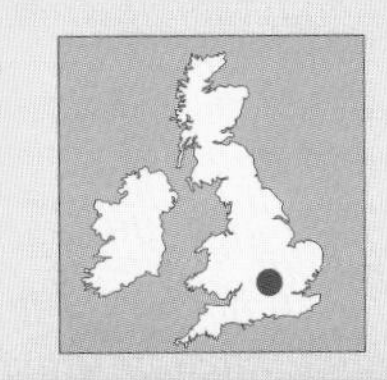

17th century farmhouse

LOVELLS AT WINDRUSH FARM

Fine facilities and impressive cuisine in acres of park and woodland

Set in 80 acres of park and woodland, Lovells is a country house hotel – and so much more. It offers a unique combination of the highest quality cuisine, accommodation which would grace the finest country house, and service only to be found when you are invited by friends.

Lovells is a delightful restaurant with rooms which also boast lounges with teak floor boards, a full size antique snooker table and delightful decor. The young chef Marcus Ashenford learnt his trade under the guidance of Michelin starred chefs like Ramon Farthing and Michel Roux. He uses the finest ingredients, local where possible, international where necessary. Independent writers are seriously impressed by his food, as are the guests.

Beside the Lovells parkland flows more than a mile of River Windrush where you can walk, fish or picnic. The land is used periodically for local horse trials and Lovells has its own specialist schooling area. The famous 15th century Minster Lovell Hall is just across the Windrush, and the village is rich in legends that include the tragic Mistletoe Bough.

As an excellent base, Lovells is located three miles east of Burford, gateway to the Cotswolds. Most important of all, Lovells, in its beautiful rural setting, offers that rarest treat of all – total relaxation!

LOCATION

From London, M40 to Junction 8, follow A40 towards Cheltenham. Shortly after bypassing Witney, turn right down road signposted to Minster Lovell. Follow signs to Minster Lovell Hall.

Minster Lovell,
Oxfordshire OX8 5RN

Telephone 01993 779802
Fax 01993 779802

PROPRIETORS

Norma Cooper and Mark Maguire

ROOM RATES

Singles £95
3 Doubles £160
Includes full breakfast, dinner and VAT

CHARGE/CREDIT CARDS

• *DC* • *MC* • *VI*

ACCOLADES

A.A. ❀❀

FACILITIES

Garden, snooker, fishing
1 meeting room/max 10 people
Golf and riding nearby

RESTRICTIONS

No facilities for disabled guests
Pets by prior arrangement

ATTRACTIONS

Minster Lovell Hall,
Blenheim Palace,
Oxford,
The Cotswolds,
Cotswold Wild Life Park

AFFILIATIONS

Independent

NEAREST

MAJOR CITY:
Oxford - 15 miles/20 mins

MAJOR AIRPORT:
London Heathrow - 45 miles/1 hr

RAILWAY STATION:
Oxford - 15 miles/20 mins

RESERVATIONS

Direct with hotel

ACCESS CODES

Not applicable

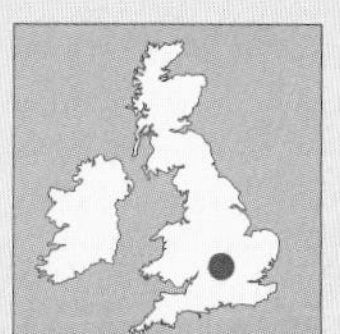

" The hay is so good and everything so neat, and the dogs so fat! "

The fifth Viscount Torrington, The Torrington Diaries

THE LYGON ARMS

16th century coaching inn

High Street, Broadway
Worcestershire WR12 7DU

Telephone 01386 852255
Fax 01386 858611

MANAGING DIRECTOR
Kirk Ritchie

ROOM RATES

2 Singles	£112 - £140
52 Doubles/Twins	£170 - £225
6 Four-posters	from £225
5 Suites	£265 - £355

Includes early morning tea, newspaper, continental breakfast and VAT

CHARGE/CREDIT CARDS

 • DC • MC • VI

ACCOLADES
E.T.B. ♛♛♛♛♛ De Luxe
R.A.C. Blue Ribbon Award ★★★★
A.A. ★★★★ ❀❀
The Good Hotel Guide

FACILITIES
Garden, croquet, outdoor tennis, gym, indoor pool, health & beauty, sauna, solarium, jacuzzi, snooker, heli-pad
5 meeting rooms/max 80 people
Hot air ballooning, golf, riding, clay pigeon shooting and archery nearby

RESTRICTIONS
Gentlemen are required to wear jacket and tie in restaurant for dinner

ATTRACTIONS
Stratford-upon-Avon, Oxford, Blenheim Palace, Warwick Castle, Hidcote Gardens, The Cotswolds

AFFILIATIONS
The Savoy Group
Leading Hotels of the World

NEAREST
MAJOR CITY:
Birmingham - 35 miles/45 mins

MAJOR AIRPORT:
London Heathrow - 90 miles/1¾ hrs
Birmingham - 40 miles/45 mins

RAILWAY STATION:
Moreton in Marsh - 8 miles/12 mins

RESERVATIONS
Toll free in US: 800-637-2869

ACCESS CODES
AMADEUS LW VKNVJ406
APOLLO LW 8427
WORLDSPAN LW 0406
SABRE LW 4740

A 16th century coaching inn of quite stunning proportions

The Lygon Arms has been welcoming visitors for over 450 years. Centrepiece of the picturesque village of Broadway, in the heart of the Cotswolds, the Inn is filled with fresh flowers, antiques, country furnishings and roaring log fires.

The bedrooms range from magnificent four-posters to award-winning contemporary rooms, decorated in country house style. Guests can choose to dine in the Great Hall, with its heraldic friezes and minstrels' gallery, or in summer al fresco on The Patio. Each offers traditional English dishes with innovative touches, whilst Goblets wine bar provides a less formal alternative.

The Inn is also the perfect setting for small conferences and top-level board meetings, being located just two hours from London and 45 minutes from Birmingham Airport. The five meeting rooms, accommodating up to 80 delegates, includes a fully air-conditioned room, with the very latest AV technology.

Those with time to relax can enjoy the adjoining Country Club with its galleried pool, spa bath, sauna, solaria, steam room, beauty treatment rooms and billiards room, or stroll in the delightful garden with its all-weather tennis court and heli-pad.

Further afield are Stratford-upon-Avon, Warwick and a cornucopia of enchanting mellow-stone villages. Outings and activities, can be arranged from riding and hot-air ballooning, to Shakespeare at Stratford and visits to private houses and gardens.

LOCATION

Take Junction 8 off the M40 from London. Broadway is on the A44 and The Lygon Arms is in the centre of the village on the right-hand side of the High Street.

" Mallory Court is a place to which my thoughts when I am busy, bothered or harrassed, turn longingly back "

Wendy Arnold, The Historic Hotels of England

Edwardian manor house

MALLORY COURT HOTEL

The three essentials of country living: hospitality, comfort and superb cuisine

Situated in the heart of England, between Stratford-upon-Avon and Warwick, Mallory Court recreates the traditions of gracious hospitality in an English country house. The house is an outstanding example of period architecture built of mellow stone with leaded-light windows. It was converted into an hotel by the present proprietors in 1976 and is generally regarded as one of the finest country house hotels in England.

Everything inside the house is polished and shining and the young attentive staff are delighted to see you when you arrive. The two lounges are furnished with comfortable sofas and armchairs and fresh flowers abound. During the winter months log fires add to the feeling of warmth and well-being. The bedrooms are luxurious, all individually decorated and provided with every thoughtful detail.

The ten acres of gardens are exquisite and lovingly maintained. They include a formal rose garden, water garden, croquet lawn, a splendid herb garden and terraces overlooking the Warwickshire countryside.

The renowned restaurant has achieved the highest accolades in all the leading food guides and is overseen by Allan Holland. The cuisine includes both classic French and British dishes and many of the vegetables, herbs and fruits used in the cooking are from the hotel's own gardens.

LOCATION

From south, 3 miles from Junction 13, M40.
From north, 3 miles from Junction 14, M40.

Harbury Lane, Bishops Tachbrook, Leamington Spa, Warwickshire CV33 9QB

Telephone 01926 330214
Fax 01926 451714

PROPRIETORS

Allan Holland and Jeremy Mort

ROOM RATES

Single occupancy	*£115 - £135*
10 Doubles/Twins	*£160 - £220*

Includes continental breakfast and VAT

CHARGE/CREDIT CARDS

• DC • MC • VI

ACCOLADES

A.A. ★★★ ❀❀❀
The Good Hotel Guide
County Restaurant of the Year 1995 - a leading guide

FACILITIES

Outdoor swimming pool, croquet, tennis, gardens, squash, heli-pad
2 meeting rooms/max 15 people
Golf, riding and fishing nearby

RESTRICTIONS

No children under 9 years
No facilities for disabled guests
No pets

ATTRACTIONS

Stratford-upon-Avon, Cotswold Villages, Warwick Castle, National Exhibition Centre

AFFILIATIONS

Relais & Chateaux

NEAREST

MAJOR CITY:
Birmingham - 30 miles/40 mins

MAJOR AIRPORT:
Birmingham - 25 miles/30 mins

RAILWAY STATION:
Leamington Spa - 2 miles/5 mins

RESERVATIONS

Direct with hotel

ACCESS CODES

Not applicable

" We can pay for accommodation anywhere, but it is not possible to buy the care you have shown us while we have been here "

Dr J Coates, Cumbria

THE MILL AT HARVINGTON

18th century mill

*Anchor Lane,
Harvington, Evesham,
Worcestershire WR11 5NR*

*Telephone 01386 870688
Fax 01386 870688*

PROPRIETORS

Simon and Jane Greenhalgh

ROOM RATES

Single occupancy £54
15 Doubles/Twins £85
Includes full breakfast and VAT

CHARGE/CREDIT CARDS

• *DC* • *MC* • *VI*

ACCOLADES

R.A.C. ★★ + Merit Awards H C & R
A.A. ★★ ❀❀ 77%
County Hotel of the Year 1996 – a leading guide
The Good Hotel Guide

FACILITIES

Garden, croquet, tennis, outdoor swimming pool, fishing
1 meeting room/max 40 people
Golf and riding nearby

RESTRICTIONS

No children under 10 years
Limited facilities for disabled guests
No pets

ATTRACTIONS

Stratford, The Cotswolds, Warwick Castle, Ragley Hall, Sudeley Castle, The Malverns

AFFILIATIONS

Independent

NEAREST

MAJOR CITY:
Birmingham - 30 miles/50 mins

MAJOR AIRPORT:
Birmingham - 32 miles/40 mins

RAILWAY STATION:
Evesham - 4 miles/5 mins

RESERVATIONS

Direct with hotel

ACCESS CODES

Not applicable

A dedication to your enjoyment, on the banks of the Avon

The village of Harvington in the fertile Vale of Evesham is recorded in William the Conqueror's Domesday Book. The Mill which has served the village since before 1750 and the fine Georgian house beside it on the banks of the Avon have been sensitively converted into a delightful hotel and an excellent restaurant.

The 15 comfortable bedrooms face the morning sun and overlook garden and river. All have en suite bathrooms, colour TV, radio, tea and coffee-making facilities, and telephone.

Menus are changed frequently to take advantage of the freshest foods available through the seasons. Full use is made of local Evesham produce; fruit, vegetables, meat, fish and game, to ensure the highest quality. From the hotel's own garden come fresh herbs: thyme, sage, rosemary and sweet English mint.

The hotel is set in almost eight acres of wooded parkland with splendid willows shading its 600 feet of river frontage. Fishing is available directly from the grounds. Heron stalk the shallows of the weir. Hares, partridges, woodpeckers, kingfishers and pheasants are to be seen. There is a hard tennis court and a heated outdoor swimming pool.

Harvington is an ideal holiday centre for Shakespeare's England. Stratford-upon-Avon is only ten miles away. For history lovers there are the medieval castles of Warwick, Kenilworth, Berkeley and Sudeley. There are stone-age burial mounds, Roman villas, Saxon villages, palaces, churches and cathedrals in plenty!

LOCATION

Harvington is only 14 miles from the M5 at Worcester, 18 miles from the M40 at Warwick. The Mill is off the B439 Evesham-Stratford road beside the river, not in the village.

“ One of the most romantic hotels in England ”

Jeff Banks, fashion designer & TV presenter

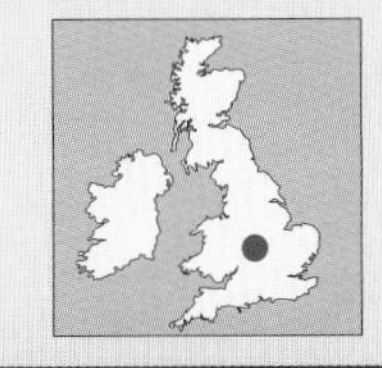

17th century manor

NAILCOTE HALL

Living in luxury surrounded by historic homes and castles

Nailcote Hall is a charming country house hotel set in 15 acres of gardens and surrounded by Warwickshire countryside. Built around 1640, the house was used by Cromwell during the Civil War and damaged by troops prior to the assault on Kenilworth Castle.

In the intimate Tudor surroundings of the Oak Room restaurant, the chef will delight you with superb cuisine, while the cellar boasts an extensive choice of international wines. Alternatively dine "under the stars" in Rick's Mediterranean style bistro.

38 en suite bedrooms offer luxury accommodation. Each is individually decorated and appointed in traditional style, and has direct dial telephone, TV, radio and hospitality tray.

Leisure facilities include indoor swimming pool, gymnasium, solarium and sauna. Outdoors, guests can enjoy the all-weather tennis courts, petanque, croquet, a nine-hole golf course and a putting green.

Ideally located in the heart of England, Nailcote Hall is within 15 minutes' drive of the castle towns of Kenilworth and Warwick, Coventry Cathedral, Birmingham International Airport and the National Exhibition Centre. Shakespeare's Stratford-upon-Avon is just 20 minutes away.

LOCATION

Situated 6 miles south of Birmingham International Airport on the B4101 Balsall Common-Coventry road within 10 minutes of the Midlands motorway network.

Nailcote Lane, Berkswell, Warwickshire CV7 7DE

Telephone 01203 466174
Fax 01203 470720

PROPRIETOR

Rick Cressman

ROOM RATES

Single occupancy	*£110*
34 Doubles/Twins	*£120*
3 Four-posters	*£140*
1 Suite	*£125 - £165*

Includes full breakfast and VAT

CHARGE/CREDIT CARDS

• DC • MC • VI

ACCOLADES

E.T.B. ♛♛♛♛ Highly Commended
R.A.C. ★★★ + Merit Awards H C & R
A.A. ★★★ ❀❀ 76%

FACILITIES

Gardens, indoor pool, croquet, tennis, 9-hole golf course, petanque, sauna, steam room, solarium, gym, heli-pad
7 meeting rooms/max 100 people
Golf and riding nearby

RESTRICTIONS

No pets

ATTRACTIONS

Warwick Castle, Kenilworth Castle, Stratford-upon-Avon, National Exhibition Centre, Coventry Cathedral

AFFILIATIONS

Independent

NEAREST

MAJOR CITY:
Coventry - 4 miles/10 mins

MAJOR AIRPORT:
Birmingham - 6 miles/10 mins

RAILWAY STATION:
Berkswell - 2 miles/5 mins
Birmingham Intl - 6 miles/10 mins

RESERVATIONS

Toll free fax in US: 800-819-0027

ACCESS CODES

Not applicable

“ This is the most comfortable, relaxing hotel I have ever stayed in ”

Tina Turner

NEW HALL

12th century moated manor house castle

Walmley Road,
Royal Sutton Coldfield,
West Midlands B76 1QX

Telephone 0121 378 2442
Fax 0121 378 4637

GENERAL MANAGERS
Ian and Caroline Parkes

ROOM RATES

4 Singles	£100 - £120
50 Doubles	£120 - £175
6 Suites	£175 - £285

Includes VAT

CHARGE/CREDIT CARDS

• DC • JCB • MC • VI

ACCOLADES
E.T.B. ♛♛♛♛♛
R.A.C. Blue Ribbon Award ★★★★
A.A. ★★★★ ❀❀
A.A. Inspectors Hotel of the Year for England 1993/4

FACILITIES
Croquet, gardens, tennis, trout lake, 9 hole golf course
4 meeting rooms/max 50 people
Golf and riding nearby

RESTRICTIONS
No children under 8 years
No pets

ATTRACTIONS
Warwick, Stratford-upon-Avon, Lichfield Cathedral, Wedgwood Pottery, Belfry Golf Centre

AFFILIATIONS
Small Luxury Hotels
A Thistle Country House Hotel

NEAREST
MAJOR CITY:
Birmingham - 8 miles/15 mins

MAJOR AIRPORT:
Birmingham - 12 miles/20 mins

RAILWAY STATION:
Birmingham - 8 miles/15 mins

RESERVATIONS
Toll free in US/Canada: 800-847-4358
Toll free in Australia: 008-062-055

ACCESS CODES
SABRE TI 16708
AMADEUS/SYSTEM 1 TI BHXNHC
WORLDSPAN TI SUTNW
APOLLO TI 13616

The oldest inhabited, moated manor house in England

New Hall, dating from the 12th century, is the oldest inhabited moated manor house in England. Personally run by Ian and Caroline Parkes, it is the holder of the prestigious RAC Blue Ribbon Award and has two AA rosettes for Food and Service. It was also the AA Hotel of the Year for England in 1993/94 and holds four AA red stars.

Ideal for romantic weekends and a touring base for visiting Warwick Castle, Stratford-upon-Avon and the Cotswolds, New Hall is 20 minutes from Birmingham International Airport, The National Exhibition Centre, the new International Convention Centre and Symphony Hall, and the Birmingham Hippodrome Theatre, home of the Royal Ballet.

Guests dine sumptuously in the 16th century oak-panelled, non-smoking restaurant, where the award-winning kitchen creates traditional and modern British cuisine.

New Hall features extensively wooded grounds with walks, a croquet lawn, nine-hole golf course, golf driving net, putting green and a flood-lit all-weather tennis court. The famous Ryder Cup Belfry Golf Centre is only one of the many championship courses that are only five minutes drive from the hotel.

LOCATION

From Exit 9 of M42 follow A4097 ignoring signs to A38 Sutton Coldfield. At B4148 traffic lights turn right. New Hall is 1 mile further on.

" You made us feel very special "

Caroline & David Lloyd

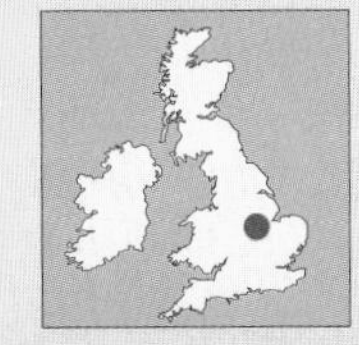

Georgian stable block

NORMANTON PARK

Historical links, with a scintillating view of Rutland Water

The largest man-made lake in Europe is in Rutland, England's smallest county and also paradoxically one of its oldest and newest! Deprived of its county status in 1974, it has now been restored to its just title to the joy of local campaigners. The county is rich in sporting and historical connections which, with the addition of the lake includes watersports. This is the home of the Belvoir Foxhound; the Normans built nearby Oakham and the Romans left a fort not four miles from Normanton Park, in which now stands this delightful hotel.

Set in five acres of parkland with a langourous stretch of lake frontage, the hotel succeeds in harmonising period decor and furnishings with all the modern comforts of life.

Dining in the Orangery at Normanton Park is a pleasant prospect indeed: the view of Rutland Water is as scintillating as the promise of the à la carte menu. The Sailing Bar and the Courtyard Patio offer a locally renowned steak and kidney pie, Melton Mowbray pies (of course) and a lighter choice of delicacies to appeal to the health conscious.

All the bedrooms are en suite and cheerfully decorated with views across Rutland Water. The effect is sublime and guaranteed to banish all symptoms of stress.

LOCATION

Take A606 off A1 signposted Oakham. Left after 3 miles on to Normanton Park Road towards Edith Weston. Hotel is on the right.

Rutland Water South Shore,
Oakham,
Rutland LE15 8RP

Telephone 01780 720315
Fax 01780 721086

PROPRIETORS

Daniel and Jane Hales and Robert Reid

GENERAL MANAGER

John Farrington

ROOM RATES

Single occupancy £49.50 - £59.50
23 Doubles/Twins £69.50 - £79.50
Includes VAT

CHARGE/CREDIT CARDS

• *MC* • *VI*

ACCOLADES

E.T.B. ♛♛♛♛ Highly Commended
A.A. ★★★ ❀ 70%
County Hotel of the Year 1996 – a leading guide

FACILITIES

Garden, fishing
3 meeting rooms/max 150 people
Golf, fitness centre, sailing, windsurfing and riding nearby

RESTRICTIONS

£10 charge for pets

ATTRACTIONS

Rutland Water, Belvoir Castle, Tolethorpe Hall, Burghley House, Rockingham Castle

AFFILIATIONS

Independent

NEAREST

MAJOR CITY:
Leicester - 17 miles/30 mins

MAJOR AIRPORT:
East Midlands - 39 miles/1hr

RAILWAY STATION:
Oakham - 6 miles/10 mins
Stamford - 9 miles/15 mins

RESERVATIONS

Direct with hotel

ACCESS CODES

Not applicable

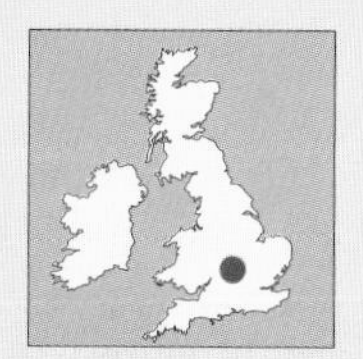

" Sheer perfection . . . faultless "

Olwyn and Bill Payne, California

NUTHURST GRANGE

Country house

Nuthurst Grange Lane,
Hockley Heath,
Warwickshire B94 5NL

Telephone 01564 783972
Fax 01564 783919

PROPRIETOR
Mr and Mrs David Randolph

ROOM RATES

Single occupancy	*£95*
13 Doubles/Twins	*£115 - £130*
1 Four-poster	*£140*
1 Suite	*£140*

Includes continental breakfast and VAT

CHARGE/CREDIT CARDS

• DC • MC • VI

ACCOLADES
E.T.B. ♛♛♛♛ Highly Commended
R.A.C. ★★★ + Merit Awards H C & R
A.A. ★★★ ❀❀❀
The Good Hotel Guide

FACILITIES
Garden, croquet, heli-pad
3 meeting rooms/max 80 people
Golf, riding and fishing nearby

RESTRICTIONS
No pets

ATTRACTIONS
Stratford-upon-Avon,
Warwick Castle,
Kenilworth Castle,
National Exhibition Centre,
The Cotswolds

AFFILIATIONS
Independent

NEAREST
MAJOR CITY:
Birmingham - 12 miles/25 mins

MAJOR AIRPORT:
Birmingham - 7 miles/15 mins

RAILWAY STATION:
Birmingham Intl - 7 miles/15 mins

RESERVATIONS
Direct with hotel

ACCESS CODES
Not applicable

Unashamed luxury in the very heart of England

A long tree-lined drive takes you to Nuthurst Grange nestling in seven and a half acres of gardens and woodlands in the heart of England.

The restaurant is the centrepiece of the hotel, providing an intimate and relaxing setting for luncheon or dinner. Chef/Patron David Randolph and his team of chefs have won many accolades for their imaginative menus which feature the freshest seasonal produce. Complemented by a fine wine list, the cuisine embraces the best of modern and classical French/British cooking. The pre-meal canapes, the selection of bread rolls, biscuits and petits fours are all home-made.

All 15 luxuriously-appointed, spacious bedrooms are furnished and decorated in soft country house style. Each has superb rural views through traditional style leaded windows. All the bedrooms have private bathrooms with air-spa baths and are provided with fruit, chocolates, biscuits and mineral water along with television, radio, direct dial telephones and room safes. Nuthurst Grange is an ideal setting and has marvellous facilities for private or business luncheons, dinners and weddings.

The seclusion of the hotel belies its easy accessibility. Just off the Stratford-upon-Avon to Birmingham road, the hotel is within 15 minutes of Birmingham International Airport and the heart of England's motorway network.

LOCATION

M42, Junction 4 and M40 Junction 16.
½ mile south of Hockley Heath on A3400, turning by hotel signboard into Nuthurst Grange Lane.

" Standards were of the highest order and we agreed it was one of the finest dinners we had ever enjoyed "

The Earl of Bradford

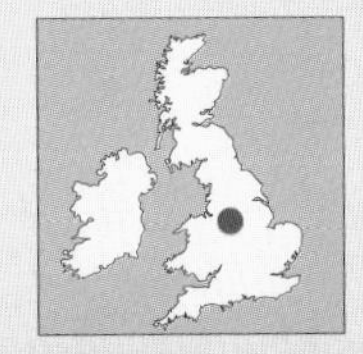

Restaurant with accommodation

An inn of excellence in the heart of England

Over the past 15 years the Wallis family have transformed this attractive former 18th century coaching inn into one of Britain's leading provincial restaurants.

The Old Beams provides accommodation of a very high standard; the beautifully decorated bedrooms are individually styled and named after famous china companies. They are furnished with the luxury of Heal's hand-made beds and en suite marbled bathrooms.

The restaurant reception area is heavily oak-beamed, where pre-dinner drinks can be enjoyed amongst an abundance of fresh flowers and by the comfort of a blazing log fire. Whether you dine in the cosy atmosphere of the restaurant or the conservatory with its Italianesque murals and grand piano, the eye for detail and excellence is clearly evident.

Nigel is a skilful chef, whose style is based on classic cuisine with a modern-day lighter interpretation and an eye-catching presentation. The many accolades confirm the care and dedication shown by Nigel and Ann Wallis.

Situated in the beautiful National Peak Park close to the famous Manifold and Dovedale Valleys, this area offers the opportunity to drive, cycle, walk or just roam in this haven in the heart of England.

LOCATION

From M1 Junction 25, take the A52 to Derby, Ashbourne, Waterhouses. The hotel is 7 miles from Ashbourne. Alternatively, from M6 Junction 15 take the A53 to Leek then the A523.

OLD BEAMS

Waterhouses, Staffordshire ST10 3HW

Telephone 01538 308254
Fax 01538 308157

PROPRIETORS

Nigel and Ann Wallis

ROOM RATES

Single occupancy £55
4 Doubles/Twins £70 - £90
1 Four-poster £90
Includes full breakfast and VAT

CHARGE/CREDIT CARDS

• DC • MC • VI

ACCOLADES

E.T.B. ♛♛♛♛ Highly Commended
A.A. ★★ ❀❀❀
The Good Hotel Guide
Ackerman-Heidseick Guide Clover Leaf Award

FACILITIES

Country garden and terrace
1 meeting room/max 10 people
Fishing nearby

RESTRICTIONS

No smoking in restaurant
No dogs

ATTRACTIONS

Alton Towers,
Chatsworth House & Haddon Hall,
World famous potteries,
Peak District National Park

AFFILIATIONS

Martell Cordon Bleu Association
Master Chefs Association

NEAREST

MAJOR CITY:
Derby - 18 miles/25 mins

MAJOR AIRPORT:
Manchester - 32 miles/50 mins
East Midlands - 30 miles/45 mins

RAILWAY STATION:
Stoke-on-Trent - 18 miles/25 mins

RESERVATIONS

Direct with hotel

ACCESS CODES

Not applicable

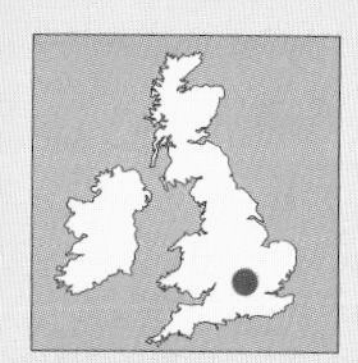

" My wife and I have spent some of our happiest times, outside our own home, at The Old Parsonage. We feel the Parsonage has been one of our real finds "

James Nelson, Cumbria

OLD PARSONAGE

17th century town house

1 Banbury Road,
Oxford,
Oxfordshire OX2 6NN

Telephone 01865 310210
Fax 01865 311262

GENERAL MANAGER
Michael Thompson

ROOM RATES

Single occupancy	*£105 - £110*
26 Doubles/Twins	*£140 - £150*
4 Suites	*£190 - £210*

Includes full breakfast and VAT

CHARGE/CREDIT CARDS

• *DC* • *MC* • *VI*

ACCOLADES
E.T.B. ♛♛♛♛♛ *Highly Commended*
The Good Hotel Guide

FACILITIES
Garden
Golf, flying and fishing nearby

RESTRICTIONS
No children
Pets by prior arrangement

ATTRACTIONS
Oxford University,
Print Room at Ashmolean Museum,
Norrington Room at Blackwells,
Museum of Modern Art,
Sheldonian Theatre

AFFILIATIONS
The Cotswold Collection

NEAREST
MAJOR CITY:
London - 53 miles/1 hr

MAJOR AIRPORT:
London Heathrow - 47 miles/1 hr

RAILWAY STATION:
Oxford - 2 miles/5 mins

RESERVATIONS
Direct with hotel

ACCESS CODES
AMADEUS/SYSTEM 1 HK OXFOLD
WORLDSPAN/SAHARA HK OLDPA
SABRE HK 30442
APOLLO HT 14857

The spirit of Oxford in the heart of this famous university city

The site on which the Old Parsonage stands dates back to 1308. The building is a much-loved Oxford landmark. It played its part in the city's history; as a sanctuary for persecuted clergy in the Middle Ages, as a stronghold for Royalists in the Civil War of the 1640's, and as a home for 19th century literati including Oscar Wilde. The historic character of the building has been preserved. The hotel is small, individually run, with a distinct personality.

Each of the 30 bedrooms is furnished in a style of its own. Many enjoy views over the secluded walled garden or the unique roof garden. Each has a luxurious marble bathroom and added extras that give a personal touch.

In the Parsonage Bar you can enjoy a light meal from an imaginative menu, a glass of wine, or simply a quiet cappuccino. Gee's Restaurant, housed in a former florist's spectacular conservatory and owned by the hotel, is less than five minutes' walk down the Banbury Road. Besides the hotel's guests, Gee's attracts a lively mixture of students, academics and townspeople. The cuisine is contemporary Mediterranean, with a variety of pastas, chargrilled steaks and fresh fish and a wide-ranging wine list.

Located between Keble and Somerville Colleges, the hotel is only a short walk from Oxford's shops, theatres, museums, art galleries, business centre and other colleges.

LOCATION

Leave the northern ring road at the roundabout at the top of Banbury Road. Follow Banbury Road through Summertown towards the city centre. The hotel is on the right, next to St Giles Church.

"As always, a treasure to enjoy and savor"

Stan David, Illinois

500-year old manor house

THE OLD RECTORY

A small hotel with unique architecture and a great past

The Old Rectory at Great Snoring, a former manor house, noted for its architectural history, stands in 1½ acres of walled garden and nestles contentedly beside the village church. This secluded haven, which dates back from 1500, promises the discerning traveller old fashioned charm with a homely warmth and friendliness.

Relaxed informality is assured, given the size of the 'hotel' – just six bedrooms, each one different from the other as governed by the unique architecture of the house. The dining room is fascinating with stone mullion windows and heavy oak beams. It is a versatile room where guests enjoy delicious dinners and hearty breakfasts.

For those who relish the idea of independence together with service, 'The Sheltons' provide the answer. These self-contained cottages are serviced on a daily basis and have the trappings of the traditional hotel but allow the guest complete freedom and flexibility. The Sheltons, named after the family responsible for the manor house, have been sympathetically constructed in the grounds of the house, which with the neighbouring church, provide a majestic back-drop for this unique development.

The Old Rectory is well placed for those visiting this special part of Norfolk.

LOCATION

Great Snoring is situated 3 miles north east of Fakenham from the A148. The Old Rectory is behind the church on the road signposted to Barsham from the village street.

Barsham Road, Great Snoring, Fakenham, Norfolk NR21 0HP

Telephone 01328 820597
Fax 01328 820048

PROPRIETOR

Rosamund M Scoles

ROOM RATES

Single occupancy	*£68*
6 Doubles/Twins	*£89.50*
4 Sheltons Cottages	*£95 - £115*

Includes early morning tea, full breakfast and VAT

CHARGE/CREDIT CARDS

• *DC* • *JCB* • *MC* • *VI*

ACCOLADES

Best of Britain
Charming Small Hotel Guide
The Good Hotel Guide

FACILITIES

Walled garden, heli-pad
Riding and fishing nearby

RESTRICTIONS

Children welcome by prior arrangement
(The Sheltons are ideal for families)
No facilities for disabled guests
No pets

ATTRACTIONS

Norfolk Heritage Coast,
Sandringham House,
Holkham Hall,
Norwich,
Cambridge

AFFILIATIONS

Independent

NEAREST

MAJOR CITY:
Norwich - 22 miles/30 mins

MAJOR AIRPORT:
London Heathrow - 115 miles/3 hrs
Stansted - 90 miles/2½ hrs

RAILWAY STATION:
King's Lynn - 22 miles/40 mins

RESERVATIONS

Direct with hotel

ACCESS CODES

SABRE HOD 14552
APOLLO HOD 59192

“ This critic can only report that her experience was very pleasant indeed ”

Paddy Burt, The Weekend Telegraph

OLD VICARAGE HOTEL

Edwardian vicarage

Worfield, Bridgnorth, Shropshire WV15 5JZ

Telephone 01746 716497
Fax 01746 716552

PROPRIETORS
Peter and Christine Iles

ROOM RATES

Single occupancy	*£67.50 - £87.50*
13 Doubles/Twins	*£95 - £130*
1 Suite	*£130*

Includes full breakfast and VAT

CHARGE/CREDIT CARDS

• *DC* • *MC* • *VI*

ACCOLADES
E.T.B. ♛♛♛♛ *De Luxe*
R.A.C. ★★★ + *Merit Awards H C & R*
A.A. ★★★ ❀❀❀ *76%*
The Good Hotel Guide
Ackerman Heidsieck Guide

FACILITIES
Croquet, garden
2 meeting rooms/max 20 people
Golf, riding and fishing nearby

RESTRICTIONS
No smoking in dining room and six bedrooms
No pets allowed in public rooms

ATTRACTIONS
Ironbridge Gorge Museums, Severn Valley Railway, Shrewsbury, Boscobel House, Ludlow, Wroxeter

AFFILIATIONS
Welsh Rarebits

NEAREST
MAJOR CITY:
Birmingham - 25 miles/50 mins
MAJOR AIRPORT:
Manchester - 50 miles/1¼ hrs
RAILWAY STATION:
Wolverhampton - 10 miles/20 mins

RESERVATIONS
Toll free fax in US: 800-873-7140

ACCESS CODES
AMAEDUS/SYSTEM 1 HK BHXOLD
APOLLO HT 20216
SABRE HK 33865

Peace and tranquillity amidst spectacular scenery

Set in two acres of grounds overlooking fields and farmland, The Old Vicarage offers guests a special experience in terms of hospitality, accommodation and the warmest of welcomes.

The pace is tranquil and enjoyable. Having found The Old Vicarage, many guests return time and again. Over the years, the hotel has been recognised by all the leading travel guides.

Dinner is always an event in The Old Vicarage. There is an emphasis on the fresh and natural with the menu changing daily. Good food deserves good wines and the extensive cellars offer outstanding examples from around the world – all at very reasonable prices.

The Iles' pride and joy are the bedrooms. Every room, named after a local village, incorporates the necessities of this century. Everything is provided in the superb en-suite bathrooms. The luxury Coach House rooms include whirlpool baths, showers and, for those on the ground floor, a private garden. All of them have views across the valley to the River Worfe.

Shropshire is a fascinating county. The historic towns and villages reflect age-old border conflicts of Celt, Roman, Saxon and Norman. More recent history is to be found at the World Heritage site of Ironbridge, birthplace of the Industrial Revolution.

LOCATION

To the east of Bridgnorth, 1 mile from A454, 2 miles from A442.

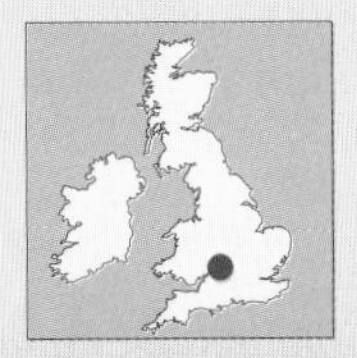

“Lovely lunch and delicious lobster and Schnitzel and duck and lime sorbet and rhubarb thingummy and fudge. Yum! Yum!”

Pru Leith

18th century country house

THE PAINSWICK HOTEL

“Sheer poetry”, said His Majesty. A sentiment as true today as ever it was

“The valleys around Painswick are sheer poetry, in this Paradise” – King Charles I's words. The stone-built village comprises mediaeval cottages lying cheek-by-jowl with the 17th and 18th century merchants' houses. Among these stood the former rectory, built in 1790 in the Palladian style which is, today, The Painswick Hotel.

The hotel has 20 luxury en suite bedrooms, all with direct-dial telephones, remote control televisions, luxury toiletries, baskets of fresh fruit, mineral water, books and magazines – amenities one expects of a top class hotel. The stunning fabrics, soft furnishings, antique furniture, period engravings and objets d'art all contribute to the sense of well-being as in a beautifully organised private house.

In the pine panelled dining room, simply delicious and tempting food is served with an emphasis on seafood, local game and Gloucestershire cheeses.

The public rooms, all with distinct elegance and character, have antique furniture and fine pictures, together with open fires. They express a quiet confidence reflecting the more leisured times in which they were built.

Painswick is a superb touring, walking, sporting and cultural centre. All the pleasures of Regency Cheltenham, Bath, Gloucester, Berkeley Castle, Broadway and Stratford-upon-Avon are within an easy drive.

LOCATION

Centre of Painswick behind Parish church. 8 miles off M5 Junction 13 take A419 to A46 north. 28 miles off M4 Junction 15 take A419 to A46 north.

Kemps Lane, Painswick, Gloucestershire GL6 6YB

Telephone 01452 812160
Fax 01452 814059

PROPRIETORS
Somerset and Helene Moore

MANAGER
Julia Robb

ROOM RATES

2 Singles	£62 - £92
15 Doubles/Twins	£87 - £130
3 Four-posters	£130

Includes full breakfast, newspaper and VAT

CHARGE/CREDIT CARDS

• MC • VI

ACCOLADES
E.T.B. ♛♛♛♛ Highly Commended
R.A.C. ★★★ + Merit Awards H C & R
A.A. ★★★ ❀❀ 72%
The Good Hotel Guide

FACILITIES
Garden, croquet
3 meeting rooms/max 100 people
Golf and riding nearby

RESTRICTIONS
No facilities for disabled guests

ATTRACTIONS
Sudeley Castle, Berkeley Castle, Bath, Stratford-upon-Avon, Cotswolds

AFFILIATIONS
The Cotswold Collection

NEAREST
MAJOR CITY:
Gloucester - 5 mile /10 mins

MAJOR AIRPORT:
London Heathrow - 90 miles/1¾ hrs
Birmingham - 70 miles/1 hr

RAILWAY STATION:
Stroud - 3 miles/5 mins

RESERVATIONS
Direct with hotel

ACCESS CODES
Not applicable

“ As good as expected and expectation was high ”

Diana & Trevor Buttery, Nottingham

THE PEACOCK HOTEL AT ROWSLEY

Country hotel

Rowsley, Nr Matlock, Derbyshire DE4 2EB

Telephone 01629 733518
Fax 01629 732671

GENERAL MANAGER

Pat Gillson

ROOM RATES

2 Singles	£75
10 Doubles/Twins	£79 - £110
1 Four-poster	£115
1 Half-tester	£115

Includes VAT

CHARGE/CREDIT CARDS

• DC • MC • VI

ACCOLADES

E.T.B. Highly Commended

FACILITIES

Garden, fishing, walking
2 meeting rooms/max 24 people
Golf, riding and mountain biking nearby

RESTRICTIONS

No facilities for disabled guests

ATTRACTIONS

Chatsworth House, Haddon Hall, Calke Abbey, The Peak District, Hardwick Hall, Stone Circle

AFFILIATIONS

Jarvis Hotels

NEAREST

MAJOR CITY:
Sheffield - 20 miles/30 mins
Chesterfield - 11 miles/20 mins

MAJOR AIRPORT:
Manchester - 30 miles/1 hr
East Midlands - 30 miles/1 hr

RAILWAY STATION:
Chesterfield - 11 miles/20 mins

RESERVATIONS

Direct with hotel

ACCESS CODES

WORLDSPAN PM 00467
APOLLO VA 18522
SABRE AA 22385

Lots of antique features – except the comfort and hospitality

Nestling in picturesque countryside on the banks of the River Derwent, the Peacock, one of Derbyshire's most charming country hotels waits to greet you.

This traditional 16th century building is full of character, providing true comfort and hospitality. Relax in the Peacock Lounge with its original antique furniture, or enjoy an aperitif in the oak beamed bar. The delightful restaurant offers a well balanced mixture of fine food and traditional English fayre, together with a selection of fine wines.

For the more energetic there is an abundance of rewarding pursuits. For the angler what better than to cast a fly over the sparkling waters of the River Wye and Derwent. For the walker, the contrast of gentle walks and rugged hills of the Peak District are ever inviting.

Within walking distance of the hotel is medieval Haddon Hall and many more famous stately homes, including Chatsworth House, are within easy reach. For those who like to browse, Bakewell offers a wealth of curios and antiques, and for the theatregoer, Buxton, Sheffield, Nottingham and Derby are within 30 minutes drive.

LOCATION

Situated on the A6 in the village of Rowsley, between Matlock and Bakewell.

"Steeped in the tranquillity of Peterstow, we were truly spoilt"

Sir Eric & Lady Stroud

Georgian rectory

PETERSTOW COUNTRY HOUSE

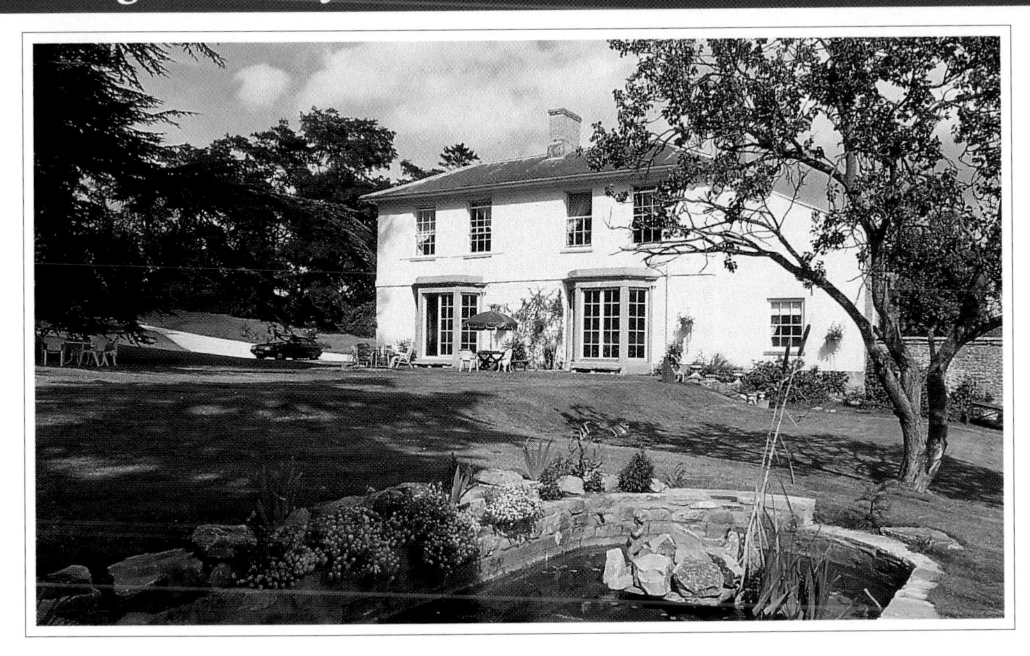

An award-winning home that's open house to the world

In 1987, Jeanne and Mike Denne fell in love with a dilapidated rectory, surrounded by 28 acres of woodland and pasture, by the side of the Church of St. Peter. With careful determination, they set about restoring the house into a delightful family home.

In 1989, they opened Peterstow Country House to share its beauty with guests from all over the world.

Upon entering the spacious hall, with its flagstone floor and grand winding staircase, the relaxed atmosphere is immediately apparent. The nine bedrooms are Georgian or Victorian style, ranging from half-tester suites to double and twin-bedded rooms.

Peterstow have justifiably enjoyed many prestigious awards for food as their chefs continually explore exciting new ways of presentation and flavour combinations. Modern English and French cuisine is the theme, with Peterstow's individualistic approach. Their wine list is carefully selected to complement the cuisine and although predominantly French, it has some fine examples of New World wines.

Set in the heart of the Wye Valley, Peterstow is surrounded by good walking country, the Welsh Marches and the Black Mountains being nearby.

LOCATION

Situated 3 miles north of Ross-on-Wye on A49 to Hereford.

Peterstow, Ross-on-Wye, Herefordshire HR9 6LB

Telephone 01989 562826
Fax 01989 567264

PROPRIETORS

Mike and Jeanne Denne

ROOM RATES

1 Single £38.50 - £69
8 Doubles/Twins £50 - £90
Includes full breakfast and VAT

CHARGE/CREDIT CARDS

• *DC* • *MC* • *VI*

ACCOLADES

E.T.B. ♛♛♛♛ Highly Commended
A.A. ★★ ❀❀ 74%
The Good Hotel Guide

FACILITIES

Gardens, clay pigeon shooting and trout lake
1 meeting room/max 40 people
Golf, riding, heli-pad and coarse fishing nearby

RESTRICTIONS

No children under 7 years
No pets

ATTRACTIONS

Wye Valley,
Symonds Yat,
Royal Forest of Dean,
Eastnor Castle

AFFILIATIONS

Independent

NEAREST

MAJOR CITY:
Hereford - 9 miles/20 mins

MAJOR AIRPORT:
Cardiff - 50 miles/1 hr

RAILWAY STATION:
Hereford - 9 miles/25 mins

RESERVATIONS

Direct with hotel

ACCESS CODES

Not applicable

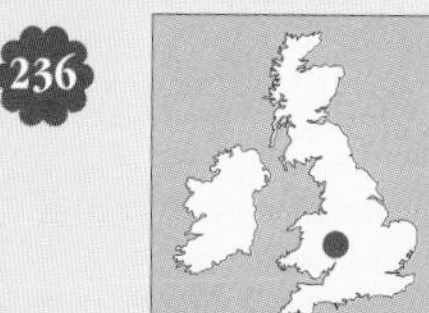

“ Like finding an oasis in the desert ”

Major Hardwicke

THE REDFERN HOTEL

Georgian house

Cleobury Mortimer,
Shropshire DY14 8AA

Telephone 01299 270395
Fax 01299 271011

OWNERS

Jon and Lis Redfern

ROOM RATES

Single occupancy	*£45 - £61*
8 Doubles/Twins	*£34 - £42.50*
1 Four-poster	*£42.50*
2 Deluxe	*£42.50*

Includes full breakfast and VAT

CHARGE/CREDIT CARDS

• DC • MC • VI

ACCOLADES

E.T.B. ♛♛♛♛ Commended
R.A.C. ★★ + Merit Awards H & R
A.A. ★★ ❀ 73%

FACILITIES

Conservatory
1 meeting room/max 20 people
Golf, riding and fishing nearby

RESTRICTIONS

No facilities for disabled guests

ATTRACTIONS

Ironbridge Industrial Museum,
Severn Valley Steam Railway,
Stokesay Castle,
Acton Scott Farm Museum

AFFILIATIONS

Minotel

NEAREST

MAJOR CITY:
Worcester - 23 miles/30 mins

MAJOR AIRPORT:
Birmingham - 35 miles/1 hr

RAILWAY STATION:
Kidderminster - 11 miles/15 mins

RESERVATIONS

Toll free fax in US: 800-654-0494

ACCESS CODES

Not applicable

Comfort and good food in an area steeped in history

There has been a community here at Cleobury Mortimer for 2,000 years. The fresh water spring which supported earlier inhabitants still flows from under the Norman Church in the centre of this small ancient market town and certainly the fields and woodlands that surround the town have changed little with the passing centuries.

The Redfern Hotel was built in 1740. It has been an hotel since 1973 when it was purchased by Jon and Lis Redfern and has over the years been developed with care into the well-known family-run hotel that it is today. The 11 attractive well appointed en suite bedrooms are comfortable and have all the facilities that one would expect. The renowned English Kitchen Restaurant, under the supervision of Richard Redfern, specialises in fresh local produce and offers a menu that changes daily.

The area is steeped in history. To the north, Ironbridge Industrial Museum on the site of the birth of the industrial revolution and where the first iron bridge in the world still stands. To the south, Worcester, “the faithful city” which was loyal to King Charles to the end. To the west, Ludlow with its castle dating back 1,000 years.

This is an ideal centre to explore the fascinating Marches area at a price that is most reasonable. For the more adventurous the hotel has its own canal narrowboat.

LOCATION

Midway between Kidderminster and Ludlow on A4117. Leave M5 at Junction 3 or 6.

" The BBC says OK "

Roy Castle

Town centre hotel

THE REGENT HOTEL

Historic Royal spa town hotel close to castles and Shakespeare country

Built in 1819 when Leamington was growing from a sleepy village into a fashionable health resort, the Regent Hotel was then the largest hotel in the world and has featured in the Guinness Book of Records.

Since that day, names that make history are inscribed in the pages of the visitors' register. In the entrance foyer is a heritage board that immortalises some 70 of the Regent's very famous patrons.

The spacious elegance of the hotel's Regency era is enriched by its classical decor and enhanced by its modern appointments. It is situated in the centre of town, and has ample free parking.

All the individually decorated bedrooms have en suite facilities, TV, direct-dial telephone, hairdryer, trouser press and hospitality tray.

The Phoenix Bar walls are decorated with hand-painted murals depicting the history of the hotel. The Vaults is a superb air-conditioned restaurant in the old wine cellars with a fixed price and à la carte menu. The Regent Hotel is honoured to have received an AA rosette for culinary standards for the last three years.

Royal Leamington Spa is close to the centre of England. Shakespeare's Stratford-upon-Avon, Warwick and Kenilworth Castles are nearby, as are the National Exhibition Centre and the Royal Showground at Stoneleigh.

LOCATION

M40 Junction 13 from London. M40 Junction 14 from Birmingham. 4 miles to town centre.

Parade,
Royal Leamington Spa,
Warwickshire CV32 4AX

Telephone 01926 427231
Fax 01926 450728

GENERAL MANAGER

John Biesok

ROOM RATES

24 Singles	*£65*
54 Doubles/Twins	*£89 - £99*
2 Four-posters	*£120*

Includes full breakfast and VAT

CHARGE/CREDIT CARDS

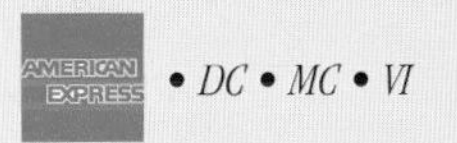

• DC • MC • VI

ACCOLADES

E.T.B. ♕♕♕♕ Commended
R.A.C. ★★★
A.A. ★★★ ❀ 75%
Best Western Connoisseur Award

FACILITIES

Games room
4 meeting rooms/max 250 people
Golf and adventure sports nearby

RESTRICTIONS

None

ATTRACTIONS

Cotswolds, Coventry Cathedral, National Exhibition Centre, Stratford-upon-Avon, Warwick Castle, Warwick Races

AFFILIATIONS

Independent

NEAREST

MAJOR CITY:
Coventry - 11 miles/15 mins

MAJOR AIRPORT:
Birmingham - 17 miles/25 mins

RAILWAY STATION:
Leamington Spa - 1 mile/3 mins

RESERVATIONS

Direct with hotel

ACCESS CODES

Not applicable

“Thank you so much for a wonderful weekend at ‘The Eagle and Child’ ”

Dinah Lampitt, Sussex

THE ROYALIST

10th century inn

**Digbeth Street,
Stow-on-the-Wold,
Gloucestershire GL54 1BN**

**Telephone 01451 830670
Fax 01451 870048**

PROPRIETORS
Matthew and Celia Fagg

MANAGER
Robert Harbord

ROOM RATES

1 Single	£40 - £50
10 Doubles/Twins	£60 - £80
1 Four-poster	£75 - £90

Includes full breakfast and VAT

CHARGE/CREDIT CARDS

• MC • VI

ACCOLADES
R.A.C. Merit Award H
A.A. QQQQ

FACILITIES
Unique historic heritage
Golf, riding and fishing nearby

RESTRICTIONS
No facilities for disabled guests

ATTRACTIONS
Warwick Castle, Cotswolds, Oxford, Blenheim Palace, Hidcote Gardens, Stratford-upon-Avon

AFFILIATIONS
Independent

NEAREST
MAJOR CITY:
Bath - 40 miles/1 hr

MAJOR AIRPORT:
London Heathrow - 65 miles/1½ hrs

RAILWAY STATION:
Moreton-in-Marsh - 4 miles/10 mins

RESERVATIONS
Direct with hotel

ACCESS CODES
Not applicable

MIDSHIRES

Witches, Knights and Crusaders . . . a thousand years of hospitality

Featured in the Guinness Book of Records as the oldest recorded inn in England, The Royalist dates from 947 AD. Behind its 17th century façade, stands the original oak-framed structure erected in the 10th century. Once owned by the Knights of St John's Hospitaliers and run as a hospice and alms house it was subsequently known as ‘The Eagle and Child’ in the 13th, 14th and 15th centuries. Besides the wealth of exposed timbers there are many reminders of this long history: marks to ward off witches, leper holes, a Babylonian ‘houris’ frieze dating from the Crusaders and an entrance to a mile-long tunnel.

This private hotel, family owned and run, provides all the comforts (en suite bathrooms, colour television, telephones) of the 20th century, whilst retaining the inherent character, atmosphere and charm of its 1000-year history. Its Coffee Shop is open all day and the bar serves a tasty selection of home-made food.

Stow-on-the-Wold is the perfect base from which to explore the Cotswolds, with Stratford-upon-Avon and Oxford well within striking distance.

The Cotswolds are enchanting, no matter which season of the year you choose to visit, and a warm welcome always awaits you at The Royalist.

LOCATION

Turn off A429 at Stow for Chipping Norton. The hotel is 300 yards on left, behind The Green.

“ Prince of the architectural gems around us is, of course, Seckford Hall at Great Bealings. This is East Anglian Elizabethan at its noblest ”

Dudley Symon, Woodbridge

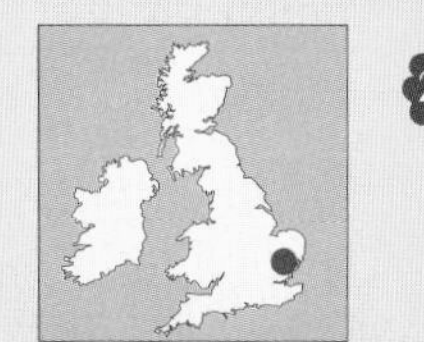

Elizabethan manor SECKFORD HALL

Dine in Tudor splendour where once Queen Elizabeth I held court

Dating from 1530, it is said that Queen Elizabeth I once held court at Seckford Hall. The Hall has lost none of its Tudor pieces, the panelled rooms, beamed ceilings, carved doors and great stone fireplaces are displayed against the splendour of English oak. Local delicacies such as the house speciality, lobster, feature on the à la carte menu.

The courtyard area was developed from the conversion of a giant Tudor barn, dairy and coach house. It now incorporates ten charming cottage style suites and a modern leisure complex which includes a heated swimming pool, exercise machines, solaria and spa bath.

Set in 34 acres of tranquil parkland with sweeping lawns and a willow-fringed lake, guests may stroll about the grounds or simply relax in the attractive terrace garden. A walk along the riverside will take the visitor to picturesque Woodbridge, with its tide mill, antique shops, yacht harbours and quaint old streets. Constable country and the Suffolk coast are nearby.

Christine and Michael look forward to welcoming you to Seckford Hall.

LOCATION

The hotel is just 7 miles north of Ipswich and is reached via the A12. It nestles in a hollow to the west of Woodbridge by-pass. Follow the by-pass until the distinctive blue and white hotel sign appears.

Woodbridge, Suffolk IP13 6NU

Telephone 01394 385678
Fax 01394 380610

PROPRIETOR
Michael Bunn

MANAGER
John Woodard

ROOM RATES

3 Singles	*£79 - £110*
12 Doubles/Twins	*£105 - £148*
7 Four-posters/Superior	*£115 - £148*
10 Suites	*£120 - £148*

Includes full breakfast, newspaper and VAT

CHARGE/CREDIT CARDS

• DC • JCB • MC • VI

ACCOLADES
E.T.B. ♛♛♛♛ Highly Commended
R.A.C. ★★★ + Merit Awards H C & R
A.A. ★★★ 73%

FACILITIES
Indoor swimming pool, gardens, gym, spa, sun-bed, golf, fishing
2 meeting rooms/max 100 people
Golf and riding nearby

RESTRICTIONS
Closed Christmas Day

ATTRACTIONS
Lavenham, Suffolk coast, Constable country, Cambridge, Norwich, Orford Castle, Sandringham, Framlingham Castle

AFFILIATIONS
Independent

NEAREST
MAJOR CITY:
London - 80 miles/1 ½ hrs

MAJOR AIRPORT:
London Heathrow - 90 miles/2¼ hrs
Stansted - 60 miles/1 ¼ hrs

RAILWAY STATION:
Ipswich - 7 miles/15 mins

RESERVATIONS
Direct with hotel

ACCESS CODES
Not applicable

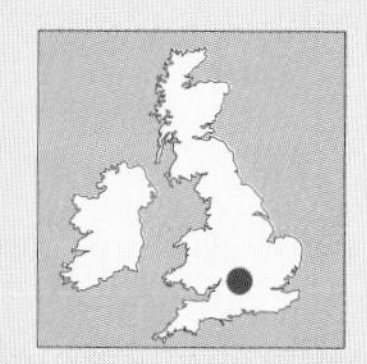

" A first class introduction to the Cotswolds which we will recommend to all our friends "

Andrew Hamlyn, Ashburton, Devon

SEYMOUR HOUSE

Georgian town house

High Street, Chipping Campden, Gloucestershire GL55 6AH

Telephone 01386 840429
Fax 01386 840369

MANAGER
Felice Tocchini

ROOM RATES

Single occupancy	£53 - £65
13 Doubles/Twins	£66 - £90
3 Suites	£132

Includes full breakfast and VAT

CHARGE/CREDIT CARDS

• MC • VI

ACCOLADES
R.A.C. ★★★ + Merit Awards H C & R
A.A. ★★★ ❀❀ 68%
Heart Beat award

FACILITIES
Garden,
Balloon Room Restaurant
1 meeting room/max 45 people
Golf and riding nearby

RESTRICTIONS
No facilities for disabled guests
No pets

ATTRACTIONS
Stratford-upon-Avon,
The Cotswolds, Blenheim Palace,
Broadway, Hidcote Gardens

AFFILIATIONS
Romantik Hotels and Restaurants

NEAREST
MAJOR CITY:
Stratford-upon-Avon - 12 miles/20 mins

MAJOR AIRPORT:
Birmingham - 32 miles/40 mins

RAILWAY STATION:
Moreton-in-Marsh -5 miles/10 mins

RESERVATIONS
Direct with hotel

ACCESS CODES
AMADEUS RM GGHTLRM
APOLLO RO HODRO/INDEX
SABRE RM YHHLRMX
SAHARA RM OIRM
WORLDSPAN RM GHTLRMQ

Brush up your Shakespeare with a Seymour House stopover

According to the historian G M Trevelyan, Seymour House Hotel is located in "the most beautiful village street now left on the island" although 'Campden' as it is affectionately known has now grown into a town which has preserved its own special charm and character.

The hotel, a listed Georgian building faced with warm Cotswold stone, dates back to the early 1700s. Recent refurbishing has been accomplished with great regard to detail and has restored this house to a welcoming and comfortable country hotel.

The Balloon Room Restaurant has a good local reputation and is featured in the main travel and food guides for recognition in quality of food, service and customer care.

Seymour House has a unique association with the Royal Shakespeare Theatre in nearby Stratford-upon-Avon and can arrange special packages to include superior hotel accommodation with breakfast, a good theatre seat and dinner prior to or after the performance in the Box Tree Restaurant situated in the theatre. The Shakespeare Stopover package can be booked for one or more nights. The popularity of the Stopover package has won acclaim for the hotel. Special Breaks at £90-£152 include full English breakfast, dinner and VAT.

LOCATION

Situated in the centre of Chipping Campden on the B4081, a mile north of A44 between Moreton-in-Marsh and Broadway.

" I want to share a wonderful discovery with your readers . . . "

Patricia Morris, Readers Write column, Los Angeles Times

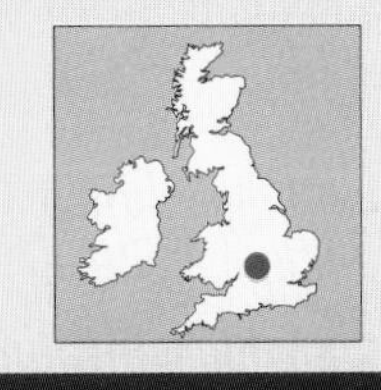

14th century abbey

THE SHAVEN CROWN

600 years of history, a medieval hall, and a family welcome

The Shaven Crown hotel is beautifully situated in the heart of The Cotswolds. Originally a 14th century hospice to Bruern Abbey, it is built of local honey-coloured stone around a central medieval courtyard garden. It has the mellowed charm of 600 years of hospitality. The hotel is owned by the Brookes family who are actively engaged in its daily running.

The pride of the Shaven Crown Hotel – in addition to its original 14th century gateway – is the medieval hall, now the residents' lounge.

All the bedrooms have tea and coffee-making facilities, TV and private bathrooms. The hotel is centrally heated throughout.

There is an intimate candlelit restaurant which serves food fresh every day. The bar offers an imaginative array of bar meals – beside the log fire – at lunch and dinner time seven days a week. In fine weather, you can choose to eat al fresco in the courtyard.

The area is justly renowned for antiques-hunting. Cheltenham and the other towns and villages of The Cotswolds are within easy reach, as are Oxford, Stratford-upon-Avon and Cirencester. Blenheim Palace, birthplace of Sir Winston Churchill, is one of the many great stately homes in the district.

LOCATION

On the A361, 4 miles north of Burford and 6 miles south of Chipping Norton.

High Street, Shipton-under-Wychwood Oxfordshire OX7 6BA

Telephone 01993 830330
Fax 01993 830330

PROPRIETOR

Mary Brookes

ROOM RATES

1 Single £33
8 Doubles/Twins £66 - £82
Inclusive of full breakfast and VAT
2 nights or more - £49.50 pp pd inclusive of dinner, full breakfast and VAT

CHARGE/CREDIT CARDS

• MC • VI

ACCOLADES

E.T.B. ♛♛♛ Commended
A.A. ★★ ❀ 61%

FACILITIES

Garden, bowling green
Golf nearby

RESTRICTIONS

No facilities for disabled guests
No pets (guide dogs allowed)

ATTRACTIONS

The Cotswolds,
Blenheim Palace,
Burford,
Bourton-on-the-Water,
Stow-on-the-Wold

AFFILIATIONS

Independent

NEAREST

MAJOR CITY:
Oxford - 26 miles/40 mins

MAJOR AIRPORT:
London Heathrow - 70 miles/1½ hrs
Birmingham - 55 miles/1¼ hrs

RAILWAY STATION:
Charlbury - 6 miles/10 mins

RESERVATIONS

Direct with hotel

ACCESS CODES

Not applicable

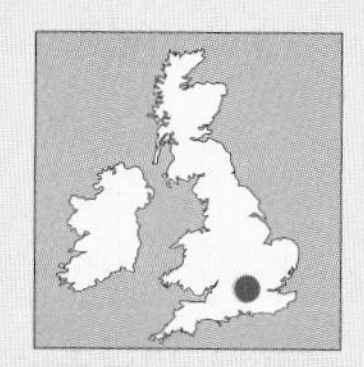

" A wonderful retreat from the hustle and bustle of London life, being only a short distance away "

Claire & Mark Grabiner, London

THE SPRINGS HOTEL

Country house

Wallingford Road, North Stoke, Oxfordshire OX10 6BE

Telephone 01491 836687
Fax 01491 836877

GENERAL MANAGER

Michael Cavilla

ROOM RATES

2 Singles	*£85 - £100*
20 Doubles/Twins	*£118 - £148*
4 Suites	*£165 - £185*

Includes full breakfast and VAT

CHARGE/CREDIT CARDS

 *• DC • MC • VI*

ACCOLADES

E.T.B. ♛♛♛♛ Highly Commended
R.A.C. ★★★ + Merit Awards H C & R
A.A. ★★★ ❀ 73%

FACILITIES

Garden, croquet, outdoor heated pool, tennis, sauna, jacuzzi, fishing
3 meeting rooms/max 50 people
Golf and riding nearby

RESTRICTIONS

No facilities for disabled guests
No pets

ATTRACTIONS

Blenheim, Oxford, Windsor, Henley-on-Thames

AFFILIATIONS

Independent

NEAREST

MAJOR CITY:
Oxford - 12 miles/20 mins

MAJOR AIRPORT:
London Heathrow - 30 miles/1 hr

RAILWAY STATION:
Reading - 12 miles/20 mins

RESERVATIONS

Direct with hotel

ACCESS CODES

Not applicable

Ducks and swans on a spring-fed lake – a very English scene

The Springs lies in a small Thames-side village midway between the M40 and M4. Its proximity to Oxford, Windsor and Henley makes it an ideal base to explore the wonderful countryside and villages of the Chilterns and Cotswolds or for a relaxing and peaceful break.

The Springs, one of the first mock-tudor houses to be built in England, lies in 30 acres of wooded grounds and formalised gardens, overlooking a spring-fed lake from which it takes its name.

In the panelled lounge, traditional furnishings and glowing log fires in winter reinforce a warm and friendly atmosphere. The en suite bedrooms are attractively decorated and are complete with every luxury. Some rooms have balconies overlooking the lake and a few have jacuzzi baths.

The magical setting of the balcony restaurant overlooking the floodlit lake with swans and ducks makes up a very English scene. The imaginative Executive Chef bases his cooking on English culinary heritage.

For the sporty, there is the use of a tennis court, a guitar shaped outdoor swimming pool, croquet and putting, and golf nearby.

Unobtrusive service and attention to detail ensures The Springs as an excellent choice of venue.

LOCATION

Just outside the market town of Wallingford on B4009, 20 minutes drive from Oxford.

"... the wonderful views offered from the large windows, the hospitality and courteousness of all the staff, again, was second to none"

M Edgeworth, Gloucestershire

Georgian mansion

STOCKS HOTEL GOLF & COUNTRY CLUB

Your home from home in the country

The elegance of this charming Georgian mansion, its food and service is one to be remembered. Stocks is located in the heart of 10,000 acres of National Trust Conservation land, and boasts excellent facilities for business or pleasure.

Intricate plasterwork, tapestries, crisp linen and porcelain set the tone of the Tapestry Restaurant, renowned for serving fine cuisine.

The championship standard 18-hole golf course was built to exacting specifications so that it has never been closed by rain since it opened. In addition to the team of PGA professionals, practice facilities and a well-stocked professional shop make the golf course one of the best in the area.

The Orangery is the ideal place to while away an hour or so with views of the surrounding parkland and golf course. There is also a terrace, situated beside the swimming pool, where lunch, afternoon tea and drinks can be served on warm summer days.

Stocks's conference and leisure facilities make it perfect for business or pleasure. All 18 bedrooms, including several suites, are individually furnished, many with garden or parkland views.

Whether your visit is for business or pleasure, the friendly, professional staff will ensure your stay is relaxing and memorable.

LOCATION

From M25 Junction 20, follow the new A41(T) dual carriageway to Tring exit. From the M1, turn off at J11 and take the A505 via Dunstable. Follow signs for Tring station/Aldbury. Stocks Hotel is signposted from Aldbury village.

Stocks Road, Aldbury, Nr Tring, Hertfordshire HP23 5RX

Telephone 01442 851341
Fax 01442 851253

GENERAL MANAGER

Nick Allam

ROOM RATES

1 Single	*£55*
12 Doubles/Twins	*£65 - £85*
2 Four-posters	*£75 - £145*
5 Suites	*£90 - £120*

Includes full breakfast

CHARGE/CREDIT CARDS

• DC • MC • VI

ACCOLADES

E.T.B. ♛♛♛ Commended

FACILITIES

Garden, 18 hole golf course, PGA game improvement centre, professional shop, croquet, tennis, outdoor pool, sauna, steam room, solarium, jacuzzi, gym, snooker, riding, livery stables, heli-pad
2 meeting rooms/max 65 people
Marquee (May-Oct)/max 180 people

RESTRICTIONS

No pets

ATTRACTIONS

Whipsnade Zoo, Ashridge Forest, Grand Union Canal, London, Woburn Safari Park

AFFILIATIONS

Independent

NEAREST

MAJOR CITY:
London - 35 miles/40 mins

MAJOR AIRPORT:
London Heathrow - 35 miles/40 mins
Luton - 10 miles/15 mins

RAILWAY STATION:
Tring - 2 miles/10 mins

RESERVATIONS

Direct with hotel

ACCESS CODES

Not applicable

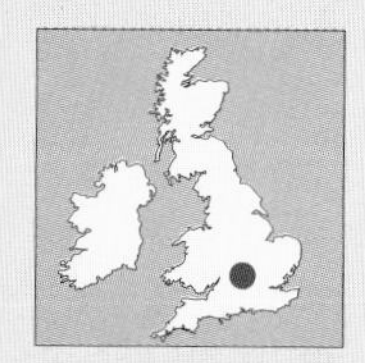

“ Flowers in the garden, meat in the hall, a bin of wine, a spice of wit, a house with lawns enclosing it ”

R L Stevenson

STUDLEY PRIORY

Elizabethan manor house

Horton-cum-Studley,
Oxfordshire OX33 1AZ

Telephone 01865 351203
Fax 01865 351613

PROPRIETOR

Jeremy R Parke

ROOM RATES

6 Singles	£88 - £95
11 Doubles/Twins	£98 - £150
1 Four-poster	£150 - £180
1 Suite	£225

Includes full breakfast and VAT

CHARGE/CREDIT CARDS

• DC • JCB • MC • VI

ACCOLADES

E.T.B. ♛♛♛♛ Highly Commended
R.A.C. ★★★ + Merit Award R
A.A. ★★★ ❀❀ 68%

FACILITIES

Croquet, gardens, golf, heli-pad
4 meeting rooms/max 100 people

RESTRICTIONS

No facilities for disabled guests
No pets

ATTRACTIONS

Oxford, Blenheim Palace, Waddeston Manor, Cotswolds, Stratford-upon-Avon

AFFILIATIONS

Thames Valley Hotels

NEAREST

MAJOR CITY:
Oxford - 7 miles/15 mins

MAJOR AIRPORT:
London Heathrow - 45 miles/50 mins

RAILWAY STATION:
Oxford - 7 miles/15 mins

RESERVATIONS

Toll free in US: 800-437-2687

ACCESS CODES

AMADEUS HK OXFSTU
APOLLO HT UDL14856
SABRE HK 31033
SAHARA/WORLDSPAN HK STUDL

MIDSHIRES

The view from your window hasn't changed much for 800 years

Studley Priory is set in 13 acres of mature grounds in the delightful village of Horton-cum-Studley located seven miles from historic Oxford and its famed university. Beautifully situated high above the Vale of Aylesbury, the hotel enjoys panoramic views of the Cotswolds and, to the east, the Chilterns Hills.

All the rooms feature remote control colour television, radio alarm clock, direct-dial telephone, hairdryer and thoughtful extras such as a hot beverage tray, cookies, fresh fruit and mineral water. Master rooms date back to the 16th century and are furnished with antiques, making them unusual rooms of character.

The award-winning Croke Restaurant offers a seasonally changing à la carte menu with an excellent table d'hôte and vegetarian menu complemented by an extensive wine list of old and new world wines.

There are an outstanding number of attractions in the area such as the university city of Oxford, Blenheim Palace with its beautifully impressive house and gardens and Stratford-upon-Avon, all within easy travelling distance. You will never be short of things to do and see.

LOCATION

7 miles from the University City of Oxford.
4 miles from A40 Headington roundabout.
Follow signs for Horton-cum-Studley.

"Warm, comfortable and welcoming . . . my favourite hotel and restaurant in Oxfordshire"

Noel Edmonds, TV presenter

Elizabethan inn

THATCHER'S INN

A quaint Elizabethan inn in beautiful Oxfordshire

Thatcher's Inn is a registered Elizabethan building dating from the 1550's in the market place at Thame. The main building is the original thatched cottage with beamed ceilings and inglenook fireplaces which give the inn such a wealth of character. There are ten en suite bedrooms, two with open fireplaces, each with its own unique charm. The four newer rooms off the courtyard, with their four-poster beds and period furnishings, echo the sense of antiquity of the original beamed rooms in the main cottage.

The landscaped courtyard features a Koi pond to soothe the traveller's soul and revive his spirits. To relax his body, there are a Californian-style hot tub with Jacuzzi and a sauna. Combine all this with the first class, friendly, efficient service and you are getting close to heaven!

The Restaurant at Thatchers offers some of the best fare anywhere in England. The menus change as the seasons and rely on the freshest of produce, most of it garnered from local sources. The inspiration comes from the Chef Patron Granville Wood who describes his cuisine as modern or progressive English. A traditional English breakfast is included in the price of your room or you can choose from an à la carte menu. Lunch is served from Mondays to Saturdays with a brunch on Sundays. But it is the evening menu that reveals the true creativity of the Chef. Put away all thoughts of dining elsewhere, the dishes here are a delight in every sense. And, should the weather smile favourably, you can dine out on the patio.

LOCATION

M40 towards Oxford. Leave at Junction 7, turn right towards Thame. At roundabout head towards town centre, turn right at bottom of hill into Lower High Street. Thatcher's is about 500 yards on right hand side with car park at the rear.

29/30 Lower High Street, Thame, Oxfordshire OX9 2AA

Telephone 01844 212146
Fax 01844 217413

CHEF/PATRON
Granville Wood

ROOM RATES

4 Singles	*£47.50 - £59.50*
2 Double/Twins	*£69.50*
4 Four-posters	*£72.50 - £79.50*

Includes full breakfast and VAT

CHARGE/CREDIT CARDS

• DC • MC • VI

ACCOLADES
Independent

FACILITIES
Garden, sauna, jacuzzi Riding and fishing nearby

RESTRICTIONS
No children
No facilities for disabled guests

ATTRACTIONS
Oxford, Cotswolds, Blenheim Palace, Waddesdon Manor, Warwick Castle, Silverstone Grand Prix Circuit

AFFILIATIONS
Independent

NEAREST
MAJOR CITY:
Oxford - 12 miles/15 mins

MAJOR AIRPORT:
London Heathrow - 40 miles/1 hr

RAILWAY STATION:
Thame-Haddenham - 5 miles/10 mins

RESERVATIONS
Direct with hotel

ACCESS CODES
Not applicable

" A once in a lifetime hotel for our once in a lifetime trip. You made us feel so welcome. Thank you "

The MacIntosh family, Minnesota

WASHBOURNE COURT HOTEL *17th century country house*

Lower Slaughter, Gloucestershire GL54 2HS

Telephone 01451 822143
Fax 01451 821045

PROPRIETOR
Michael Pender

MANAGER
Ahmet Ulun

ROOM RATES

Single occupancy	*£78*
12 Doubles/Twins	*£88 - £98*
6 Suites	*£135*
5 Superiors	*£115 - £135*

Includes full breakfast and VAT

CHARGE/CREDIT CARDS

• MC • VI

ACCOLADES
E.T.B. Highly Commended
A.A. ★★★ 72%

FACILITIES
Tennis, gardens, heli-pad
2 meeting rooms/max 14 people
Golf, riding, fishing, quad biking, clay pigeon shooting and hot air ballooning nearby

RESTRICTIONS
No facilities for disabled guests

ATTRACTIONS
Blenheim Palace, Stratford-upon-Avon, Bath, Oxford, The Old Roman Fosseway, Cotswolds

AFFILIATIONS
Independent

NEAREST
MAJOR CITY:
Oxford - 25 miles/40 mins
MAJOR AIRPORT:
London Heathrow -75 miles/1 ¼ hrs
Birmingham - 55 miles/45 mins
RAILWAY STATION:
Kingham - 5 miles/10 mins

RESERVATIONS
Direct with hotel

ACCESS CODES
Not applicable

MIDSHIRES

A true gem right in the heart of The Cotswolds

Washbourne Court is a truly magnificent 17th century hotel standing in four acres of grounds alongside the River Eye in the centre of Lower Slaughter – undoubtedly one of the most beautiful and unspoilt of all the Cotswold villages. Whatever the season, there is a special magic about the village and the hotel. The building has retained all the original charm and character that can only be acquired with age – some 400 years.

The Pender family own and manage the hotel and their aim is to provide a friendly and personal service at an affordable price. All 23 bedrooms have an individual character with private bathrooms and, of course, every modern convenience. Some have jacuzzis and private lounges.

The intimate riverside restaurant offers the finest of modern English style of cuisine and only the best of fresh local produce is used. The ambience and atmosphere is one to be savoured.

Lower Slaughter is famous for its outstanding scenic beauty, and is the perfect location for exploring the beautiful north Cotswolds and nearby villages.

If you are in search of peace, tranquillity and the epitome of English country life – then Washbourne Court is your style of hotel.

LOCATION

About a half mile off the A429 between Stow-on-the Wold and Bourton-on-the-Water. (Signed to The Slaughters.)

“ Truly a haven of peace and tranquillity – with superb service ”

Howard Cragg, Sussex

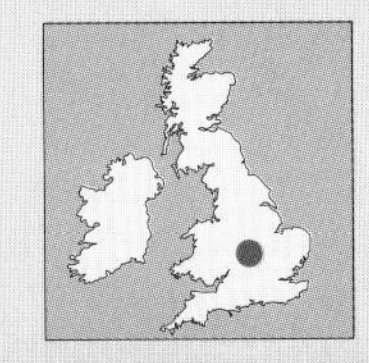

Country mansion with golf course

WELCOMBE HOTEL

Shakespeare once owned the grounds. Theodore Roosevelt stayed here

Just 1½ miles from Stratford-upon-Avon, this magnificent Jacobean-style mansion stands within its own 157-acre parkland estate, much of which was owned by William Shakespeare. The Welcombe was built in 1869 as a country house. Theodore Roosevelt was a guest here in 1910.

Today, the Welcombe has a reputation for maintaining the very highest international standards. There are 75 double rooms of which many are suites or luxuriously-appointed superior doubles that feature marble bathrooms and four-posters.

The renowned restaurant has large bay windows overlooking the gardens. Before or after dining, drinks can be taken either in the Trevelyan Terrace Bar, where there is often a pianist playing the baby grand, or the magnificent oak-panelled lounge.

The private estate includes an excellent 18-hole, par 70 golf course, all-weather floodlit tennis courts and extensive formal gardens with lakes and a waterfall. The Golf Clubhouse overlooks the putting green. Horse riding and other leisure pursuits may be arranged in the immediate vicinity.

The Welcombe provides the perfect base for visiting the Cotswolds, the splendours of the Heart of England and all that is Shakespeare.

LOCATION

1½ miles from centre of Stratford-upon-Avon on A439 to Warwick.

Warwick Road, Stratford-upon-Avon, Warwickshire CV37 0NR

Telephone 01789 295252
Fax 01789 414666

CONTACT

Jon Moore and Jane Lee

ROOM RATES

1 Single	*£110*
59 Doubles/Twins	*£150*
9 Luxury Doubles	*£275*
6 Suites	*£195 - £500*

Includes full breakfast and VAT

CHARGE/CREDIT CARDS

• DC • MC • VI

ACCOLADES

E.T.B. ♛♛♛♛♛ Highly Commended
R.A.C. ★★★★ + Merit Awards H C & R
A.A. ★★★★ ❀❀ 70%

FACILITIES

Tennis, gardens, snooker, heli-pad
18-hole par 70 golf course, putting green
6 meeting rooms/max 120 people
Riding, fishing, swimming and gym nearby

RESTRICTIONS

None

ATTRACTIONS

Royal Shakespeare Theatre, Shakespeare's Birthplace, Anne Hathaway's Cottage, Warwick Castle

AFFILIATIONS

Grand Heritage Hotels

NEAREST

MAJOR CITY:
Birmingham - 28 miles/35 mins

MAJOR AIRPORT:
Birmingham - 25 miles/30 mins

RAILWAY STATION:
Stratford-upon-Avon - local

RESERVATIONS

Direct with hotel

ACCESS CODES

Not applicable

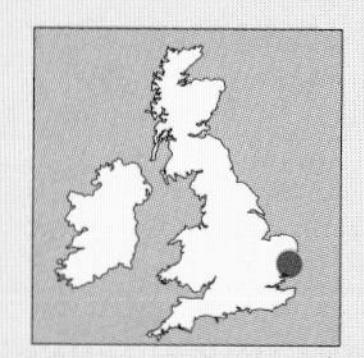

“ The room was delightful, the service excellent and the dinner superb. If only I could persuade your chef to part with the recipe for asparagus pancake ”

Sheila Carter, West Yorkshire

WENTWORTH HOTEL

Coastal country house hotel

Wentworth Road, Aldeburgh, Suffolk IP15 5BD

Telephone 01728 452312
Fax 01728 454343

PROPRIETOR
Michael Pritt

ROOM RATES
7 Singles £48.50 - £60
31 Doubles/Twins £87 - £108
Includes full breakfast and VAT

CHARGE/CREDIT CARDS

• DC • MC • VI

ACCOLADES
E.T.B. ♛♛♛ Highly Commended
A.A. ★★★ 68%

FACILITIES
Terrace garden
Golf nearby

RESTRICTIONS
No children
Limited facilities for disabled guests

ATTRACTIONS
Snape Maltings Concert Hall and River Complex, Suffolk coast, Constable country, Framlingham Castle, Lavenham, Minsmere Bird Reserve

AFFILIATIONS
Consort Hotels

NEAREST
MAJOR CITY:
Ipswich - 25 miles/40 mins

MAJOR AIRPORT:
London Heathrow - 100 miles/2½ hrs
Norwich - 50 miles/1¼ hrs

RAILWAY STATION:
Saxmundham - 8 miles/10 mins

RESERVATIONS
Direct with hotel

ACCESS CODES
Not applicable

A meeting place for art, music, sprats and a Marmalade Cat

The Wentworth Hotel sits right on the edge of the beautiful Suffolk coast, looking out over Aldeburgh Beach. Since 1920, it has been run by the Pritt family and Michael Pritt, third generation and present owner, has managed to modernise without spoiling the special country house atmosphere. Log fires, antique furniture and signed Russell Flint prints all contribute to the Wentworth's unique character.

Original touches abound. Each bedroom has a copy of Orlando The Marmalade Cat, a much-loved children's story set in Owlbarrow (Aldeburgh). Some rooms are also provided with binoculars to give an even better view of the sea.

Food at the Wentworth is a blend of traditional English and French with the emphasis on local produce. Fresh from Aldeburgh Beach come lobsters, crabs and the famous Aldeburgh sprats – a traditional dish at the Lord Mayor's Banquet in London. The wine list is compiled by Adnams of Southwold, 'Wine Merchants of the Year' in 1991, 1992 and 1994.

The hotel has strong links with Aldeburgh Music Festival, founded by Benjamin Britten and Peter Pears, and is a meeting place for performers and concert-goers. Among those who have stayed at the Wentworth are Lord Laurence Olivier, Julian Bream, Dame Peggy Ashcroft and Kathleen Ferrier.

LOCATION

Take the A12 towards Felixstowe. After crossing the Orwell Bridge, continue for 3-4 miles and turn left to Lowestoft. Turn right on to the A1094 to Aldeburgh and go straight over mini-roundabout. Turn left at the bottom of the hill into Wentworth Road. The hotel is 300 yards on.

"Thank you and all your staff for what proved a wonderful weekend"

Piet Pulford, Lamborghini Club UK

Manor house

WESTON MANOR HOTEL

An archetypal baronial hall, once the home of Henry VIII

Weston Manor has been the showpiece of the lovely village of Weston-on-the-Green, six miles from Oxford, since the 11th century. The ancestral home of the Earls of Abington and Berkshire, it was once the home of Henry VIII. The manor house has been sympathetically restored retaining its fine architectural features and historic charm.

It is set in 13 acres of beautiful gardens and grounds. Facilities include a well-kept croquet lawn and an outdoor heated swimming pool open during summer months.

The charming en suite bedrooms offer guests every modern convenience; many of them retain antique furniture and they all have garden views, private bathrooms and elegant surroundings.

The baronial hall, with its magnificent vaulted ceiling and original 15th century linenfold oak panelling, is the setting for the best of traditional and modern English cuisine and classic wines. The conference facilities offer business clientele modern support facilities and peaceful surroundings.

Weston Manor is ideally situated for visits to Blenheim Palace, Woodstock, Broughton Castle, Waddesdon Manor and the university city of Oxford.

LOCATION

35 minutes drive from the M25, 45 minutes from Birmingham and the NEC and 2 hours drive from Manchester. B430 – 2 miles from Junction 9 on the M40, just off the A34.

Weston-on-the-Green, Oxford, Oxfordshire OX6 8QL

Telephone 01869 350621
Fax 01869 350901

GENERAL MANAGER

Dudley Osborn

ROOM RATES

4 Singles	*£90*
29 Doubles	*£110*
2 Four-posters	*£145*
1 Suite	*£145*

Includes full breakfast and VAT

CHARGE/CREDIT CARDS

• *DC* • *MC* • *VI*

ACCOLADES

A.A. ★★★ ❀ *68%*

FACILITIES

Outdoor swimming pool, croquet, gardens, squash, heli-pad
5 meeting rooms/max 40 people
Golf nearby

RESTRICTIONS

No facilities for disabled guests
No pets

ATTRACTIONS

Blenheim Palace, Oxford University, Stratford-upon-Avon, Shakespeare country, The Cotswolds, Silverstone

AFFILIATIONS

Best Western
Thames Valley Hotels

NEAREST

MAJOR CITY:
Oxford - 6 miles/10 mins
London - 65 miles/1¼ hrs

MAJOR AIRPORT:
London Heathrow - 50 miles/1 hr

RAILWAY STATION:
Oxford - 6 miles/10 mins

RESERVATIONS

Toll free in US: 800-437-2687

ACCESS CODES

WORLDSPAN HK WESTO

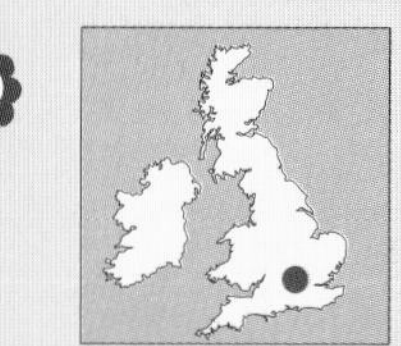

"Our stay was more than a pleasure – it was an absolute delight. Thank you again for such carefully considered hospitality"

Anthony "Spike" Milligan

WHITE HART HOTEL

Ancient coaching inn

High Street,
Dorchester-on-Thames,
Oxfordshire OX10 7HN

Telephone 01865 340074
Fax 01865 341082

GENERAL MANAGER
Mark Stott

ROOM RATES

2 Singles	*£55*
13 Doubles/Twins	*£85*
2 Four-posters	*£85 - £120*
3 Suites	*£120*

Includes full breakfast and VAT

CHARGE/CREDIT CARDS

• DC • MC • VI

ACCOLADES
E.T.B. ♛♛♛♛ *Highly Commended*
R.A.C. ★★★
A.A. ★★★ ❀❀ *62%*

FACILITIES
2 meeting rooms/max 50 people
Riding, speedboats and waterskiing, boating, sailing, clay pigeon shooting and fishing nearby

RESTRICTIONS
No facilities for disabled guests
Pets welcome in hotel, but not in bar or restaurant

ATTRACTIONS
Dorchester Abbey, Oxford, The Cotswolds, Henley-on-Thames, Blenheim Palace, Windsor Castle

AFFILIATIONS
Independent

NEAREST
MAJOR CITY:
Oxford - 10 miles/15 mins

MAJOR AIRPORT:
London Heathrow - 40 miles/55 mins
Oxford - 13 miles/15 mins

RAILWAY STATION:
Didcot Parkway - 12 miles/20 mins

RESERVATIONS
Direct with hotel

ACCESS CODES
Not applicable

The best of English welcomes in historic River Thames countryside

Rich in character, The White Hart offers visitors the warmest of English welcomes. Following centuries of experience the hotel is seasoned in providing every hospitality and courtesy. The White Hart also enjoys a reputation for exemplary cuisine; and selected suppliers ensure that the cellar invariably stocks at least 50 of the world's finest wines.

The varied arrangements of the suites are charming relics of ancient construction, but all have been tastefully modernised. Every room is en-suite, with TV, telephone and tea and coffee making facilities provided. However, convenience is not provided at the expense of character. A building of such antiquity cannot house an elevator, so the rating will never rise above three stars; yet the cordial hospitality of the White Hart cannot be bettered. An idyllic haven for your weekend breaks and longer holidays, the White Hart is also the perfect business meeting venue, offering every facility to the conference guest.

The construction date of the White Hart is lost to time, but the history of Dorchester is better known. The iron age village was settled by the Romans who left valuable archeological artefacts. The pride of Dorchester is the magnificent abbey, dating from the 11th century. This quintessential English village is a delightful retreat.

LOCATION

From Junction 11 of the M4, drive towards Reading, then head towards Oxford on the A4074. Or, from Junction 6 of the M40, follow the B4009 towards Benson, then turn right onto the A4074. Dorchester is signposted from this road.

"Brian and Tina are two of the most welcoming and hospitable hosts in the Cotswolds"

Drew Smith, Editor of Taste magazine, Wiltshire

Elizabethan inn

THE WILD DUCK

An attractive 15th century inn of great character

The Wild Duck is a mellow Cotswold stone Elizabethan Inn. A typical local English inn with a warm and welcoming ambience, rich in colours and hung with old oil portraits of English ancestors. Large open log fires burn in the bar and the oak panelled residents' lounge in wintertime.

The garden is secluded, delightful and perfect for 'alfresco' dining in the summer. The bar offers six real ales and the wine list is extensive and innovative.

The country-style dining room offers fresh seasonal food; game in winter and fresh fish delivered overnight from Brixham in Devon, which can include such exotic fare as parrot fish and tilapia.

There are nine bedrooms, two of which have four-poster beds and overlook the garden. All rooms have direct-dial telephone, colour TV and tea/coffee-making facilities.

Within one mile, The Wild Duck is surrounded by the Cotswold Water Park, with over 80 lakes providing fishing, swimming, sailing, water and jet-skiing. Polo at Cirencester Park is a regular event and every March, Cheltenham holds the Gold Cup Race Meeting. Horse trials at Gatcombe Park and Badminton are also held annually.

LOCATION

From M4 take Junction 17 and follow Cirencester signs. Before Cirencester, turn right at Kemble and follow signs to Ewen.

Drakes Island,
Ewen, Cirencester,
Gloucestershire GL7 6BY

Telephone 01285 770310
Fax 01285 770310

OWNERS

Brian and Tina Mussell

ROOM RATES

Single occupancy	*£48*
7 Doubles/Twins	*£65*
2 Four-posters	*£75*

Includes continental breakfast and VAT

CHARGE/CREDIT CARDS

• *MC* • *VI*

ACCOLADES

E.T.B. ♛♛♛ Commended
R.A.C. ★★★
Inn of the Year - leading guides

FACILITIES

Gardens
Golf, riding and fishing nearby

RESTRICTIONS

Children 5-10 years sharing double room - £10 extra
No facilities for disabled guests
£5 charge for dogs

ATTRACTIONS

Slimbridge Wild Fowl Sanctuary,
Gatcombe Horse Trials,
The Cotswolds,
Gloucestershire docks

AFFILIATIONS

Independent

NEAREST

MAJOR CITY:
Bath - 25 miles/35 mins

MAJOR AIRPORT:
London Heathrow - 70 miles/1¾ hrs
Bristol - 40 miles/45 mins

RAILWAY STATION:
Kemble - 3 miles/3 mins

RESERVATIONS

Direct with hotel

ACCESS CODES

Not applicable

"I was very impressed with the wonderful hospitality shown me by all the Woodlands Manor family"

Richard Montgomery, New Jersey

WOODLANDS MANOR

Manor house

***Green Lane,
Clapham,
Bedford MK41 6EP***

***Telephone 01234 363281
Fax 01234 272390***

PROPRIETOR

Keith A Timewell

ROOM RATES

8 Singles from £59.50
16 Doubles/Twins £75 - £90
1 Suite £90
Includes full breakfast and VAT

CHARGE/CREDIT CARDS

• *DC* • *MC* • *VI*

ACCOLADES

R.A.C. ★★★+ Merit Awards H C & R
A.A. ★★★ 72%

FACILITIES

Garden, croquet, heli-pad
3 meeting rooms/max 25 people
Golf, riding and fishing nearby

RESTRICTIONS

No children under 7 years
No pets

ATTRACTIONS

Woburn Abbey,
Warwick Castle,
Bunyan Museum,
Oxford, Cambridge,
Bushmead Priory,
Wrest Park House and Gardens

AFFILIATIONS

Independent

NEAREST

MAJOR CITY:
London - 50 miles/1 hr

MAJOR AIRPORT:
Luton - 30 miles/30 mins

RAILWAY STATION:
Bedford - 2 miles/5 mins

RESERVATIONS

Direct with hotel

ACCESS CODES

Not applicable

Serendipidy – the art of discovering a delight by accident

The first hint of a pleasant, relaxing stay at this hotel comes from the address: Green Lane. Environmentally, it is green. This handsome period house is set serenely within acres of wooded grounds and well beyond the frenetic sounds of the world we live in. And yet, who would believe it is just two miles from the centre of John Bunyan's home town of Bedford.

Surrounded by well-stocked and well-kept gardens, it is almost assured that whichever bedroom you are given, there's a splendid view. These rooms are all en suite and every modern facility is thoughtfully provided. The decor and furnishings reflect the admirable taste of the owners, the Timewell family – another propitious name connected with this property!

Robert Tarry (and why not!) is the charming house manager whose easy, welcoming style belies a true professional.

And this includes the pleasures to be found in the sumptuous dining room – an indulgent combination of great comfort and excellent food which is described as "traditional English with a French flair" – lovely fresh flavours that cry out for the taste of good wine. No problem here; the wine vaults will oblige with interest.

Woburn Abbey, one of the great stately homes of England, is nearby as are Oxford and Cambridge. So why not combine serendipidy with a little learning?

LOCATION

Clapham village is 2 miles north of the centre of Bedford on the A6.

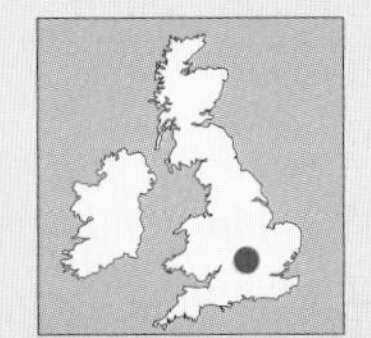

"I can thoroughly recommend Wroxton House to businessmen and people looking for a relaxing, friendly and very comfortable country house"

Mr J A Oldfield, Executive Chairman, Aston Martin Lagonda Limited

17th century thatched house

WROXTON HOUSE HOTEL

Wroxton St Mary,
Nr Banbury,
Oxfordshire OX15 6QB

Telephone 01295 730777
Fax 01295 730800

GENERAL MANAGER

Roger Swatkins

ROOM RATES

5 Singles	*£75 - £85*
24 Doubles	*£85 - £112*
2 Four-posters	*£112 - £125*
1 Suite	*£112 - £125*

Inlcudes full breakfast and VAT

CHARGE/CREDIT CARDS

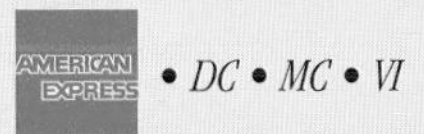

• DC • MC • VI

ACCOLADES

E.T.B. ♛♛♛♛♛ Commended
R.A.C. ★★★
A.A. ★★★ 68%

FACILITIES

Golf and riding nearby

RESTRICTIONS

No children
No facilities for disabled guests

ATTRACTIONS

Oxford, Stratford-upon-Avon, The Cotswolds, Silverstone, Warwick and Broughton Castles, Upton House, Blenheim Palace,

AFFILIATIONS

Best Western
Thames Valley Hotels

NAEREST

MAJOR CITY:
Oxford - 30 miles/35 mins

MAJOR AIRPORT:
Birmingham - 42 miles/40 mins

RAILWAY STATION:
Banbury - 3 miles/5 mins

RESERVATIONS

Direct with hotel

ACCESS CODES

AMADEUS/SYSTEM 1 BW BHX294
SABRE BW 18418
APOLLO BW 05965
WORLDSPAN BW 83294

Cotswold traditions and care, midway between Oxford and Stratford

Built of honeyed local stone, restoration has linked three village houses to a charming clock tower wing and conservatory lounge. The character of the hotel is created by a team of carefully selected staff, who combine attentive service with friendliness and informality.

The original timbers are preserved in many of the older of the 32 en suite rooms. Comfortable bathrooms provide fluffy towels, pot pourri and bath oils.

Guests may dine by candlelight in the intimate restaurant, set in three adjoining rooms, where a traditional Cotswold atmosphere is evoked by original beams, inglenooks, carved oak recesses, horse brasses and pewter. Expertly prepared menus display chef Frank Peigne's personal interpretation of modern French cuisine. From the home-baked bread and home-grown herbs to a carefully chosen wine cellar emphasising quality and value, the standards are perfection.

Located midway between Stratford-upon-Avon and Oxford, Wroxton House provides an ideal base for exploring this part of England. Banbury itself is a bustling part of England with many memories of the Civil War period.

There are 15 magnificent mansions and gardens, including Blenheim, Broughton and Upton, within half an hour's drive. So is Silverstone motor racing circuit. Golf, gliding and horse riding are all available in the neighbourhood.

LOCATION

Junction 11 M40, follow A422 towards Stratford for 3 miles.

"Beware – we'll send you more Hawaiian tourists. It was delightful, 'mahalo' for all your extra care"

Dr & Mrs Leslie Correa, Hawaii

YE OLDE SALUTATION INN

14th century inn

Market Pitch, Weobley, Herefordshire HR4 8SJ

Telephone 01544 318443
Fax 01544 318216

PROPRIETORS
Chris and Frances Anthony

ROOM RATES

3 Doubles	£58
1 Four-poster	£62
1 Cottage	£62

Includes full breakfast and VAT

CHARGE/CREDIT CARDS

• DC • JCB • MC • VI

ACCOLADES
E.T.B. Highly Commended
A.A. ★★ 74%
Heartbeat award - Environmental Health Services
Les Routiers Corps d'Elite Award 1994/5
The Good Hotel Guide

FACILITIES
Garden, gym
Golf, riding and fishing nearby

RESTRICTIONS
Children minimum age 14 years
No smoking in bedrooms and restaurant
No facilities for disabled guests
Pets by arrangement

ATTRACTIONS
Hay-on-Wye (second hand book shops), Black Mountains, Brecon Beacons

AFFILIATIONS
Independent

NEAREST
MAJOR CITY:
Hereford 12 miles/15 mins

MAJOR AIRPORT:
Birmingham 50 miles/1½ hrs

RAILWAY STATION:
Hereford 12 miles/15 mins

RESERVATIONS
Direct with hotel

ACCESS CODES
Not applicable

Down among the cattle, apples and hops and still undiscovered by tourism

Ye Olde Salutation Inn is a black and white timber-framed building dating back over 500 years, set in the medieval village of Weobley in rural Herefordshire. This area of the Welsh Marches is largely unspoiled by tourism and is famous for its cattle, cider orchards and hops. Combining a former ale and cider house and an adjoining cottage, the inn offers a traditional setting and a friendly atmosphere in which to enjoy superb food and comfortable accommodation.

All four bedrooms are en suite and one has a four-poster bed. A self-catering cottage is also available. There is a spacious residents' lounge, a delightful bar with an inglenook fireplace, and an additional public bar.

Everything here is cooked to order, using only the freshest produce, the cooking is mainly English in style although French influence is also apparent. The menu offers a comprehensive choice with something to suit every taste, and the composition and presentation of each dish is of a very high standard. Particularly delicious desserts are also served. A wide selection of carefully chosen wines is available to complement your meal.

LOCATION

Weobley is 12 miles north west of Hereford, just off the Leominster – Brecon road, on the A4112. Ye Olde Salutation Inn is in the village centre facing Broad Street.

West Country

Berry Pomeroy Castle dates from the 14th century and was the home of a Norman family. It was burned down in 1708 but remains a symbol of Devon's romantic past. The castle is about five miles inland from Torquay.

Heritage sites

The following heritage sites can be found on the map overleaf. The key numbers show where they are located.

AVON

Sir Bevil Grenville's Monument	1
Lansdown, Stanton Drew Circles and Cove	2
Stoney Littleton, Long Barrow	3

CORNWALL

Ballowall Barrow, St Just	4
Dupath Well House, Callington	5
Halliggye Fogou	6
Launceston Castle	7
Pendennis Castle	8
Restormel Castle	9
St Catherine's Castle, Fowey	10
St Mawes Castle	11
Tintagel Castle	12

DEVON

Berry Pomeroy Castle	13
Bowhill	14
Dartmouth Castle	15
Lydford Castles and Saxon Town	16
Mount Batten Tower	17
Okehampton Castle	18
Totnes Castle	19

DORSET

Abbotsbury Abbey Remains	20
Fiddleford Manor	21
Maiden Castle	22
Portland Castle	23
St Catherine's Chapel, Abbotsbury	24

SOMERSET

Cleeve Abbey	25
Farleigh Hungerford Castle	26
Glastonbury Tribunal	27
Muchelney Abbey	28
Nunney Castle	29

WILTSHIRE

Avebury Museum	30
Bratton Camp and White Horse	31
Ludgershall Castle and Cross	32
Old Sarum	33
Old Wardour Castle	34
Stonehenge	35

COLOUR KEY TO HOTEL SYMBOLS

The rosettes on the map indicate the location of each hotel; the numbers within show the page number of the hotel. The colour of the rosette is a rough guide to the price of a twin or double room (see colour key below).

- Double room: up to £75 per night
- Double room: £76 - £125 per night
- Double room: £126 - £175 per night
- Double room: from £176+ per night

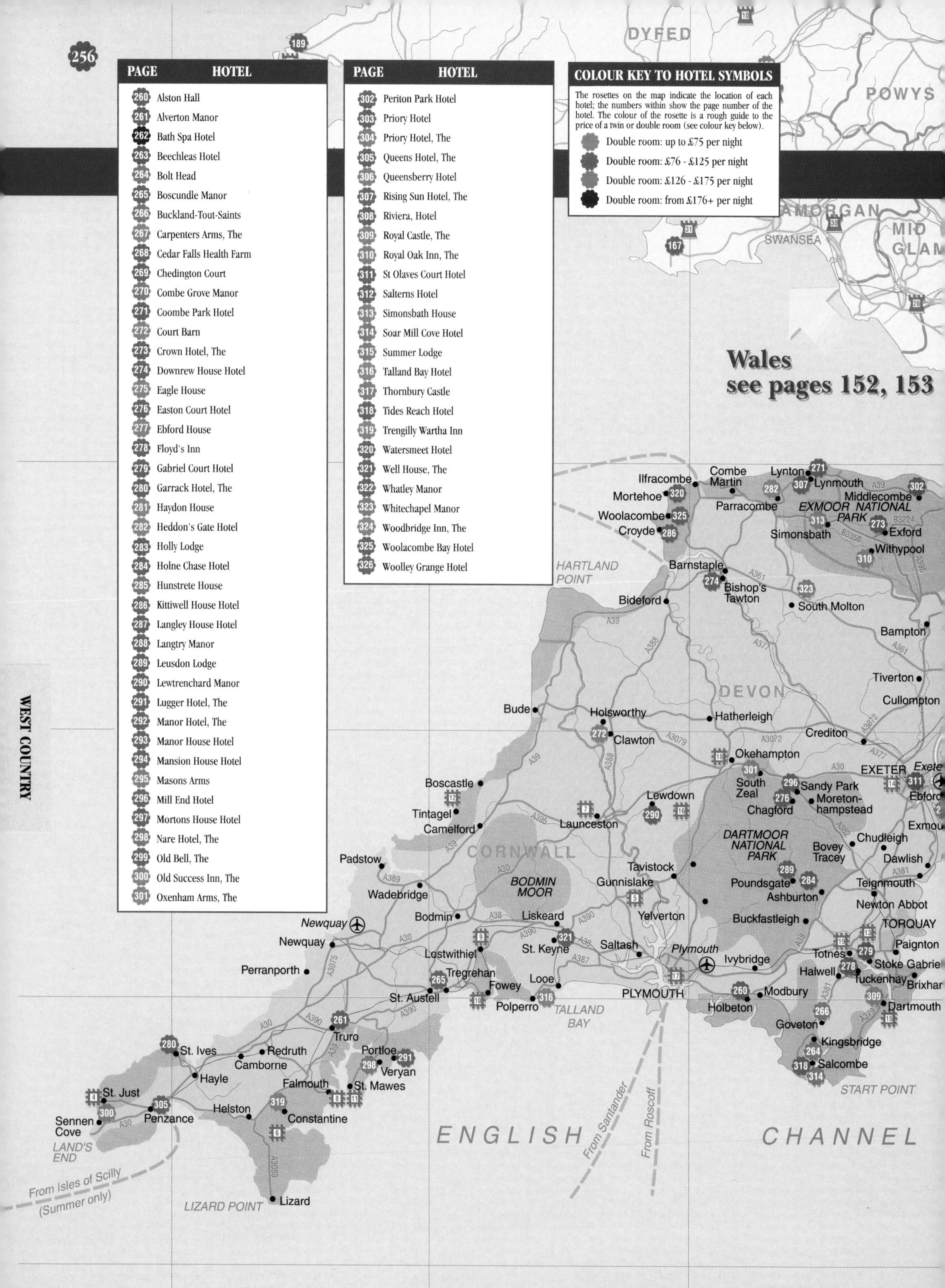

Wales see pages 152, 153

DYFED
POWYS
GLAMORGAN
MID GLAM
SWANSEA
DEVON
CORNWALL
EXMOOR NATIONAL PARK
DARTMOOR NATIONAL PARK
BODMIN MOOR
HARTLAND POINT
LAND'S END
LIZARD POINT
START POINT
TALLAND BAY
ENGLISH CHANNEL
From Isles of Scilly (Summer only)
From Santander
From Roscoff
Ilfracombe
Combe Martin
Lynton
Lynmouth
Mortehoe
Woolacombe
Croyde
Parracombe
Middlecombe
Simonsbath
Exford
Withypool
Barnstaple
Bishop's Tawton
Bideford
South Molton
Bampton
Tiverton
Cullompton
Bude
Holsworthy
Clawton
Hatherleigh
Crediton
Okehampton
South Zeal
Sandy Park
Chagford
Moretonhampstead
EXETER
Ebford
Boscastle
Tintagel
Camelford
Lewdown
Launceston
Exmouth
Chudleigh
Bovey Tracey
Dawlish
Padstow
Wadebridge
Tavistock
Gunnislake
Poundsgate
Ashburton
Teignmouth
Newton Abbot
Bodmin
Liskeard
Yelverton
Buckfastleigh
TORQUAY
Newquay
Lostwithiel
St. Keyne
Saltash
Plymouth
Ivybridge
Totnes
Paignton
Stoke Gabriel
Perranporth
Tregrehan
Fowey
Looe
Halwell
Tuckenhay
Brixham
St. Austell
Polperro
PLYMOUTH
Modbury
Holbeton
Dartmouth
Truro
Goveton
St. Ives
Redruth
Camborne
Portloe
Veryan
Kingsbridge
Hayle
Falmouth
St. Mawes
Salcombe
St. Just
Penzance
Helston
Constantine
Sennen Cove
Lizard

WEST COUNTRY

WEST COUNTRY
GLOUCESTERSHIRE
Midshires see pages 192, 193
CHELTENHAM
GLOUCESTER
GWENT
NEWPORT
CARDIFF
SOUTH GLAMORGAN
BRISTOL CHANNEL
OXFORDSHIRE
BERKSHIRE
READING
BASINGSTOKE
South see pages 328, 329
HAMPSHIRE
EASTLEIGH
SOUTHAMPTON
FAREHAM
PORTSMOUTH
GOSPORT
AVON
WILTSHIRE
SOMERSET
DORSET
Lechlade
Cricklade
Thornbury
Malmesbury
Chipping Sodbury
SWINDON
Wootton Bassett
Avonmouth
Portishead
Mangotsfield
Clevedon
BRISTOL
Bristol
Corsham
Chippenham
Avebury
Marlborough
WESTON-SUPER-MARE
BATH
Bathford
Bradford on-Avon
Melksham
Devizes
Congresbury
Hunstrete
Monkton Combe
Wolley Green
North Newnton
Stanton Wick
Cheddar
Midsomer Norton
Radstock
Trowbridge
Burnham-on-Sea
Ludgershall
Frome
Westbury
Watchet
Wells
Warminster
Shepton Mallet
Amesbury
Glastonbury
Bridgwater
Wiveliscombe
Bishops Lydeard
Castle Cary
Mere
Wilton
Salisbury
Wincanton
Taunton
Podimore
Ilchester
Shaftesbury
Wellington
Sherborne
Ilminster
Yeovil
Crewkerne
Chard
Evershot
Chedington
Blandford Forum
Honiton
Wimborne Minster
Bournemouth
Axminster
POOLE
Ottery St Mary
Bridport
Lyme Regis
Dorchester
Christchurch
Seaton
Branscombe
West Bexington
BOURNEMOUTH
Sidmouth
Wareham
Studland
Abbotsbury
Budleigh Salterton
Weymouth
Corfe Castle
Swanage
Fortuneswell
Easton
BILL OF PORTLAND
From Guernsey, and Jersey
From St. Malo (Summer only)
From Cherbourg
WEST COUNTRY
ISLES OF SCILLY
St. Martin's
Hugh Town
Isles of Scilly (St. Mary's)
miles 0 2 4
kms 0 2 4 6
Islands see page 449
PAGE HOTEL
Please refer to the Islands, page 449, to find hotels located on the islands shown on this map.
462 St Martin's Hotel
KEY
Motorways
'A' Roads
Railways
Airports
National Boundaries
County Boundaries
Heritage Sites
English Heritage Sites
Ferry Routes
Urban Areas
National Parks and Areas of Outstanding Natural Beauty
Each grid square equals 30 miles (approx. 50 km)
Maps produced by Arka Cartographics Limited. Copyright 1995
27/28, Hartfield Road, Forest Row, East Sussex RH18 5DY England
0 Miles 30
0 Kilometres 50

Avebury Stone Circle, near Marlborough, Wiltshire, is possibly the most important prehistoric site in Europe. Many of the great Sarsen stones weigh over 40 tons and form a circle of one mile in circumference. The site, built about 1800 BC, predates Stonehenge by some 200 years.

COUNTIES

Avon

Cornwall

Devon

Dorset

Somerset

Wiltshire

Palaces, Stately Homes, Historic Houses

Bishop's Palace, Wells, Somerset. Fortified 13th c palace, chapel and ruins. Home of Bishops of Bath & Wells for over 700 years.

Bowood House, Calne, Wiltshire. 18th c house by Robert Adam. Paintings, Victoriana, porcelain.

Cotehele Manor House, nr Calstock, Cornwall. Built 1485-1627. Original Tudor gateway, tower and Great Barn.

Dartmouth Castle, Devon. First castle designed and built specifically for artillery in 1481. In use until Second World War.

Dunster Castle, Somerset. A castle has been on this Exmoor site for over 1,000 years. Home of the Luttrell family for 600 years.

Dyrham Park, Wiltshire. Mansion built 1691-1710. The rooms have little changed; the deer have been here since the Saxons.

Montacute House, Somerset. Built 1588-1601 by Phelps family. Furniture, portraits, tapestries, plasterwork, panelling.

Mount Edgcumbe House, Cremyll, Cornwall. Tudor mansion house. Grade I listed garden. 800-acre parkland.

Pendennis Castle, Falmouth, Cornwall. Built against 'pretensed invasion' by Henry VIII in 1539. Withstood 23-week siege in Civil War.

Powderham Castle, Kenton, Devon. 1390. Georgian interiors, china, furnishings and paintings.

The West Country lives up to its reputation as a marvellous place for holidays. Starting with the natural attractions of magnificent coastline and mild weather, it is a region enriched with some of the country's finest cathedrals and castles. It is a land holding much of England's history and a great deal of its romance. You are never far from the sea, yet within 20 miles you can find rugged isolation on Dartmoor, Bodmin Moor, Exmoor in Lorna Doone's valley (Somerset) or Thomas Hardy's Wessex (Dorset). The region's love of art is abundantly shown in the many superb collections of paintings and sculptures in the galleries, museums and stately homes.

At Stonehenge are the Bronze Age standing stones, up to 21 ft high, where sunworshippers gathered at the dawn of history. Salisbury, with its high cathedral spire, was once capital of Wessex. Sir Walter Raleigh's castle ennobles the ancient town of Sherborne. At Glastonbury Abbey in Somerset the seeds of Christianity were sown in England. Wells has England's first Gothic cathedral. Nearby are the historic port of Bristol and elegant Bath Spa. Glorious Devon has stunning scenery and superb seaside resorts. Cornwall, separated by the River Tamar from England for all but five miles, has its own language and a fascinating individuality. The huge granite mass of Land's End is the country's most westerly point.

For all the profusion of the holiday activities in the West Country, the pace of life remains relaxed. Every afternoon sumptuous cream teas with scones, strawberry jam and cream are on offer. Sample Somerset 'scrumpy' cider and Dorset Blue Vinny blue-veined cheese. There's always time to enjoy them, and talk to the people of the West Country as friends.

Wilton House, Wiltshire. Elizabethan home of Earls of Pembroke for over 400 years. Cube Rooms. Art collection.

Museums, Galleries & Modern Highspots

American Museum in Britain, Bath, Avon. 17th c furnished rooms. Silver, pewter, glass. Historical maps, folk art gallery.

Avebury Museum, Wiltshire. One of Britain's most important collections of pre-historic architecture. Stone circle circa 1800BC.

Avon Wildlife Trust, Willsbridge Mill, Avon. 18th c corn mill housing "hands on" exhibition. Nature trail.

Charlestown Shipwreck Centre, Cornwall. Visual history of town and dwellers. Outstanding display of shipwreck material.

Dartmoor High Moorland Visitor Centre, Princetown, Devon. Life-size characters, computer inter-active displays, photographs.

Great Western Railway Museum, Swindon, Wiltshire. Historic GWR engines, nameplates, posters from 'God's Wonderful Railway'.

Perry's Cider Mills, Dowlish Wake, Somerset. Working cider farm, with old cider presses, farm tools and photographs.

Salisbury & South Wiltshire Museum, Salisbury. History of Old Sarum and Salisbury, Romans and Saxons, in Grade I listed building.

TOURIST OFFICE INFORMATION

Further information about the South West will be gladly supplied by:

West Country Tourist Board,
60 St David's Hill, Exeter EX4 4SY
Tel: 01392 76351

Southern Tourist Board,
40 Chamberlayne Road, Eastleigh, Hampshire SO50 5JH
Tel: 01703 620006

For international offices, please turn to page 480

Tintagel Castle, Cornwall, legendary home of King Arthur, the "Once and future King". There was a celtic monastery here in the 6th century. The 12th century walls from the chapel and the 13th century castle still stand sentinel over this rugged and beautiful coast.

Totnes Castle, Devon, was built as a motte and bailey castle by the Normans in the 12th century. The keep and its impressive ramparts, dating from the 14th century, have wonderful views of the Dart Valley.

Tank Museum, Wareham, Dorset. Over 250 armoured fighting vehicles. Video theatres.

Churches & Cathedrals

Australia Chapel, Bathampton, Avon. Grave of Admiral Arthur Philip, first governor of New South Wales.

Culbone Church, St Beuno, Somerset. This tiny church on vast Exmoor measures just 35ft by 12ft.

Exeter Cathedral, Devon. Gothic decorated. World's longest unbroken stretch of Gothic vaulting. Medieval carved figures.

Salisbury Cathedral, Wiltshire. Gothic cathedral 1258. 404 ft spire added in 14th c. Ancient clock mechanism 1386. Magna Carta.

St Mary Redcliffe, Bristol, Avon. 1280. Queen Elizabeth I called it England's 'fairest, goodliest and most famous'. American chapel.

Truro Cathedral, Cornwall. Victorian Gothic cathedral by John Pearson, built 1850-1910.

Wells Cathedral, Somerset. Dating from 12th c. Early English Gothic style. West Front has 296 groups of medieval sculpture.

Wimborne Minster, Dorset. St Norman to Late Gothic. Striking Quarter Jack Clock.

Wolford Chapel, Dunkeswell, Devon. Built 1802 by General Simco, first Lieutenant Governor of Ontario, Canada.

Parks & Gardens

Bath Botanical Gardens, Avon. One of Britain's finest collections of plants on limestone.

Hestercombe Gardens, Cheddon Fitzpaine, Somerset. Multi-terraced garden created by Sir Edward Lutyens and Gertrude Jekyll at the turn of the century.

Pentewan, Cornwall. The Lost Gardens of Heligan is an immense garden restoration project.

Plant World, Newton Abbot, Devon. Unique 'Map of the World' gardens. Rare and unusual plants in nursery.

Stourhead House, Stourton, Wiltshire. Landscaped garden laid out 1741-80. Lakes, temples, rare trees and plants.

Thomas Hardy's Cottage Garden, Higher Bockhampton, Dorset. In this setting, he wrote "Far from the Madding Crowd".

Sport & Outdoors

Angling. Shark fishing off Falmouth, freshwater on Tamar, Parrett, Exe and Lyn.

Cheddar Gorge, Somerset. Climb Jacob's Ladder. Go down to the stalactites and stalagmites. Join in adventure caving.

Cricket. Big hitting on the comparatively small County Ground in Taunton, Somerset.

Rugby Union. Britain's strongest club is Bath, Avon.

Steam Trains. Dart Valley Railway, Buckfastleigh, Devon. Easter, then May-Sep. East Somerset Railway, Cranmore, Somerset. Apr-Oct.

Surfing. Newquay, Cornwall. White-crested Atlantic rollers. Championship events.

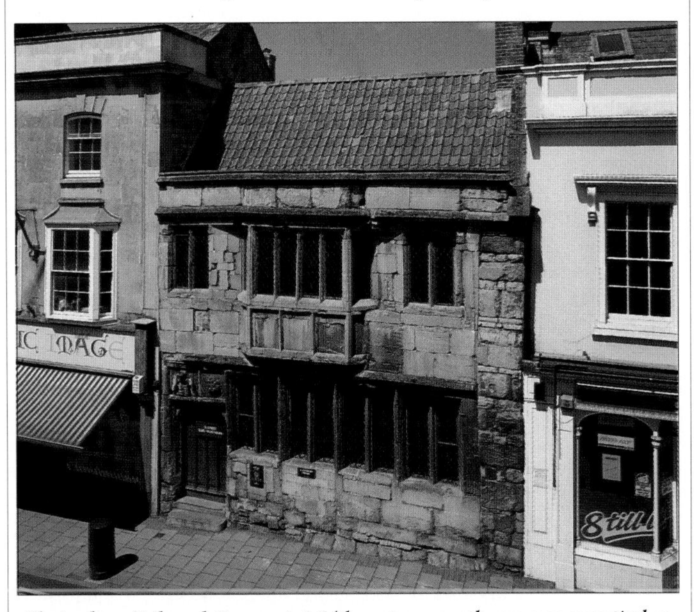

Glastonbury Tribunal, Somerset. A 14th century courthouse was once timber-fronted. The ashlar stone face was added by Bishop Bere in 1500. Today, it houses a museum of antiquities from the Iron Age.

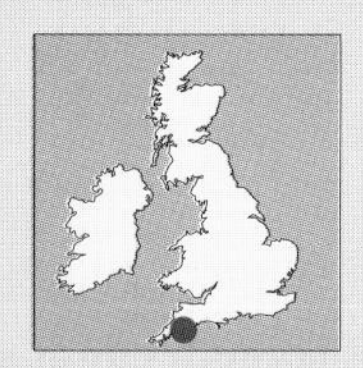

“Within a few days, it didn't feel like a hotel at all, but more like a home we could return to after our long shooting days”

Lindsay Doran, film producer

ALSTON HALL

Edwardian manor

Alston, Holbeton,
Nr Plymouth,
Devon PL8 1HN

Telephone 01752 830555
Fax 01752 830494

MANAGING DIRECTOR

Tim Pettifer

ROOM RATES

8 Doubles £100
12 Superior doubles £110 - £120
Includes full breakfast and VAT

CHARGE/CREDIT CARDS

• DC • MC • VI

ACCOLADES

E.T.B. ♛♛♛♛ Commended
A.A. ★★★ ❀ 67%

FACILITIES

Garden, croquet, tennis, mini-gym, indoor and outdoor pools, sauna, solarium, aromatherapy
2 meeting rooms/max 70 people
Fishing, riding, sailing and shooting nearby

RESTRICTIONS

No facilities for disabled guests
Pets £7.50 per day

ATTRACTIONS

Mount Batten Tower, Mayflower Steps, Saltram House, Shire Horse Centre, Berbecks Museum, Dartmoor National Park

AFFILIATIONS

Independent

NEAREST

MAJOR CITY:
Plymouth - 13 miles/30 mins

MAJOR AIRPORT:
Plymouth - 13 miles/30 mins

RAILWAY STATION:
Plymouth - 13 miles/30 mins

RESERVATIONS

Direct with hotel

ACCESS CODES

Not applicable

In 1620 the pilgrims set sail not far from here. But look what they left behind!

South Devon has long been the playground for the British. The variety and concentration of leisure facilities is second to none in the country: watersports, shooting, riding, fishing and golf amongst many others. To fail to mention Alston Hall would be to deny the area of a most singular attraction.

The building, which includes an oak-panelled hall, minstrels gallery and stained glass windows, is a splendid tribute to the Edwardian era. Alston Hall was once the family home of Dame Lucille Sayers whose presence still pervades the house and, more particularly, the garden, for she was a renowned expert in Peonies.

The Peony Room restaurant is the place to indulge your gourmet inclinations. Like all art forms, the preparation is all taken very seriously and presented for your critical appreciation. The food is fresh and local, the menus inspired and the wine list endorses this dedication to excellence.

To work up a healthy appetite, The Alston Hall Leisure Club, which includes all-weather tennis courts, is on hand and available free of charge to residents.

And, after the exertions of the day, whether at Alston Hall or the myriad facilities nearby, you can look forward to the sumptuous comfort of your delightful en suite bedroom where every facility is thoughtfully provided.

LOCATION

A38 towards Plymouth. Take B3210 at Wrangaton. After Ermington join A379 in direction of Plymouth. Left after 1 mile. 1st right after Battisborough Cross.

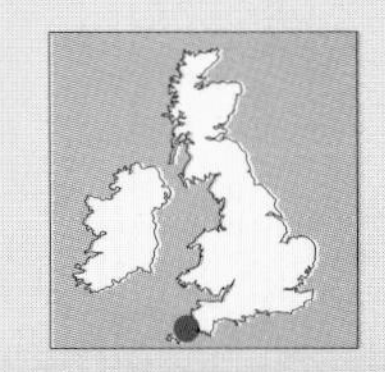

" A really excellent hotel. The meals and service equal the Waldorf Astoria, New York "

Frank & Margaret Blatchford, Victoria, Australia

Cornish country manor

ALVERTON MANOR

The charm and character of another age

Alverton Manor is a truly impressive sight. Built in its present form during the early 19th century, the manor was for many years occupied by the Sisters of the Epiphany, until being restored to its former glory. Located on a hillside setting, the hotel boasts fine period sandstone walls, attractive mullioned windows and an original Cornish Delabole slate roof. The building is Grade II listed, and considered of special historical interest.

Alverton Manor is outstandingly comfortable in a discreet, elegant way. It has been lovingly restored and is beautifully appointed, yet retains the character and charm of another age. Each of the hotel's 34 bedrooms has been individually designed to provide a special and unique ambience. All the bedrooms are comprehensively furnished with the amenities one expects from a modern luxury hotel.

Alverton Manor is renowned for its excellent cuisine, which is contemporary English and French. The restaurant has recently been awarded an AA Rosette for its high standards.

Truro has some of the best-preserved Georgian houses in Britain and its own three-spired cathedral. The many reminders from Cornwall's stirring history include Henry VIII's castle at Pendennis. The sparkling blue sea, sub-tropical flowers and palm trees of the Cornish Riviera are all virtually on the doorstep of Alverton Manor.

LOCATION

Situated on the A390 approach road to Truro from St Austell, the hotel is located on your right hand side as you approach the first major roundabout on entering Truro.

Tregolls Road,
Truro,
Cornwall TR1 1XQ

Telephone 01872 76633
Fax 01872 222989

PROPRIETOR
Michael Sagin

ROOM RATES

6 Singles	*£63*
16 Doubles/Twins	*£99*
8 Deluxe Doubles/Twins	*£109*
4 Suites	*£130*

Includes full breakfast and VAT

CHARGE/CREDIT CARDS

• DC • JCB • MC • VI

ACCOLADES
E.T.B. ♛♛♛♛ Highly Commended
R.A.C. ★★★
A.A. ★★★ ❀ 71%

FACILITIES
Garden, snooker
5 meeting rooms/max 200 people
Golf, fishing and riding nearby

RESTRICTIONS
Dogs by prior arrangement

ATTRACTIONS
Truro and Truro Cathedral,
Isles of Scilly,
Pendennis Castle,
St Mawes Castle

AFFILIATIONS
Independent

NEAREST
MAJOR CITY:
Truro - ½ mile/3 mins

MAJOR AIRPORT:
Exeter - 90 miles/1½ hrs
Newquay - 12 miles/20 mins

RAILWAY STATION:
Truro - 1 mile/5 mins

RESERVATIONS
Direct with hotel

ACCESS CODES
Not applicable

"This beautiful hotel has made our special week in Bath quite perfect"

Joanna Lumley, actress

Bath Spa Hotel

19th century Georgian mansion

Sydney Road,
Bath BA2 6JF

Telephone 01225 444424
Fax 01225 444006

MANAGER
Robin Sheppard

ROOM RATES

7 Singles	£119 - £139
78 Doubles/Twins	£149 - £169
5 Four posters	£219 - £229
8 Suites	£269 - £329

Includes VAT

CHARGE/CREDIT CARDS

• DC • JCB • MC • VI

ACCOLADES
E.T.B. ♛♛♛♛♛ *De Luxe*
R.A.C. ★★★★★
A.A. ★★★★★ ❀❀ *66%*
Caterer & Hotelkeeper Hotel of the Year 1994

FACILITIES
Garden, croquet, tennis, sauna, indoor swimming pool, creche, valet and chauffeur service, jacuzzi, gym, health and beauty
7 meeting rooms/max 120 people
Golf and riding nearby

RESTRICTIONS
None

ATTRACTIONS
Roman Baths, Museum of Costume, Georgian crescents, antique markets, Bath, Longleat, American Museum

AFFILIATIONS
Forte Grand Meridien
Leading Hotels of the World

NEAREST
MAJOR CITY:
Bath

MAJOR AIRPORT:
London Heathrow - 90 miles/2 hrs

RAILWAY STATION:
Bath - 1 mile/5 mins

RESERVATIONS
Toll free in US/Canada: 800-578-7878

ACCESS CODES
SABRE FE 21430
APOLLO FE 5645
WORLDSPAN FE 0026
AMADEUS/SYSTEM 1 FE BRS026

Georgian style and splendour in the 20th century

An immaculately restored 19th century mansion, the Bath Spa is a handsome hotel set amidst seven acres of tranquil gardens. Panoramic views of the formal gardens, ponds and gentle fountains surround you.

In the Colonnade, distinctive murals and exotic palms create an informal and relaxing alfresco atmosphere.

The Vellore Restaurant contains the heart of the house, centre stage to a stunning menu of contemporary, yet highly individual dishes. Lovers of fine food and wine will enjoy accomplished meals punctuated by fastidious service and epicurean skill.

There are 98 bedrooms including eight majestic suites. The hotel offers the full modern amenities you would expect of an RAC five star Hotel of the Year, while still retaining the character of a homely country house.

You will receive complimentary membership of The Laurels Health and Leisure Spa for the duration of your stay. Qualified staff are on hand to arrange exercise programmes, relaxing massages and pampering beauty treatments. There is a swimming pool and a jacuzzi to help soothe the nerves, while a tennis court for the energetic and a croquet lawn for the dastardly are available in the grounds. Quality golf is a mere three iron drive away at Sham Castle and the best club rugby in the country is but a five minute walk. There are seven meeting rooms providing capacious surroundings for up to 120 delegates.

LOCATION

The hotel is on Sydney Road, a mere 10 minutes stroll from the centre of Bath.

"I really can't find words to express our delight at our three day stay with you in your exquisite hotel"

Mr & Mrs F A Collins, Broadstone

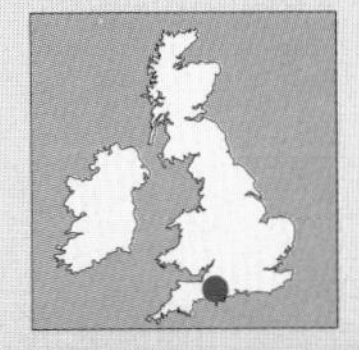

Georgian town house

BEECHLEAS

Quality comforts with the atmosphere of yesteryear in Thomas Hardy country

Beechleas is a delightful Georgian Grade II listed town house hotel, situated five minutes' walk from the centre of Wimborne Minster. This historic market town has an interesting twin-towered church, built on the site of its old Saxon Abbey during the 12th and 13th century.

Beechleas offers the traditional welcome of a good family hotel. The Coach House features cosy beamed rooms with all the atmosphere of yesteryear but with the added comforts of today.

The charming restaurant, overlooking a pretty walled garden, features genuine English cooking, with some French influence. The restaurant has been awarded two prestigious Red Rosettes. Welcoming log fires during the chillier months enhance a warm and friendly ambience as does the conservatory in spring and summer.

Beechleas is perfectly situated for visiting the beautiful Thomas Hardy countryside. The hotel exclusively offers Thomas Hardy tours by Range Rover arranged with a local guide. National Trust properties within easy reach include Kingston Lacey House, Corfe Castle and the Iron Age defensive earthworks of Badbury Rings. Walking, riding, fishing and golf are close by. Sailing can range from nearby coastal coves such as Lulworth, to further trips as far as the Needles. Sandy beaches, shopping at Poole and Bournemouth, the New Forest and Purbeck Hills are all within 20 minutes' drive.

LOCATION

From London, follow signs to Wimborne along A31. From the large roundabout proceed along Wimborne Road West B3073, which becomes Leigh Road after 2 miles. At next roundabout turn left (sign-posted to Poole A349). Beechleas is on your right hand side.

17 Poole Road,
Wimborne Minster,
Dorset BH21 1QA

Telephone 01202 841684
Fax 01202 849344

PROPRIETOR

Josephine McQuillan

ROOM RATES

Single occupancy £61.50 - £81.50
9 Doubles/Twins £80 - £100
Includes newspaper, early morning tea, breakfast and VAT

CHARGE/CREDIT CARDS

• *DC* • *MC*

ACCOLADES

R.A.C. ★★ + Merit Awards H C & R
A.A. ★★ ❀❀
The Good Hotel Guide

FACILITIES

Garden
1 meeting room/max 12 people
Fishing, walking and riding nearby

RESTRICTIONS

No facilities for disabled guests
Pets by discretion on application

ATTRACTIONS

Kingston Lacey House, Purbecks, New Forest, Poole Harbour, Brownsea Island, Wimborne Minster

AFFILIATIONS

Independent

NEAREST

MAJOR CITY:
Winchester - 42 miles/45 mins

MAJOR AIRPORT:
London Gatwick -109 miles/2 hrs 10 mins

RAILWAY STATION:
Poole - 6 miles/10 mins

RESERVATIONS

Direct with hotel

ACCESS CODES

Not applicable

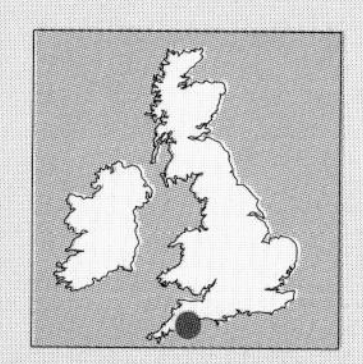

“ The welcome, warmth and attentiveness of your staff was unparalleled . . . the views and the beauty of its location exceptional ”

Senior Supt P Burbidge-King, Hong Kong

BOLT HEAD

Private hotel

South Sands, Salcombe,
Devon TQ8 8LL

Telephone 01548 843751
Fax 01548 843060

PROPRIETOR
Colin D Smith

MANAGER
Alan Messeder

ROOM RATES

3 Singles	£62 - £82
22 Doubles	£124 - £164
1 Family Suite	£169 - £294
1 Superior Double	£144 - £184

Includes full breakfast, dinner and VAT

CHARGE/CREDIT CARDS

• DC • MC • VI

ACCOLADES
E.T.B. ♛♛♛♛ Commended
R.A.C. ★★★ + Merit Award H
A.A. ★★★ ❀ 74%

FACILITIES
Heated outdoor pool, gardens
Golf, riding, fishing and beach nearby

RESTRICTIONS
No facilities for disabled guests
Pets at discretion of management

ATTRACTIONS
Overbecks Gardens,
Plymouth Hoe,
Dartmoor National Park,
Castle Drogo

AFFILIATIONS
Best Western

NEAREST
MAJOR CITY:
Plymouth - 20 miles/45 mins

MAJOR AIRPORT:
London Heathrow - 210 miles/3½ hrs
Plymouth - 20 miles/45 mins

RAILWAY STATION:
Totnes - 25 miles/45 mins

RESERVATIONS
Direct with hotel

ACCESS CODES
Not applicable

Panoramic sea views overlooking Britain's maritime heritage

The Bolt Head Hotel is magnificently situated with panoramic views over Salcombe Estuary, the sea and surrounding coastline. The Hotel adjoins National Trust property incorporating Overbecks Gardens & Museum and miles of unspoilt coastal paths for breathtaking walks.

The 28 bedrooms are all en suite with hair-dryer, remote control colour television with satellite, radio, telephone and tea and coffee-making facilities. There are superior rooms and also family suites with facilities for baby-listening. Most rooms have sea views.

You can relax in the bar, lounge, on the sun terrace or in the restaurant and enjoy the view whilst sipping an aperitif before sampling some of chef's fine food and good wine from the extensive cellar.

The hotel has an outdoor heated swimming pool, surrounded by palm trees, with loungers for sunbathing. There is a games room with table tennis and a pool table. The safe sandy beach at South Sands is just below the hotel. The hotel is less than one hour's drive from Plymouth where the Pilgrim Fathers made their historic voyage to America and from where Sir Francis Drake sailed to defeat the Spanish Armada. There are four good golf courses within 40 minutes drive. Horse riding, sailing, wind-surfing and fishing can all be arranged and the hotel has its own moorings.

The hotel is closed from mid-November until March.

LOCATION

7 miles from Kingsbridge on the western side of the Salcombe Estuary. Take the A38 then A381 to Totnes/Kingsbridge/Salcombe.

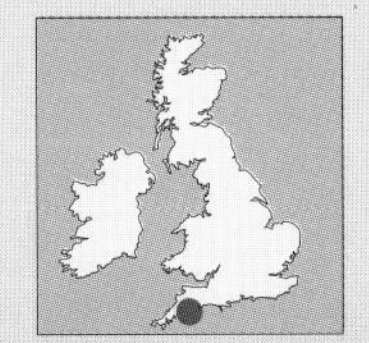

"We felt like guests of considerate, discriminating and charming friends – we wish we had had the foresight to have stayed longer – a wonderful place"

Professor Clayton, Massachusetts

18th century manor house

BOSCUNDLE MANOR

Cornish magic and Mary's culinary flair

Come and experience the magic of Cornwall at Boscundle Manor, a beautiful small 18th century manor house set in ten acres of secluded grounds.

All the rooms are attractively furnished with antiques, pictures and family possessions. The bedrooms are extremely comfortable, the double rooms having spa baths and showers. The grounds include two practice golf holes (for guests' use only), over a mile of pathways and the remains of the main Engine House and chimney of the Wheal Eliza tin mine.

Andrew and Mary Flint bought the property on the first day they saw it and have now been here for over 17 years. Mary is the chef and aims to provide her guests with fresh local food, cooked with loving care and served as imaginatively as possible. There is an extensive wine list of over 150 wines which is particularly strong on clarets.

Although the Flints do not attempt to provide a formal hotel service, their personal involvement and enthusiasm create a relaxed and happy atmosphere. The fact that many of their guests return time and time again speaks for itself. They are always delighted to help guests make the best use of their time in Cornwall and to discover some of its unique magic.

LOCATION

2 miles east of St Austell off the A390 on road signposted to Tregrehan.

Tregrehan, St Austell,
Cornwall PL25 3RL

Telephone 01726 813557
Fax 01726 814997

PROPRIETORS
Andrew and Mary Flint

ROOM RATES

2 Singles	£50 - £65
5 Doubles	£80 - £110
3 Suites	£110 - £140

Includes full breakfast and VAT

CHARGE/CREDIT CARDS

• MC • VI

ACCOLADES
E.T.B. ♛♛♛♛ Highly Commended
R.A.C. ★★ + Merit Awards H C & R
A.A. ★★ ❀ 78%
The Good Hotel Guide

FACILITIES
Outdoor swimming pool, croquet and gardens, snooker, golf, gym, heli-pad
Golf, riding and tennis nearby

RESTRICTIONS
No facilities for disabled guests

ATTRACTIONS
Coastal walks, Lanhydrock Gardens, Fowey, Charlestown and Mevagissey Villages, St Mawes and Restormel Castles

AFFILIATIONS
Independent

NEAREST
MAJOR CITY:
Truro - 14 miles/30 mins

MAJOR AIRPORT:
London Heathrow - 280 miles/4 hrs
Newquay - 19 miles/40 mins

RAILWAY STATION:
St Austell - 2 miles/5 mins

RESERVATIONS
Toll free in US/Canada: 800-544-9993

ACCESS CODES
Not applicable

"We will never return to England without visiting Buckland-Tout-Saints"

Franco Ghezzi, California

BUCKLAND-TOUT-SAINTS

300-year old mansion

Goveton, Kingsbridge, Devon TQ7 2DS

Telephone 01548 853055
Fax 01548 856261

PROPRIETORS

John and Tove Taylor

ROOM RATES

1 Single	£60 - £75
5 Doubles/Twins	£120 - £150
5 Superior Doubles	£140 - £170
3 Suites	£160 - £190

Includes early morning tea, full breakfast, dinner and VAT

CHARGE/CREDIT CARDS

• DC • MC • VI

ACCOLADES

R.A.C. ★★★ + Merit Awards H C & R
A.A. ★★★ ❀❀ 77%
The Good Hotel Guide

FACILITIES

Gardens, croquet, putting green, heli-pad
2 meeting rooms/max 30 people
Golf, riding and fishing nearby

RESTRICTIONS

No facilities for disabled guests

ATTRACTIONS

Dartmouth, Dartmouth Golf & Country Club, Dartmoor, Exeter, Plymouth, Mayflower Sailing

AFFILIATIONS

The Celebrated Hotels Collection

NEAREST

MAJOR CITY:
Plymouth - 20 miles/45 mins

MAJOR AIRPORT:
London Heathrow - 220 miles/3½ hrs
Exeter - 40 miles/1 hr 10 mins

RAILWAY STATION:
Totnes - 12 miles/25 mins

RESERVATIONS

Toll free in US: 800-322-2403

ACCESS CODES

Not applicable

You'll appreciate how little has changed and how much for the better

1990 was the tri-centenary of the restoration of Buckland-Tout-Saints. William and Mary were then on the throne of England. Even in 1690, the estate had been in existence 600 years before this manor house was restored by Sir John Southcote.

Now, situated in its lovely gardens in the heart of the South Devon countryside, Buckland-Tout-Saints offers you a tradition that has grown out of the lavish country house entertaining of bygone days, when the owner of a country estate would invite his guests down to be wined and dined and waited upon. Today, that feeling of being a privileged guest in a private house, in an atmosphere that is elegant yet informal, is something Buckland-Tout-Saints tries hard to preserve for you.

The Taylors take special pride in their chefs whose culinary skills produce imaginative dishes, using only the best of local Devon produce. The hotel's cellars provide the finest wines to complement the food.

The hotel offers many country house pursuits, including a croquet lawn and putting green. Golf and swimming can be arranged at the Dartmouth Golf and Country Club. Buckland is conveniently located for Plymouth and Exeter; the many joys of South Devon and Dartmoor are very near.

LOCATION

Take A381 to Kingsbridge. Situated 2 miles north of Kingsbridge. After Halwell and The Mounts, turn left at hotel sign.

" Gosh, they really have got it all just right, haven't they? "

Paddy Burt, The Daily Telegraph

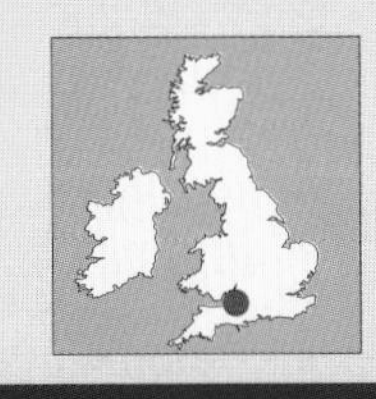

THE CARPENTERS ARMS

In the tradition of a country inn, enjoy good food, real ales and fine company

This charming inn lies in the hamlet of Stanton Wick on the edge of the Mendip Hills and overlooks the Chew Valley. The Carpenters Arms is a unique combination of a traditional English pub, superb food and twelve delightful bedrooms, all with their own bathrooms.

Ideally situated for touring Bath, Bristol and Wells, The Carpenters Arms offers a relaxing environment for those seeking the peace of the countryside. The business executive, keen to escape the tedium of large impersonal hotels, will also find a haven of rest and relaxation.

Good food, real ales and fine wines make The Carpenters Arms a very popular venue. Guests have a choice of two dining rooms and, from the menu in the restaurant, you can choose from a varied and interesting selection of freshly prepared dishes in a warm and inviting atmosphere. If you wish to enjoy the 'olde world' atmosphere on a less expensive scale, dine in the Coopers Parlour where the quality of fayre is just as high and the manner less formal.

The nearby theatres, the antique shops, the museums, the cathedrals and the stately homes make The Carpenters Arms the perfect location for touring.

LOCATION

In the beautiful Chew Valley countryside, close to Bath. Turn off the A37 Wells to Bristol road at Pensford. Alternatively turn off the A368 Bath to Weston-super-Mare road.

Stanton Wick, Nr Pensford, Somerset BS18 4BX

Telephone 01761 490202
Fax 01761 490763

PROPRIETORS

Nigel Pushman and Michael Ruthven

ROOM RATES

Single occupancy £49.50
12 Doubles/Twins £65.50
Includes full breakfast, morning newspaper and VAT

CHARGE/CREDIT CARDS

• DC • MC • VI

ACCOLADES

R.A.C. ★★★

FACILITIES

Outdoor patio
2 meeting rooms/max 40 people
Golf, riding, fishing, hot air ballooning and clay pigeon shooting nearby

RESTRICTIONS

No facilities for disabled guests
No pets

ATTRACTIONS

Bath, Bristol, Longleat, Cheddar Gorge, Wookey Hole, Wells, Glastonbury

AFFILIATIONS

Independent

NEAREST

MAJOR CITY:
Bristol- 7 miles/20 mins

MAJOR AIRPORT:
London Heathrow - 120 miles/2 hrs
Bristol - 5 miles/10 mins

RAILWAY STATION:
Bristol Temple Meads - 7 miles/20 mins

RESERVATIONS

Direct with hotel

ACCESS CODES

Not applicable

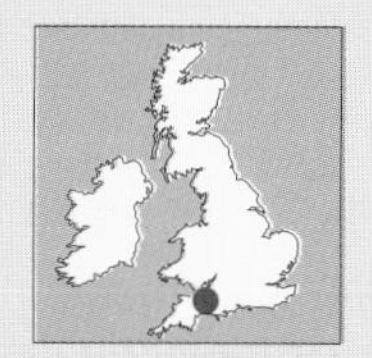

"You are so fortunate to have Cedar Falls so near, look how far I have to travel to enjoy the facilities, but it's a must for me before a tour"

Guy Mitchell, Las Vegas

CEDAR FALLS HEALTH FARM

18th century manor

Bishops Lydeard,
Taunton,
Somerset TA4 3HR

Telephone 01823 433233
Fax 01823 433338

PROPRIETOR
Mr R Smith

RATES PER PERSON

11 Singles	*£89 - £135*
22 Doubles	*£79 - £125*
1 Suite	*£135*
1 Double Suite	*£125*

Includes continental breakfast, lunch, dinner, complimentary treatments, and VAT on minimum of two night's stay

CHARGE/CREDIT CARDS

• MC • VI

ACCOLADES
Premier Health Farm established since 1982

FACILITIES
18 hole golf course, tennis, indoor/outdoor pools, fishing, cycling, exercise classes, gymnasium, over 50 beauty treatments, Reflexology, Aromatherapy Hypnotherapy, Reiki, Kinesiology
44 acres of gardens and grounds

RESTRICTIONS
No children under 16 years
No pets

ATTRACTIONS
Willow and Wetlands Centre, West Steam Railway, Dunster Castle, Combe Sydenham Country Park

AFFILIATIONS
Independent

NEAREST
MAJOR CITY:
Bristol - 44 miles /1 hr
Exeter - 40 miles/1 hr

MAJOR AIRPORT:
London Heathrow - 150 miles/2 ½ hrs

RAILWAY STATION:
Taunton - 5 miles/15 mins

RESERVATIONS
Direct with hotel

ACCESS CODES
Not applicable

Beneficial, therapeutic and healthy – relaxing in The Quantocks

At Cedar Falls Health Farm you choose to do as much or as little as you want. The 18th century Manor set in 44 acres of woodlands was once a favourite weekend venue of Sir Winston Churchill and Lord Baden Powell. The 18 hole golf course, trim and cycle tracks, fishing, whirlpool, indoor and outdoor swimming pools, give the visitor plenty to do while enjoying the tranquillity of the surroundings. At the end of the day, relax in the panelled Red Dining Room and enjoy a healthy nutritious three course meal.

In addition to the more traditional beauty treatments of facial, manicure, pedicure, body wrap, waxing, make-up, and electrolysis to name a few, Cedar Falls gives you the opportunity to step back and assess your hectic lifestyle, and consider ways to change it to benefit your whole body and mind.

Your programme begins with a choice of a complimentary full body massage or half hour facial for each night's stay. Cedar Falls offers Slendertone, Lonithermie and Frigi Thalgo slimming treatments and advice from their dietician.

In the Natural Therapy Clinic they offer, Kinesiology, Aromatherapy, Reflexology, Hypnotherapy, Reiki, Iridology, Holistic massage, Sports Therapy and Manual Lymphatic Drainage.

Most evenings there are talks and demonstrations on matters relating to health and beauty – the most popular being those on stress management and natural therapy treatments.

LOCATION

From London and south Wales take M4/M5. Leave M5 at Junction 25. Follow signs for Minehead (A358). Pass right turn for Bishops Lydeard, ½ mile on turn right into Cedar Falls.

" One of the finest hotels in England "

Dr T Hunt, Canada

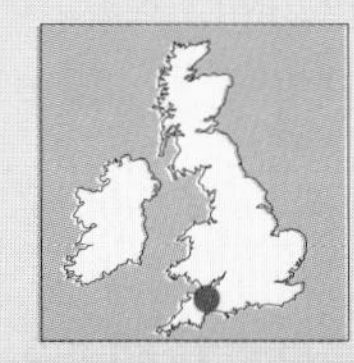

Jacobean style manor house

CHEDINGTON COURT

A tranquil ambience with a relaxing air of informality

This Jacobean style manor house is a traditional country house hotel nestling under a leafy ridge 600 feet up and enjoying one of the most impressive views in southern England. The ten-acre garden which contains a massive sculptured yew hedge, a 1,000-year old yew tree, pools, a grotto and water garden, terraces and balustrades, combines a subtle blend of the well-tended and the wild.

The welcoming interior with fine Persian rugs, antiques and stone fireplaces, creates an atmosphere of comfortable, yet distinctive, informality and relaxation. The well-furnished and spacious bedrooms, with books and attractive fabrics, have wonderful views over the gardens and beyond. The style of cooking is English and French; the menu changes daily and caters for vegetarians. The acclaimed wine list shows over 500 wines from around the world including many half bottles and many at modest prices.

The nine-hole (soon to be extended to 18 holes) par 74 golf course is on 90 acres of beautiful parkland skilfully using the natural features of the rolling countryside and offering interesting and challenging golf to players of all abilities. The surrounding wooded hills provide a sensational backdrop of changing colours throughout the year. There is also a pitch and putt course and a large practice area.

LOCATION

The hotel is ¼ mile off the A356 at Winyard's Gap, 4½ miles south east of Crewkerne.

Chedington, Beaminster, Dorset DT8 3HY

Telephone 01935 891265
Fax 01935 891442

PROPRIETORS

Hilary and Philip Chapman

ROOM RATES

Single occupancy £57 - £77
10 Doubles £94 - £134
Includes full breakfast and VAT

CHARGE/CREDIT CARDS

• *JCB* • *MC* • *VI*

ACCOLADES

E.T.B. ♛♛♛♛ Highly Commended
The Good Hotel Guide

FACILITIES

Croquet, gardens, snooker, jacuzzi, golf, heli-pad, vegetarian dishes available
1 meeting room/max 20 people
Riding, tennis and swimming nearby

RESTRICTIONS

No facilities for disabled guests

ATTRACTIONS

Montacute House, Forde Abbey
Abbotsbury Swannery and sub-tropical gardens,
Dorset coastal path,
Yeovilton Air Museum

AFFILIATIONS

Romantik Hotels & Restaurants

NEAREST

MAJOR CITY:
Yeovil - 11 miles/25 mins

MAJOR AIRPORT:
London Heathrow - 110 miles/2¼ hrs
Exeter - 35 miles/45 mins

RAILWAY STATION:
Crewkerne - 4 miles/10 mins

RESERVATIONS

Direct with hotel

ACCESS CODES

AMADEUS SYSTEM 1 RM CHE
APOLLO RO CHEDINGTON
SABRE RM 37221
WORLDSPAN RM CHEDI
SAHARA RO 43493

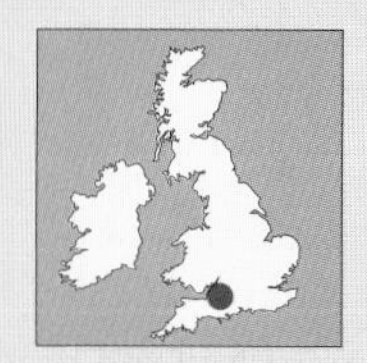

"The most delightful situation in the vicinity of Bath"

John Wesley, 1781

COMBE GROVE MANOR

Country house hotel & spa

**Brassknocker Hill,
Monkton Combe, Bath,
Avon BA2 7HS**

**Telephone 01225 834644
Fax 01225 834961**

GENERAL MANAGER

Antonio Parrilla

ROOM RATES

Single occupancy £98
37 Doubles £98 - £175
2 Four-posters £185 - £225
2 Suites £195
Includes contintental breakfast, use of spa and leisure facilities and VAT

CHARGE/CREDIT CARDS

• DC • MC • VI

ACCOLADES

E.T.B. ♛♛♛♛♛ Highly Commended
R.A.C. ★★★★ + Merit Award C
A.A.★★★★ ❀❀ 68%

FACILITIES

Garden, indoor/outdoor tennis, croquet, indoor/outdoor pool, sauna, jacuzzi, gym, health & beauty, children's menus and creche, courtesy limousine, heli-pad
3 meeting rooms/max 100 people
Golf, riding, fishing and shooting nearby

RESTRICTIONS

No pets
No facilities for disabled guests

ATTRACTIONS

The Cotswolds, Stonehenge, Bath, Wells, Longleat

AFFILIATIONS

Independent

NEAREST

MAJOR CITY:
Bath - 2 miles/5 mins

MAJOR AIRPORT:
London Heathrow - 100 miles/2 hrs

RAILWAY STATION:
Bath Spa - 2 miles/5 mins

RESERVATIONS

Toll free fax in US: 800-945-8470

ACCESS CODES

Not applicable

Something for everyone on the very edge of Bath

Combe Grove Manor is an historical manor house nearly 300 years old whose fir groves were noted by John Wesley. Today, it offers all the services you would expect from a luxury country house hotel.

It is conveniently situated just two miles from Bath in the heart of the West Country. A visit should include a tour of the Roman Baths built by the Romans nearly 2,000 years ago. Also within easy reach are Salisbury, Stonehenge, the Cotswolds and many stately homes.

Combe Grove Manor is set in 82 acres of landscaped gardens and woodlands and enjoys spectacular panoramic views. It has been sympathetically refurbished featuring antiques and traditional fabrics. The rooms in the manor house have all been individually designed and furnished, including two four-poster rooms and two suites with jacuzzi baths. There are 31 additional rooms in the newly built Swiss chalet-style Garden Lodge, many of which have their own private terrace.

Guests have unlimited access to unrivalled spa facilities including indoor and outdoor swimming pools, tennis courts (2 indoor), gymnasium, aerobics studio, hydro spa, steam room, sauna, solaria, a practice golf course and an 18 station driving range. There are also beauty salons where a full range of treatments are available, featuring Clarins products.

LOCATION

Two miles south of the city of Bath. For detailed directions guests are advised to contact hotel reception.

"Everyone should have this lovely experience at least once in their life"

Mel & Lois Kerner, USA

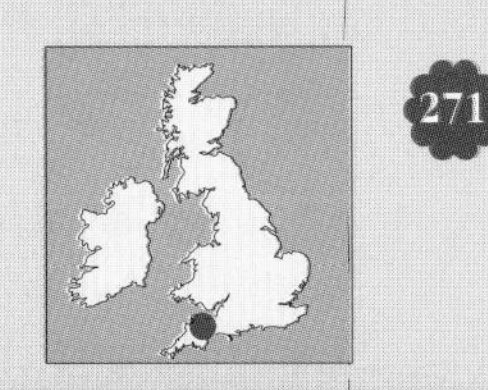

17th century hunting lodge

COMBE PARK

Scrumptious home cooking among the wildlife of North Devon

Owners Shirley and David Barnes and John Walley, and their staff, would be delighted to welcome you to Combe Park Hotel. The house dates back to the 17th century and is now a small family-run hotel set in a picturesque National Trust valley. The Hoar Oak Water fronts the house, and the brown trout in the river keep the herons happy!

The nine bedrooms occupy the first and second floors. All are individual and have private facilities. They all look out on to natural scenery: over the river to the Oak Wood, over the terraced garden to the valley, or down the drive to where a small herd of deer gathers at the start and end of each day.

The cuisine of Shirley Barnes has won AA Red Rosette awards for four consecutive years. The secret is fresh food cooked from the oven to the plate, featuring starters that include home-made soups right through to hard-to-resist puddings such as jam roly poly, bread and butter pudding and a more discreet exotic fruit salad.

Apart from the food, the allure of Combe Park is its ideal setting for a walking holiday. Bird watchers can bring binoculars to see a buzzard wheeling away in the sky, and fly-catchers, tree-creepers and perhaps even a lesser spotted woodpecker. There are stables nearby for the best way to see Exmoor (on horseback, like Carver Doone). You can fish for salmon or trout on the East Lyn, within easy walking distance. The area is known as the little Switzerland of England, and remains an unspoilt retreat of old England.

LOCATION

M5 Junction 25 (Taunton) follow A358, then A39 to Lynmouth via Minehead and Porlock.

Hillsford Bridges,
Lynton,
Devon EX35 6LE

Telephone 01598 752356

PROPRIETORS

Shirley and David Barnes
John Walley

ROOM RATES

9 Doubles/Twins £85 - £92
Includes dinner, full breakfast and VAT

CHARGE/CREDIT CARDS

Cash or cheque only

ACCOLADES

A.A. ★ ❀ 74%

FACILITIES

Garden
Fishing, birdwatching, walking, riding and beaches nearby

RESTRICTIONS

No children under 12 years
No facilities for disabled guests

ATTRACTIONS

Exmoor National Park,
Arlington Court,
Lynton Cliff railway,
Cleeve Abbey

AFFILIATIONS

Independent

NEAREST

MAJOR CITY:
Exeter - 56 miles/1½ hrs

MAJOR AIRPORT:
London Heathrow - 190 miles/3½ hrs
Bristol - 72 miles/1¼ hrs

RAILWAY STATION:
Taunton - 44 miles/1 hr 5 mins

RESERVATIONS

Direct with hotel

ACCESS CODES

Not applicable

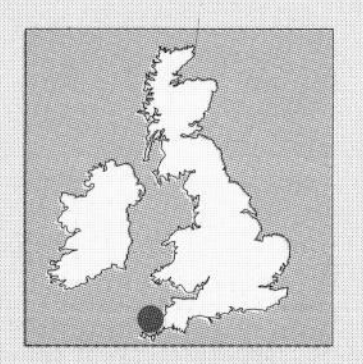

"What a lovely peaceful place!"

Lulu, London

COURT BARN

Victorian country house

Clawton, Holsworthy,
Devon EX22 6PS

Telephone 01409 271219
Fax 01409 271309

PROPRIETOR

Robert and Susan Wood

ROOM RATES

1 Single	£30 - £45
6 Doubles/Twins	£55 - £75
1 Four-poster	£70 - £80

Includes full breakfast and VAT

CHARGE/CREDIT CARDS

• DC • JCB • MC • VI

ACCOLADES

E.T.B. ♛♛♛♛ Highly Commended
R.A.C. ★★ + Merit Award R
A.A. ★★ ❀ 72%

FACILITIES

Garden, croquet, badminton, lawn tennis, putting green
Golf, riding, fishing, sailing and indoor pool nearby

RESTRICTIONS

No facilities for disabled guests

ATTRACTIONS

Boscastle, Clovelly, Tintagel, Roadford and Tamar Lakes, Bodmin Moor, Heritage coast, Exmoor and Dartmoor National Parks, RHS Rosemoor and Devon Gardens

AFFILIATIONS

Independent

NEAREST

MAJOR CITY:
Exeter - 35 miles/50 mins

MAJOR AIRPORT:
London Heathrow - 210 miles/3½ hrs
Exeter - 35 miles/50 mins

RAILWAY STATION
Exeter - 35 miles/50 mins

RESERVATIONS

Direct with hotel

ACCESS CODES

Not applicable

For ardent lovers of the unexplored

Built as the 'Sanctuary' around the 16th century, and later known as 'Court Baron', the present house was partly rebuilt in 1853, renamed 'Court Barn', and had its own chapel. It is a small, but delightful country house, set in five acres of park-like grounds with an aura of peace and quietude.

There are eight en suite bedrooms, two lounges, two dining rooms and a bar. Court Barn is known for its warm welcome and personal service.

A crackling log fire in at least one of the lounges all year round creates the perfect setting in which to relax and enjoy good food and pleasant company.

The elegant breakfast room has views across the croquet lawn to the 12th century Clawton church. The restaurant is furnished with antiques, and is perfect for enjoying the fresh, quality food prepared each day to create their delicious five-course dinners. They are justifiably proud of the many national awards (1989 to 1995) for their wine list of 375 wines, the Tea Council awards for their teas and the AA Rosette.

Lovers of unspoilt countryside, safe, Blue Flag beaches, nature trails, cycle trails, National Trust and National parks will enjoy this unexplored part of Devon and Cornwall.

Court Barn helps you to unwind from stress and appreciate the old-fashioned values of quality, comfort and hospitality at prices you remember years ago!

LOCATION

2½ miles south of Holsworthy off A388, turn towards North Tamerton for ½ mile. Hotel is next to 12th century Clawton Church.

"It is extremely rare to have the pleasure of eating and relishing such superb food"

Hugo Jeune, Lynmouth

Coaching inn

THE CROWN HOTEL

Lovingly restored to its former glory and beyond

In years gone by, the Crown Hotel was probably the most famous hotel on Exmoor. One of the original coaching inns, it catered in great comfort for travellers from all walks of life and all countries around the globe.

Situated in the middle of Exford, one of the prettiest villages on the moor and known as the capital of Exmoor, the Crown is very much the centre of village life and holds many fond memories for the older residents.

The Crown has now been completely refurbished to its former glory and been brought sympathetically into the 20th century. Comfortable lounges and bedrooms are complemented by a restful and luxurious dining room where Simon Whitley, the Head Chef, serves some of the most wonderfully exciting food on Exmoor.

The hotel still maintains its original stable yard which guests may use when bringing their horses to Exmoor. As well as riding pursuits, all manner of country sports, including game shooting and clay pigeon shooting, can be arranged by the hotel.

LOCATION

Take Junction 25 on M5 and follow signs for Taunton. Take the A358 out of Taunton, then the B3224 via Wheddon Cross into Exford.

Exmoor National Park, Exford, Somerset TA24 7PP

Telephone 0164 3831554
Fax 0164 3831665

OWNER

Michael Bradley and John Atkin

ROOM RATES

3 Singles	*£36 - £40*
14 Doubles/Twins	*£72 - £90*

Includes full breakfast and VAT

CHARGE/CREDIT CARDS

• MC • VI

ACCOLADES

R.A.C. ★★★

A.A. ★★★ ❀❀ *71%*

FACILITIES

Garden, stables
Riding, fishing, game shooting and clay pigeon shooting nearby

RESTRICTIONS

No facilities for disabled guests
No dogs allowed in public rooms

ATTRACTIONS

Tarr Steps ancient clapper bridge,
Lorna Doone Valley,
Dunster Castle,
Valley of the Rocks

AFFILIATIONS

Independent

NEAREST

MAJOR CITY:
Taunton - 25 miles/45 mins

MAJOR AIRPORT:
London Heathrow - 163 miles/2¾ hrs
Bristol - 63 miles/1½ hrs

RAILWAY STATION:
Taunton - 25 miles/45 mins

RESERVATIONS

Direct with hotel

ACCESS CODES

Not applicable

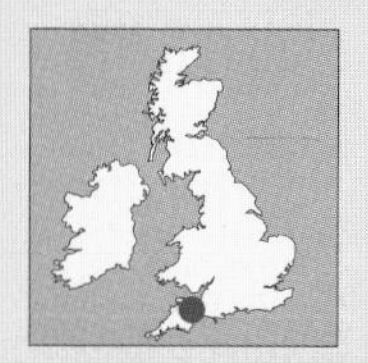

"Downrew House makes a marvellous base from which to tour, but be warned: you may be tempted never to leave the house and grounds"

R M Beckett, Chicago

DOWNREW HOUSE HOTEL

Queen Anne house

Bishops Tawton, Barnstaple, Devon EX32 0DY

Telephone 01271 42497
Fax 01271 23947

OWNER
Clifford Johnson

ROOM RATES

Single occupancy	£54 - £68
11 Doubles	£92 - £120
1 Suite	£104 - £130

Includes full breakfast, dinner and VAT

CHARGE/CREDIT CARDS

• MC • VI

ACCOLADES
E.T.B. ♛♛♛♛
R.A.C. ★★

FACILITIES
Outdoor pool, croquet, tennis, gardens, small golf course, snooker
1 meeting room/max 40 people
Riding and fishing nearby

RESTRICTIONS
None

ATTRACTIONS
Rosemoor Gardens (Royal Horticultural Society), Arlington Court, Lynton/Lynmouth

AFFILIATIONS
Independent

NEAREST
MAJOR CITY:
Exeter - 40 miles/50 mins

MAJOR AIRPORT:
Bristol - 85 miles/1½ hrs
Exeter - 45 miles/1 hr

RAILWAY STATION:
Barnstaple - local

RESERVATIONS
Direct with hotel

ACCESS CODES
Not applicable

Care and attention to detail are the hallmarks of this delightful hotel

Downrew is a small Queen Anne country house hotel three miles south of Barnstaple, situated on the slopes of the Codden Hill. The original buildings date from 1640 and were enlarged in 1705.

It stands in twelve acres of meadowland, well-kept gardens and has its own five-hole golf course. The atmosphere is warm and friendly and the food and service are quite exceptional.

The dining room's magnificent bow window looks over lawns, rose beds and the surrounding countryside. On clear days, Dartmoor, some 35 miles to the south, can be seen. It is an ideal base to explore the whole of North Devon, both its beautiful and rugged coastline and the Exmoor National Park.

Tourist attractions include the Royal Horticultural Society Gardens at Rosemoor, Arlington Court belonging to the National Trust and Dartington Crystal. Clovelly is only 15 miles away and Lynton and Lynmouth some 20 miles.

The resident proprietor and his son have worked at London's Grosvenor House and at The Dorchester respectively. They have now opted for a quieter way of life in North Devon.

You may be sure that you will be made very welcome and well looked after.

LOCATION

Situated 1½ miles off the A377 Barnstaple to Exeter road, signposted Cobberton in the village of Bishops Tawton.

“ We enjoyed the incredibly friendly atmosphere and the personal attention in this elegant establishment ”

Robin & Tom Liston, Los Altos

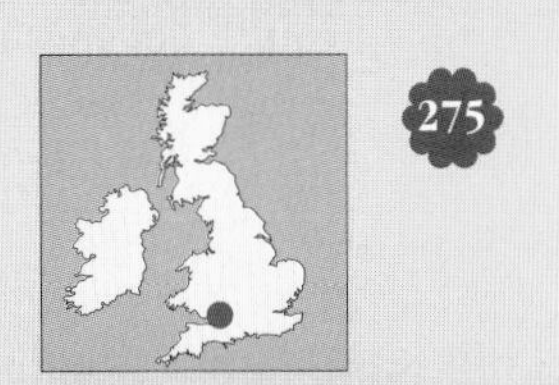

Georgian mansion

EAGLE HOUSE

Church Street, Bathford, Bath, Avon BA1 7RS

Telephone 01225 859946
Fax 01225 859946

PROPRIETORS
John and Rosamund Napier

ROOM RATES

2 Singles	£36 - £45
7 Doubles/Twins	£45 - £70
1 Suite	£75 - £99

Includes continental breakfast and VAT
Free accommodation for children sharing parents' room

CHARGE/CREDIT CARDS

• MC • VI

ACCOLADES
E.T.B. ♛♛ Commended
The Good Hotel Guide

FACILITIES
Croquet, gardens, tennis
1 meeting room/max 40 people
Golf, riding and hot air ballooning nearby

RESTRICTIONS
No facilities for disabled guests

ATTRACTIONS
Bath, The Cotswolds, Longleat House, Stourhead Gardens

AFFILIATIONS
Independent

NEAREST
MAJOR CITY:
London - 100 miles/2 hrs
MAJOR AIRPORT:
London Heathrow - 85 miles/1½ hrs
Bristol - 18 miles/45 mins
RAILWAY STATION:
Bath - 3½ miles/10 mins

RESERVATIONS
Direct with hotel

ACCESS CODES
Not applicable

WEST COUNTRY

Courtesy in mellow surroundings on the outskirts of Bath

Eagle House, a small Georgian mansion, is three miles from Bath in the charming, walled village of Bathford. The house with its lovely garden is elegant and comfortable but not fussy.

The owners, John and Rosamund Napier, have an informal but caring approach. Often people bring their own drink and are sometimes surprised that they are supplied with ice and glasses and encouraged to use the lovely, octagonal drawing-room. Breakfast, the only meal served, starts early and goes on late and special requests are catered for.

The accent is on personal service and John, who trained at the Savoy Hotel in London, his wife and helpers take time to advise guests on the best pubs, restaurants, and beauty spots. Families are very welcome, both in the house and the attractive walled garden cottage.

Bathford is ideal for visiting Bath without being caught up in the bustle of the centre. Eagle House has plentiful parking and the village has an excellent bus service to the city.

Real log fires, home-baked croissants and wonderful wholemeal bread from the village bakery are among ingredients which bring customers back to Eagle House time and time again.

LOCATION

3 miles out of Bath on A4 towards London, turn right on to A363. After 150 yards, fork left up hill for 250 yards. Church Street is the first on right.

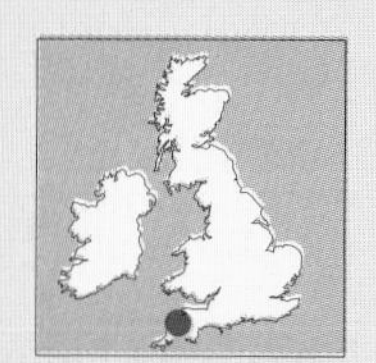

"I often try, and always fail to define the peculiar charm of Easton Court – something more than comfort – a tranquillity which makes it uniquely agreeable for both work and rest"

Evelyn Waugh, author

EASTON COURT HOTEL

Tudor house

Easton Cross, Chagford, Devon TQ13 8JL

Telephone 01647 433469
Fax 01647 433469

PROPRIETORS

Graham and Sally Kidson

ROOM RATES

1 Single	*£51 - £64*
5 Doubles	*£94 - £116*
2 Four-posters	*£110 - £122*

Includes full breakfast, dinner and VAT

CHARGE/CREDIT CARDS

• DC • MC • VI

ACCOLADES

A.A. ★★ ❀ 69%

Ashley Courtenay - Hotel of Distinction

FACILITIES

Walled cottage garden
Golf, riding and fishing nearby

RESTRICTIONS

Children under 12 not accepted
Well behaved dogs welcome

ATTRACTIONS

Castle Drogo,
Finch Foundry,
Teign Gorge,
Becky Falls

AFFILIATIONS

Independent

NEAREST

MAJOR CITY:
Exeter - 18 miles/30 mins

MAJOR AIRPORT:
London Heathrow - 175 miles/3¾ hrs
Exeter - 18 miles/30 mins

RAILWAY STATION:
Exeter - 18 miles/30 mins

RESERVATIONS

Direct with hotel

ACCESS CODES

Not applicable

On the edge of Dartmoor and inspirational in more ways than one!

Easton Court Hotel is a lovely old thatched Tudor house of great charm and character which nestles on the eastern edge of the Dartmoor National Park, a short distance from the picturesque ancient stanary town of Chagford. The oldest part of the hotel dates from around 1450 and great care has been taken to preserve the original structure with its thatched roof, granite walls, oak beams, ancient doorway and great inglenook fireplace. These elements combine to give Easton Court a quite unique atmosphere of peace and tranquillity.

Easton Court has been a haven to many literary personalities over the years and has lent inspiration to the writing of several books, including Evelyn Waugh's 'Brideshead Revisited'.

A short walk from the hotel brings you to the majestic Teign River gorge, down which it is possible to walk past the commanding presence of Castle Drogo to the popular beauty spot of Fingle Bridge.

The hotel has seven comfortable bedrooms all with en suite facilities and all have tea and coffee making units and colour television. In the hotel's intimate candle lit dining room you may enjoy an unhurried five course evening meal prepared by the resident chef and complemented by an extensive wine list.

As a family run hotel, Easton Court seeks to offer a friendly personal service to all its guests. Here the aim is to provide comfort and good food in an atmosphere of peace, relaxation and informality. Special rates are also available for short breaks of two or more nights.

LOCATION

From the A30 Exeter to Okehampton road take the A382 exit at Whiddon Down. Follow signs to Moretonhampstead and the hotel will be found after 3 miles opposite the turning for Chagford village.

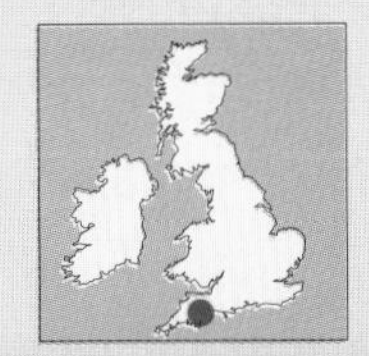

“Thank you for making me feel so welcome. I enjoyed my visit enormously, and you, your family and your staff certainly looked after us tremendously well”

Rt Hon John Major, Prime Minister

Country house

EBFORD HOUSE

The very essence of Devon hospitality and comfort

Set in 1½ acres of mature landscaped gardens, the Ebford House excels in providing elegant comfort, together with the finest modern English creative cuisine.

Each of the 16 en suite bedrooms is individually designed to the highest standards. A well equipped leisure and fitness area is offered, as well as a choice of restaurants and bars. This Devon country house is celebrated for its friendly welcome, caring attention and award winning restaurant.

A short country walk before dinner will take you to the delightful riverside village of Topsham. Nestled next to the River Exe, this ancient and once important river port dates back to the Middle Ages. Today, its importance lies in water sports and recreation with an ever increasing number of visitors being drawn to its quaint little streets and wonderful architecture.

Nearby, Exeter matches the city of York for depth of historical importance, and when staying at Ebford House you are in fact only a seven minute drive from Exeter city centre, with its fabulous cathedral and courtyard, Roman ruins, and the history-rich old quays, together with a wealth of museums and churches.

Devon is famous for its fishing, sailing and bird-watching, and the hotel can arrange your golf and horse-riding.

LOCATION

On the A376 Exmouth road just 2 miles from the M5 Junction 30, 5 miles from the city airport and railway station and 1 mile from Topsham.

Exmouth Road,
Ebford, Exeter,
Devon EX3 0QH

Telephone 01392 877658
Fax 01392 874424

PROPRIETORS

Mr D T and Mrs J M Horton

ROOM RATES

3 Singles £58 - £68
13 Doubles £65 - £90
Includes full breakfast and VAT

CHARGE/CREDIT CARDS

 *• MC • VI*

ACCOLADES

E.T.B. ♛♛♛♛ Commended
A.A. ★★★ ❀❀ 67%

FACILITIES

Gardens, sauna, gym, jacuzzi
2 meeting rooms/max 30 people
Golf, riding, fishing, birdwatching, sailing and walking nearby

RESTRICTIONS

No children allowed
No facilities for disabled guests

ATTRACTIONS

Exeter, Exeter Cathedral, A La Ronde and Bradley Houses, Dartmoor National Park, Bowhill, Plymouth, Killerton

AFFILIATIONS

Logis of Great Britain

NEAREST

MAJOR CITY:
Exeter - 4 miles/10 mins

MAJOR AIRPORT:
London Heathrow - 170 miles/3 hrs
Exeter - 4 miles/10 mins

RAILWAY STATION:
St Davids - 4 miles/12 mins

RESERVATIONS

Direct with hotel

ACCESS CODES

Not applicable

"The setting is beautiful, the food and wine were superb and the service was something that many grander establishments can only dream of"

J Stowers, Devon

FLOYD'S INN

16th century inn

Bow Creek,
Tuckenhay,
Totnes,
Devon TQ9 7EQ

Telephone 01803 732350
Fax 01803 732651

PROPRIETOR
Keith Floyd

GENERAL MANAGER
Mike Atkinson

ROOM RATES

Dart Cabin	*£125*
Khun Akorn Chamber	*£125*
Dukes Suite	*£175*

Includes continental breakfast and VAT

CHARGE/CREDIT CARDS
MC • VI

ACCOLADES
Independent

FACILITIES
Snooker, sauna, sun-bed
Fishing nearby

RESTRICTIONS
No facilities for disabled guests

ATTRACTIONS
Berry Pomeroy Castle,
Totnes Castle,
Dartmouth Castle,
Dartmoor National Park,
Exeter Cathedral

AFFILIATIONS
Independent

NEAREST
MAJOR CITY:
Plymouth - 30 miles/35 mins

MAJOR AIRPORT:
Plymouth - 30 miles/35 mins

RAILWAY STATION:
Totnes - 4 miles/10 mins

RESERVATIONS
Direct with hotel

ACCESS CODES
Not applicable

The world comes for the food. The shrewd stay on for a night or two

Located on the side of the picturesque Bow Creek and surrounded by woodland, Keith Floyd's delightful pub (dating back to 1550) has a relaxed, unconventional feel to it. You should allow time to wend your way gently through the leafy lanes and arrive with time to enjoy this idyllic location.

You can dine in the ever-popular George's restaurant, George being the wine-sipping teddy bear seated at one of the tables suitably attired with bow tie and yellow checked waistcoat. You might try the likes of lobster soufflé with vodka sauce, followed by fillet of roe deer with red cabbage and chestnuts, finishing with delicious roast pears with fig ice cream, or try some of the 'canteen meals' which feature international 'fun' food and specialities from Floyd's far flung travels such as Thai or Italian dishes.

If you don't want to drive home after dinner, stay in one of the three themed bedrooms in Floyd's barn. The Dart Cabin is nautical with anchor and ship's telegraph, the Khun Akorn Chamber (Thai style) has satin sheets, carved wooden screens and draped four-poster bed, while the Dukes Suite boasts sumptuous surroundings and dark antique furniture.

For those wishing to linger longer, as seems to be the pattern here, reduced rates are available for stays of more than one night.

LOCATION

From Torbay take the A381 Dartmouth/ Kingsbridge road. Take turnoff for Tuckenhay. Turn left and follow lane for a couple of miles to crossroads. Turn right down the hill, over Bow Bridge, past Watermans Arms and Floyd's is on the left.

“At last, enchanting England. We've found heaven!”

Max Malden, Calgary

GABRIEL COURT HOTEL

500 years of heritage and a sunny disposition

For nearly 500 years this was the home of the Churchward family, the Squires of Stoke Gabriel.

In 1928 the house was converted into an hotel and since then has earned an excellent reputation for its hospitality and comfort. Appealing essentially to those who like peace and quiet it is, nevertheless, a wonderful base for exploring the many and varied tourist attractions which abound in a 30 miles radius. Dartmoor, the Heritage Coast, National Trust properties, Totnes and Dartmouth, to name but a few.

The hotel overlooks the very pretty village of Stoke Gabriel which stands by the River Dart. Its age has not been exactly chronicled but from records it would appear that there has been a Church in the village since the tenth century.

Set in its own grounds and surrounded by a high stone wall, the hotel faces south and enjoys all available sunshine.

The food is English cooking at its best with Salmon from the Dart, sea fish landed at Brixham and an abundance of game from nearby Estates. Vegetables are often from the hotel's own garden. The table d'hôte menu is changed daily and offers an excellent choice.

The Beacom family look forward to making your acquaintance and will warmly welcome you to Gabriel Court.

LOCATION

Leave A38 at Buckfastleigh. Take A384 to Totnes, then A385 towards Paignton. Turn right towards village at Parker's Arms.

Stoke Gabriel, Near Totnes, Devon TQ9 6SF

Telephone 01803 782206
Fax 01803 782333

PROPRIETOR

Mr O M Beacom

ROOM RATES

2 Singles	*£55*
17 Doubles/Twins	*£79*

Includes full breakfast and VAT

CHARGE/CREDIT CARDS

• *DC* • *MC* • *VI*

ACCOLADES

R.A.C. ★★★ + Merit Award H
A.A. ★★★ 71%
Logis – Three fireplaces

FACILITIES

Garden, croquet, tennis, outdoor pool
1 meeting room/max 20 people
Golf, riding, walking and fishing nearby

RESTRICTIONS

No facilities for disabled guests

ATTRACTIONS

Dartmoor National Park, Totnes, River Dart, Dartmouth and their castles, Coleton Fishacre, South Devon coastline

AFFILIATIONS

Logis of Great Britain

NEAREST

MAJOR CITY:
Plymouth - 28 miles/40 mins

MAJOR AIRPORT:
London Heathrow - 190 miles/3¾ hrs
Exeter - 28 miles/40 mins

RAILWAY STATION:
Totnes - 4 miles/15 mins

RESERVATIONS

Direct with hotel

ACCESS CODES

Not applicable

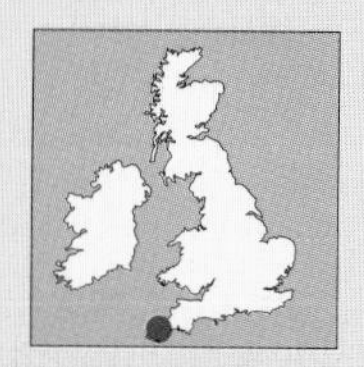

"As usual everything, especially the cuisine, was superb, outshone only by Kilby hospitality"

Joyce & Bob Hinze, USA

THE GARRACK HOTEL

Cornish coastal hotel

Burthallan Lane, St Ives, Cornwall TR26 3AA

Telephone 01736 796199
Fax 01736 798955

PROPRIETORS

The Kilby Family
(John, Frances, Michael, Stephen)

ROOM RATES

Single occupancy	*£58 - £61*
14 Doubles/Twins	*£99 - £102*
2 Four-posters	*£99 - £122*
2 with spa bath	*£116 - £122*

Includes full breakfast and VAT

CHARGE/CREDIT CARDS

• *DC* • *MC* • *VI*

ACCOLADES

E.T.B. ♛♛♛♛ *Commended*
A.A.★★★ ❀ *64%*
The Good Hotel Guide

FACILITIES

Garden, indoor pool, spa, sauna, solarium, gym, all day licensed coffee shop and restaurant
1 meeting room/max 30 people
Golf, riding, walking and fishing nearby

RESTRICTIONS

Dogs by prior arrangement

ATTRACTIONS

Tate Gallery, St. Ives, Newlyn, Orion Gallery, Lands End, St. Michaels Mount, Cornish coastal path

AFFILIATIONS

Relais du Silence (France)
Hospitality Hotels of Cornwall
Logis of Great Britain

NEAREST

MAJOR CITY:
Truro - 25 miles/45 mins

MAJOR AIRPORT:
Exeter - 110 miles/ 2¼ hrs
London Heathrow - 300 miles/6 hrs

RAILWAY STATION:
St Ives - 1 mile/3 mins

RESERVATIONS

Toll free in UK: 0500 011325

ACCESS CODES

Not applicable

The connoisseur's choice for seeing Cornwall and south-west England

Those who live in rural England say to the visitor from overseas "come and see the real England!" Of all the counties, Cornwall is unique, both for its history and its scenery. It is a land of contrasts from its rugged coastline, precipitous cliffs and often angry seas, to lazy wooded creeks, small fishing harbours, sandy coves and beautiful bathing beaches.

Originally a private house known in the Cornish language as Chy-an-Garrack, which translates into English as The House on the Rock, it was the home of Lady Ebury prior to becoming a hotel in 1947. Since then the Kilby family has made many changes: new bedrooms have been added and a small leisure centre with swimming pool, sauna and solarium.

It is now a secluded, vine covered granite building standing in two acres of gardens high above Porthmeor Beach with fabulous views of St Ives Bay and the coastal landscape beyond. Of the 18 en suite bedrooms, some have four-poster beds and some have personal spa baths. The hotel is proud of its reputation for good culinary standards, recognised by an award of a rosette by the AA for the past four years, and for an extensive wine list. The hotel is dedicated to providing comfort in tranquil and beautiful surroundings accompanied by good food, good service and good company where the customers interests are paramount. As a base for visiting the many attractions including the renowned Tate Gallery, St Ives and the Garrack have no equal.

LOCATION

From the A30, take 2nd exit signposted to St Ives. Turn left at 2nd mini-roundabout onto B3311 for 4¼ miles then join B3306 towards St Ives. Turn third left after petrol station and proceed 400 yards where hotel is signposted.

“ Bursting with hospitality ”

Judith Chalmers, “100 Irresistible Weekends”

Edwardian town house

HAYDON HOUSE

Jane Austen wrote about the secrets of Bath . . . here's another

Bath needs little introduction as one of the loveliest cities in the world with so much more to enjoy than simply taking the waters, as in Roman times, or the wider range of secret pleasures available in Jane Austen's day. Nowadays, it holds one more secret . . . a secret you should know – Haydon House.

From the outside, Haydon looks like any other Edwardian house, so typical of the residential streets of Bath. Inside, however, an oasis of tranquillity and elegance awaits you, where high standards of hospitality prevail.

The reception rooms are tastefully furnished with antiques, whilst the five guest bedrooms are decorated to a very high standard. All rooms have private facilities, colour television and direct-dial telephone and a generous hospitality tray offering complimentary home-made shortbread and a decanter of sherry.

Innovative breakfasts are stylishly served and there is a lovely garden in which to relax.

The hosts' aim at Haydon is to make your stay, however short or long, truly happy and memorable by providing a secluded retreat from which you can readily dip into and enjoy all the pleasures of Georgian Bath, yet escape the throng.

LOCATION

In the centre of the Georgian city of Bath.

9 Bloomfield Park, Bath, Avon BA2 2BY

Telephone 01225 444919
Fax 01225 427351

PROPRIETORS

Gordon and Magdalene Ashman-Marr

ROOM RATES

Single occupancy	*£40 - £55*
4 Doubles/Twins	*£55 - £75*
1 Suite	*£65 - £75*

Includes full breakfast and VAT

CHARGE/CREDIT CARDS

• *JCB* • *MC* • *VI*

ACCOLADES

E.T.B. ♛♛ Highly Commended
R.A.C. Highly Acclaimed
A.A. Premier Selected
The Good Hotel Guide

FACILITIES

Sun terrace and gardens
Golf and riding nearby

RESTRICTIONS

No smoking throughout
Children by prior arrangement
No facilities for disabled guests
No pets

ATTRACTIONS

Bath,
Wells Cathedral,
Glastonbury,
Cotswolds, Avebury
Salisbury, Stonehenge

AFFILIATIONS

Independent

NEAREST

MAJOR CITY:
Bath

MAJOR AIRPORT:
London Heathrow - 90 miles/1½ hrs
Bristol - 15 miles/30 mins

RAILWAY STATION:
Bath Spa - 1 mile/5 mins

RESERVATIONS

Direct with hotel

ACCESS CODES

Not applicable

“ A glimpse of paradise at Heddon’s Gate ”

Paddy Burt, The Daily Telegraph

HEDDON’S GATE HOTEL

Country house

**Heddon’s Mouth,
Parracombe, Barnstaple,
Devon EX31 4PZ**

**Telephone 01598 763313
Fax 01598 763363**

PROPRIETOR

Bob Deville

ROOM RATES

1 Single	£27 - £38
9 Doubles/Twins	£50 - £76
1 Four-poster	£50 - £76
3 Suites	£59 - £96

Includes full breakfast, afternoon tea and VAT

CHARGE/CREDIT CARDS

• MC • VI

ACCOLADES

E.T.B. Highly Commended

The Good Hotel Guide

FACILITIES

Gardens

Riding and coastal walks nearby

RESTRICTIONS

No children under 10 years

No smoking in the dining room

No facilities for disabled guests

ATTRACTIONS

Lorna Doone Country, Lynton & Lynmouth, Arlington Court, Exmoor National Park

AFFILIATIONS

Independent

NEAREST

MAJOR CITY:
Exeter - 45 miles/1½ hrs

MAJOR AIRPORT:
London Heathrow - 200 miles/4½ hrs
Bristol - 95 miles/2½ hrs

RAILWAY STATION:
Barnstaple - 16 miles/40 mins

RESERVATIONS

Direct with hotel

ACCESS CODES

Not applicable

An Exmoor hideaway in Lorna Doone country

Exmoor, home of Lorna Doone! An unspoilt land of contrasts, from high rolling moorland to deep valleys with their tumbling streams. Diverse wildlife, too, from buzzards soaring high to the wild Red Deer. Exmoor, with its dramatic coastal scenery, is the most beautiful of the English National Parks.

Heddon’s Gate Hotel has stunning views of the western hills of Exmoor. Sitting high above the valley which runs down to the sea half a mile away at Heddon’s Mouth, it is three miles from the nearest village of Parracombe.

This Edwardian house has been run as an hotel for over 25 years by proprietor/cook Bob Deville who has created an atmosphere very ‘English’ in character. Bob’s loyal team is local and he uses the best of Exmoor’s produce – Devonshire cream and milk, Somerset bacon and cheeses.

Heddon’s Gate is a very comfortable place, with en suite bedrooms, peaceful lounges with log fires, and outside, terraced lawns, gardens and ample car parking. Every day a complimentary traditional English afternoon tea is offered to all guests. Heddon’s Gate is for those seeking to experience Exmoor hospitality at its best.

A final note: the approach to Heddon’s Gate Hotel is via steep and winding lanes and may not be suitable for just a one night stay!

LOCATION

From A39, 3 miles west of Lynton, take unclassified road signposted ‘Martinhoe and Woody Bay’. Left at next crossroads, go downhill for 2 miles – private drive on right.

“ A haven of tranquillity and comfort, the highlight of our British visit ”

Dan Elinghausen, Chicago

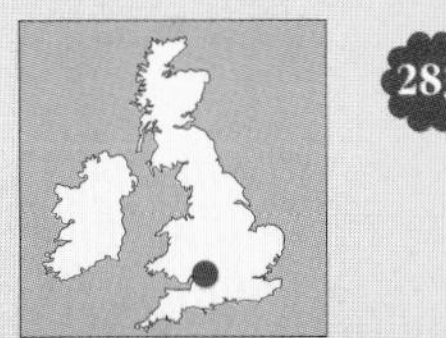

Victorian town house

HOLLY LODGE

So much of England's heritage on your award-winning doorstep!

Holly Lodge is a large Victorian town house set in its own grounds and enjoys magnificent views over the world heritage city of Bath. It was rescued from semi-dereliction in 1986 by Carrolle Sellick and George Hall and now boasts seven individually designed rooms, some with queen size beds and others with specially built four-posters. All the rooms have luxury bathrooms, TV and satellite movies, direct-dial telephones, hot drink facilities and a host of extras.

You can enjoy imaginatively prepared breakfasts in the conservatory breakfast room and relax in the beautiful lounge or the floodlit gazebo in the evenings. Holly Lodge is strictly no smoking.

Twice nominated by the West Country Tourist Board for the 'England for Excellence' Award, Holly Lodge features in many well-known guide books and is graded 'De Luxe' by the English Tourist Board.

Holly Lodge is conveniently placed for touring a wide variety of attractions – Stonehenge, The Cotswolds, Southern Wales, Wells and the Mendip Hills, all within a 40 mile radius of Bath. The centre of Bath, with its magnificent architecture, Roman remains and fine shops is on the doorstep.

LOCATION

½ mile south west of Bath city centre off A367 Wells Road.

8 Upper Oldfield Park,
Bath,
Avon BA2 3JZ

Telephone 01225 424042
Fax 01225 481138

PROPRIETOR

Mr George Hall

ROOM RATES

1 Single £48 - £55
6 Doubles £75 - £85
Includes full breakfast and VAT

CHARGE/CREDIT CARDS

 • *DC* • *MC* • *VI*

ACCOLADES

E.T.B. ♛♛ De Luxe
A.A. QQQQQ Premier Selected
West Country Tourist Board
England for Excellence Award 1993
The Good Hotel Guide

FACILITIES

Gardens
Golf, riding and health spas nearby

RESTRICTIONS

No children
No pets
No smoking

ATTRACTIONS

Castle Combe,
Bath, Cotswolds,
Wells Cathedral,
Stonehenge

AFFILIATIONS

Independent

NEAREST

MAJOR CITY:
Bath - ½ mile/5 mins

MAJOR AIRPORT:
London Heathrow - 90 miles/1½ hrs
Bristol - 13 miles/40 mins

RAILWAY STATION:
Bath Spa - ½ mile/5 mins

RESERVATIONS

Direct with hotel

ACCESS CODES

Not applicable

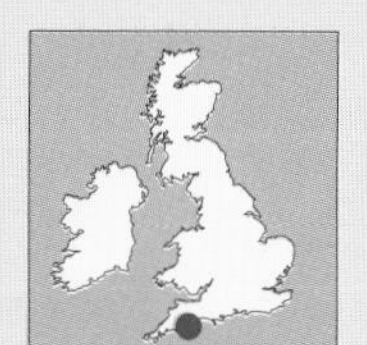

"What more could anyone want, or ever hope to find!"

Joy & Peter Riley, Bristol

HOLNE CHASE HOTEL

Victorian country house

Nr Ashburton,
Devon TQ13 7NS

Telephone 01364 631471
Fax 01364 631453

PROPRIETORS

Sebastian and Philippa Hughes

ROOM RATES

1 Single	£50 - £70
11 Doubles	£90 - £110
1 Four-poster	£115
1 Suite	£115

Includes full breakfast and VAT

CHARGE/CREDIT CARDS

• DC • MC • VI

ACCOLADES

E.T.B. ♛♛♛♛ Highly Commended
R.A.C. ★★★
A.A. ★★★ ❀ 64%
The Good Hotel Guide

FACILITIES

Croquet, gardens, heli-pad
salmon fishing (March-Sept)
Riding nearby

RESTRICTIONS

No smoking in restaurant
No dogs in public rooms

ATTRACTIONS

Dartmoor National Park, Buckfast Abbey, Dartington Hall, Totnes, Totnes Castle, Plymouth, Dartmouth Castle

AFFILIATIONS

Logis of Great Britain
Relais du Silence

NEAREST

MAJOR CITY:
Exeter/Plymouth - 22 miles/30 mins

MAJOR AIRPORT:
Bristol - 90 miles/1 hr 40 mins
Plymouth - 20 miles/45 mins

RAILWAY STATION:
Newton Abbot - 10 miles/20 mins

RESERVATIONS

Toll free in US: 800-989-7676

ACCESS CODES

Not applicable

A peculiarly secluded and romantic situation

Holne Chase was opened as a private hotel in 1934. White's Directory of Devon declared Holne Chase House to be in "a peculiarly secluded and romantic situation" back in 1849. Today, there seems little reason to change this description.

High Dartmoor – described as Southern Britain's last wilderness – is close by and Holne Chase itself is within the protected environment of the Dartmoor National Park. This means plenty of pedestrian access to an area that is said to have the highest concentration of Neolithic remains in Northern Europe. The hotel is particularly well-suited to be a centre for touring South West England.

Sebastian Hughes has lived in the locality for many years so they have a fair idea of what goes on nearby. They have a productive kitchen garden which supplies the restaurant; the cooking is described as "honest with natural flavours" and is complemented with an interesting wine list. The comfy sitting rooms with log fires on cold days and individually furnished bedrooms, complete a picture of calm contentment and pleasant well-being.

The connections of Devon with lands across the seas are the stuff of History: Drake and the Mayflower steps in Plymouth, Morewellham Quay at the upper limit of navigation on the Tamar and, more recently, the historic preparations for the Normandy Landings in 1944 around Torcross and Slapton.

LOCATION

3 miles north of Ashburton on Princetown road.

"Old Sir Francis, he lived like a hog at Hownstret in Somerset"

John Evelyn, 1646

18th century country estate

HUNSTRETE HOUSE

All the blessings of good living on a mature, productive estate

The "Houndstreet" estate has a colourful and well-recorded history dating back to 963AD. John Evelyn referred to "Old Sir Francis (Popham), he lived like a hog at Hownstret in Somerset, with a moderate pittance". Rest assured guests will find some welcome changes.

The house is largely 18th century, set in 92 acres of deer park, woodland, and six acres of gardens at the edge of the Mendips – eight miles from both Bath and Bristol. Within the gardens are croquet lawns, herbaceous borders, trellises, pergolas, glasshouses, a tennis court and a heated pool.

The walled gardens and orchards, in which over 50 varieties of fruit and vegetables grow, provide much of the fresh produce for the kitchens which have an outstanding reputation. The breads and preserves are homemade, cheeses and butter come from local farms, fish is fresh daily from Bristol.

The drawing room and library are splendidly furnished with antiques, original paintings and collections of fine porcelain. The dining room looks into the flower-filled courtyard where guests may dine in the warmer months.

Individually decorated in the style of an English country house, the 23 bedrooms look over the rolling hills. The atmosphere is of a private house. The service is impeccable but friendly, the style relaxed yet refined.

LOCATION

M4 at Junction 18. Take A46 to Bath. Leave Bath on A4 to Bristol then take A39 to Wells and Weston. Hunstrete is 5 miles on right.

Hunstrete, Chelwood, Nr Bristol, Avon BS18 4NS

Telephone 01761 490490
Fax 01761 490732

GENERAL MANAGER

Richard Carr

ROOM RATES

1 Single	*from £115*
18 Doubles/Twins	*£150 - £180*
2 Four-posters	*£230 - £250*
2 Suites	*£230 - £250*

Includes full breakfast and VAT

CHARGE/CREDIT CARDS

• DC • MC • VI

ACCOLADES

R.A.C. ★★★★ *+ Merit Awards H C & R*
A.A. ★★★ ❀❀❀

FACILITIES

Garden, croquet, outdoor pool, tennis, riding, heli-pad
3 meeting rooms/max 70 people
Golf and fishing nearby

RESTRICTIONS

Children by arrangement
No pets

ATTRACTIONS

Bath, Wells, Bristol, Longleat, Glastonbury

AFFILIATIONS

Arcadian Hotels

NEAREST

MAJOR CITY:
Bath - 8 miles/15 mins

MAJOR AIRPORT:
London Heathrow - 90 miles/2 hrs
Bristol - 15 miles/40 mins

RAILWAY STATION:
Bath - 8 miles/15 mins

RESERVATIONS

Direct with hotel

ACCESS CODES

Not applicable

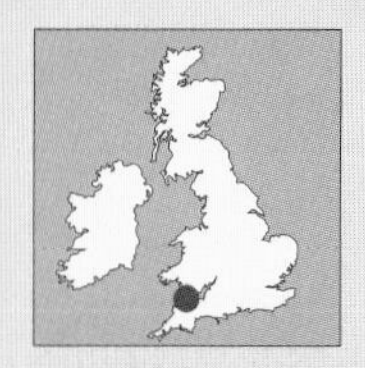

"Nice to return again and enjoy Kittiwell's care, comfort and cuisine"

Mr Emeroth, Stockholm

KITTIWELL HOUSE HOTEL

16th century longhouse

Croyde,
Devon EX33 1PG

Telephone 01271 890247
Fax 01271 890469

PROPRIETORS

J D and Y Lang

ROOM RATES

Single occupancy £34 - £38
9 Doubles/Twins £96 - £108
3 Four-posters £96 - £108
Includes table d'hôte dinner, full breakfast and VAT

CHARGE/CREDIT CARDS

• *JCB* • *MC* • *VI*

ACCOLADES

R.A.C. ★★ + Merit Awards H & R
A.A. ★★ ❀ 71%
The Good Hotel Guide

FACILITIES

Garden
Golf, riding and clay shooting nearby

RESTRICTIONS

No facilities for disabled guests

ATTRACTIONS

Arlington Court,
Saunton Sands,
Exmoor and Dartmoor National Parks,
Clovelly, Lee Bay,
Rosemore Gardens,
Dartington Glass

AFFILIATIONS

Independent

NEAREST

MAJOR CITY:
Exeter - 50 miles/1 hr

MAJOR AIRPORT:
London Heathrow - 200 miles/3 hrs
Bristol - 100 miles/1½ hrs

RAILWAY STATION:
Barnstaple - 9 miles/12 mins

RESERVATIONS

Direct with hotel

ACCESS CODES

Not applicable

History comes alive in one of the most romantic areas of England

Kittiwell House was a 16th century thatched roof Devon Longhouse. Sympathetically renovated to enhance the old world character of interior and exterior, it has charm in every corner. Kittiwell is privately run by its resident proprietors who still believe in good old fashioned service and friendship.

All the bedrooms have been recently renovated and refurbished to a high standard. All have full central heating with variable temperature control, tea and coffee making facilities, radio, clock alarm and colour TV. For the romantic, there are rooms with four-poster beds in the older section of the hotel "Under The Thatch".

The restaurant has a low heavy beamed ceiling and wood-panelled walls. The table d'hôte menu is charged daily with a choice of starters, main dishes and desserts. The extensive à la carte offers fish, poultry, game and vegetarian dishes. The wine list is wide and international.

This is Tarka country, and there are numerous Tarka trails for walkers and cyclists, passing through some of Devon's loveliest countryside, so evocatively described by Henry Williamson in his book "Tarka the Otter". Saunton golf course, widely regarded as the Best in the West, is just three miles from the hotel. Fishing, bathing, clay pigeon shooting, walking and horse riding are all nearby. Exmoor and Dartmoor are both within easy reach, as are Clovelly, Lee Bay and the rugged coastline of Lynton and Lynmouth.

LOCATION

½ mile from Croyde village post office in the direction of Georgeham. Located on the left hand side.

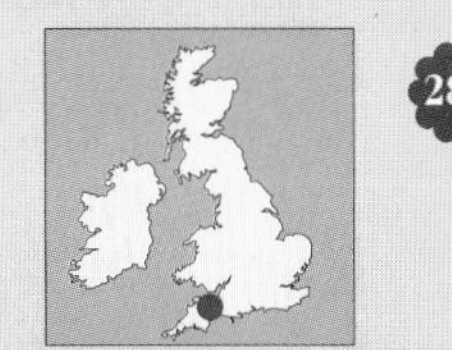

“ A stay at Langley House certainly is one of the better things in life ”

Johan & Ingrid Van Brabant, Belgium

16th century house

LANGLEY HOUSE HOTEL

Langley Marsh, Wiveliscombe, Nr Taunton, Somerset TA4 2UF

Telephone 01984 623318
Fax 01984 624573

PROPRIETORS

Peter and Anne Wilson

ROOM RATES

1 Single	£62.50 - £68.50
5 Doubles/Twins	£83 - £114.50
1 Four-poster	£102 - £114.50
1 Family Suite	£114.50 - £125

Includes full breakfast and VAT

CHARGE/CREDIT CARDS

• MC • VI

ACCOLADES

A.A. ★★ ❀❀
The Good Hotel Guide
County Restaurant of the Year 1993 – a leading guide

FACILITIES

Garden, croquet, tennis
1 meeting room/max 16 people
Riding, fishing and shooting nearby

RESTRICTIONS

No facilities for disabled guests

ATTRACTIONS

Exmoor National Park, Glastonbury, Wells, Knightshayes Gardens, Dunster Castle

AFFILIATIONS

Selected British Hotels

NEAREST

MAJOR CITY:
Exeter - 25 miles/40 mins

MAJOR AIRPORT:
London Heathrow - 150 miles/2¾ hrs
Exeter - 25 miles/40 mins

RAILWAY STATION:
Taunton - 10 miles/20 mins

RESERVATIONS

Toll free in US: 800-323-5463

ACCESS CODES

Not applicable

WEST COUNTRY

A multi-prize-winning gem amongst some of the richest history in Britain

Langley House is a 16th century retreat set in four acres of award winning gardens on the edge of Exmoor National Park. Alterations in the 18th century have invested the house with period charm and elegance. Owners Peter and Anne Wilson have excelled in the conversion of Langley House into a small highly rated country house hotel.

The eight bedrooms, each with private bathroom, are individually decorated (Langley won the Wedgwood/BTA Interior Design Award) and have peaceful garden views and many personal touches including fresh flowers. Peter Wilson cooks in the modern English style. The beamed restaurant is critically acclaimed and in 1995 was awarded two rosettes from the AA.

It has been said that in order to see the full range of Britain's scenery one need only travel to Somerset. Exmoor's heather clad moors and deep ravines remind one of Scotland. The golden warm stone of Ham and the Blackdowns resemble the Cotswolds. The levels equate to East Anglia and Cambridgeshire. The rugged coasts are akin to Cornwall, the Mendips are like parts of Wales. Yet only Somerset has the rich history and heritage and can trace man earlier than any other part of this Kingdom. From Iron Age to Bronze Age; from Romans to Christ; King Arthur and Camelot, the bloody civil war – Somerset has lived history and no visit to Britain is complete without a journey to her fairest county. Langley House is the perfect base for such a visit.

LOCATION

B3227 Taunton to Wiveliscombe. Follow sign to Wiveliscombe town centre. Turn right at town centre, Langley House is ½ mile out of town on the right.

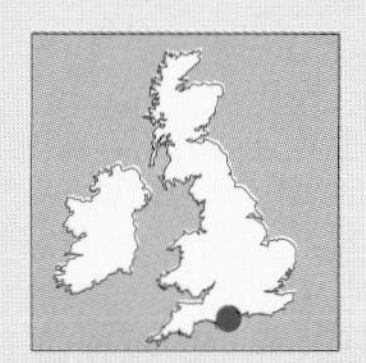

“ Very occasionally you stumble upon a rare gem of an hotel where the building, food, service and history blend to form something quite exceptional – such is Langtry Manor ”

Out & About Magazine

LANGTRY MANOR

Victorian country house

Derby Road, Bournemouth, Dorset BH1 3QB

Telephone 01202 553887
Fax 01202 290115

PROPRIETOR
Pamela Hamilton Howard

GENERAL MANAGER
Tara Howard

RATES PER PERSON

Single occupancy	*£69.50*
10 Doubles/Twins	*£59.50*
2 Four-posters	*£69.50*
3 Suites	*£79.50*
King Edward VII Suite	*£89.50*

Includes full breakfast, dinner and VAT

CHARGE/CREDIT CARDS

• DC • JCB • MC • VI

ACCOLADES
R.A.C. ★★★ + Merit Awards H C & R
A.A. ★★★ ❀ 68%

FACILITIES
Gardens
Golf, riding, fishing and beaches nearby

RESTRICTIONS
Children and pets by arrangement

ATTRACTIONS
Beaulieu Motor Museum, Palace House, Hardy country, Lord Mountbatten's Broadlands, Hardy's cottage, New Forest, Isle of Wight

AFFILIATIONS
Independent

NEAREST
MAJOR CITY:
Bournemouth - 1 mile/5 mins

MAJOR AIRPORT:
London Heathrow - 98 miles/1½ hrs

RAILWAY STATION:
Bournemouth - ¾ mile/3 mins

RESERVATIONS
Direct with hotel

ACCESS CODES
Not applicable

History and elegance in the romantic love nest of a king

Built in1877 by the then Prince of Wales (later King Edward VII) for his favourite Lillie Langtry as a love nest; this beautiful home is located on a quiet tree-lined avenue by the sea. Langtry Manor has been lovingly restored by the Howard family in the style of the finest Country House Hotels.

Intertwined hearts bearing the initials of Lillie and Prince Edward are scratched into a window pane. This and other historic features make this a house well worth the visit.

All bedrooms and suites are individually designed for your comfort, some with a four-poster bed or jacuzzi. You can even stay in the King's own suite.

The magnificent Dining Hall with its Minstrels Gallery and stained glass windows is complemented by delicious food and fine wines. The staff are chosen primarily for their ability to make you feel an honoured guest in a friendly, welcoming home.

Weekend stays include an Edwardian Banquet at which all six mouth-watering courses are displayed for your choice by staff in Edwardian dress. A short son-et-lumière gives a flavour of the history of this lovely house and its famous occupants.

Langtry Manor is justly famous for its Welcome and Celebration Weekends. A delightful experience from £59.50 per person per night that includes a candlelit dinner on Friday and an Edwardian banquet on Saturday . . . plus those unexpected little touches.

LOCATION

5 minutes walk from Bournemouth Central Station and East Cliff Sands.

" Peaceful, comfortable, wonderful food – who could ask for more? "

John & Penny Hankinson, New Forest, Hampshire

19th century country house

LEUSDON LODGE

A pleasant prospect of comfort and well-being on the top of Dartmoor

Built in the 19th century, Leusdon Lodge is situated in an elevated position in the Dartmoor National Park with wonderful views over the surrounding countryside. It enjoys perfect peace and quiet with farmland and wooded valleys all around, yet is only seven miles from Ashburton.

The house is comfortably furnished and has the feel of a family home. There are attractive fabrics, interesting pictures and antiques. The seven bedrooms, all with en suite bathrooms, are decorated to a high standard. Top quality beds combined with healthy Devon air ensure a good night's sleep.

Meals are served in the panelled dining room where the menu changes daily and offers plenty of choice. Great care is taken in the preparation of the food which uses quality local produce including vegetables from the kitchen garden. Special diets are catered for. The wine list features both New World and European wines. For an aperitif, there is a cosy sitting room warmed by a log fire in winter.

Special Breaks are available to make the most of the local area: walking on the open moor, riding, fly fishing, golf, racing at Newton Abbot and Haldon. There are Iron Age and prehistoric sites to visit as well as stately homes and gardens such as Castle Drogo, Killerton and Knightshayes.

LOCATION

Leave A38 at the Peartree Cross to Ashburton. Follow signs to River Dart Country Park, Princetown, and Two Bridges. Through village of Poundsgate and, 400 yards on, turn right, signposted to Leusdon then fork right and turn right at end of small common. Go 300 yards downhill to hotel.

Leusdon, Poundsgate, Nr Ashburton, Newton Abbot, Devon TQ13 7PE

Telephone 01364 631304
Fax 01364 631599

PROPRIETORS

Ivor and Miranda Russell

ROOM RATES

7 Doubles/Twins £60 - £120
Includes full breakfast and VAT

CHARGE/CREDIT CARDS

• MC • VI

ACCOLADES

E.T.B. ♛♛♛ Commended
International Food and Wine Society – Restaurant Award

FACILITIES

Croquet, gardens
Room for disabled guest
1 meeting room/max 10 people
Riding and fishing nearby

RESTRICTIONS

No smoking in dining room
No pets in public rooms

ATTRACTIONS

Dartmoor National Park, Buckfast Abbey, Killerton & Knightshayes Gardens, Hound Tor, Castle Drogo

AFFILIATIONS

Independent

NEAREST

MAJOR CITY:
Exeter - 30 miles/40 mins
Plymouth - 23 miles/35 mins

MAJOR AIRPORT:
London Heathrow - 229 miles/4¼ hrs
Exeter - 35 miles/50 mins

RAILWAY STATION:
Newton Abbot - 14 miles/35 mins

RESERVATIONS

Direct with hotel

ACCESS CODES

Not applicable

"In a lifetime of travel, I do not remember more beautiful surroundings or more gracious treatment"

Cordelia May, Pennsylvania

LEWTRENCHARD MANOR

17th century manor house

Lewdown, Nr Okehampton, Devon EX20 4PN

Telephone 01566 783256
Fax 01566 783332

PROPRIETORS
James and Sue Murray

ROOM RATES

Single occupancy	*£75 - £95*
5 Doubles/Twins	*£100 - £130*
2 Four-posters	*£130*
1 Suite	*£140*

Includes full breakfast and VAT

CHARGE/CREDIT CARDS

• *DC* • *MC* • *VI*

ACCOLADES
A.A. ★★ ❀❀
The Good Hotel Guide

FACILITIES
Croquet, gardens, heli-pad, fishing
2 meeting rooms/max 50 people
Riding nearby

RESTRICTIONS
Children under 8 by arrangement
No facilities for disabled guests
Pets accepted by prior arrangement

ATTRACTIONS
Dartmoor National Park, Lydford Gorge, Cotehele House, Buckland Abbey

AFFILIATIONS
Pride of Britain

NEAREST
MAJOR CITY:
Exeter/Plymouth - 30 miles/45 mins

MAJOR AIRPORT:
London Heathrow - 195 miles/3½ hrs
Exeter/Plymouth - 30 miles/45 mins

RAILWAY STATION:
Exeter/Plymouth - 30 miles/45 mins

RESERVATIONS
Toll free fax in US: 800-635-3608

ACCESS CODES
Not applicable

Grandeur and good living in a Jacobean manor

Built by the Monk family, on the site of an earlier house, this Jacobean manor was embellished by the Victorian writer, hymn writer and folklorist, Sabine Baring Gould. There are granite mullion windows with 19th century stained glass and high ceilings with decorative plasterwork set off by rich oak panelling. Bedrooms, some with four-posters, are tastefully decorated and the views are of formal and informal gardens and beyond the pastures of Lewtrenchard Estate.

The grand oak staircase descends from the long gallery to the imposing entrance hall that gleams with brass. In the panelled lounge, you will find the proprietors, James and Sue Murray who love to chat to guests. The public rooms are comfortable and elegant and there are log fires and fresh flowers everywhere.

In the dining room, with its crisp pink and white linen, you can enjoy classic French cooking with modern interpretations.

The Murrays offer clay pigeon shooting, fishing and croquet in the grounds and there are riding, golf and tennis facilities nearby. Guests can be met at both Exeter and Plymouth stations and airports.

Lewtrenchard Manor is very well placed for many National Trust properties, Dartmoor and the Devon or Cornish coast. It is a most relaxing retreat in very peaceful surroundings.

LOCATION

From Exeter take A30 for Okehampton – Bodmin. After 25 miles take slip road marked to Tavistock/Plymouth. Turn right and immediately left, signed for Lewdown. After 6 miles turn left to Lewtrenchard. Follow signs.

“ This is quite the most enjoyable stay that I’ve had in an hotel and I’ve travelled and stayed world wide! ”

L M Deuchar, Wiltshire

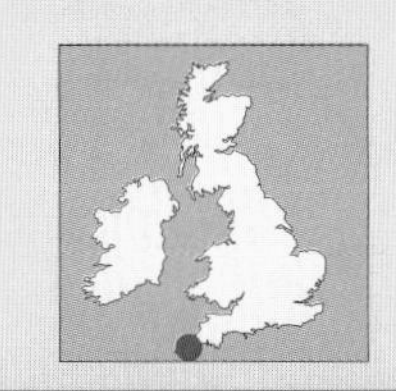

17th century seaside inn

THE LUGGER HOTEL

Complete relaxation in a romantic setting

Dominating a cove, The Lugger Hotel sits at the very water's edge of the picturesque fishing village of Portloe in a great unspoilt part of Cornwall. Untouched by time, this quiet community is surrounded by cliffs, water and breathtaking views – a nature-lovers' dream.

Portloe lays in the heart of the beautiful Roseland Peninsula, and is close to the attractive villages of St Mawes and Veryan, famous for their round thatched cottages.

Originally a 17th century inn reputed to have been the haunt of smugglers, it has been in the Powell Family for three generations and is now a comfortable well-appointed hotel, where care has been taken to preserve its intimate atmosphere. There are 19 tastefully furnished bedrooms, all with en suite facilities.

The cocktail bar, once used by fisherman and smugglers, overlooks the harbour. Here one can enjoy a delicious fresh crab sandwich, for lunch or perhaps afternoon tea. You can also relish a drink whilst taking in the sea air on the terrace overhanging the beach.

The restaurant has panoramic views and offers varied and exciting menus of anglo-continental dishes specialising in local seafood. There is an extensive wine list including a locally produced Cornish wine. Coffee is served with homemade sweetmeats after your meal in the oak-beamed lounge which adjoins the bar and the restaurant.

LOCATION

Turn off A390 St Austell to Truro road on to B3287 to Tregony. Then take A3078 (St Mawes road) and after two miles, fork left for Veryan and Portloe, turning left at T-junction for Portloe.

Portloe, Nr Truro, Cornwall TR2 5RD

Telephone 01872 501322
Fax 01872 501691

PROPRIETORS
The Powell Family

GENERAL MANAGER
Stephen Powell

ROOM RATES

3 Singles	*£57 - £70*
14 Doubles/Twins	*£114 - £140*
2 Mini Suites	*£132 - £144*

Includes full breakfast, dinner and VAT

CHARGE/CREDIT CARDS

• DC • JCB • MC • VI

ACCOLADES
E.T.B. ♛♛♛♛ Highly Commended

FACILITIES
Sauna, solarium
Riding, tennis and bowls nearby

RESTRICTIONS
No children under 12 years
No facilities for disabled guests
Non-smoking restaurant
No pets

ATTRACTIONS
St Just in Roseland,
St Mawes Castle,
Lands End, Penzance,
Pendennis Castle,
Trelissick Gardens

AFFILIATIONS
Hospitality Hotels of Cornwall

NEAREST
MAJOR CITY:
Truro - 12 miles/25 mins

MAJOR AIRPORT:
London Heathrow - 220 miles/5 hrs
Newquay - 20 miles/35 mins

RAILWAY STATION:
Truro - 12 miles/25 mins

RESERVATIONS
Direct with hotel

ACCESS CODES
Not applicable

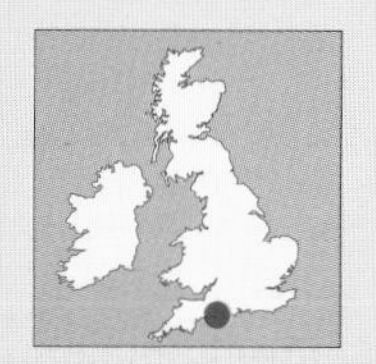

"A dream of Dorset made real"

Maurice Dodd, London

THE MANOR HOTEL

11th century manor house

West Bexington, Dorchester, Dorset DT2 9DF

Telephone 01308 897616
Fax 01308 897035

PROPRIETORS

Richard and Jayne Childs

ROOM RATES

1 Single £43 - £46
12 Doubles/Twins £76 - £78
Includes full breakfast and VAT

CHARGE/CREDIT CARDS

• DC • MC • VI

ACCOLADES

E.T.B. ♛♛♛♛ *Commended*
A.A. ★★ ❀ *67%*

FACILITIES

Garden
2 meeting rooms/max 70 people
Golf, riding and fishing nearby

RESTRICTIONS

No facilities for disabled guests
No pets

ATTRACTIONS

Abbotsbury Gardens,
Hardy Country,
Hardy's Monument,
Abbotsbury Swannery,
Brewers Quay

AFFILIATIONS

Independent

NEAREST

MAJOR CITY:
Exeter - 40 miles/1 hr

MAJOR AIRPORT:
London Heathrow - 110 miles/2½ hrs
Exeter - 50 miles/1½ hrs

RAILWAY STATION:
Dorchester - 11 miles/30 mins

RESERVATIONS

Direct with hotel

ACCESS CODES

Not applicable

A dream of Dorset

The 'Manor' is the ancient Manor House of Bessington, now West Bexington. An old stone building, mellowed by nine centuries of sun and sea, it dates back far enough to have a starred rating in the Domesday Book – but comforts and facilities have been considerably improved since then. The charmingly appointed rooms are redolent of sea, country gardens, and crisp fresh linen. The original cellar now earns its keep as a friendly bar, offering a bar menu more imaginative than most since it, and the dining room cuisine, is in the hands of a master chef with a reputation which is the envy of his peers.

West Bexington dips a toe in the sea in Lyme Bay and the residents' lounge overlooks a flowered garden, the great sweep of Chesil Bank and the uncluttered slumbering miles of west Dorset. It's a meandering drive off the old coast road, a road which has more than its fair share of scenic grandeur, linking Portland to Lyme Regis. Within easy reach are the sandy stretches of Weymouth, Charmouth and Lyme Regis.

Nearby West Bay offers boating and sea fishing from a harbour vibrant with the colourful bobbing of fishing craft. Locally, golf, riding, shooting or just plain old mooching about are all on offer. Historic towns and stately homes and gardens grace the surrounding Dorset landscape. All in all the proprietors, Richard and Jayne Childs, could hardly disagree with the frequent visitor who described The Manor as a dream of Dorset made real.

LOCATION

500 yards from Chesil Beach off B3157 Bridport to Weymouth coast road, turning towards sea at The Bull, Swyre.

“ Everything was perfect, including the weather ”

Robert Johnson, Surrey

Gothic manor house

MANOR HOUSE HOTEL

Magnificent sea views combined with limitless, relaxing pursuits

The Manor House is set in 20 acres of secluded gardens and grounds nestling in one of the most beautiful coastal positions in Britain. A rambling and romantic Gothic manor house in the unspoilt village of Studland, the oldest parts of the building date from circa 1750.

Since 1950, it has been the home of the Rose family who have added many refinements, providing the visitor with all the amenities of a modern hotel, while retaining all the old age charm of a beautiful country house.

The oak panelled dining room adjoins the light and airy conservatory dining area with stunning views to the sea. Fresh local seafood is always featured on the menu and sweets and pastries are prepared daily. There is a comfortably furnished lounge and a cosy oak panelled residents' bar where you can enjoy a tasty bar lunch or a quiet drink after dinner.

All the bedrooms, including the Westminster bedroom with its wall carvings and four-poster bed, are en suite with colour television, tea and coffee making facilities, telephone and hair dryer. The 20 double bedrooms are comfortably furnished with restful decor. Many rooms have magnificent sea views across the bay. The gardens and grounds are a delightful feature affording peace and seclusion.

A truly magnificent setting with woodland and coastal walks and the unspoiled natural beauty. The local area offers three miles of sandy beach below the hotel, links golf courses, horseriding, coastal walks, and bird watching in RSPB reserves.

LOCATION

To Bournemouth and over Sandbanks ferry to Studland. Take 1st left in village or A351 Wareham to Corfe Castle, then B3351 to Studland and 2nd right in village.

Studland, Nr Swanage, Dorset BH19 3AU

Telephone 01929 450288
Fax 01929 450288

OWNER/PROPRIETOR

Richard Rose

ROOM RATES

Single occupancy	*£65 - £75*
12 Doubles/Twins	*£96 - £130*
4 Four-posters	*£120 - £140*
2 Suites	*£125 - £145*

Includes full breakfast, dinner and VAT

ACCOLADES

E.T.B. ♕♕♕ Commended
R.A.C. ★★
A.A. ★★ ❀ 65%

CHARGE/CREDIT CARDS

• MC • VI

FACILITIES

Garden, croquet, tennis, heli-pad
1 meeting room/max 50 people
Golf, riding, fishing, walking and watersports nearby

RESTRICTIONS

No children under 5 years
No smoking in dining room in evenings
No facilities for disabled guests

ATTRACTIONS

Bournemouth, Poole, New Forest, Brownsea Island

AFFILIATIONS

Independent

NEAREST

MAJOR CITY:
Bournemouth - 9 miles/20 mins

MAJOR AIRPORT:
Bournemouth - 11 miles/30 mins

RAILWAY STATION:
Wareham - 10 miles/25 mins

RESERVATIONS

Direct with hotel

ACCESS CODES

Not applicable

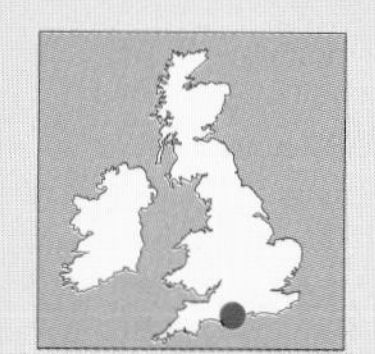

“ This is a wonderful, wonderful hotel. I can't fault it ”

Jilly Cooper, author

THE MANSION HOUSE HOTEL

18th century town house

Thames Street, Poole, Dorset BH15 1JN

Telephone 01202 685666
Fax 01202 665709

PROPRIETOR
Robert J Leonard

GENERAL MANAGER
Mrs Jackie Godden

ROOM RATES
9 Singles £75 - £80
19 Doubles £110 - £120
Includes full breakfast, early morning tea, newspaper and VAT

CHARGE/CREDIT CARDS

• DC • JCB • MC • VI

ACCOLADES
E.T.B. ♛♛♛♛ Highly Commended
A.A.★★★ ❀❀ 79%
AA Courtesy & Care Award 1995
The Good Hotel Guide

FACILITIES
Private dining club
3 meetings rooms/max 50 people
Golf, riding and fishing nearby

RESTRICTIONS
No facilities for disabled guests

ATTRACTIONS
Poole Old Town, Corfe Castle, Hurst Castle, 'Hardy' country, The New Forest, Abbotsbury Abbey

AFFILIATIONS
Best Western

NEAREST
MAJOR CITY:
London - 110 miles/2¼ hrs

MAJOR AIRPORT:
London Heathrow - 100 miles/2¼ hrs

RAILWAY STATION:
Poole - 1 mile/5 mins

RESERVATIONS
Direct with hotel

ACCESS CODES
Not applicable

Premier hospitality beside the world's second largest natural harbour

The Mansion House Hotel and Dining Club, as the name implies, is the original 'Mayoral House' of Old Poole dating back to the Georgian era.

Poole, in Dorset, has great links with the 'New World' and the Lester family, who built the Mansion House around 1780. They made their fortune from their maritime ties with the Newfoundland cod-fish traders of the 18th Century. The famous 'cod fillet fireplace' commemorates their close connection across the water. Poole itself is the world's second largest natural harbour and is at the heart of Dorset's Thomas Hardy country and near William the Conqueror's New Forest.

So The Mansion House, a country house in an historic town, exemplifies that link with the past. Its converted 28 bedrooms, whilst containing all modern amenities, are all individually designed, furnished sympathetically and many named after a famous Georgian figure.

The hotel is privately owned by Robert and Valerie Leonard. Their Dining Club, to which hotel guests enjoy temporary membership, is recognised as the premier 'eating house' in Poole and naturally specialises in local seafood.

Terms are surprisingly modest yet quality is not diminished. A short stay at The Mansion House will linger in the memory!

LOCATION

In Poole, Dorset. Trains from Waterloo take 1 hr 40 mins; direct daytime InterCity trains link Poole with the Thames Valley, Birmingham, the North and Scotland.

“ A beautiful coastal inn steeped in history, charm and warmth ”

Mrs Lucy Hamilton

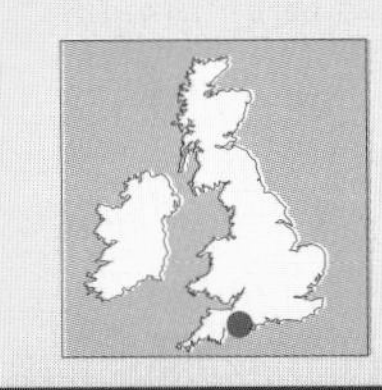

14th century smugglers' inn

THE MASONS ARMS

Traditional Devonshire inn in the midst of acres of National Trust land

The Masons Arms was established around 1360 as an inn for travelling smugglers. It provided an ideal stopping point in the remote village of Branscombe with shelter, good food and warmth.

Today, its proprietor, Murray Inglis, has kept its charm and warmth, offering exceptional cuisine together with individual thatched cottage accommodation furnished with genuine antiques.

The sumptuous meals are prepared to the highest standards with the freshest produce including locally landed shell and wet fish. Whether you choose to eat in the restaurant (awarded the AA rosette for cuisine) or the bar with open log fire, a member of their team of friendly staff will help you select one of many fine wines to accompany your meal.

Situated in the heart of glorious Devon countryside, the hotel is a haven for followers of country pursuits. There are acres of National Trust coastal walkways stretching for hundreds of miles and the local shoots offer a great deal of sport for the hearty.

If you prefer a more leisurely break the surrounding villages provide much interest and history, whilst the beautiful city of Exeter with its famous cathedral is only 30 minutes away.

LOCATION

Take the A303 to Honiton. Follow signs to A3052. After Sidmouth, turn right to Branscombe, just after sign for Salcombe Regis.

Branscombe,
Devon EX12 3DJ

Telephone 01297 680300
Fax 01297 680500

PROPRIETOR

Murray Inglis

ROOM RATES

Single occupancy	*£32 - £50*
19 Doubles/Twins	*£44 - £80*
1 Four-poster	*£44 - £80*

Includes full breakfast and VAT

CHARGE/CREDIT CARDS

MC • VI

ACCOLADES

A.A. ★★ ❀ 72%.

FACILITIES

Garden, fishing, heli-pad
1 meeting room/max 120 people
Leisure club, riding and golf nearby

RESTRICTIONS

None

ATTRACTIONS

Cricket St Thomas,
Crealy Country Park,
Exeter Cathedral,
Killerton

AFFILIATIONS

Independent

NEAREST

MAJOR CITY:
Exeter - 20 miles/30 mins

MAJOR AIRPORT:
Exeter - 15 miles/20 mins

RAILWAY STATION:
Axminster - 12 miles/15 mins

RESERVATIONS

Direct with hotel

ACCESS CODES

Not applicable

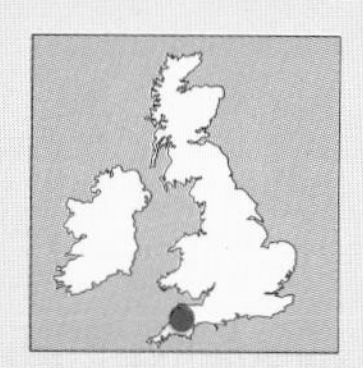

"It was a charming hotel, with a very nice personal conduct, for us it was the best"

J J C Van Lier, Gravehague, Holland

MILL END HOTEL

Country house

Sandy Park, Chagford,
Nr Newton Abbot,
Devon TQ13 8JN

Telephone 01647 432282
Fax 01647 433106

PROPRIETORS

Hazel and Nicholas Craddock

ROOM RATES

2 Singles £45 - £50
14 Doubles/Twins £70 - £90
Includes full breakfast and VAT

CHARGE/CREDIT CARDS

• DC • JCB • MC • VI

ACCOLADES

E.T.B. ♛♛♛♛ Highly Commended
R.A.C. ★★★ + Merit Awards H C & R
A.A. ★★★ ❀ 75%
The Good Hotel Guide

FACILITIES

Gardens
Fishing - salmon/sea trout
Golf and riding nearby

RESTRICTIONS

No facilities for disabled guests
No dogs in public rooms

ATTRACTIONS

Drogo Castle, Exeter,
Rosemoor Gardens,
Dartmoor National Park,
Exeter Cathedral

AFFILIATIONS

Independent

NEAREST

MAJOR CITY:
Exeter - 20 miles/35 mins

MAJOR AIRPORT:
London Heathrow - 175 miles/4 hrs
Exeter - 25 miles/50 mins

RAILWAY STATION:
Exeter - 20 miles/35 mins

RESERVATIONS

Direct with hotel

ACCESS CODES

Not applicable

Mill End is quintessentially English but its guests are international

In many ways Mill End is like many good English country house hotels. It has a beautiful setting, standing as it does on the banks of the moorland River Teign. It is not too large, having only 16 rooms. It provides excellent food and comfortable lodgings.

But Mill End Hotel is special.

First and foremost it is unashamedly old fashioned English. From the chintz covers in the large lounge to the traditional English gardens, and the mildly eccentric guests, it is an establishment that could only be found in England.

Secondly, the restaurant only uses the freshest, highest quality ingredients, carefully prepared on the premises on the day you eat them – that is the Mill End promise. They are justly proud of their award winning cheese selection, and they list over 140 wines.

The best recommendation, however, is its dedicated band of guests, including one doughty American couple who have returned from the mid west to stay at the hotel every year for the last 13 years.

But very best of all, a visit to Mill End, with all its charm and understated quality, will not need a second mortgage to settle the bill.

LOCATION

Dartmoor National Park (Teign Valley). The hotel can be reached easily from the Exeter-Okehampton road (A30) at Whiddon Down. NB: The hotel is NOT in Chagford; do not turn into Chagford from A382.

"Thank you to all at Mortons House for yet another lovely holiday in my favourite hotel and in my favourite part of the country"

Anne Johnson-Rooks, Kent

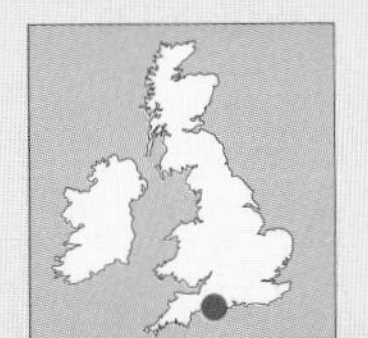

Elizabethan manor

MORTONS HOUSE HOTEL

Stay in the fairytale capital of the ancient Isle of Purbeck

Corfe Castle is the old fairytale capital of the "Isle of Purbeck", where Edward, first king of all England, was martyred in 978 AD. It gave its name to the unspoilt village, built in Purbeck stone and dominated by the ruins of the Norman castle. Mortons House was built in 1590 in the shape of an 'E' to honour Queen Elizabeth I. It was extended in 1666, probably with stone from the castle and is linked to it by underground tunnels.

There are 17 bedrooms, each with private bathroom, TV, telephone and tea and coffee-making facilities. For special occasions, four-poster beds, spa baths and suites are available.

Mortons House is proud of the commendations received for its traditional English cuisine. Local specialities such as Dorset Cheddar and Dorset Blue Vinny cheeses play an important part on the menus. As do fruit and vegetables fresh from the local market gardens.

The magnificent unspoilt area of the Purbeck coastline offers miles of idyllic country walking with many bird and wildlife sanctuaries. Golf, tennis and other sporting activities on land and sea are available in the area.

Mortons House is within easy reach of Poole, and Bournemouth with its leisure and shopping attractions. It is an ideal centre for touring the south of Dorset, a county steeped in history and boasting a wealth of stately and literary homes, museums and historic sites.

LOCATION

The hotel is prominently situated on the A351 in the village of Corfe Castle, midway between Wareham and Swanage.

Corfe Castle,
Dorset BH20 5EE

Telephone 01929 480988
Fax 01929 480820

PROPRIETORS
David and Hilary Langford

ROOM RATES
Single occupancy £60 - £70
15 Doubles/Twins £80 - £96
2 Suites £110 - £130
Includes full breakfast and VAT

CHARGE/CREDIT CARDS

• DC • MC • VI

ACCOLADES
E.T.B. ♛♛♛ Highly Commended
A.A. ★★★ ❀ 67%

FACILITIES
Garden, croquet
2 meeting rooms/max 45 people
Golf, riding, watersports, tennis and fishing nearby

RESTRICTIONS
No facilities for disabled guests
No smoking in dining room

ATTRACTIONS
Corfe Castle,
Poole Harbour,
Brownsea Island,
Arne Bird Reserve,
Kingston Lacey House,
Compton Acres

AFFILIATIONS
Independent

NEAREST
MAJOR CITY:
Salisbury - 45 miles/1 hr

MAJOR AIRPORT:
Bournemouth - 22 miles/30 mins

RAILWAY STATION:
Wareham - 5 miles/10 mins

RESERVATIONS
Direct with hotel

ACCESS CODES
Not applicable

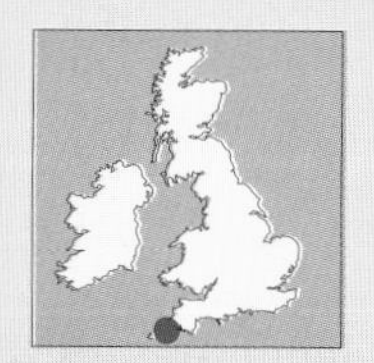

" The Nare is one of those rare hotels where the guests are put unashamedly first! "

David Uren, Hampshire

THE NARE HOTEL

Country house by the sea

Carne Beach, Veryan, Nr Truro, Cornwall TR2 5PF

Telephone 01872 501279
Fax 01872 501856

PROPRIETORS
Mr and Mrs T N Gray

GENERAL MANAGER
Mrs Daphne Burt

ROOM RATES

6 Singles	*£50 - £109*
28 Doubles	*£100- £188*
2 Suites	*£250 - £400*

Includes early morning tea, full breakfast, afternoon tea and VAT

CHARGE/CREDIT CARDS

• *MC* • *VI*

ACCOLADES
R.A.C. ★★★★ + *Merit Awards H & R*
A.A. ★★★★ ❀ *74%*
The Good Hotel Guide

FACILITIES
Garden, tennis, indoor/outdoor pools, sauna, jacuzzi, gymnasium, snooker, beach fishing, heli-pad
2 meeting rooms/max 50 people
Riding, fishing and coastal path walking nearby

RESTRICTIONS
No children under 7 years in restaurant for dinner

ATTRACTIONS
St Mawes Castle,
St Just in Roseland Church,
Pendennis Castle,
Restormel Castle

AFFILIATIONS
Independent

NEAREST
MAJOR CITY:
Truro - 12 miles/25 mins

MAJOR AIRPORT:
London Heathrow - 220 miles/4 hrs
Newquay - 20 miles/35 mins

RAILWAY STATION:
Truro - 12 miles/25 mins

RESERVATIONS
Direct with hotel

ACCESS CODES
Not applicable

One of the most beautifully situated hotels in the British Isles

The charming Nare Hotel is in Gerrans Bay, near St Mawes, close to a safe sandy beach with wonderful cliff walks, and is well situated for visiting Cornwall's glorious gardens and historic houses, most within a radius of 20 miles.

The Nare is renowned for its tranquil atmosphere and elegance of an English country house with antiques, fresh flowers, log fires and afternoon teas in the drawing room, combined with courteous old fashioned service by long-term caring staff.

Facilities include indoor and outdoor heated swimming pools, gymnasium, sauna, solarium, an all-weather tennis court, concessionary golf at Truro and riding stables nearby.

The hotel restaurant offers the finest English cuisine with local farm produce and delicious sea food specialities from Cornish waters. The fabulous food, together with a carefully chosen list of interesting wines, has won The Nare the coveted AA Rosette for Cuisine.

The hotel courtesy car will meet guests at Newquay Airport or Truro Station by prior arrangement.

LOCATION

From A390 take B3287 to Tregony. From Tregony follow the St. Mawes road for 2 miles. First left through Veryan village, then 1 mile straight down to the sea and Nare Hotel.

" This is my favourite hotel in all of England "

Rosemary Lowcock, Sherborne, Dorset

13th century inn

THE OLD BELL

Upholding the ancient traditions of good innkeeping

The Old Bell was established by the Abbot of Malmesbury during the reign of King John as a place to refresh guests who came to consult the Abbey's library.

Situated at the edge of the Cotswolds, this Grade I listed building may well be England's most ancient hotel. Inside, the hall boasts a medieval stone fireplace, while each bedroom is decorated and furnished to an individual style and character. A classic and imaginative menu exemplifies the best in English cooking, with meals ranging from four-course dinners complemented by fine wines in the Edwardian dining room, to informal snacks on the terrace.

The oak beamed lounges, which were built in the 16th century for the steward of Malmesbury Abbey, open on to a quiet terrace and a traditional English garden complete with gazebo. Families are particularly welcomed at The Old Bell, with no charge for children sharing parents' rooms. A playroom staffed by nannies and children's menus are also available.

Malmesbury is only 30 minutes from Bath and is close to a number of other beautiful villages such as Castle Combe, Bourton on the Water and Lacock.

LOCATION

From M4 Junction 17 take A429 towards Cirencester. After 4 miles follow the signs to Malmesbury town centre. The Old Bell is situated adjacent to the Abbey.

Abbey Row, Malmesbury
Wiltshire SN16 0AG

Telephone 01666 822344
Fax 01666 825145

OWNERS

Nicholas Dickinson and Nigel Chapman

ROOM RATES

4 Singles £60 - £70
28 Doubles/Twins £75 - £125
Includes full breakfast and VAT

CHARGE/CREDIT CARDS

• DC • JCB • MC • VI

ACCOLADES

E.T.B. ♛♛♛♛ Highly Commended
R.A.C. ★★★
A.A. ★★★ ❀❀ 75%

FACILITIES

Garden
3 meeting rooms/max 50 people
Fishing and riding nearby

RESTRICTIONS

No facilities for disabled guests

ATTRACTIONS

Lacock, Bath,
Bowood House,
Westonbirt Arboretum,
The Cotswolds

AFFILIATIONS

Independent

NEAREST

MAJOR CITY:
Bath - 27 miles/45 mins

MAJOR AIRPORT:
London Heathrow - 80 miles/1 hr 20 mins
Bristol - 35 miles/45 mins

RAILWAY STATION:
Chippenham - 9 miles/15 mins

RESERVATIONS

Direct with hotel

ACCESS CODES

Not applicable

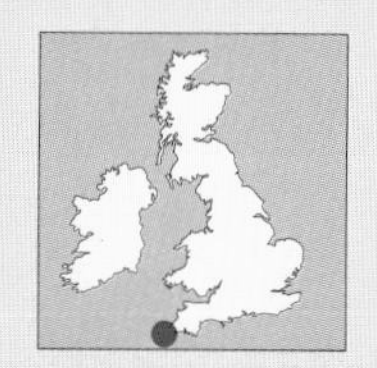

"I wish to thank you for a very enjoyable and relaxing stay. My wife and I would also like to thank your helpful staff who were very professional and obliging"

Wesly Forsythe, Tewkesbury

THE OLD SUCCESS INN

17th century fisherman's inn

Sennen Cove,
Nr Penzance,
Cornwall TR19 7DG

Telephone 01736 871232
Fax 01736 871457

PROPRIETOR
R B Warren

MANAGER
Martin Brookes

RATES PER PERSON
2 Singles £19
10 Doubles/Twins £32 - £36.50
Includes full breakfast and VAT

CHARGE/CREDIT CARDS

• DC • MC • VI

ACCOLADES
E.T.B. ♛♛♛ *De Luxe*
R.A.C. ★★
A.A. ★★ *66%*

FACILITIES
Golf, surfing and fishing nearby

RESTRICTIONS
No facilities for disabled guests

ATTRACTIONS
Whitesands Beach,
Minack Theatre,
Land's End,
St Michael's Mount

AFFILIATIONS
Les Routiers

NEAREST
MAJOR CITY:
Truro - 30 miles/40 mins

MAJOR AIRPORT:
Newquay - 44 miles/55 mins

RAILWAY STATION:
Penzance - 9 miles/12 mins

RESERVATIONS
Direct with hotel

ACCESS CODES
Not applicable

The bay where the dolphins play

Sennen Cove is one of the most beautiful and lesser known bays in Cornwall, just a short distance from Land's End and a few miles from Penzance. Hidden away from the main road down a winding lane with cliffs on either side, Sennen suddenly appears, white sands, exquisite blue seas where dolphins come to play. Nestling in this lovely bay is the Old Success Inn, originally an old fisherman's inn, now attractively modernised.

There are twelve comfortable bedrooms, all en suite, and two have four-poster beds. Several have views overlooking the bay. Both the restaurant and bar offer excellent home cooked food with good local fish dishes.

Sennen is popular for surfing and other water sports. There are also some fine walks around the cliffs to Land's End. Visitors regularly make flights to the Isles of Scilly from Land's End and, for a really different experience in the summer, visitors can enjoy excellent plays and musicals at the Minack Theatre, carved out of the side of the cliffs at Porthcurno Bay.

Sennen is a delightful spot for those on honeymoon or just wanting a weekend away from it all. The Old Success is open all year round including Christmas and has short breaks running throughout the year.

LOCATION

Off the A30, 1 mile from Lands End.

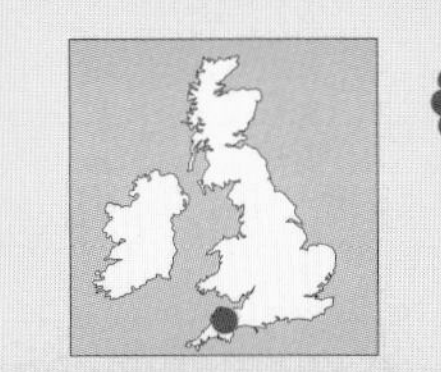

" . . . as he drove slowly down through the village to where stood the Oxenham Arms, the stateliest and most ancient abode of the hamlet "

Eden Phillpots, "The Beacon"

12th century manor house

THE OXENHAM ARMS

Explore Devon and Dartmoor from this ancient hostelry

When one looks down on South Zeal from the nearby hills of Dartmoor, most of the property boundaries are clearly seen to be unchanged from the original layout of the village when established in the 12th century; and in the centre of the village is the "Great House" – the Oxenham Arms. Built around a 5000-year old granite monolith which still can be seen in the little family room behind the bar, and used for centuries as a hospice for lay monks, the property later became the dower house of the Burgoynes whose heiress carried it to the Oxenham family, after whom it is named. The monogram of the Burgoynes can be seen cut into the granite surround of the entrance gate added in Tudor times along with the arched entrance porch.

Should a reincarnated Elizabethan pay a return visit, he would find many features unchanged – massive granite walls, heavy oak beams, low ceilings, granite mullion windows, great open fires, even the old carp-holding well in the garden. But no doubt he would be perplexed by electricity, plumbing, television, telephones, fax machine, and being offered fish fresh that day from the Barbican in Plymouth.

Surrounded by splendid walking country, this is an ideal base for exploring Dartmoor, the north and south coasts of Devon, Castle Drogo, and over 30 National Trust and Heritage properties in the region. The Henry family, owners for over twenty years, wait to welcome you to this ancient hostelry.

LOCATION

In centre of rural village in Dartmoor National Park, just off A30, 18 miles west of Exeter.

South Zeal, Okehampton, Devon EX20 2JT

Telephone 01837 840244
Fax 01837 840791

PROPRIETOR

James H Henry

ROOM RATES

Single occupancy	*£40 - £45*
7 Doubles/Twins	*£50 - £60*
1 Four-poster	*£50 - £60*

Includes full breakfast and VAT

CHARGE/CREDIT CARDS

• DC • MC • VI

ACCOLADES

E.T.B. ♛♛♛ Commended
R.A.C. ★★
A.A. ★★ 65%
The Good Hotel Guide

FACILITIES

Garden
Golf, riding and fishing nearby
Walking on Dartmoor

RESTRICTIONS

No facilities for disabled guests

ATTRACTIONS

Dartmoor National Park
Castle Drogo,
Dupath Well House,
Okehampton Castle

AFFILIATIONS

Independent

NEAREST

MAJOR CITY:
Exeter - 18 miles/25 mins

MAJOR AIRPORT:
Bristol - 90 miles/1½ hrs
Exeter - 18 miles/25 mins

RAILWAY STATION:
Exeter St Davids - 18 miles/25 mins

RESERVATIONS

Direct with hotel

ACCESS CODES

Not applicable

“ One of the most comfortable places on earth ”

George Hill, Times Travel

PERITON PARK HOTEL

Victorian country house

Middlecombe, Exmoor,
Nr Minehead,
Somerset TA24 8SW

Telephone 01643 706885
Fax 01643 706885

PROPRIETORS

Richard and Angela Hunt

ROOM RATES

8 Doubles/Twins £80 - £90
Includes full breakfast and VAT

CHARGE/CREDIT CARDS

• MC • VI

ACCOLADES

A.A. ★★ ❀❀ 75%
The Good Hotel Guide

FACILITIES

Croquet, gardens,
riding, heli-pad
1 meeting room/max 24 people
Golf and fishing nearby

RESTRICTIONS

No children under 12 years old
Dogs in ground floor room only

ATTRACTIONS

Dunster Castle,
Knightshayes,
Arlington Court,
Montacute House

AFFILIATIONS

Logis of Great Britain

NEAREST

MAJOR CITY:
Bristol - 60 miles/1½ hrs

MAJOR AIRPORT:
London Heathrow - 160 miles/3 hrs
Bristol - 55 miles/1½ hrs

RAILWAY STATION:
Taunton - 25 miles/35 mins

RESERVATIONS

Direct with hotel

ACCESS CODES

Not applicable

Hunting, shooting and fishing . . . and excellent cuisine

Bordering on the northern fringe of the Exmoor National Park, the elevated position of this handsome Victorian country residence allows guests magnificent views of the surrounding countryside. Through the dawn mist, the early riser may be rewarded with a glimpse of Red Deer grazing on the moorland below the hotel.

Retaining all of its original character and elegance, the hotel has spacious and light rooms with all the creature comforts you would expect: a comfortable drawing room with roaring log fire and a panelled dining room where you may enjoy some of the finest food on Exmoor.

The cuisine is in the country house style with menus that change with the season to reflect the best of West Country produce – fresh fish, local game, delicately cooked vegetables, local cheeses and Somerset wine.

Exmoor is for lovers of the countryside with miles of varied, unspoilt, breathtaking landscape. Its combination of rugged coastline, heathered moorland, wooded valleys and clear rivers makes this the perfect retreat from the trials of everyday life.

Riding can be arranged with a number of stables as can hunting to hounds with one of six local packs, or fishing for the wily brown trout or salmon. Game shooting is also available in season and clay shooting throughout the year.

LOCATION

1¼ miles west of Minehead on A39.

“ The Priory is the sort of hotel I'd recommend other hoteliers to stay in ”

Paddy Burt, Daily Telegraph

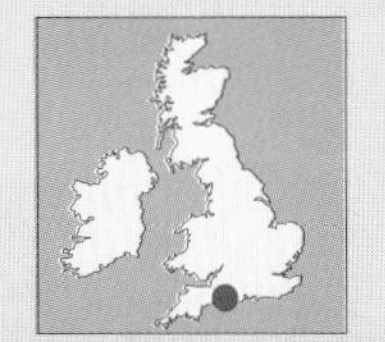

16th century priory

PRIORY HOTEL

Steeped in history, an idyllic sanctuary for the world-weary

Dating from the early 16th century, the one-time Lady St Mary Priory has offered sanctuary to travellers for years. A far cry from the hustle and bustle of city life, The Priory stands in four acres of immaculate gardens on the banks of the River Frome, surrounded by idyllic Dorset countryside.

Steeped in history, The Priory has undergone a sympathetic conversion to an hotel which is charming yet unpretentious. Each bedroom is distinctively styled with family antiques lending character. Many rooms have commanding views of the Purbeck Hills. A 16th century clay barn has been transformed into the Boathouse, consisting of two spacious luxury suites at the river's edge.

Tastefully furnished, the drawing room residents' lounge and intimate bar, together create a convivial atmosphere. The Greenwood Dining Room is open for breakfast and lunch, while dinner is served in the vaulted cellars. There are moorings for guests arriving by boat.

Dating back to the 9th century, the market town of Wareham has more than 200 listed buildings. Corfe Castle, Lulworth Cove, Poole and Swanage are all close by.

LOCATION

Wareham is on the A351 to the west of Bournemouth and Poole. The hotel is beside the River Frome to the east of Wareham.

Church Green, Wareham,
Dorset BH20 4ND

Telephone 01929 551666
Fax 01929 554519

PROPRIETORS
Stuart and John Turner

ROOM RATES
Single occupancy £80 - £105
3 Singles £70
12 Doubles/Twins £90 - £135
2 Four-posters £160
2 Suites £185
Includes morning tea/coffee, newspaper, full breakfast and VAT

CHARGE/CREDIT CARDS

• DC • MC • VI

ACCOLADES
E.T.B. ♛♛♛♛ De Luxe
R.A.C. ★★★★ + Merit Awards H C & R
A.A. ★★★ ❀❀
The Good Hotel Guide

FACILITIES
Croquet, gardens
1 meeting room/max 20 people
Fishing, sailing, riding, cycling and golf nearby

RESTRICTIONS
Children by prior arrangement
No facilities for disabled guests
No pets

ATTRACTIONS
Corfe, Purbeck, Hurst and Portland Castles, Lulworth Cove, Kingston Lacey, Poole Harbour, Wareham, Dorchester, Hardy Country

AFFILIATIONS
Independent

NEAREST
MAJOR CITY:
Salisbury - 35 miles/45 mins

MAJOR AIRPORT:
London Heathrow - 100 miles/1 ½ hrs

RAILWAY STATION:
Wareham - 1 mile/3 mins

RESERVATIONS
Direct with hotel

ACCESS CODES
Not applicable

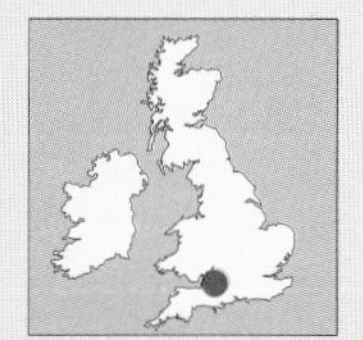

"I rate the Priory the best hotel in town"

David Wickers, The Sunday Times

THE PRIORY HOTEL

Country house style

Weston Road, Bath,
Avon BA1 2XT

Telephone 01225 331922
Fax 01225 448276

GENERAL MANAGER

Thomas L Conboy

ROOM RATES

3 Singles	£85 - £120
15 Doubles/Twins	£155 - £190
3 Junior Suites	£225

Includes continental breakfast and VAT

CHARGE/CREDIT CARDS

• DC • MC • VI

ACCOLADES

E.T.B. ♛♛♛♛ De Luxe
A.A. ★★★ ❀❀
The Good Hotel Guide

FACILITIES

Outdoor swimming pool, croquet, gardens
3 meeting rooms/max 70 people
Golf nearby

RESTRICTIONS

Pets by arrangement

ATTRACTIONS

Heritage City of Bath, Costume Museum, Royal Crescent, Botanical Gardens, Royal Victoria Park, Longleat House and Garden, Dyrham Park

AFFILIATIONS

The Celebrated Hotels Collection

NEAREST

MAJOR CITY:
Bath - 1 mile/5 mins
London - 105 miles/2 hrs

MAJOR AIRPORT:
London Heathrow - 90 miles/1½ hrs
Bristol - 40 miles/45 mins

RAILWAY STATION:
Bath Spa - 1 mile/5 mins

RESERVATIONS

Toll free in US: 800-322-2403

ACCESS CODES

Not applicable

A little Eden in the Roman City of Bath

Built in 1835 of Bath stone in the Gothic style, The Priory is one of a row of elegant residences on the west side of the city. Discreetly located in a quiet part of the city adjoining Royal Victoria Park and the Botanical Gardens, the hotel enjoys the tranquillity of its extensive grounds and yet is within half a mile of some of Europe's finest architecture, and many other delights that make Bath such an attractive city. This combination of a peaceful location and proximity to a unique cultural centre, make The Priory an ideal base from which to benefit from the best of both worlds.

The Priory Restaurant is internationally renowned and has consistently received numerous awards over the years. The cuisine is mainly French classical supplemented by local and national dishes. Adjoining the restaurant are two spacious reception rooms and the elegant drawing room with its French doors leading on to the garden.

The recently refurbished bedrooms are all tastefully appointed, and most have garden views. Each one, named after a flower or shrub, has antique furniture and works of art to complement the luxurious furnishings.

Theatres, museums, antique shops, and the Roman Baths are just a few of the many attractions which you can enjoy from the comfort of The Priory.

LOCATION

From London leave the M4 at Junction 18 and follow signs to Bath on A46. The A4 London road leads into the city. The hotel is located on the west side of Bath in Weston Road, 300 yards west of the Royal Victoria Park.

“ Friendliness and service outstanding ”

Professor Snell, Birmingham

Victorian seaside hotel

THE QUEENS HOTEL

Fine fish and fitness amongst the landmarks of Cornwall

Penzance is a great base from which to tour Cornwall. The Queens Hotel is also an ideal place to rest and relax in a warm, friendly atmosphere in this family owned hotel. A Victorian-style building with all the modern amenities expected of a three star hotel.

All of the bedrooms have en suite facilities and many with magnificent sea views across Mounts Bay and Newlyn Harbour.

The hotel is situated on Penzance's Promenade and the restaurant overlooks the bay providing excellent food and wine. Fresh local fish dishes are a speciality.

The hotel has a health club incorporating sauna and solarium, as well as a snooker room and games room for the less energetic.

This part of Cornwall has so much to offer visitors. St Michael's Mount, the most famous landmark in Cornwall, is just a short drive away and can be walked to when the tide is low. Lands End is also very near as is the Minack Theatre, a wonderful open air theatre carved out of the hillside which regularly puts on performances of Shakespeare and well-known musicals. Throughout Cornwall there are beautiful gardens, English Heritage and National Trust properties open for most of the year.

Getting there is not difficult: the roads are broad and the trains are frequent, mostly express to Penzance from London and other major cities around Britain.

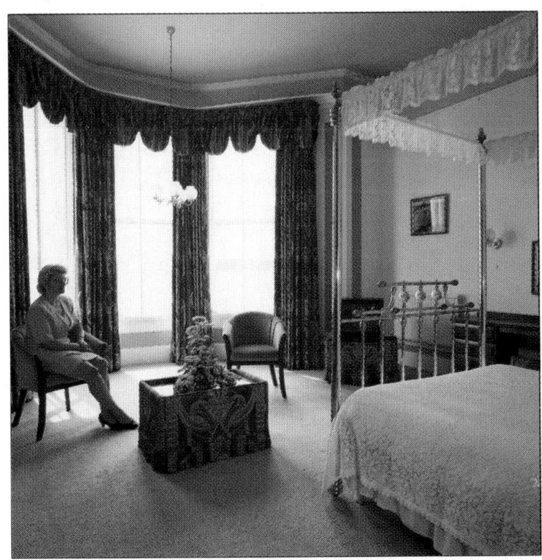

LOCATION

Follow A30 to Penzance. Once in Penzance follow signs for car park and sea front. The Queens is located halfway along The Promenade.

The Promenade, Penzance, Cornwall TR18 4HG

Telephone 01736 62371
Fax 01736 50033

GENERAL MANAGER

Vyvyan Jenkin

ROOM RATES

16 Singles	*£35 - £47*
46 Doubles/Twins	*£62 - £91*
3 Four-posters	*£91 - £103*

Includes full breakfast and VAT

CHARGE/CREDIT CARDS

• DC • MC • VI

ACCOLADES

E.T.B. ♛♛♛♛ Commended
R.A.C.★★★
A.A. ★★★

FACILITIES

Health Club, snooker, games room
3 meeting rooms/max 200 people
Riding and fishing nearby

RESTRICTIONS

No facilities for disabled guests
No dogs in bars or restaurants
Dogs to be kept on a leash in public areas

ATTRACTIONS

St Michael's Mount,
Tate Gallery,
Land's End, St Ives,
Trebah Gardens

AFFILIATIONS

Independent

NEAREST

MAJOR CITY:
Truro - 25 miles/25 mins

MAJOR AIRPORT:
London Heathrow - 300 miles/5½ hrs
Newquay - 45 miles/1 hr

RAILWAY STATION:
Penzance - 1 mile/5 mins

RESERVATIONS

Toll free in UK: 0500 121265

ACCESS CODES

Not applicable

“ Our stay at the Queensberry ranks as our most memorable hotel stay in England ”

Heather Cameron, New York

QUEENSBERRY HOTEL

Regency house

**Russel Street, Bath,
Avon BA1 2QF**

**Telephone 01225 447928
Fax 01225 446065**

PROPRIETORS
Stephen and Penny Ross

ROOM RATES
Single occupancy £80 - £92
22 Doubles £98 - £164
Includes continental breakfast and VAT

CHARGE/CREDIT CARDS

• MC • VI

ACCOLADES
R.A.C. ★★★ + Merit Awards H C & R
A.A. ★★★ ❀❀ 79%
The Good Hotel Guide 'County Hotel of The Year' 1994 – a major guide

FACILITIES
Courtyard garden
1 meeting room/max 20 people
Golf and riding nearby

RESTRICTIONS
No facilities for disabled guests
No pets

ATTRACTIONS
Bath, Roman Baths, Stonehenge, Wells, Longleat, Stourhead Gardens

AFFILIATIONS
Selected British Hotels

NEAREST
MAJOR CITY:
Bath

MAJOR AIRPORT:
London Heathrow - 90 miles/1¾ hrs
Bristol - 15 miles/30 mins

RAILWAY STATION:
Bath Spa - 1 mile/5 mins

RESERVATIONS
Toll free in US: 800-323-5463

ACCESS CODES
Not applicable

An architecturally acclaimed house in the Roman city of Bath

The Queensberry – luxurious, decorative and intimate – a few minutes' walk from the Roman Baths but itself in the heart of Georgian Bath. Built by John Wood of Royal Crescent fame, for the Marquis of Queensberry in 1772, the house retains its splendid period plasterwork and fireplaces, all now complemented by Penny Ross's interiors. There is a delightful courtyard garden, drawing room and cocktail bar.

The focal point of the hotel is The Olive Tree Restaurant which Chef/Patron Stephen Ross describes as a contemporary restaurant – informal, modestly priced, with English cooking that combines excellent local produce with the robust flavours of the Mediterranean.

The Queensberry could not be better placed for visiting the highlights of Bath; the Roman Baths, Theatre Royal, Assembly Rooms and Royal Crescent are minutes' walk from the hotel. A meander downhill takes you past the antiques markets, the best shops outside London and on to Bath Abbey.

After testing Bath's waters, we are sure that you will want to make a return visit to The Queensberry.

LOCATION

M4 to Junction 18, A46 to Bath. Turn right at T-junction and at mini-roundabout take the right hand fork to next lights. Turn sharp right at Landsdown Road, 2nd left into Bennett Street Russel Street is 1st right.

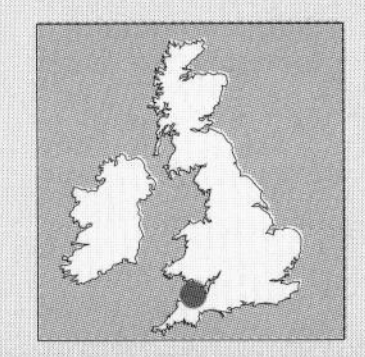

"It is the sheer charm of the Rising Sun that earned it the title 'Inn of the Year'"

Daily Mail

Thatched smuggler's inn

THE RISING SUN HOTEL

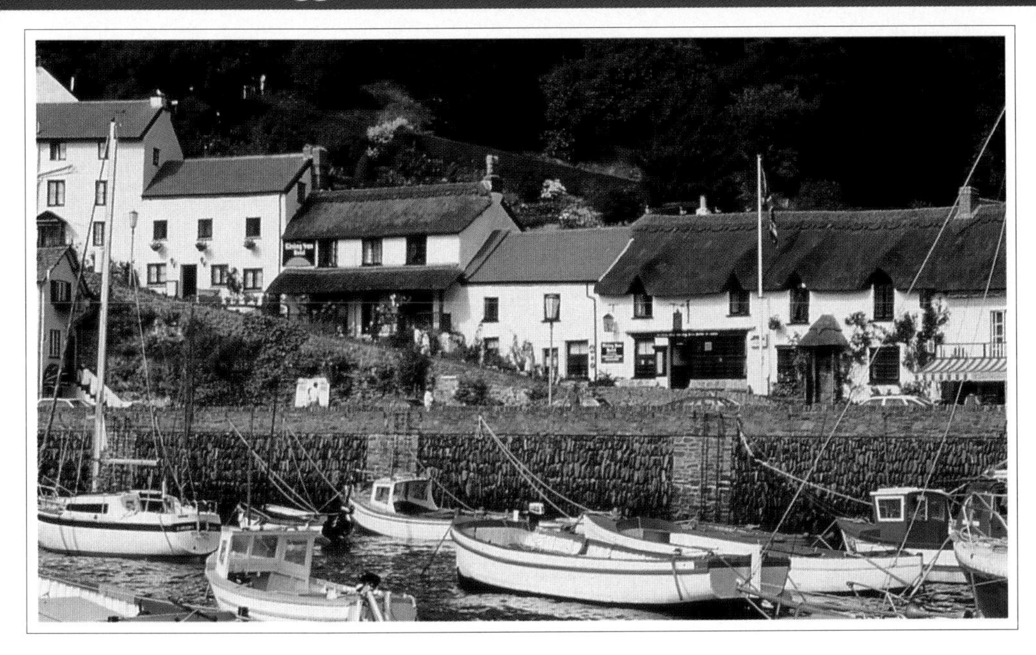

Picture postcard setting – boats bobbing in the harbour – too romantic for words

An award-winning 14th century thatched smugglers inn overlooking a tiny picturesque harbour and Lynmouth Bay with its stunning backdrop of the highest hogback cliffs in England, and situated on the edge of Exmoor National Park where herds of deer, wild ponies and birds of prey roam free.

The Rising Sun Hotel is steeped in history with oak panelling, crooked ceilings, thick walls and creaky uneven oak floorboards. It was in one of these rooms that R. D. Blackmore wrote several chapters of his West Country classic "Lorna Doone".

The romantic poet Percy Bysshe Shelley spent his honeymoon in 1812 with his child bride Harriet at the inn's cottage (partly to dodge his irate parents-in-law). He wrote of it, "The climate is so mild that myrtles of immense size twine up our cottage and roses blow in the open air in winter".

Lynmouth Bay lobster, local game and salmon fished from the hotel's private stretch of river and served in the romantic, candlelit oak-panelled dining room, all add to the atmosphere of quintessential British innkeeping at its best.

LOCATION

Leave the M5 motorway at Junction 23 (signposted Minehead) and follow the A39 to Lynmouth.

Harbourside, Lynmouth, North Devon EX35 6EQ

Telephone 01598 753223
Fax 01598 753480

PROPRIETOR

Hugo Jeune

ROOM RATES

2 Singles	*£45*
7 Doubles/Twins	*£79 - £95*
2 Four-posters	*£95 - £99*
1 Suite	*£115*

Includes full breakfast and VAT

CHARGE/CREDIT CARDS

• DC • MC • VI

ACCOLADES

E.T.B. ♛♛♛ Highly Commended
R.A.C. ★★ + Merit Awards H C & R
A.A. ★★ ❀❀ 70%
The Good Hotel Guide

FACILITIES

Fishing

RESTRICTIONS

No children under 5 years
Pets by arrangement

ATTRACTIONS

Lynmouth,
Clovelly, Exmoor,
Arlington Court,
Killerton Gardens,
Lorna Doone country,
Dartington Glass

AFFILIATIONS

Independent

NEAREST

MAJOR CITY:
Barnstaple - 18 miles/40 mins

MAJOR AIRPORT:
Bristol - 75 miles/2 hrs
Exeter - 55 miles/1¼ hrs

RAILWAY STATION:
Barnstaple - 18 miles/30 mins

RESERVATIONS

Direct with hotel

ACCESS CODES

Not applicable

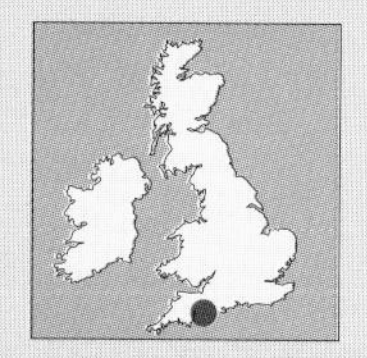

"Unsurpassed in service and friendliness . . . superb cuisine . . . The Riviera is truly lovely in every respect and continues to be one of our favourite hotels"

Patricia Polidor, New York

HOTEL RIVIERA

Luxury hotel

The Esplanade, Sidmouth, Devon EX10 8AY

Telephone 01395 515201
Fax 01395 577775

OWNER

Peter S Wharton

ROOM RATES

7 Singles	£67 - £90
18 Doubles/Twins	£118 - £164
2 Suites	£162 - £182

Includes full breakfast, dinner and VAT

CHARGE/CREDIT CARDS

• DC • MC • VI

ACCOLADES

E.T.B. ♛♛♛♛ De Luxe
R.A.C. ★★★★ + Merit Awards H C & R
A.A. ★★★★ ❀ 70%

FACILITIES

Patio
1 meeting room/max 85 people
Golf, riding, fishing, tennis, croquet and game shooting nearby

RESTRICTIONS

None

ATTRACTIONS

Killerton House,
Exeter Cathedral,
Bicton Park and Gardens,
Dartmoor and Exmoor National Parks

AFFILIATIONS

Independent

NEAREST

MAJOR CITY:
Exeter - 13 miles/30 mins
London - 165 miles/3½ hrs

MAJOR AIRPORT:
London Heathrow - 153 miles/3 hrs
Exeter - 10 miles/30 mins

RAILWAY STATION:
Exeter - 13 miles/30 mins

RESERVATIONS

Direct with hotel

ACCESS CODES

Not applicable

A luxury hotel where traditional values are kept alive

Picture an unspoilt seaside town in the glorious English county of Devon. Where cricket is still played on the village green. Where a stroll along the promenade is akin to taking a gentle journey back in time. Where afternoon tea, served with strawberries and cream, is as much of a tradition to its country folk as is the Changing of the Guard to a Londoner.

If Sidmouth provides a pleasant reminder of a more gracious age, then the Riviera is the epitome of that golden era of courtesy, elegance and discreet luxury hotels. Staring proudly out to sea from its prominent seafront position on a handsome Regency esplanade, the Riviera has a style and presence that is utterly unique. Its special charm bids you welcome from the instant you enter its bow-fronted, deep-carpeted foyer to the very last moment of your visit. The personal attention from the staff, many of whom have worked at the Riviera for many years, lends a warm family atmosphere – while the hotel's old-fashioned values bring back guests time after time.

Whatever the season, the Hotel Riviera is the perfect choice for the discerning in search of relaxation and quieter pleasures. How better to bring each day to a close than with an aperitif in the lounge, accompanied by soft music from the resident pianist; a meal in the elegant restaurant where – naturally enough – seafood is a speciality; followed by a traditional English nightcap in the welcoming luxury of the Regency Bar.

LOCATION

Sidmouth is 13 miles from M5, Junction 30 (then follow A3052).

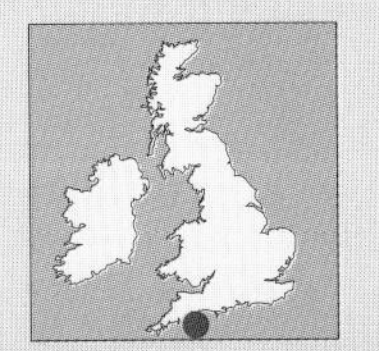

“ A superb hotel in a magnificent location, combining features of the past with modern comforts ”

John Guatieri, Bristol

17th century coaching inn THE ROYAL CASTLE

Priest holes, Elizabethan furniture, Tudor fireplaces and a Royal past

Right on the quayside, in the heart of Dartmouth, is The Royal Castle, now an hotel but originally built in the 1630's as two merchant's houses. Following several visits by the Prince of Wales – later to be crowned Edward VII – 'Royal' was conferred upon the hotel in 1902.

The hotel has many reminders of its rich history: tudor fireplaces, a magnificent staircase, priest holes and a 300-year old Lyndstone Range all survive as relics of the past; there are many fine pieces of antique furniture too: map chests, oak coffers, Elizabethan chairs and tables. The original four-poster and brass beds are still in use.

Nigel and Anne Way took over the hotel in 1983 and continue its centuries' old tradition of fine English innkeeping. 25 luxury en suite bedrooms are uniquely decorated and furnished with a choice of bath, shower or jacuzzi room. All the latest facilities are included to help make your stay a pleasure, whatever the time of year.

The traditional restaurant on the first floor overlooks the estuary, and specialises in the best of the region's produce and locally caught seafood. The frequently changing menu is prepared by the head chef, cooked to order, and served by formal, but friendly staff.

In keeping with the hotel's great history, there are still two busy bars serving choice food, fine ales and select wines, all of which contribute to the hotel's wonderfully historic ambience.

LOCATION

Summer: via Totnes on A3122 Other seasons: via A379/B3205 to Kingswear Car Ferries (peak season delays).

The Quay, Dartmouth, Devon TQ6 9PS

Telephone 01803 833033
Fax 01803 835445

OWNERS

Nigel and Anne Way

RATES PER PERSON

Single occupancy	*£54.50 - £64.50*
14 Doubles	*£49.50 - £69.50*
7 Four-posters	*£50 - £57*
4 Family rooms	*£38 - 66.50*

Includes full breakfast, dinner and VAT

CHARGE/CREDIT CARDS

• MC • VI

ACCOLADES

E.T.B. ♛♛♛ Highly Commended
R.A.C. ★★★ + Merit Award H
A.A. ★★★ 69%

FACILITIES

Jacuzzi
2 meeting rooms/max 50 people
Golf, fishing and boating nearby

RESTRICTIONS

No facilities for disabled guests
Pets by prior arrangement

ATTRACTIONS

Dartmouth,
South Devon Coast,
River Dart,
Totnes and Berry Pomeroy Castles,
Dartmoor National Park,
Plymouth

AFFILIATIONS

Independent

NEAREST

MAJOR CITY:
Exeter - 35 miles/45 mins

MAJOR AIRPORT:
London Heathrow - 200 miles/3½ hrs
Exeter - 35 miles/45 mins

RAILWAY STATION:
Totnes - 12 miles/30 mins

RESERVATIONS

Toll free fax in US: 800-275-7153

ACCESS CODES

Not applicable

" A culinary match for London's West End "

Godfrey Smith, The Sunday Times

THE ROYAL OAK INN

17th century inn

Exmoor National Park,
Withypool,
Somerset TA24 7QP

Telephone 01643 831506/7
Fax 01643 831659

PROPRIETORS
Michael and Dolly Bradley

ROOM RATES

2 Singles	*£32 - £34*
6 Doubles/Twins	*£35 - £38*

Includes full breakfast and VAT

CHARGE/CREDIT CARDS

• DC • MC • VI

ACCOLADES
R.A.C. ★★ + Merit Awards C & R
A.A. ★★ ❀ 71%

FACILITIES
Stabling for guests' horses, horse and hunter hire
1 meeting room/max 20 people
Hunting, game shooting and clay pigeon shooting nearby

RESTRICTIONS
No children under 8
No facilities for disabled guests
Dog's bedding must be provided

ATTRACTIONS
Tarr Steps, ancient Clapper Bridge, Dunster Yarn Market and Castle, Lorna Doone Valley/Valley of Rocks

AFFILIATIONS
Independent

NEAREST
MAJOR CITY:
Taunton - 27 miles/45 mins
MAJOR AIRPORT:
London Heathrow - 165 miles/2¾ hrs
Bristol - 65 miles/1½ hrs
RAILWAY STATION:
Taunton - 27 miles/45 mins

RESERVATIONS
Direct with hotel

ACCESS CODES
Not applicable

Lorna Doone was written here. Gen Eisenhower pondered D Day here.

"There is nothing which has yet been contrived by man by which so much happiness is produced as by a good tavern or inn."

- Samuel Johnson

Since this quotation, times have certainly changed, but hopefully the hospitality, comfort and excellent food afforded by The Royal Oak inn have not. The inn has been renowned for its comfort and food for approximately three centuries.

Set in the beautiful village of Withypool in the middle of Exmoor it is an ideal base from which to ride, hunt, shoot, fish or simply walk and enjoy the calm and beauty of the moors with its sparkling rivers and fertile valleys.

R D Blackmore, author of 'Lorna Doone', was so taken by Withypool that he stayed at the inn whilst writing his famous novel in 1866. General Eisenhower became a familiar figure at the Royal Oak when his troops were training on Exmoor for the D Day landings.

Withypool, with the river Barle meandering through, is quiet and relaxed and within easy reach of local beauty spots such as the ancient and undateable footbridge at Tarr Steps, Dunkery Beacon, historic Dunster Castle and the renowned Somerset and North Devon beaches.

LOCATION

Exit Junction 27 on M5 and travel on A361 to South Molton. At South Molton, turn right for North Molton then Withypool.

" Central to our enjoyment of the weekend was the excellence of the cooking. It was delicious "

The Daily Mail

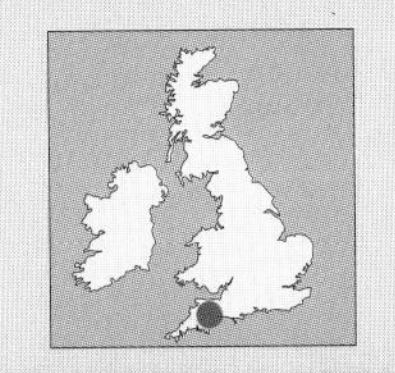

Georgian town house

ST OLAVES COURT HOTEL

A gourmet's haven within the sound of the cathedral bells of Exeter

St Olaves Court, famous for its restaurant and home from home atmosphere, stands just 400 yards from Exeter Cathedral. It is a lovely Georgian building with just 15 en suite rooms that stands in its own walled garden – an oasis in the city centre. It has become such a favourite that it is almost considered a special address – unassuming from the outside with a warm welcome within.

The rooms are very well cared for and range from single and twins to luxurious double bedrooms with jacuzzi. The hotel has been discreetly furnished, partly with antiques. The service is first rate; one guest commented, "we found it by accident, but there was nothing accidental about the levels of service".

Central to the enjoyment of St Olaves is the excellence of the cooking. The candlelit restaurant – one of the best in south west England – is renowned for its outstanding cuisine. The Head Chef, winner of the young Irish Chef of the Year competition, achieves taste, texture and colour as well as excellence in presentation.

St Olaves Court Hotel is ideally placed for exploring the City of Exeter as well as the famous South Devon coastline, the beauties of Dartmoor National Park and visiting the famous National Trust gardens.

That so many guests return each year is the best accolade of all.

LOCATION

From Exeter city centre follow signs to "Mary Arches P". Hotel entrance is directly opposite.

Mary Arches Street, Exeter, Devon EX4 3AZ

Telephone 01392 217736
Fax 01392 413054

PROPRIETORS

Raymond and Ute Wyatt
and Peter Collier

ROOM RATES

1 Single £60 - £80
14 Doubles/Twins £70 - £110
Includes continental breakfast and VAT

CHARGE/CREDIT CARDS

• *DC* • *MC* • *VI*

ACCOLADES

R.A.C. ★★★ + *Merit Award H & R*
A.A. ★★★ ❀❀ *69%*
The Good Hotel Guide
Frommers England

FACILITIES

Secluded walled gardens
4 meeting rooms/max 80 people
Golf and riding nearby

RESTRICTIONS

None

ATTRACTIONS

Exeter, Bowhill,
Exeter Cathedral,
North Devon coast,
Dartmoor National Park

AFFILIATIONS

Independent

NEAREST

MAJOR CITY:
Exeter

MAJOR AIRPORT:
London Heathrow - 180 miles/3 hrs
Exeter - 7 miles/12 mins

RAILWAY STATION:
Exeter - 1 mile/5 mins

RESERVATIONS

Toll free in US: 800-543-4135

ACCESS CODES

Not applicable

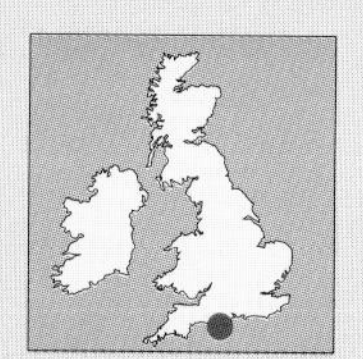

"A delightful experience 'oft to be repeated'"

Nina Howe, Basingstoke

Salterns Hotel

Waterside hotel

Salterns Way, Poole,
Dorset BH14 8JR

Telephone 01202 707321
Fax 01202 707488

PROPRIETORS
Beverley Helliwell-Smith and John Smith

ROOM RATES

10 Singles	£66
10 Doubles/Twins	£86

Includes VAT

CHARGE/CREDIT CARDS

• DC • MC • VI

ACCOLADES
R.A.C. ★★★ + Merit Awards H C & R
A.A. ★★★ ❀❀ 80%
A.A. Courtesy & Care Award 1993

FACILITIES
Garden, snooker, heli-pad
3 meeting rooms/max 120 people
Golf and fishing nearby

RESTRICTIONS
No facilities for disabled guests
Pets by arrangement

ATTRACTIONS
Corfe Castle, Stonehenge, Thomas Hardy country, Poole pottery

AFFILIATIONS
Best Western

NEAREST
MAJOR CITY:
London - 90 miles/2 hrs 20 mins

MAJOR AIRPORT:
London Heathrow - 100 miles/2½ hrs
Hurn - 8 miles/30 mins

RAILWAY STATION:
Poole - 2 miles/10 mins

RESERVATIONS
Direct with hotel

ACCESS CODES
Not applicable

Difficult to imagine that this stunning location could be bettered

The setting of this hotel never ceases to appeal, located on the water's edge with stunning views across the lovely harbour of Poole. It would be difficult to imagine that this charming location could be bettered, for here you have found the perfect choice.

Salterns Hotel, with its south facing position, sits in fourteen acres of marina, with its own waterside patio, lawn and pretty borders of carefully kept shrubs.

The waterside restaurant is a perfect blend of elegance and beauty serving, without doubt, the best food in the area, and certainly it can boast of having one of the finest chefs in England. Nigel Popperwell rejoined Salterns in May 1995 after a six year break. His superb food and Beverley Smith's outstandingly high levels of customer care make Salterns a choice not easily matched. The 20 bedrooms offer high standards of comfort and luxury with a host of complimentaries to anticipate the guests' every need.

A feature of Salterns Hotel is its themed rooms; 'Bluebell' and 'Buttercup' are amongst the favourites, although the 'Duck' room also has its following.

Great care and attention has been devoted to the creation of Salterns, offering a standard which has now become the hallmark of Salterns' success.

LOCATION

Leave Poole in the direction of Sandbanks, B3369. After approximately 1½ miles turn right into Salterns Way at Lilliput.

"Our second stay and most certainly not our last. A memorable weekend, perfect surroundings, friendly service, a delightful ambience and superb food"

Digby & Sandra Brecknell, Florida

17th century private house

SIMONSBATH HOUSE HOTEL

In the centre of the wild, natural beauty of the Forest of Exmoor

Simonsbath House was the first house in the Forest of Exmoor. It was built in 1654 by James Boevey, a wily London merchant of Huguenot extraction, on the spot where all the tracks across the moor appeared to meet.

The present owners, Sue and Mike Burns bought Simonsbath in 1985, and have made it their home and a comfortable family-run hotel that still retains the attractive features of an interesting and historic old house. You will find four-poster beds, velvet drapes and oak panelling, log fires and delicious home-cooked food. Your bedroom is furnished and decorated with beautiful fabrics and linens, fresh fruit and bottled water on the dressing table, magazines by your bed. From your window you look out on picture postcard scenery: beech forests of ever-changing hue, a crystal river bubbling through the valley, and fold after fold of heather clad hills.

This is the country of the wild Red Deer, the last surviving herds in England, the game bird, the rainbow trout and the salmon. It is the country of Lorna Doone, with many beauty spots on the "Lorna Doone Trail" to fire your imagination. Within reach are the magnificent cathedrals of Exeter and Wells, the cradle of Christianity at Glastonbury, Bath, and Devon's sandy beaches. Enjoy them and return ravenous in the late afternoon to a home-made tea of scones, strawberry jam and clotted cream.

LOCATION

Take Junction 25 on M5 and follow signs for Taunton. Take the A358 out of Taunton, then the B3224 via Wheddon Cross and Exford through to Simonsbath.

Simonsbath, Nr Minehead, Somerset TA24 7SH

Telephone 01643 831259
Fax 01643 831557

PROPRIETORS

Mike and Sue Burns

RATES PER PERSON

Single occupancy	*£44 - £60*
4 Doubles/Twins	*£39 - £45*
3 Four-posters	*£39 - £45*

Includes full breakfast and VAT

CHARGE/CREDIT CARDS

• *DC* • *MC* • *VI*

ACCOLADES

E.T.B. ♛♛♛♛ *Highly Commended*
A.A. ★★ ❀ *75%*
The Good Hotel Guide

FACILITIES

Garden
Fishing and riding nearby

RESTRICTIONS

No children under 10 years
No facilities for disabled guests
No pets

ATTRACTIONS

Exmoor National Park, Lorna Doone Valley, Tarr Steps ancient clapper bridge, Dunster Castle, Arlington Court, Knighthayes Court, Valley of the Rocks

AFFILIATIONS

Independent

NEAREST

MAJOR CITY:
Taunton - 34 miles/40 mins

MAJOR AIRPORT:
London Heathrow - 200 miles/3 hrs

RAILWAY STATION:
Taunton - 34 miles/40 mins

RESERVATIONS

Direct with hotel

ACCESS CODES

Not applicable

" Whether the dish be one of virtuoso spontaneity or supremely classical the Makepeaces can be relied upon for the finest dining experience "

Leslie Faull, Commander de la Commanderie des Cordons Bleus

SOAR MILL COVE HOTEL

Country hotel by the sea

Salcombe, Devon TQ7 3DS

Telephone 01548 561566
Fax 01548 561223

PROPRIETOR
Keith A Makepeace

ROOM RATES
Single occupancy £70 - £110
14 Doubles/Twins £120 - £160
2 Suites £180 - £268
Includes full breakfast, Devon cream tea upon arrival and VAT

CHARGE/CREDIT CARDS

• *MC* • *VI*

ACCOLADES
E.T.B. ♛♛♛♛♛
R.A.C. ★★★ + *Merit Awards H C & R*
A.A. ★★★ ❀❀ *75%*
The Good Hotel Guide

FACILITIES
Garden, own beach, tennis, indoor/outdoor pools
Golf, riding, salmon (coarse, sea, river, lake) fishing nearby

RESTRICTIONS
Disabled guests by prior arrangement
Pets by prior arrangement

ATTRACTIONS
Dartmoor National Park, Dartmouth, Plymouth, Totnes Castle, Dartmouth Castle, Overbecks Museum and Gardens, National Shire Horse Centre

AFFILIATIONS
Independent

NEAREST
MAJOR CITY:
Plymouth - 22 miles/40 mins

MAJOR AIRPORT:
London Heathrow - 210 miles/4 hrs
Plymouth - 22 miles/40 mins

RAILWAY STATION:
Totnes - 18 miles/35 mins

RESERVATIONS
Direct with hotel

ACCESS CODES
Not applicable

Lovely hotel in glorious situation fronting its own sandy bay

Imagine walking to only the sound of birds and the waves breaking upon the golden sand. A late breakfast on your private terrace whilst watching the lobster pots being brought in. Then strolling amongst the sea pinks to a dramatically beautiful beach surrounded by 20,000 acres of National Trust coastline indented with sandy bays and bubbling streams.

Ride a thoroughbred over sheltered meadows; enjoy a round of golf with a backcloth of sea islands; play lawn tennis in this beautiful Devon coombe followed by English afternoon tea in the rose arbour.

Later, dinner in the elegant restaurant prepared by the award-winning brigade of Keith Stephen, Maitre Association Culinaire Francaise.

Leave time on other days to explore Dartmoor and the Plymouth of Drake, Elizabeth and Raleigh, the many ancient Wool towns and harbourside villages of this beautiful southernmost tip of Devon – the land where Dartmoor comes down to the sea.

All this in one lovely hotel, a beautiful bedroom with its own patio doors opening onto the garden, and that special caring service which an established family tradition brings. Special three-day breaks are available from £180 per person, which include dinner, breakfast and VAT.

LOCATION

From A381 Kingsbridge to Salcombe Road at village of Malborough turn right and after church bear left at junction. It is then just 2 miles to the sea and the hotel.

" Oh to be in England now that Summer Lodge is here! "

Peter Stephens, Ottawa

Georgian dower house

SUMMER LODGE

The house that Thomas Hardy built in the county he wrote about

Dorset sighs with relief as the world passes it by. The names of unspoilt thatched villages mark the course of long, winding streams. It is the county of the famous and infamous; the Tolpuddle Martyrs and their Star Chamber persecutor, Judge Jeffries. To the discerning eye of England's aristocracy, Dorset was the preferred county for their stately homes, the Earls of Ilchester, for example, who built Summer Lodge as a dower house.

Thomas Hardy brought the area to life in such classics as *Tess of the d'Urbevilles* and, in his capacity as an architect, gave new life to Summer Lodge by adding the sitting room and the master bedroom.

The house is charming and lovingly restored and converted into a luxurious hotel by owners Nigel and Margaret Corbett who offer guests a friendly welcome, encouraging them to relax as if in their own home. The bedrooms have views over the walled gardens or overlook the village rooftops to the fields beyond.

Looking out over the garden through french windows is the dining room whose well-earned three rosettes say it all about the cuisine: fresh local produce is combined with the culinary expertise of Head Chef Timothy Ford to create his distinctive brand of English cooking.

The coast lies 12 miles south and there are many fine National Trust properties and outstanding gardens in the locality open to the public, including John Makepeace's furniture at Parnham House, and Jane Austen's and John Fowles' much written about Lyme Regis.

LOCATION

1 mile west of A37, halfway between Dorchester and Yeovil. In village take Summer Lane turning.

Evershot, Dorset DT2 OJR

Telephone 01935 83424
Fax 01935 83005

PROPRIETORS
Nigel and Margaret Corbett

MANAGER
Alison Barden

ROOM RATES

3 Singles £135
14 Doubles £195 - £255
Includes early morning tea, newspaper, full breakfast, Dorset cream tea, dinner and VAT

CHARGE/CREDIT CARDS

• *DC* • *MC* • *VI*

ACCOLADES
E.T.B. ♛♛♛♛ De Luxe
R.A.C. ★★★ + Merit Awards H C & R
A.A. ★★★ ❀❀❀
The Good Hotel Guide

FACILITIES
Outdoor pool, croquet, tennis, gardens
1 meeting room/max 20 people
Golf, riding and fishing nearby
Pheasant, deer and clay-pigeon shooting nearby

RESTRICTIONS
None

ATTRACTIONS
Kingston Lacey, Stourhead Gardens, Dorchester and Hardy's Cottage, Cerne Giant (The Rude Man of Dorset), Corfe Castle, Abbotsbury Swannery

AFFILIATIONS
Relais & Châteaux

NEAREST
MAJOR CITY:
Bath - 50 miles/1¼ hrs

MAJOR AIRPORT:
London Heathrow - 100 miles/2 hrs

RAILWAY STATION:
Dorchester - 10 miles/15 mins

RESERVATIONS
Direct with hotel

ACCESS CODES
Not applicable

" The food was excellent, neither 'gourmet' nor home-cooking, with menus suited for a long stay – different every night "

The Good Hotel Guide

TALLAND BAY HOTEL

Cornish manor house

Talland-by-Looe, Cornwall PL13 2JB

Telephone 01503 272667
Fax 01503 272940

PROPRIETORS

Barry and Annie Rosier

RATES PER PERSON

2 Singles	£35 - £45
16 Doubles/Twins	£40 - £70
2 Four-posters	£40 - £70

CHARGE/CREDIT CARDS

• DC • MC • VI

ACCOLADES

E.T.B. ♛♛♛♛ Highly Commended
R.A.C. ★★★ + Merit Award H
A.A. ★★★ ❀ 71%
The Good Hotel Guide César Award 1996

FACILITIES

Garden, croquet, sauna, outdoor pool, putting green, table tennis
1 meeting room/max 20 people
Golf, riding, sailing, boating, sea fishing and tennis nearby

RESTRICTIONS

No children under 5 years in dining room at night
Well behaved pets by prior arrangement – not in public rooms

ATTRACTIONS

Restormel Castle, Bodmin Moor, St Catherine's Castle, Fowey, Dupath Well House, Callington

AFFILIATIONS

Independent

NEAREST

MAJOR CITY:
Plymouth - 25 miles/30 mins

MAJOR AIRPORT:
Plymouth - 25 miles/30 mins

RAILWAY STATION:
Liskeard - 10 miles/15 mins

RESERVATIONS

Direct with hotel

ACCESS CODES

Not applicable

A rare example of a country house in a quite stunning location

Talland Bay Hotel is a delightful old Cornish manor house, parts of which date back to the 16th century, and is a rare example of a true country house hotel by the sea. In a rural setting, surrounded by over two acres of beautiful landscaped gardens, the hotel enjoys glorious views over the two dramatic headlands of Talland Bay.

Bedrooms, which have been recently redecorated, are individually furnished to a high standard; many have lovely garden and sea views, one has a large private balcony. and several have private gardens. Lounges open on to a south facing terrace by a heated outdoor swimming pool, so that during fine weather the hotel takes on an almost Mediterranean air.

Dinner menus are imaginative and incorporate much fresh regional produce – seafood from Looe, including lobster and crab, tender Cornish lamb and west country cheese – complemented by a list of some one hundred carefully selected wines from around the world. Tasty light luncheons are served throughout the year, together with a traditional luncheon on Sundays, and in the summer months, a cold buffet.

Talland Bay is a magically peaceful spot from which to explore this part of Cornwall; there are breathtaking cliff coastal walks at the hotel's doorstep leading to Looe, Polperro and beyond. There are wonderful subtropical gardens such as the famous "Lost Gardens of Heligan", great National Trust and privately owned houses and castles. For the sports minded there are several excellent golf courses, sailing, sea fishing and riding.

LOCATION

From Plymouth take the A38 south. Then the B3251 to Looe. Head towards Polperro for 2 miles. Left at crossroads .

"Each year we visit, we marvel at how such near perfection can be surpassed and it always is!"

Dody & Frank Viola, Michigan

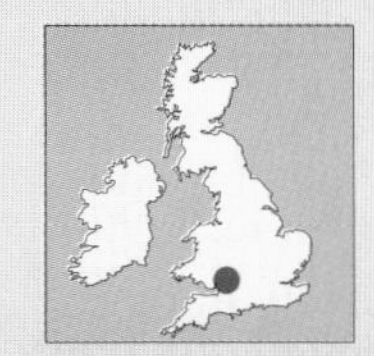

Tudor castle

THORNBURY CASTLE

Step through the centuries into the splendour of a Royal castle

The building of Thornbury Castle, commenced in 1511 by Edward Stafford, 3rd Duke of Buckingham, ended in 1521 when he was beheaded by Henry VIII. Buckingham's vast estates, including Thornbury, were confiscated by the King who stayed here with Anne Boleyn in 1535. Henry's daughter, Mary Tudor, lived here as a princess and when she became Queen she returned the Castle to the descendants of the late Duke.

Today, this Tudor castle-palace stands serenely in 15 acres, with distant views of the Severn Estuary and the hills of south Gloucestershire and Wales. Fine old panelling, tapestries and paintings enrich the interiors. There are 18 carefully restored bedchambers, most overlooking the oldest Tudor garden in England or the vineyard. Many have sumptuous four-poster beds and huge Tudor fireplaces.

The three intimate dining rooms have a gracious ambience to suit the superb cuisine.

Thornbury is an ideal base from which to discover the many historic sites, villages and towns located within an hour's drive of the castle, or cross the Severn Bridge into Wales and explore that beautiful country.

The Castle has recently been granted a license to perform marriage ceremonies.

LOCATION

From London, go west on the M4 to the intersection of the M5 (exit 20). Take the A38 north. After 6 miles take the B4061 to Thornbury. At the bottom of the High Street bear left into Castle Street. After 300 yards, the Castle entrance will be found to the left of the church.

Thornbury, Avon BS12 1HH

Telephone 01454 281182
Fax 01454 416188

PROPRIETORS
The Baron and Baroness of Portlethen

ROOM RATES

2 Singles	£75 - £95
7 Doubles/Twins	£95 - £145
8 Four-posters	£160 - £220
1 Suite	£175 - £210

Includes continental breakfast, early morning tea, newspaper and VAT

CHARGE/CREDIT CARDS

• DC • MC • VI

ACCOLADES
R.A.C. Blue Ribbon Award ★★★
A.A. ★★★ ❀❀
The Good Hotel Guide

FACILITIES
Croquet, gardens, heli-pad,
Licensed for weddings
2 meeting rooms/max 28 people
Golf, tennis, shooting, riding, ballooning, off-road safaris nearby

RESTRICTIONS
No children under 12 unless known
No facilities for disabled guests
No pets

ATTRACTIONS
Berkeley Castle, Chepstow Castle, Slimbridge Wildfowl Trust, The Cotswolds, Bath, Bristol, Wye Valley, Tintern Abbey

AFFILIATIONS
Pride of Britain
The Celebrated Hotels Collection

NEAREST
MAJOR CITY:
Bristol - 15 miles/20 mins
Bath - 23 miles/45 mins

MAJOR AIRPORT:
London Heathrow - 120 miles/2 hrs
Bristol - 21 miles/35 mins

RAILWAY STATION:
Bristol Parkway - 12 miles/15 mins

RESERVATIONS
Toll free fax in US: 800-635-3613

ACCESS CODES
APOLLO HT 41651
SABRE HK 36355
WORLDSPAN HK THORN

“ Completely relaxed, wholly pampered and now totally addicted ”

George Turner III, Washington

TIDES REACH HOTEL

Contemporary hotel

South Sands, Salcombe, Devon TQ8 8LJ

Telephone 01548 843466
Fax 01548 843954

PROPRIETOR
Roy Edwards

MANAGER
John Edwards

ROOM RATES
Single occupancy £60 - £90
35 Doubles/Twins £104 - £192
3 Family Suites £174 - £254
Includes full breakfast, dinner and VAT

CHARGE/CREDIT CARDS

• DC • MC • VI

ACCOLADES
E.T.B. ♛♛♛♛♛ Highly Commended
R.A.C. ★★★ + Merit Awards H C & R
A.A. ★★★ ❀ 79%
The Good Hotel Guide

FACILITIES
Indoor pool, gardens, squash, snooker, fitness centre, sauna, hair & beauty salon, windsurfing, sailing, waterskiing Golf, riding and beaches nearby

RESTRICTIONS
No children under 8 years
No smoking in restaurant
No facilities for disabled guests

ATTRACTIONS
Dartmoor National Park, South Devon coast, Plymouth, Dartmouth and Totnes Castle, Overbeck Museum and Gardens, National Shire Horse Centre

AFFILIATIONS
Independent

NEAREST
MAJOR CITY:
Plymouth - 24 miles/40 mins
MAJOR AIRPORT:
London Heathrow - 220 miles/4½ hrs
Plymouth - 24 miles/40 mins
RAILWAY STATION:
Totnes - 20 miles/30 mins

RESERVATIONS
Direct with hotel

ACCESS CODES
Not applicable

More than just an hotel, an ideal holiday location

A warm welcome awaits you at The Tides Reach Hotel. This elegant and luxuriously appointed hotel has been under the personal supervision of the owners, Mr and Mrs Roy Edwards, for more than 25 years. They have built up an enviable reputation for cuisine and standards of service complementing the hotel's situation which must be one of the most naturally beautiful in the British Isles.

Set in a commanding position, facing south in the tree-fringed sandy cove of South Sands, you could not wish for a more ideal location for a short break or relaxing holiday. The hotel stands just inside the mouth of the outstandingly scenic Salcombe Estuary.

At Tides Reach, one of the most important ingredients is the service – not just the extent to which it is available but also the manner in which it is carried out. To this end, the highly trained staff, carefully chosen for their caring and courteous service, are dedicated to making your stay a pleasant and memorable one.

In the Garden Room Restaurant the connoisseur of fine food and wine will find great satisfaction. Fresh fish and carefully selected local produce are expertly prepared to uphold the hotel's international reputation.

LOCATION

Leave A38 at Totnes, then follow A381 to Kingsbridge and thereafter to Salcombe as signposted.

“ Whenever I visit Cornwall the friendly welcome and good food at Trengilly Wartha is something to look forward to ”

Brenda, Baroness Dean of Thornton-le-Fylde

Country inn and restaurant — TRENGILLY WARTHA INN

The taste is unashamedly Gallic; the welcome delightfully Cornish

Trengilly Wartha is situated in a small hamlet in an Area of Outstanding Natural Beauty, about one mile from the village of Constantine. The hotel's name translated literally means, 'the settlement above the trees'. Nestling in the wooded valley of Polpenwith Creek the inn includes six acres of beautiful gardens and meadows.

Five of the six bedrooms have private bathrooms and all have a television, radio, direct-dial telephone and tea and coffee making facilities.

The restaurant is designed to mirror the atmosphere and style of a well-run French family hotel. The fixed price menu offers a good choice of innovative and imaginative dishes which change frequently to take advantage of fresh local produce, especially fish. The owners' long time personal interest in wines ensures a varied and original selection. One exception to the Gallic theme are the breakfasts which are most definitely traditionally English.

The Trengilly's bar is very much a friendly Cornish local inn. Being a Freehouse, they offer a broad selection of beers and have gained a good reputation for real ales. They always have four or five available served direct from the stillages. A good list of wines by the glass is supplemented by farm ciders, fruit wines and over 30 malt whiskies.

The bar menu includes both popular local dishes as well as some more unusual ones. There you can dine by a blazing fire in winter or under a vine shaded pergola in summer.

LOCATION

Situated just north of the Helford River. Approach Constantine via Gweek from the west and Penryn from the east. Follow signs into the valley to the hotel.

Constantine, Falmouth, Cornwall TR11 5RP

Telephone 01326 340332
Fax 01326 340332

PROPRIETORS

Nigel and Isabel Logan
Michael and Helen Maguire

ROOM RATES

6 Doubles/Twins £45 - £61
Includes full breakfast and VAT

CHARGE/CREDIT CARDS

• DC • JCB • MC • VI

ACCOLADES

E.T.B. ♛♛♛ Commended
A.A. QQQ
The Good Hotel Guide

FACILITIES

Garden, petanque
2 meeting rooms/max 40 people
Golf, riding and fishing nearby

RESTRICTIONS

No facilities for disabled guests

ATTRACTIONS

Tate Gallery,
St Ives,
Seal Sanctuary,
Mounts Bay,
Trebah and Glendurgan Gardens

AFFILIATIONS

Logis of Great Britain

NEAREST

MAJOR CITY:
Plymouth - 70 miles/1¾ hrs

MAJOR AIRPORT:
Exeter - 90 miles/2 hrs
Newquay - 20 miles/1 hr

RAILWAY STATION:
Falmouth - 7 miles/20 mins

RESERVATIONS

Direct with hotel

ACCESS CODES

Not applicable

"Hotel fine – food lovely – glad we stayed here . . . the beach at the bottom of the garden had the best rock pools in the entire world"

Margot Norman, The Times

WATERSMEET HOTEL

Edwardian country house

Mortehoe, Woolacombe, North Devon EX34 7EB

Telephone 01271 870333
Fax 01271 870890

PROPRIETORS
Mr and Mrs J B Wheeldon

MANAGER
Neil Bradley

ROOM RATES

4 Singles	£61 - £86
20 Doubles	£114 - £154
1 Suite	£126 - £174

Includes full breakfast, dinner and VAT

CHARGE/CREDIT CARDS

• MC • VI

ACCOLADES
E.T.B. ♛♛♛♛ Highly Commended
R.A.C. ★★★ + Merit Awards H C & R
A.A. ★★★ ❀❀ 76%

FACILITIES
Outdoor pool, croquet, lawn tennis, gardens, fishing, private access to beach
Golf nearby

RESTRICTIONS
Children under 8 take high tea, not dinner
Pets by arrangement

ATTRACTIONS
Mortehoe Village, Lorna Doone Valley, Dartington Glass, Arlington Court, Exmoor National Park, Saunton Championship Golf Course

AFFILIATIONS
Independent

NEAREST
MAJOR CITY:
Exeter/Taunton - 56 miles/1 ½ hrs

MAJOR AIRPORT:
London Heathrow - 250 miles/4 hrs
Exeter - 60 miles/1 ½ hrs

RAILWAY STATION:
Barnstaple - 16 miles/20 mins

RESERVATIONS
Direct with hotel

ACCESS CODES
Not applicable

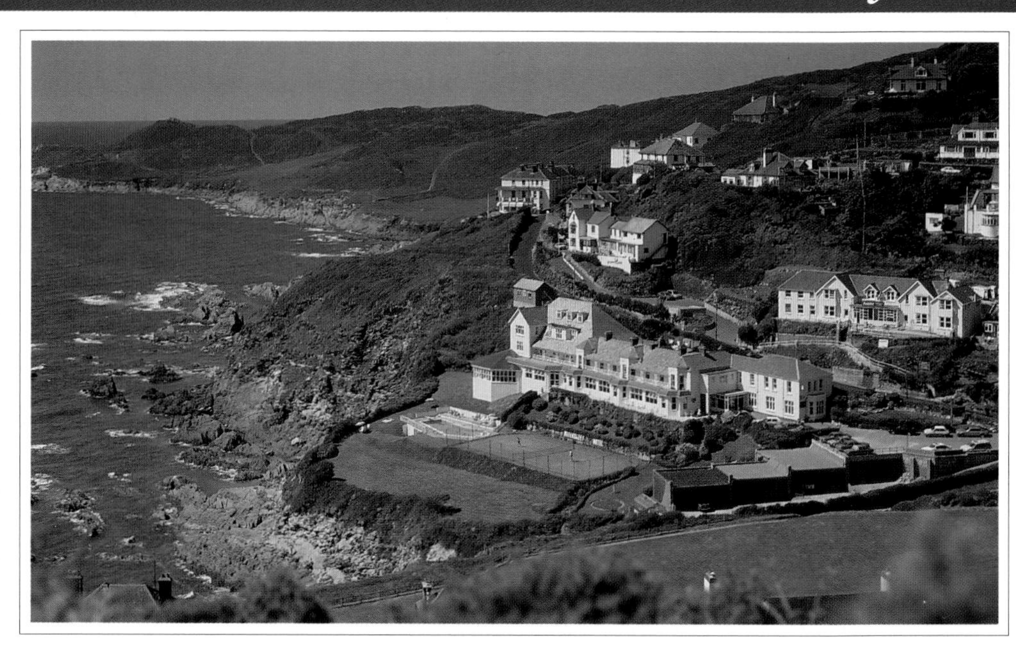

Edwardian elegance on the Atlantic coast touching the mystery of Exmoor

Built as a gentleman's country residence in 1907, the house has been tastefully restored to its former Edwardian elegance. Its position was carefully chosen and is one of the few places on the North Devon coast to face south, looking along three miles of Woolacombe sands to Hartland Point. With three acres of waterfront garden and steps leading to the secluded beach, Watersmeet attracts both guests who like to relax and do nothing and those who prefer to walk, ride, golf, shoot, hunt or simply swim and surf in the Atlantic rollers at the bottom of the garden.

From the golden sands of Woolacombe to the majestic cliffs of Trentishoe and the open moor behind, this special part of England is an unspoilt haven of peace and relaxation. The slanting trees, the stone circles, the Beast of Exmoor, the Doone Valley – all shrouded in mystery. This is the real England.

The village of Mortehoe is listed in the famous Domesday Book written in 1086. Of particular interest is the village church built in the 12th century which has one of the finest examples of a medieval barrel roof in England. Somewhat later, Woolacombe was used during the Second World War by the American Armed Forces training for the Normandy landings. An elegant memorial stone records the event. Major Finn remembers, "When I first saw Woolacombe beach, I thought I was in California or Florida. It seemed to be an ideal vacation site."

LOCATION

Quietly situated on the coast between Woolacombe and Mortehoe. Take A361 from Barnstaple. After about 10 miles, follow signs to Mortehoe.

Historic Houses
Castles & Gardens 1996

The Premier Guide to Britain's National Heritage

Please return to:

UK Office
SPECIALIST MARKETING DEPARTMENT
Reed Information Services
Windsor Court
East Grinstead House
East Grinstead
West Sussex
RH19 1XA
UNITED KINGDOM
TEL: (+44) 1342 335872
FAX: (+44) 1342 335948

USA Office
Howard Holmes
c/o Reed Reference Publishing
121 Chanlon Road
New Providence
New Jersey 07974
USA

TEL: (+1) 908 771 8785
FAX: (+1) 908 771 8755

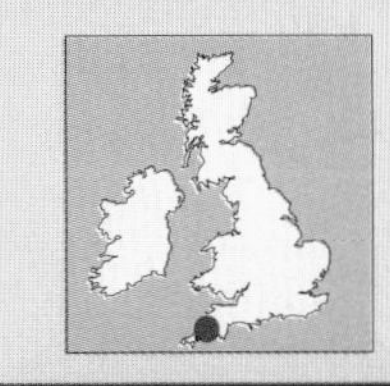

" One of the great pleasures of exploration is the contrast between extremes. I can think of nothing I have enjoyed more than eating at the superb Well House after a spell in the wilderness " Robin Hanbury-Tenison

Victorian country manor

THE WELL HOUSE

Discover romantic Cornwall from this delightful secluded manor

An intimate seven-bedroomed Victorian country manor, The Well House is tucked away down a country lane deep in Cornwall's Looe Valley, just beyond the River Tamar. Its facade, wrapped in rambling wisteria and jasmine trailers, is just one of the hotel's continuous series of delights that include top quality service, modern luxury and impeccable standards of comfort.

The dining room, with its magnificent bay windows and sun terrace overlooking the lawns, has a contemporary style which is echoed in the cooking though the traditions of the area are clearly in evidence. Cornish fish soup and freshly caught sea bass, turbot or lobster, along with wild boar, partridge and local English cheeses are all a feature of the daily changing menu at this internationally acclaimed restaurant.

Near the picturesque villages of Looe, Polperro and Fowey, the hotel is set in four acres of gardens, with an all-weather tennis court, swimming pool and croquet lawn – in a spectacular setting. Excellent fishing, riding and golf can be found nearby and the coastline offers matchless scenery and walking territory.

LOCATION

From Liskeard, take the B3254 to St Keyne, 3 miles south of Liskeard. Take the left fork by the church and the hotel is ½ mile from there.

St Keyne, Liskeard, Cornwall PL14 4RN

Telephone 01579 342001
Fax 01579 343891

PROPRIETOR

Nick Wainford

ROOM RATES

Single occupancy £60
8 Doubles £76.50 - £105
Includes continental breakfast and VAT

CHARGE/CREDIT CARDS

• *MC* • *VI*

ACCOLADES

A.A. ★★ ❀❀❀
The Good Hotel Guide
Courvoisier's Book of the Best

FACILITIES

Garden, croquet, tennis, outdoor swimming pool
1 meeting room/max 20 people
Golf, riding and fishing nearby

RESTRICTIONS

No children under 8 at dinner
No facilities for disabled guests

ATTRACTIONS

Fishing villages of Looe, Polperro and Fowey, Restormel and Cothele Castles, Lands End, St Michaels Mount

AFFILIATIONS

Pride of Britain

NEAREST

MAJOR CITY:
Plymouth - 16 miles/25 mins

MAJOR AIRPORT:
London Heathrow - 220 miles/3½ hrs
Plymouth - 16 miles/25 mins

RAILWAY STATION:
Liskeard - 3 miles/5 mins

RESERVATIONS

Direct with hotel

ACCESS CODES

Not applicable

" . . . and we left with the impression that we had just spent a delightful weekend with friends "

Arthur Moore

WHATLEY MANOR

17th century manor house

Easton Grey, Malmesbury, Wiltshire SN16 0RB

Telephone 01666 822888
Fax 01666 826120

DIRECTOR
Peter Kendall

ROOM RATES
Single occupancy £85 - £96
18 Doubles/Twins £112 - £136
1 Four-poster £136
Includes full breakfast and VAT

CHARGE/CREDIT CARDS

• *DC* • *MC* • *VI*

ACCOLADES
R.A.C. ★★★ + Merit Awards C & R
A.A. ★★★ 74%

FACILITIES
Outdoor pool, croquet, tennis, gardens, sauna, solarium, jacuzzi, snooker
2 meeting rooms/max 40 people

RESTRICTIONS
No facilities for disabled guests

ATTRACTIONS
Bath, Launceston Castle, Avebury, Ashdown House, Oldbury Castle, Lacock Abbey, Cirencester, The Cotswolds

AFFILIATIONS
Selected British Hotels

NEAREST
MAJOR CITY:
Bath - 20 miles/30 mins
Oxford - 45 miles/1 hr

MAJOR AIRPORT:
London Heathrow - 80 miles/1½ hrs

RAILWAY STATION:
Chippenham - 12 miles/15 mins

RESERVATIONS
Toll free in US: 800-323-5463

ACCESS CODES
AMADEUS HK BRSWHA
APOLLO/SABRE HK 32048
SAHARA HT 14854
WORLDSPAN HK WHATL

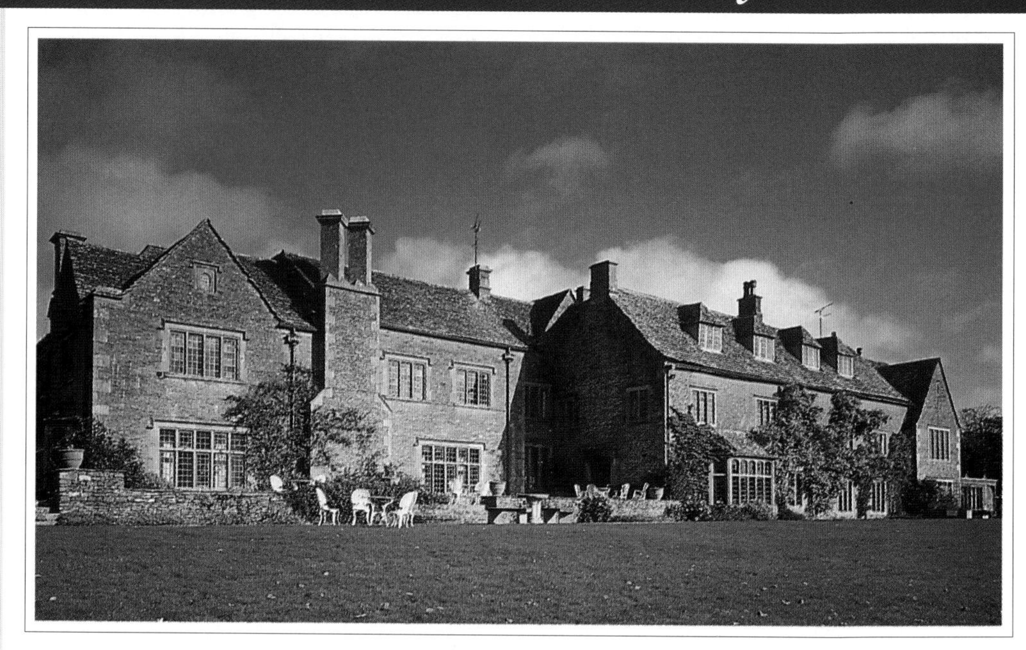

A Grade II listed building close to Bath and The Cotswolds

This manor house dates back to the 17th century and, today, provides visitors with the very best of country house comfort in traditional and unspoiled surroundings.

The large bedrooms, which look out over the gardens and estate, are comfortable with period furniture and all, of course, with private bathrooms. There are two panelled lounges, both with winter log fires, a book-lined library bar and a welcoming restaurant. Recreational facilities include swimming pool, tennis court, sauna, solarium and jacuzzi. In the old Saddle Room, still with the racks for polo sticks, there is now a snooker table.

Whatley Manor is easily reached from London (two hours) and both Heathrow and Gatwick airports. Bath and Cirencester are 30 minutes and Oxford, Stratford-upon-Avon and Salisbury are all within a couple of hours' drive.

A country house hotel should offer good cuisine, real comfort and unobtrusive service, but, above all, be a place to relax and unwind in an atmosphere that is both welcoming and informal. Whatley Manor is all of this.

LOCATION

On the edge of the Cotswolds, between Cirencester and Bath, Whatley Manor is on the B4040 about 3 miles west of Malmesbury and 6 miles from Junction 17 on M4.

" Our stay was enjoyably effortless as if we were family friends "

Sir John Harvey-Jones

Elizabethan manor house

WHITECHAPEL MANOR

History and haute cuisine in the grand manner

One of the few country hotels to achieve the miraculous combination of the grand and the homely, Whitechapel combines this rare quality with classic standards of service and cuisine within an idyllic setting. Listed Grade I, Whitechapel Manor, an Elizabethan manor house, is quintessentially English. The entrance hall displays a perfect Jacobean carved oak screen and, throughout the rest of the house, the William and Mary plasterwork and panelling complete with painted overmantels, is remarkable for its beauty and lusty country character.

All around is tranquil, unspoilt countryside rising up to the National Park of Exmoor and the most dramatic coastline in England. Whitechapel is the ideal position from which to explore the moors, coast, ancient woodland valleys, numerous gardens, Exmoor's villages (much is National Trust) and the wildlife, including the native Red Deer.

Return to enjoy afternoon tea on the terraced lawns or by the open fire in the great hall. Sit there as evening draws in to choose from the dinner menu which favours local game and superb seafood – a menu which has gained a well-earned international reputation. The atmosphere is relaxed, staff are professional and friendly and the gentle welcome by the Shaplands helps make your stay pleasurable and refreshing.

LOCATION

Come off the M5 at Junction 27 and take the A361 towards Barnstaple. After 30 miles, turn right at the roundabout.

Nr South Molton, North Devon EX36 3EG

Telephone 01769 573377
Fax 01769 573797

PROPRIETORS

John and Patricia Shapland

GENERAL MANAGER

Steve Evans

ROOM RATES

2 Singles	*£70 - £85*
6 Doubles	*£110 - £150*
1 Four-poster	*£170*
1 Suite	*£170*

Includes full breakfast, early morning tea, newspaper and VAT

CHARGE/CREDIT CARDS

• DC • JCB • MC • VI

ACCOLADES

E.T.B. Highly Commended
R.A.C. Blue Ribbon Award ★★
A.A. ★★
The Good Hotel Guide
Ackerman Heidsieck Clover Leaf Award

FACILITIES

Croquet and gardens
2 meeting rooms/max 40 people
Riding and fishing nearby

RESTRICTIONS

No smoking in dining room
No pets

ATTRACTIONS

Royal Horticultural Society's 'Rosemoor', Exmoor National Park, Dartington Glass, Arlington Court

AFFILIATIONS

Pride of Britain

NEAREST

MAJOR CITY:
Exeter - 35 miles/45 mins

MAJOR AIRPORT:
London Heathrow - 200 miles/3 hrs
Exeter - 40 miles/45 mins

RAILWAY STATION:
Tiverton Parkway - 28 miles/30 mins

RESERVATIONS

Toll free in US: 800-323-7308

ACCESS CODES

AMADEUS/SYSTEM 1 HK EXTWHI
SABRE HK 34713
WORLDSPAN HK 41208
APOLLO HK WHITM

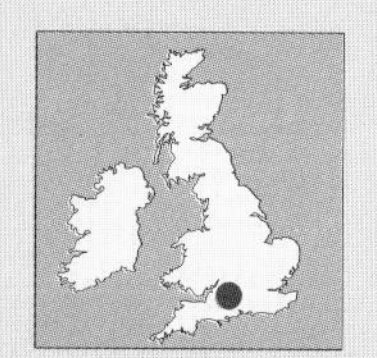

“ Spoilt for choice ”

Gordon Blue, Wiltshire Gazette & Herald

THE WOODBRIDGE INN

16th century inn

North Newnton,
Nr Pewsey,
Wiltshire SN9 6JZ

Telephone 01980 630266
Fax 01980 630266

PROPRIETORS
Lou and Terri Vertessy

ROOM RATES

Single occupancy	*£25 - £30*
3 Doubles/Twins	*£30 - £35*

Includes full breakfast and VAT

CHARGE/CREDIT CARDS

• *DC* • *MC* • *VI*

ACCOLADES
E.T.B. Commended
R.A.C. Acclaimed
A.A. QQ Rated
Wiltshire Pub of the Year 1993

FACILITIES
Gardens, fly fishing, billiards, petanque
1 meeting room/max 10 people
Golf, riding, hang-gliding nearby

RESTRICTIONS
No facilities for disabled guests
No smoking in restaurant
No pets (except Guide Dogs)

ATTRACTIONS
Bath, Stonehenge,
Avebury Stone Circles,
Salisbury Cathedral,

AFFILIATIONS
Logis of Great Britain
Les Routiers

NEAREST
MAJOR CITY:
Devizes - 10 miles/15 mins

MAJOR AIRPORT:
London Heathrow - 60 miles/1 ¼ hrs
Bristol - 60 miles/1 ¼ hrs

RAILWAY STATION:
Pewsey - 3 miles/5 mins

RESERVATIONS
Toll free in US: 800-989-7676

ACCESS CODES
Not applicable

Award-winning country inn between Stonehenge and Avebury

The Woodbridge Inn is situated in the heart of Pewsey Vale, an area designated as having ‘Outstanding Natural Beauty’.

This 16th century inn is ideally placed in tranquil countryside, on the banks of the Hampshire River Avon, midway between Stonehenge and the equally famous Avebury Stone Circles.

The river is well-stocked with wild trout and grayling and dry-fly fishing can be arranged on the premises. On a clear day, the White Horse on the hillside at Alton Barnes can be seen from the house. Inside, there are things to do – bar billiards, darts, and various table games. Outside, there is Boules – French petanque – (boules supplied), fishing on the river and a children's play area.

For refreshments, why not try one of the four (or all) traditional ales pulled by handpump. There is also a good range of imported beers, stout, low and non-alcoholic drinks, liqueurs, aperitifs and digestifs.

At The Woodbrige Inn you will find a rare, if not unique array of dishes, which should satisfy the traditionalist to the adventurous, as well as the vegetarian.

The dishes feature Mexican, Cajun, Thai and Indonesian, Chinese, Japanese, French, Italian, Hungarian, as well as English cuisines, so there is always something to please everyone.

LOCATION

3 miles south of Pewsey on the A345, just 10 miles from Stonehenge.

"The Woolacombe Bay Hotel is a credit to tourism in the West Country and the North Devon area in particular"

Mr Chris Fulford, West Country Tourist Board inspector

19th century hotel

WOOLACOMBE BAY HOTEL

Where old-world charm and modern pleasures meet

Rugged moors, rocky tors, hedges decked in Spring with wild violets. Endless walks along stunning beaches and headlands. Picturesque villages with old world charm and hostelries with locals yarning the day away . . . come and feel the freedom of Devon.

Set in six acres of quiet gardens gently leading to Woolacombe's three miles of golden sands, this seaside hotel, built in the halcyon days of the mid-1800s, exudes a relaxed air of friendliness and good living, comfort and service in the traditional style. Since it was used as the headquarters of the American Army Officers during the Second World War (and from whence training for the landings of the Normandy beaches took place) it has been extensively but sensitively modernised, combining discreetly, old fashioned ambience and modern charm.

The leisure facilities are extensive and superb. You can be pampered in luxury by the beautician and masseur; exercise in the new "hot house" Fitness Centre under qualified instructors in a choice of disciplines – Aerobics, fitness training or the Trim Trail. In addition, you will find heated swimming pools, golf, tennis and squash – all on site. More relaxing activities include leisurely games of snooker or bowls and, in the high season, a Children's Club.

Of course there is also the chance to simply catch up on a good book in the spacious lounges, or just having a snooze. Further afield, guests can charter the MV Frolica for fishing or an excursion to Lundy Island. The choice is absolutely yours at Woolacombe Bay .

LOCATION

Exit M5 at Junction 27. Follow A361 through Barnstaple towards Ilfracombe. Take B3343 off Mullacott Cross roundabout for Woolacombe. Follow signs for Woolacombe. The hotel is situated in centre of village.

South Street, Woolacombe, Devon EX34 7BN

Telephone 01271 870388
Fax 01271 870613

OWNER/PROPRIETORS

Mr and Mrs R M Lancaster

ROOM RATES

1 Single £55 - £100
34 Doubles/Twins £110 - £200
1 Four-poster £160 - £200
28 Family room prices on application
Includes full breakfast, dinner and VAT

CHARGE/CREDIT CARDS

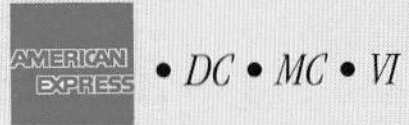

• DC • MC • VI

ACCOLADES

E.T.B. ♛♛♛♛♛ Highly Commended
R.A.C. ★★★
A.A. ★★★ 67%

FACILITIES

Garden, croquet, tennis, squash, indoor and outdoor pools, golf, bowls, health & beauty, gym
3 meeting rooms/max 200 people
Golf, riding, fishing and shooting nearby

RESTRICTIONS

No facilities for disabled guests
No pets

ATTRACTIONS

Arlington Court, Rosemore Gardens, Dartington Glass, Exmoor

AFFILIATIONS

Independent

NEAREST

MAJOR CITY:
Exeter/Plymouth - 56 miles/1½ hrs

MAJOR AIRPORT:
London Heathrow - 200 miles/4 hrs
Exeter/Bristol - 56 miles/1½ hrs

RAILWAY STATION:
Barnstaple - 15 miles/20 mins

RESERVATIONS

Direct with hotel

ACCESS CODES

Not applicable

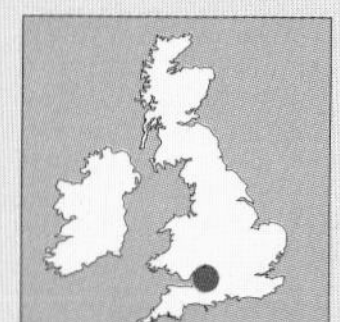

" It's difficult not to fall under the spell of Woolley Grange "

A well-known hotel guide

WOOLLEY GRANGE HOTEL

17th century manor house

Woolley Green,
Bradford-on-Avon,
Wiltshire BA15 1TX

Telephone 01225 864705
Fax 01225 864059

E-Mail woolley@eworld.com

PROPRIETORS
Nigel and Heather Chapman

ROOM RATES

1 Single	£80
17 Doubles/Twins	£95 - £135
2 Suites	£145

Includes full breakfast, early morning tea, newspaper and VAT

CHARGE/CREDIT CARDS

• DC • MC • VI

ACCOLADES
E.T.B. ♛♛♛♛ Highly Commended
A.A. ★★★ ❀❀❀ 75%
A.A. 'English Hotel of the Year' 1993
The Good Hotel Guide

FACILITIES
Outdoor swimming pool, croquet, tennis, gardens, games room, nursery, a collection of bicycles
2 meeting rooms/max 40 people
Riding and fishing nearby

RESTRICTIONS
No facilities for disabled guests
Dogs not allowed in dining room

ATTRACTIONS
Bath, Longleat, Stourhead, Bowood, Stonehenge, Wells, Lacock

AFFILIATIONS
Independent

NEAREST
MAJOR CITY:
Bath - 8 miles/10 mins

MAJOR AIRPORT:
London Heathrow - 90 miles/1½ hrs

RAILWAY STATION:
Bath - 8 miles/10 mins

RESERVATIONS
Toll free in US: 800-848-7721

ACCESS CODE
Not applicable

A splendid place for adults to relax – and the children will love it too!

Founded in 1989 by husband and wife team, Nigel and Heather Chapman, Woolley Grange is an award-winning luxury hotel, quite unlike any other. The home of the Baskerville family for 200 years, Woolley Grange is today home to the Chapmans, their four young children and two Springer Spaniels.

Within the Jacobean walls of this 17th century Cotswold stone manor house, there exists a stylish yet unusually relaxed atmosphere. You can anticipate very good food from a renowned English chef, Peter Stott, and a warm welcome from the whole family.

It's a place for adults to take their pleasures and also a place where children ask to be brought back to time and again. The Woolley Bears Den has a huge games room and a nursery supervised by nannies all day. Lunch and high tea are served in the nursery.

Only 10 minutes from Bath, 30 minutes from Stonehenge and 45 minutes from Salisbury; Woolley is set in rolling countryside on the fringe of the historic and undiscovered Saxon hillside town of Bradford-on-Avon, a local centre for antiques.

This is patently a family home where the qualities that make Woolley so special for those who live there, can be shared by guests.

LOCATION

On the B3105 1 mile north east of Woolley Green. Signpost Woolley Green.

The South

HMS Victory, flagship of the British Navy that fought and won the battle of Trafalgar under the command of Admiral Lord Horatio Nelson on the 24th October 1805. The battle ended the threat of a French invasion of Britain and established Britain's naval supremacy.

Heritage sites

The following heritage sites can be found on the map overleaf. The key numbers show where they are located.

BERKSHIRE

Donnington Castle	1

KENT

Dover Castle	2
Deal Castle	3
Dymchurch Martello Tower	4
Eynsford Castle	5
Lullingstone Roman Villa	6
Rochester Castle	7
Reculver Towers and Roman Fort	8
Walmer Castle and Gardens	9

HAMPSHIRE

Calshot Castle	10
Fort Brockhurst	11
Hurst Castle	12
Netley Abbey	13
Portchester Castle	14
Portsmouth: Royal Garrison Church	15
Silchester Roman City Walls and Amphitheatre	16
Titchfield Abbey	17
Wolvesey: Old Bishop's Palace	18

SURREY

Farnham Castle Keep	19
Waverley Abbey	20

SUSSEX

Battle Abbey and Site of The Battle of Hastings	21
Bramber Castle	22
Boxgrove Priory	23
Bayham Abbey	24
Pevensey Castle	25

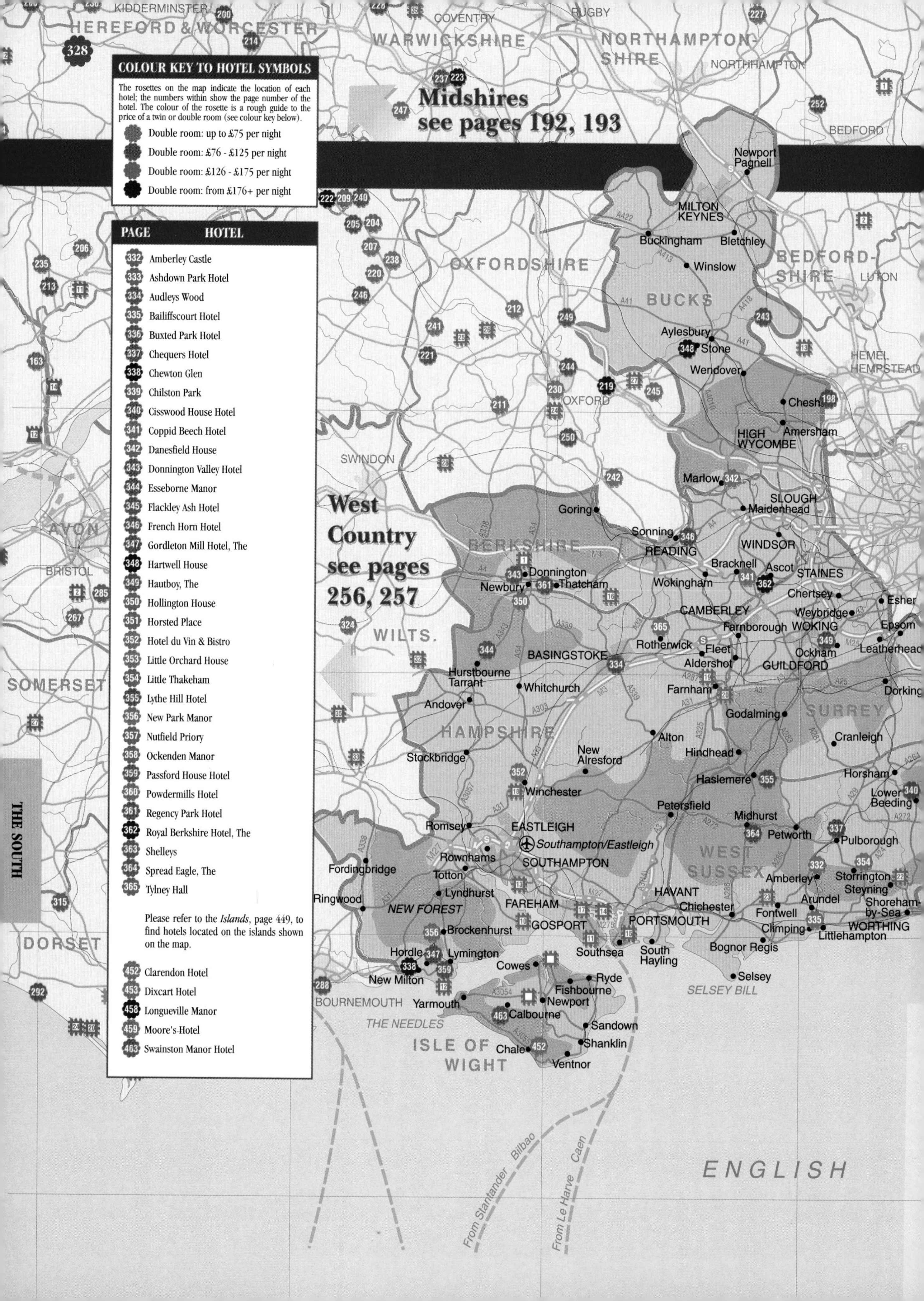
COLOUR KEY TO HOTEL SYMBOLS
The rosettes on the map indicate the location of each hotel; the numbers within show the page number of the hotel. The colour of the rosette is a rough guide to the price of a twin or double room (see colour key below).
Double room: up to £75 per night
Double room: £76 - £125 per night
Double room: £126 - £175 per night
Double room: from £176+ per night
PAGE HOTEL
332 Amberley Castle
333 Ashdown Park Hotel
334 Audleys Wood
335 Bailiffscourt Hotel
336 Buxted Park Hotel
337 Chequers Hotel
338 Chewton Glen
339 Chilston Park
340 Cisswood House Hotel
341 Coppid Beech Hotel
342 Danesfield House
343 Donnington Valley Hotel
344 Esseborne Manor
345 Flackley Ash Hotel
346 French Horn Hotel
347 Gordleton Mill Hotel, The
348 Hartwell House
349 Hautboy, The
350 Hollington House
351 Horsted Place
352 Hotel du Vin & Bistro
353 Little Orchard House
354 Little Thakeham
355 Lythe Hill Hotel
356 New Park Manor
357 Nutfield Priory
358 Ockenden Manor
359 Passford House Hotel
360 Powdermills Hotel
361 Regency Park Hotel
362 Royal Berkshire Hotel, The
363 Shelleys
364 Spread Eagle, The
365 Tylney Hall
Please refer to the Islands, page 449, to find hotels located on the islands shown on the map.
452 Clarendon Hotel
453 Dixcart Hotel
458 Longueville Manor
459 Moore's Hotel
463 Swainston Manor Hotel
Midshires see pages 192, 193
West Country see pages 256, 257
THE SOUTH
HEREFORD & WORCESTER
WARWICKSHIRE
NORTHAMPTON-SHIRE
OXFORDSHIRE
BUCKS
BEDFORD-SHIRE
BERKSHIRE
WILTS.
HAMPSHIRE
SURREY
WEST SUSSEX
SOMERSET
AVON
DORSET
ISLE OF WIGHT
ENGLISH
KIDDERMINSTER
COVENTRY
RUGBY
NORTHHAMPTON
BEDFORD
LUTON
HEMEL HEMPSTEAD
Newport Pagnell
MILTON KEYNES
Buckingham
Bletchley
Winslow
Aylesbury
Stone
Wendover
Chesham
Amersham
HIGH WYCOMBE
OXFORD
SWINDON
BRISTOL
Marlow
SLOUGH
Maidenhead
Goring
Sonning
READING
WINDSOR
Bracknell
Ascot
STAINES
Wokingham
Donnington
Newbury
Thatcham
Chertsey
Esher
CAMBERLEY
Weybridge
Epsom
Farnborough
WOKING
Leatherhead
Rotherwick
Fleet
Ockham
Aldershot
GUILDFORD
BASINGSTOKE
Hurstbourne Tarrant
Whitchurch
Farnham
Dorking
Andover
Godalming
Alton
Cranleigh
Stockbridge
New Alresford
Hindhead
Haslemere
Horsham
Winchester
Lower Beeding
Petersfield
Midhurst
Romsey
EASTLEIGH
Southampton/Eastleigh
Petworth
Pulborough
Fordingbridge
Rownhams
SOUTHAMPTON
Totton
Amberley
Storrington
Steyning
Lyndhurst
HAVANT
Ringwood
NEW FOREST
FAREHAM
Chichester
Arundel
Shoreham-by-Sea
Fontwell
PORTSMOUTH
Brockenhurst
GOSPORT
Climping
WORTHING
Littlehampton
Hordle
Lymington
Southsea
South Hayling
Bognor Regis
Cowes
New Milton
Ryde
Selsey
Fishbourne
SELSEY BILL
BOURNEMOUTH
Yarmouth
Newport
Calbourne
THE NEEDLES
Sandown
Shanklin
Chale
Ventnor
From Stantander Bilbao
From Le Harve Caen

SOUTH

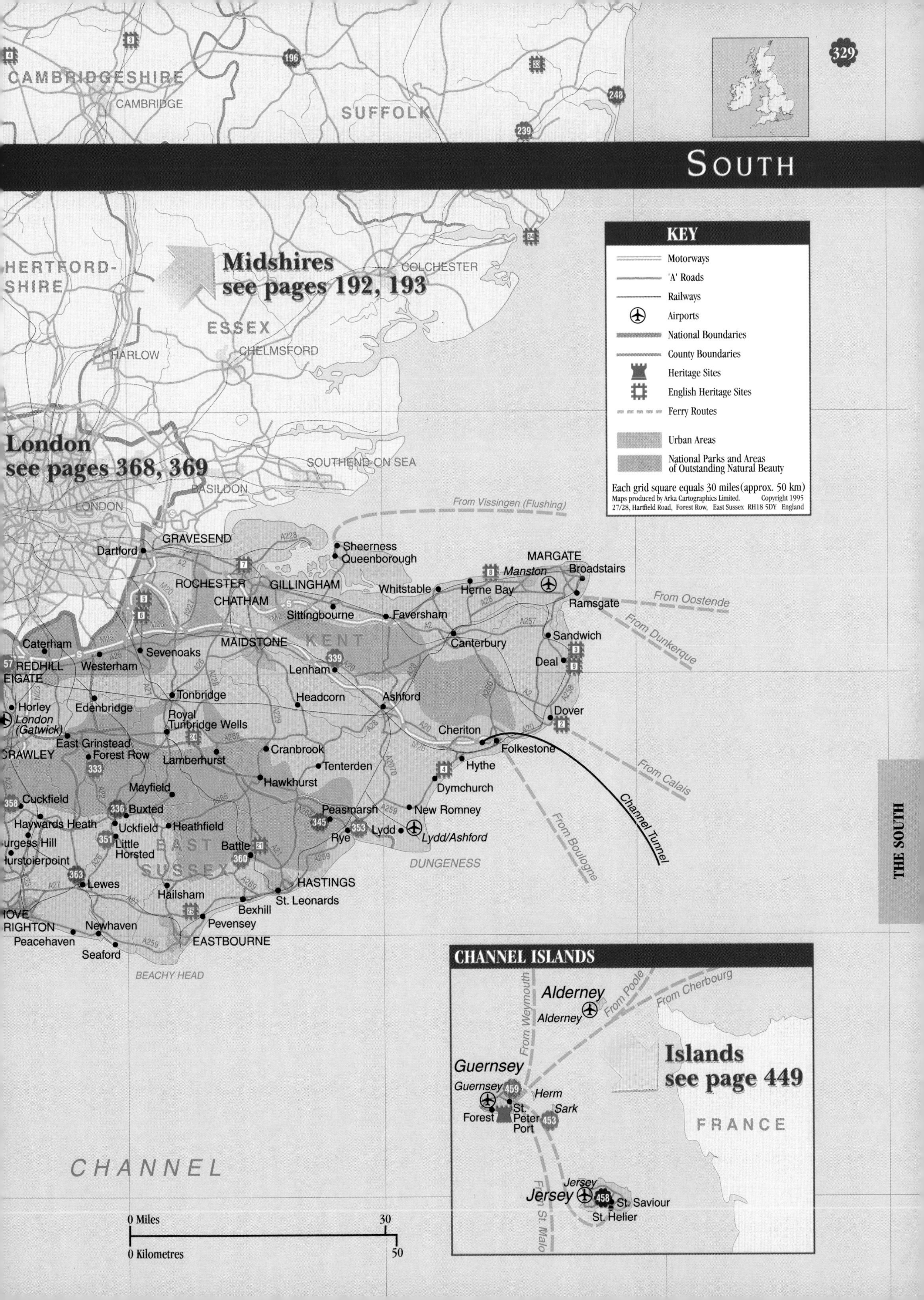

CAMBRIDGESHIRE
CAMBRIDGE
SUFFOLK
HERTFORD-SHIRE
Midshires see pages 192, 193
COLCHESTER
ESSEX
HARLOW
CHELMSFORD
London see pages 368, 369
SOUTHEND-ON SEA
BASILDON
LONDON
KEY
Motorways
'A' Roads
Railways
Airports
National Boundaries
County Boundaries
Heritage Sites
English Heritage Sites
Ferry Routes
Urban Areas
National Parks and Areas of Outstanding Natural Beauty
Each grid square equals 30 miles (approx. 50 km)
Maps produced by Arka Cartographics Limited. Copyright 1995
27/28, Hartfield Road, Forest Row, East Sussex RH18 5DY England
From Vissingen (Flushing)
GRAVESEND
Dartford
Sheerness
Queenborough
MARGATE
Manston
Broadstairs
ROCHESTER
GILLINGHAM
Whitstable
Herne Bay
CHATHAM
Sittingbourne
Faversham
Ramsgate
From Oostende
From Dunkerque
Sandwich
Caterham
MAIDSTONE
KENT
Canterbury
REDHILL
Westerham
Sevenoaks
Lenham
Deal
EIGATE
Tonbridge
Headcorn
Ashford
Horley
Edenbridge
Dover
London (Gatwick)
Royal Tunbridge Wells
Cheriton
Folkestone
East Grinstead
RAWLEY
Forest Row
Lamberhurst
Cranbrook
Tenterden
Hythe
From Calais
Hawkhurst
Dymchurch
Mayfield
Cuckfield
Buxted
Peasmarsh
New Romney
Channel Tunnel
Haywards Heath
Uckfield
Heathfield
Rye
Lydd
Lydd/Ashford
From Boulogne
urgess Hill
Little Horsted
EAST SUSSEX
Battle
urstpierpoint
DUNGENESS
Lewes
HASTINGS
Hailsham
St. Leonards
Bexhill
OVE
RIGHTON
Newhaven
Pevensey
Peacehaven
EASTBOURNE
Seaford
BEACHY HEAD
CHANNEL
0 Miles 30
0 Kilometres 50
CHANNEL ISLANDS
Alderney
Alderney
From Weymouth
From Poole
From Cherbourg
Guernsey
Islands see page 449
Guernsey
Herm
Sark
Forest
St. Peter Port
FRANCE
Jersey
Jersey
St. Saviour
St. Helier
From St. Malo
THE SOUTH

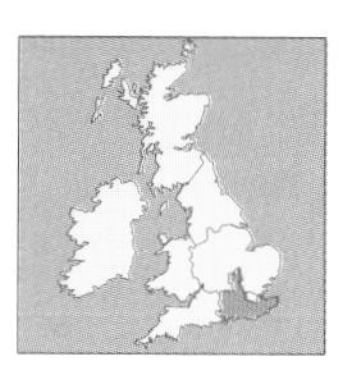

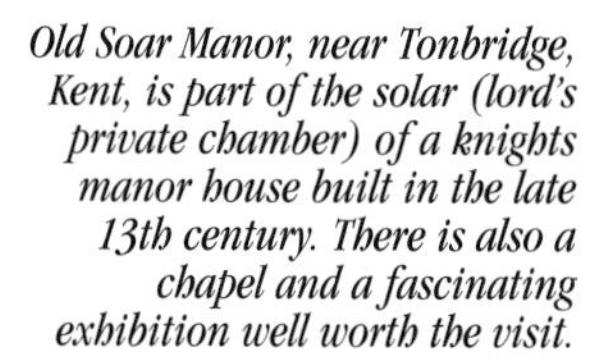

Old Soar Manor, near Tonbridge, Kent, is part of the solar (lord's private chamber) of a knights manor house built in the late 13th century. There is also a chapel and a fascinating exhibition well worth the visit.

COUNTIES

Berkshire

Buckinghamshire

Hampshire

Kent

Surrey

Sussex

A schoolboy in a much loved railway poster says "Summer comes sooner in the South". The South has Britain's lowest rainfall, and yet its gardens flourish and the fields are green. Within the (usually!) sunny scenery are historic cities, castles and stately homes, cottages and village inns. The Duke of Norfolk's Arundel Castle towers high over its domain in West Sussex. Deep in Dorset's countryside, Sir Walter Raleigh's castle ennobles the ancient town of Sherborne. In Kent, you can join pilgrims at Canterbury Cathedral where Thomas a Becket was murdered. In Hampshire, Alfred the Great's capital Winchester was once Britain's fifth largest town. Not far away is the New Forest, the royal hunting preserve of William the Conqueror.

The sea has always been in our blood. History and high drama are to be found in the seaports and rocky cliffs. You can board Nelson's flagship 'Victory' in Portsmouth, visit the ancient town of Hastings where William conquered, walk on the White Cliffs of Dover where Napoleon and Hitler did not. Illustrious royal visitors led the way south in the 18th century when the value of sea air was proclaimed by Dr Richard Russell, "Doctor Brighton". Today, seaside resorts like Brighton, Bournemouth, Eastbourne and Bognor, recognising they should not live by summer alone, offer superb shopping and entertainment.

The South has a tradition of hospitality. While you are here, don't miss sampling some Southern specialities such as Blue Vinny blue-veined cheese in Dorset, Victoria plums and Cox's Orange Pippin apples from Kent. In that county too are more than 10,000 acres of hop fields, which give British beer its individual flavour and partly explains the popularity of the many village inns and country pubs where local people meet and talk with their friends and visitors.

Castles, Stately Homes, Historic Houses

Bateman's, Burwash, E Sussex. 17th c Sussex ironmaster's house. Home of Rudyard Kipling.

Canterbury Heritage Museum, Kent. Treasures from 2,000 years in medieval building on River Stour. Saxon gold.

Chartwell, Westerham, Kent. Home of Sir Winston Churchill. His study, uniforms, photographs. Garden with lake and Golden Rose walk.

Chilworth Manor House, Surrey. 14th c walled garden laid out by Sarah, Duchess of Marlborough on old monastery site.

Hastings Castle, E Sussex. Fragmentary remains of Norman castle built by William the Conqueror. 1066 story interpretation.

Hever Castle, Kent. Childhood home of Anne Boleyn, much restored by Astor family. Moat, fine interior, topiary maze.

Jordans, Buckinghamshire. William Penn burial ground and exhibition. Quaker Meeting House and Wrest Park Mansion nearby.

Leeds Castle, Leeds, Kent. Supremely beautiful 12th c castle on two islands in lake. Tapestries, art treasures.

Lewes Castle, E Sussex. Early Norman motte and shell keep with 12th c towers and 14th c barbican gateway. Descriptive displays.

Portchester Castle, Hampshire. Roman-Saxon shore fort. Norman additions.

Royal Pavilion, Brighton, E Sussex. Eastern style palace of Prince Regent, built by Nash.

Southsea Castle, Portsmouth, Hampshire. Fort built by Henry VIII in 1545 as part of national coastal defences.

Windsor Castle, Berkshire. The chief royal Residence, built by William the Conqueror. Queen Victoria is buried in its Home Park.

Museums, Galleries & Modern Highspots

Brighton Museum & Art Gallery, Sussex. 1873 Moorish design building with fine collections of ceramics, art nouveau, art deco.

Canterbury Tales, Canterbury, Kent. Audiovisual evocation of Chaucer's pilgrims on journey to Thomas Becket's shrine.

Dickens Centre, Rochester, Kent. Unique experience of life and characters of Britain's greatest Victorian novelist.

Eastbourne Heritage Centre, Sussex. How the town became "Empress of Watering Places". Old penny-in-slot machines.

Martello Tower Visitor Centre, Folkestone, Kent. A defense structure built 1805 to guard against invasion by Napoleon.

National Motor Museum, Beaulieu, Hampshire. Motoring history from 1896. Abbey ruins.

Rye Town Sound & Light Show, E Sussex. The dramatic story of smugglers and revenue men.

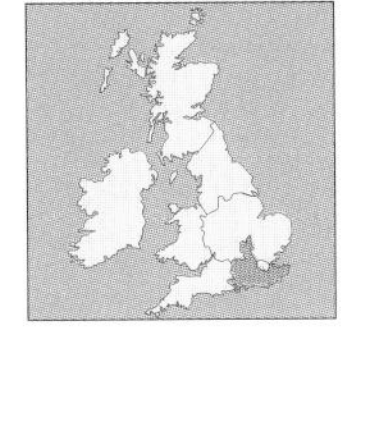

TOURIST OFFICE INFORMATION

Further information about the South will be gladly supplied by:

Heart of England Tourist Board,
Woodside, Larkhill Road,
Worcester, WR5 2EQ
Tel: 01905 763436

Southern Tourist Board,
40 Chamberlayne Road, Eastleigh,
Hampshire SO5 5JH
Tel: 01703 620006

For international offices, please turn to page 480

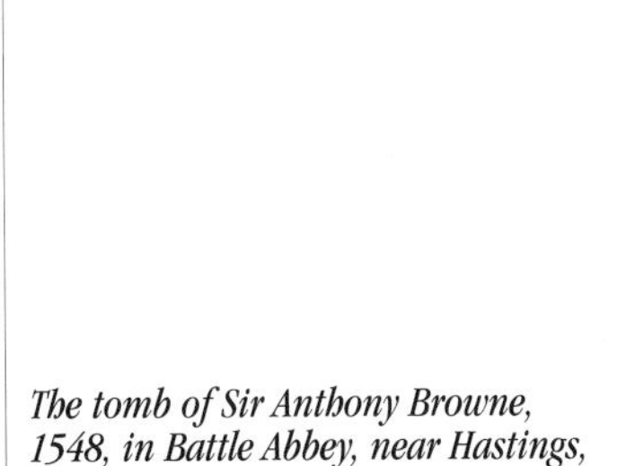

The tomb of Sir Anthony Browne, 1548, in Battle Abbey, near Hastings, Kent. William the Conqueror slayed King Harold here and became the first Norman King of England in 1066. He swore he would build an abbey if he won and did so on the spot where his adversary died.

White Cliffs Experience, Dover, Kent. Invasions and threats from Roman times to Second World War.

Churches & Cathedrals

Canterbury Cathedral, Kent. Founded 597. Norman crypt, Superb medieval stained glass. Mother Church of Anglican Communion.

Chantry Chapel, Buckingham. Rebuilt in 1475, retaining a magnificent Norman doorway.

Chichester Cathedral, W Sussex. Mainly Norman architecture. Detached bell tower.

Guildford Cathedral, Surrey. New Anglican cathedral, consecrated 1961. Notable glass engravings.

Portsmouth Cathedral, Hampshire. Strong seafaring links. Tomb of unknown sailor from the Mary Rose.

Rochester Cathedral, Kent. Consecrated 604. Present building dates from 1077.

St Nicholas, Brockenhurst, Hampshire. Oldest Norman church in the New Forest, mentioned in Domesday Book.

Winchester Cathedral, Hampshire. Started in 1079, completed 1404. Huge perpendicular nave. Site of Saxon church built by King Alfred.

Windsor, Berkshire. St George's Chapel, built 1475. Chapel of the Order of the Garter. Burial place of ten sovereigns.

Parks & Gardens

Queen Eleanor's Garden, Winchester Castle. Reconstruction of 13th c garden.

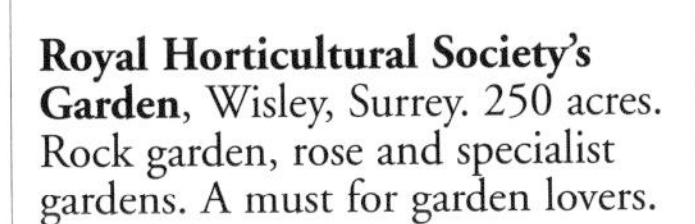

Royal Horticultural Society's Garden, Wisley, Surrey. 250 acres. Rock garden, rose and specialist gardens. A must for garden lovers.

Sheffield Park Gardens, Danehill, W Sussex. 100 acres of landscaped gardens with lakes on five levels. Rhododendrons, azaleas, waterlilies.

Sissinghurst Garden, Kent. Created by Vita Sackville-West round her Elizabethan mansion.

Stowe Landscape Gardens, Buckingham. One of Europe's finest, with works by Vanbrugh, Kent and Gibbs.

Windsor Great Park, Berkshire. 4,800 spacious acres beside Windsor Castle, with starling roost and heronry.

Sport & Outdoors

Horse Racing. The Derby is held on Epsom Downs, Surrey on the first Saturday of June.

Show Jumping. Hickstead, E Sussex – the Hickstead Derby is famous for the fearsome height of its fences.

Veteran Car Run. Brighton, E Sussex. 1st Sunday in Nov. Historic vehicles make their way down from London in May.

The Royal Pavilion, Brighton, Sussex, was built by John Nash in 1811 in the pseudo-Indian style. The fairytale palace became a Royal residence for George III and is as eccentric inside as it is out. It was said that Queen Victoria loathed it and it ceased to be a Royal residence in 1845. Today it houses a large exhibition and memorabilia of the Georgian period.

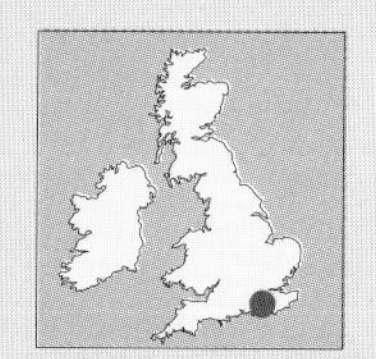

"Amberley Castle – the friendliest castle in the world

Mrs R Simpson

AMBERLEY CASTLE

10th century castle

Amberley,
Nr Arundel,
West Sussex BN18 9ND

Telephone 01798 831992
Fax 01798 831998

PROPRIETORS
Joy and Martin Cummings

GENERAL MANAGER
Gordon Riddell

ROOM RATES

11 Doubles	*£130 - £195*
2 Twins	*£160 - £250*
2 Four-posters	*£250 - £275*

Includes full breakfast and VAT

CHARGE/CREDIT CARDS

• DC • MC • VI

ACCOLADES
R.A.C. Blue Ribbon Award ★★★
A.A. ★★★ ❀❀
Country Hotel of the Year 1995 – a leading guide

FACILITIES
Garden, croquet, en-suite jacuzzis, heli-pad
3 meeting rooms/max 50 people
Golf, riding, shooting and fishing nearby

RESTRICTIONS
No facilities for disabled guests

ATTRACTIONS
Arundel Castle, Petworth, Amberley Chalk Pits, Goodwood House

AFFILIATIONS
Small Luxury Hotels

NEAREST
MAJOR CITY:
London - 55 miles/1 hr 10 mins

MAJOR AIRPORT:
London Gatwick - 30 miles/45 mins

RAILWAY STATION:
Amberley - 1 mile/5 mins

RESERVATIONS
Toll free in US/Canada: 800-525-4800

ACCESS CODES
AMADEUS/SYSTEM 1 LX LONAMB
WORLDSPAN LX ESHAC
AXESS LX 5631
SABRE LX 26404
APOLLO LX 4517

Peace and serenity within the 60 foot walls of a 900-year-old castle

For more than 900 years, Amberley Castle has stood in its serene landscape of undulating downland and hauntingly beautiful water meadows. Built originally by Bishop Luffa of Chichester as a country retreat, the magnificent building has extended hospitality to Henry VIII, Charles II and Elizabeth I.

Lovingly restored by its resident owners, Joy and Martin Cummings, Amberley Castle was transformed into the only English medieval castle hotel in 1988. With its 15 individually designed rooms, each with jacuzzi bath en suite, Amberley Castle offers superb luxury and every convenience expected by today's discerning travellers, while retaining all its authentic grandeur.

The 12th century Queen's Room restaurant, with its elegant barrel vaulted ceiling and 17th century mural, provides a splendid setting for award-winning castle cuisine. The imaginative Executive Head Chef Simon Thyer bases his cooking on English culinary heritage with a modern-day interpretation.

Located just 60 miles from London and conveniently accessible by air and channel ferry ports, Amberley Castle lies on the edge of one of the prettiest Sussex downland villages, amidst a host of historic landmarks such as Arundel Castle and Petworth House. There is shopping and internationally-acclaimed theatre in Brighton and Chichester, Glorious Goodwood for horse racing, Cowdray Park for polo – and much more besides.

LOCATION

Amberley Castle is on the B2139, off the A29 between Fontwell and Bury.

" Again, thank you all for making our weekend so specially wonderful. We felt to be part of the family . . . "

Dr Loveday

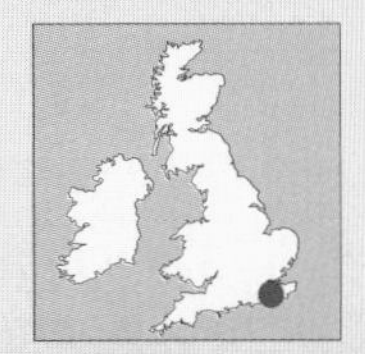

Victorian mansion ASHDOWN PARK HOTEL

Much to see and do from this Victorian showpiece

Built in 1867 and restored in the 1990s, this impressive mansion is set in 186 acres of beautiful countryside in the heart of Ashdown Forest. Whether staying for a weekend, a wedding reception, honeymoon or for business, Ashdown Park Hotel is the complete venue. The gilt and embossed ceilings of the lounges, the tranquil view from the leaded windows and open fires complete the friendly and welcoming atmosphere.

In these beautiful surroundings you can relax and enjoy a drink before or after a delectable meal in the award-winning Anderida Restaurant.

Great thought has gone into the design of the 95 bedrooms – every room has individual characteristics, is beautifully decorated and en suite. From the elegance of the four-poster bedrooms the views of Ashdown Park stretch out, providing the perfect setting for honeymooners and romantics.

Relaxation is assured – the swimming pool, beauty salon, sauna, snooker and gentle walks are invitingly to hand. For the more energetic there are squash courts, gymnasium, tennis courts and a nine-hole golf course. Ashdown Park is ideally situated for a wide variety of interests and activities. Historic Hever Castle, Penshurst Place and Tunbridge Wells are within easy reach, as are the Bluebell Railway, Brighton with its exotic Pavilion, Glyndebourne for opera lovers and Lingfield Race Course for the sport of kings.

LOCATION

Leave M23, Junction 10. Take A264 to East Grinstead then the A22 to Eastbourne. 2 miles south of Forest Row, turn left at Wych Cross to Hartfield. Ashdown Park is on the right hand side.

Wych Cross, Forest Row, East Sussex RH18 5JR

Telephone 01342 824988
Fax 01342 826206

GENERAL MANAGER

Graeme C Bateman

ROOM RATES

7 Singles	*£94 - £120*
61 Doubles/Twins	*£115 - £145*
24 Suites	*£155 - £230*
6 Four-posters	*£280*

Includes full breakfast and VAT

CHARGE/CREDIT CARDS

• DC • MC • VI

ACCOLADES

E.T.B. ♛♛♛♛♛ De Luxe
R.A.C. Blue Ribbon Award ★★★★
A.A. ★★★★ ❀❀
Hotel of the Year 1994 - Southeast England Tourist Board

FACILITIES

Garden, croquet, squash, snooker, indoor swimming pool, sauna, jacuzzi, gym, health & beauty, tennis, 9-hole golf
15 meeting rooms/max 200 people
Golf and riding nearby

RESTRICTIONS

No pets

ATTRACTIONS

Hever Castle, Sheffield Park, Wakehurst Place, Tunbridge Wells

AFFILIATIONS

Small Luxury Hotels

NEAREST

MAJOR CITY:
Lewes - 10 miles/20 mins

MAJOR AIRPORT:
London Gatwick - 14 miles/20 mins

RAILWAY STATION:
East Grinstead - 5 miles/10 mins

RESERVATIONS

Toll free in US/Canada: 800-355-6161

ACCESS CODES

SABRE LX 38628
AMADEUS LX LGWAPH
WORLDSPAN/SAHARA LX LGWAD
APOLLO LX 44666
SYSTEM 1 LX LON100
AXCESS LX 5657

“ The staff create a very friendly atmosphere ”

A G & P Field, Birmingham

AUDLEYS WOOD

Victorian house

Alton Road,
Basingstoke,
Hampshire RG25 2JT

Telephone 01256 817555
Fax 01256 817500

GENERAL MANAGER
Robert Hunter

ROOM RATES
69 Doubles/Twins £95 - £125
2 Four-posters £165
Includes VAT

CHARGE/CREDIT CARDS

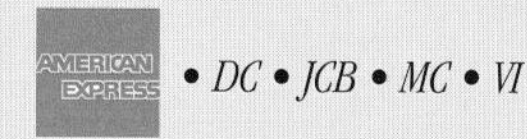

• DC • JCB • MC • VI

ACCOLADES
E.T.B. ♛♛♛♛♛ De Luxe
R.A.C. ★★★★ + Merit Awards C & R
A.A. ★★★★ ❀❀ 72%

FACILITIES
Garden, croquet, heli-pad
5 meeting rooms/max 65 people
Golf and riding nearby

RESTRICTIONS
Pets by prior arrangement

ATTRACTIONS
Jane Austen Museum, The Vyne, Winchester, Watercress Line

AFFILIATIONS
A Thistle Country House Hotel

NEAREST
MAJOR CITY:
Winchester - 18 miles/25 mins

MAJOR AIRPORT:
London Heathrow - 37 miles/50 mins
Eastleigh - 20 miles/35 mins

RAILWAY STATION:
Basingstoke - 2 miles/5mins

RESERVATIONS
Toll free in US/Canada: 800-847-4358
Toll free in Australia: 800-062-055

ACCESS CODES
AMADEUS/SYSTEM 1 TI LHRAUD
APOLLO TI 13619
SABRE TI 20421
WORLDSPAN TI BNKAH

A majestic example of Victorian comfort and style

When Henry Adolphus Simonds bought Audleys Wood as his family home in 1899, he bought a spacious brick-faced house surrounded by woods and farmland, just 1½ miles south of Basingstoke on the Alton Road.

In true Victorian tradition the house has a covered porte cochère entrance, much notable interior wood panelling, a magnificent conservatory, cosy fireplaces and plenty of space.

The conservatory has now become a renowned restaurant – a light, vaulted room, complete with minstrel's gallery – and the wood panelled rooms have become discreet meeting rooms and lounges. Some of the oak panelling dates from the mid-1600's and is reputed to have come from Tewkesbury Abbey a century ago.

On the first floor are the original bedrooms – some now converted into luxury four-poster bed suites. The hotel has another 71 beautifully decorated, spacious bedrooms each featuring a marble-tiled bathroom, bathrobes and luxury toiletries, satellite TV, minibar, trouser press, hair dryer and refreshments tray.

The food and wine are similarly aimed to please the discerning guests. The menus are extensive and Chef Cleveland has developed an outstanding reputation for quality and innovation. General Manager, Robert Hunter, has laid down an extensive cellar and has placed many interesting items on the hotel's wide-ranging wine list.

LOCATION

Situated along the A339 Alton Road, 1½ miles south of Basingstoke off the M3 Junction 6. Audleys Wood is situated on right, ⅓ mile after the Venture roundabout.

" *This is our favourite place on earth* "

Mark Elliott, London

Medieval manor house

BAILIFFSCOURT HOTEL

Truly a coastline medieval retreat

Gothic mullioned windows wink through the trees along the approach to Bailiffscourt. As you walk under the gnarled 15th century beams you can sense the dignity of the Middle Ages. Yet Bailiffscourt is an extraordinary architectural fantasy – a medieval manor built in the 1930s at immense cost to satisfy a caprice of the late Lord Moyne, from materials dating as far back as the 13th century.

Bailiffscourt has to be experienced to fully appreciate the unique atmosphere and special charm which captivates its guests. The 20 bedrooms are luxuriously furnished, many with four-poster beds, oak beams and log fires for winter nights. There is a truly magnificent master suite with cathedral ceiling, four-poster bed, open log fire and two baths side-by-side.

A special feature is the walled-courtyard filled with climbing roses, occasionally visited by the peacocks who have made Bailiffscourt their home for many years. Thatched cottages and mellow stone buildings are grouped around the courtyard and surrounded by 23 acres of idyllic parkland bordering the beach.

The innovative young head chef is receiving the highest accolades for his imaginative cuisine and the restaurant is renowned for its superb food accompanied by the finest wines.

LOCATION

Off the A259 at Climping, near Arundel, 'next to the sea'.

Climping, Nr Arundel, West Sussex BN17 5RW

Telephone 01903 723511
Fax 01903 723107

DIRECTORS

Sandy and Anne Goodman

ROOM RATES

1 Single from	*£80*
25 Doubles	*£110 - £225*
1 Suite	*£250*

Includes full breakfast and VAT

CHARGE/CREDIT CARDS

• DC • MC • VI

ACCOLADES

E.T.B. ♛♛♛♛♛ De Luxe
R.A.C. ★★★ + Merit Awards H C & R
A.A.★★★ ❀❀❀ 77%
The Good Hotel Guide

FACILITIES

Outdoor pool, croquet, tennis, gardens, heli-pad
2 meeting rooms/max 40 people
Golf, riding and fishing nearby

RESTRICTIONS

No facilities for disabled guests

ATTRACTIONS

Arundel Castle,
Petworth,
Chichester,
Brighton,
Goodwood House

AFFILIATIONS

Grand Heritage Hotels

NEAREST

MAJOR CITY:
Chichester - 8 miles/15 mins

MAJOR AIRPORT:
London Gatwick - 35 miles/45 mins

RAILWAY STATION:
Littlehampton - 3 miles/5 mins

RESERVATIONS

Toll free in US: 800-HERITAGE

ACCESS CODES

Not applicable

"Thanks for a lovely three week stay"

Richard Briers, actor

BUXTED PARK HOTEL

Georgian mansion

Buxted, Uckfield,
East Sussex TN22 4AY

Telephone 01825 732711
Fax 01825 732770

GENERAL MANAGER
Mark Robson

ROOM RATES

2 Singles	*£75*
34 Doubles/Twins	*£95*
7 Master Rooms/Suites	*from £125*

Includes full breakfast and VAT

CHARGE/CREDIT CARDS

• DC • MC • VI

ACCOLADES
Awards pending

FACILITIES
Garden, lakes, croquet, putting, sauna, gym, outdoor swimming pool, jacuzzi, health & beauty, snooker, heli-pad
6 meeting rooms/max 170 people
Cinema with seating for 54
Golf and fishing nearby

RESTRICTIONS
No smoking restaurant
Pets by prior arrangement

ATTRACTIONS
Glyndebourne,
Brighton Royal Pavilion,
Bluebell Railway,
Sheffield Park Gardens,
Ashdown Forest

AFFILIATIONS
Independent

NEAREST
MAJOR CITY:
London - 48 miles/1½ hrs

MAJOR AIRPORT:
London Gatwick - 28 miles/40 mins

RAILWAY STATION:
Buxted - ½ mile/2 mins

RESERVATIONS
Direct with hotel

ACCESS CODES
Not applicable

Queen Victoria loved it here . . . and so will you

Acres of beautiful Sussex countryside stretch before this splendid Georgian mansion, where every view from its graceful terraces is quite magnificent. It was these glorious vistas which drew both Queen Victoria and Queen Mary, wife of George V, back to Buxted Park time and again.

Built in 1725 – a period of distinctive, elegant architecture – Buxted Park has been sympathetically refurbished and restored to enhance its grandeur. It is set on the edge of Ashdown Forest in 312 acres of private gardens, lakes and parkland where fallow deer roam free and wildlife abound.

Guest bedrooms are comfortably furnished and provide all the facilities demanded by today's discerning traveller. Two restaurants offer superior dining (al fresco, in the Summer, is an added option). Afternoon tea – that great British tradition – can be taken in one of several drawing rooms and you are sure to find your favourite drink in the delightful bar.

For the energetic, there's a well-equipped gymnasium and a host of outdoor leisure pursuits. For those seeking rest and relaxation, there are some excellent walks and a lovely outdoor pool with an extensive lounging area (an indoor swimming pool will be open by Spring '96). And, for those who wish simply to be pampered, there's a wide range of beauty treatments from which to choose.

Discover for yourself why Queen Victoria loved it so much.

LOCATION

Buxted Park is on the A272 a mile north of Uckfield and is approached by a long private drive (clearly signposted).

“ My home . . . away from home ”

F A Barber, Gloucestershire

16th century historic house

CHEQUERS HOTEL

The quintessential small English hotel graced with period antiques

Chequers is first recorded as changing hands in 1548, and, in the stewardship of the present owner, John Searancke, has become a fine example of the quintessential small English hotel. Gracefully improved and extended over the years, the hotel stands at the heart of the local conservation area, facing out across the Arun Valley towards the South Downs. The hotel is Grade II listed as of historic interest.

Luxurious bedrooms, mostly now with en-suite bathrooms, are appointed to a high standard, with colour TV, trouser press, hair-drier, hospitality tray, and other thoughtful extras to ensure that your stay is comfortable. The warm and relaxing atmosphere is further enhanced by fine period antiques and a blazing log fire in the lounge.

Chequers Restaurant serves fresh market produce from a daily changing menu. There is also an all day Coffee Shop for lighter meals.

Recent additions have included the nine acre meadow right outside the hotel. Wild flowers abound in the Spring, there are lovely walks and views, and the meadow becomes the focal point of the village come Guy Fawkes Night.

Chequers is an hour or so south of London, by car or by main line train, and surrounded by glorious countryside. There is so much to see and do at all times of the year. Go and explore for yourself.

LOCATION

The hotel is just north of the village centre at the top of the hill, opposite the church.

Church Place, Pulborough, West Sussex RH20 1AD

Telephone 01798 872486
Fax 01798 872715

PROPRIETOR

John Searancke

ROOM RATES

1 Single	£49.50 - £54.50
6 Doubles/Twins	£75 - £85
1 Four-poster	£85
2 Family	£85.50

Includes full breakfast and VAT

CHARGE/CREDIT CARDS

• DC • MC • VI

ACCOLADES

E.T.B. ♛♛♛♛ Highly Commended
R.A.C. ★★ + Merit Awards H & C
A.A. ★★ ❀ 71%

FACILITIES

Gardens, conservatory
9 acre meadow, heli-pad
1 meeting room/max 20 people
Golf, riding and fishing nearby

RESTRICTIONS

None

ATTRACTIONS

Arundel Castle,
Goodwood House,
Petworth House

AFFILIATIONS

Minotel
Logis of Great Britain

NEAREST

MAJOR CITY:
Brighton - 20 miles/35 mins

MAJOR AIRPORT:
London Gatwick - 18 miles/30 mins

RAILWAY STATION:
Pulborough - ½ mile/5 mins

RESERVATION

Toll free in US: 800-989-7676
Toll free in UK: 0800-387394

ACCESS CODES

Not applicable

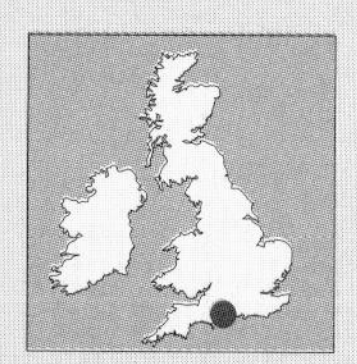

"This is THE luxury hotel. The service is astonishing . . . the cooking is luxury hotel stuff, done with a flair and talent that is rare"

Jonathan Meades, The Times

CHEWTON GLEN

Georgian country house

New Milton,
Hampshire BH25 6QS

Telephone 01425 275341
Fax 01425 272310

PROPRIETORS
Brigitte and Martin Skan

MANAGING DIRECTOR
Peter Crome

ROOM RATES
35 Doubles/Twins £195 - £300
18 Suites £300 - £395
Includes VAT

CHARGE/CREDIT CARDS

• DC • MC • VI

ACCOLADES
R.A.C. Blue Ribbon Award ★★★★★
A.A. ★★★★★ ❀❀❀
The Good Hotel Guide

FACILITIES
Garden, indoor/outdoor pool, croquet, indoor/outdoor tennis, health and beauty, gym, golf, putting, snooker room and jogging trail
3 meeting rooms/max 100 people
Riding and golf nearby

RESTRICTIONS
No children under 7 yrs
No pets

ATTRACTIONS
Stonehenge, Kingston Lacey, Broadlands, Winchester and Salisbury Cathedrals, Wilton House, Exbury Gardens, Beaulieu Motor Museum

AFFILIATIONS
Relais & Châteaux
Leading Hotels of the World

NEAREST
MAJOR CITY:
Southampton - 20 miles/35 mins

MAJOR AIRPORT:
London Heathrow - 88 miles/1¾ hrs

RAILWAY STATION:
New Milton - 1½ miles/8 mins

RESERVATIONS
Toll free in US: 800-344-5087
Toll free fax in US: 800-398-4534
Toll free in Germany: 0130-810890

ACCESS CODES
LW

Excellence, style and imagination in perfect harmony

A very warm welcome awaits you at Chewton Glen. Even before you get out of your car, you will be made to feel at ease immediately. Staff are meticulously selected and trained to treat guests in a professional and friendly style so that the atmosphere of a large private house pervades.

Great emphasis is placed on the quality and service of the food and wines and every kind of accolade from far and wide has been bestowed upon the Marryat Restaurant. The finest local seasonal produce is always used and the cooking is a delicious meld of classical cuisine and the modern, healthy and lighter style. Mark Walter, Chewton Glen's Chef Sommelier and winner of the Champagne Ruinart UK Wine Waiter of the Year Award 1994, has compiled a list of over 500 very interesting vintages.

All rooms are individually decorated and tastefully furnished with antiques and in the bedrooms and bathrooms; nothing is overlooked – there is scarcely an amenity you can imagine that has not been included. Balconies or terraces from most rooms afford an opportunity to enjoy the beautiful views of the surrounding parkland.

The Health Club was added in 1990, providing a sanctuary where both body and mind can be refreshed in a friendly atmosphere of peace and calm.

There are endless things to do at Chewton Glen. Play golf, either in the hotel grounds or on the numerous excellent courses nearby, explore the New Forest and its villages, visit stately homes and gardens, or take a day's tour in the hotel's chauffeur-driven Jaguar.

LOCATION

Take the M27 towards Bournemouth; A337 to Lyndhurst then A35 for Bournemouth. Drive 10 miles, ignoring signs to New Milton, turn left at the Walkford and Highcliffe sign. Go through Walkford, then take second turning on left 'Chewton Farm Road'.

"One of the most romantic hotels in England"

Travel Editor, Daily Mail

18th century manor house

CHILSTON PARK

Sandway, Lenham, Maidstone, Kent ME17 2BE

Telephone 01622 859803
Fax 01622 858588

PROPRIETORS
Judith and Martin Miller

GENERAL MANAGER
Peter K Hawkes

ROOM RATES

27 Doubles	£98.50 - £170
7 Four-posters	£155 - £170
4 Suites	£185

Includes full breakfast and VAT

CHARGE/CREDIT CARDS

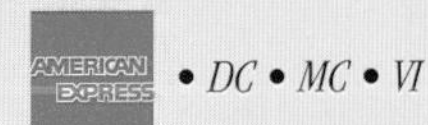

• DC • MC • VI

ACCOLADES
R.A.C. ★★★

FACILITIES
Garden, croquet, tennis, snooker, fishing, heli-pad
4 meeting rooms/max 120 people

RESTRICTIONS
No facilities for disabled guests
Pets by arrangement

ATTRACTIONS
Leeds Castle, Canterbury, Sissinghurst, Chartwell

AFFILIATIONS
Travel Resources Sterling Hotel Group

NEAREST
MAJOR CITY:
Canterbury - 21 miles/35 mins

MAJOR AIRPORT:
London Gatwick - 42 miles/55 mins
Headcorn - 6 miles/15 mins

RAILWAY STATION:
Lenham - 1 miles/5 mins

RESERVATIONS
Toll free in US/Canada: 800-637-7200

ACCESS CODES
AMADEUS/SYSTEM 1 LONCHI
APOLLO WR 41434
WORLDSPAN 2 LONCP
SABRE WR 34861
SAHARA LONCP

Romantic heritage in the Garden of England

Chilston Park Country House is the classic country house. A listed Grade 1 mansion house set in acres of parkland in the heart of the Kent countryside. This family home will make you step back in time with an atmosphere of warmth and light flickering from chandeliers and log fires. Gleaming wood and family portraits set off this treasure trove of antiques, creating what has been described as one of the most romantic hotels in England. The 38 bedrooms are individually styled, having lake or parkland views. There are four suites and many rooms have four-poster beds.

In the unique candle-lit dining rooms, staff in period uniforms serve the superb cuisine, complemented by fine wines.

There are activities such as archery, clay pigeon shooting and hot air ballooning in the grounds.

Located close to Junction 8 of the M20. Chilston Park is ideally situated for visiting Leeds Castle, Chartwell, and exploring a fascinating variety of castles, gardens, vineyards and the Cathedral city of Canterbury, as well as Kent's coastline, just half an hour from the Eurotunnel.

LOCATION

Take Junction 8 of the M20 and drive to Lenham village. Turn right at the village square and follow the signs to Chilston.

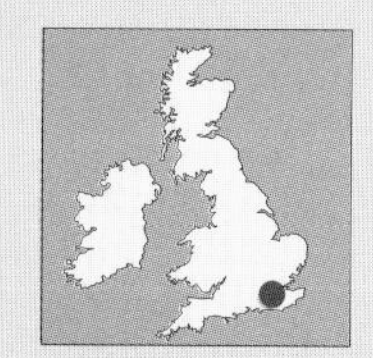

“ Excellent (always) ”

P Moore, Surrey

CISSWOOD HOUSE HOTEL

Edwardian country house

Sandygate Lane, Lower Beeding, Nr Horsham, West Sussex RH13 6NF

Telephone 01403 891216
Fax 01403 891621

PROPRIETORS
Othmar and Elizabeth Illes

ROOM RATES

8 Singles	*£70 - £80*
18 Doubles/Twins	*£90 - £110*
6 Four-posters	*£99 - £110*
2 Suites	*£133 - £135*

Includes continental breakfast and VAT

CHARGE/CREDIT CARDS

• MC • VI

ACCOLADES
Independent

FACILITIES
Indoor pool, croquet, garden
4 meetings rooms/max 200 people
Golf nearby

RESTRICTIONS
Children under 12 years by special arrangement
No facilities for disabled guests
No pets allowed

ATTRACTIONS
Leonards Lee and Nymans Gardens, Arundel Castle, Hever Castle, Goodwood Races, Ashdown Forest

AFFILIATIONS
Independent

NEAREST
MAJOR CITY:
Horsham - 3 miles/5 mins

MAJOR AIRPORT:
London Gatwick - 12 miles/20 mins

RAILWAY STATION:
Horsham - 3 miles/5 mins

RESERVATIONS
Direct with hotel

ACCESS CODES
Not applicable

A high standard of cuisine and comfort in a house built by Harrods

Cisswood House was built in 1928 as the country house for the former chairman of Harrods Sir Woodman Burbidge. The house was built in about 1928 and craftsmen from Harrods were used throughout to create the marvellous wood and plaster work.

Othmar, the chef/proprietor and Elizabeth Illes converted Cisswood House into an hotel in 1979. They offer a very high standard of cuisine in the delightful 'Garden Restaurant' and friendly discreet service and excellent value for money. The menu reflects the seasonal produce available and is cooked freshly in the new classical tradition with generous portions and delicious flavours. It is complemented by a very interesting wine list.

Cisswood has a large local following as well as welcoming visitors from abroad.

The bedrooms are all individually designed and are all en suite, some with spa baths and six with four-poster beds. There are two luxury suites with large separate sitting rooms. Each bedroom has colour TV, drinks fridge and telephone.

Banqueting and Conference facilities for 150 are available in the oak panelled Courtyard Suite, which can be sub-divided.

The hotel is set in 12 acres of grounds and gardens and is convenient for Gatwick Airport, approximately 12 miles south.

LOCATION

At the junction of the A281 and A279, 3 miles east of Horsham.

“ Having stayed in many fine hotels, this one in my opinion excels. It is perhaps of note that this is the first occasion I have felt strongly enough to write ”

Giles Harvey, Metheringham

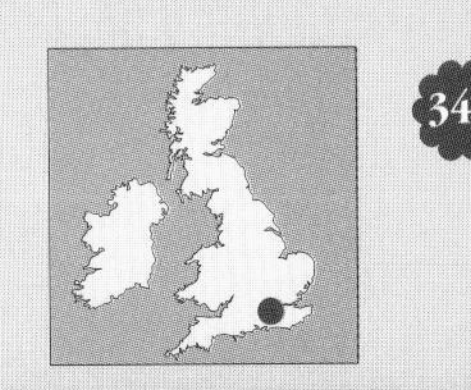

Unique alpine design

COPPID BEECH HOTEL

An hotel? Or a resort? It's worth going out of your way to find out!

There are many reasons for choosing your hotel, but rarely an hotel for its own sake alone, regardless of its location. The Coppid Beech is one such exception and, indeed, might be better described as a resort given its range of facilities.

This uniquely designed property provides an exclusive, comfortable setting in which to relax and unwind. A tour of the premises reveals the full extent of the pleasures on offer. There's a well-equipped leisure club complete with beauty salon, gym, swimming pool, jacuzzi and sauna. Next door, you will find an ice rink and a dry ski slope. With golf, fishing and riding nearby, you will not be short of things to do during the day. The Keller Bar, The Night Club and Rowans Restaurant are there to delight you by night.

Dining is a memorable experience; imaginative dishes with a choice of fresh, seasonal fare and a variety of fresh produce are the pride and passion of the Executive Chef who influences the selection of wines for your pleasure.

When it's time to retire, you will find your en suite luxury bedroom spacious and splendidly appointed with all the comforts that today's travellers expect, including satellite TV and mini-bar.

The combination of such a variety of facilities, the dedicated staff, the excellence of the cuisine and, above all, the warmth of the hospitality will have you coming back for more!

LOCATION

From Junction 10 off the M4 take Wokingham/Binfield exit on to the A329. At Coppid Beech roundabout take 1st exit left for Binfield and right at mini-roundabout. Hotel is on the right.

John Nike Way,
Bracknell,
Berkshire RG12 8TF

Telephone 01344 303333
Fax 01344 301200

GENERAL MANAGER
Alan Blenkinsopp

ROOM RATES

44 Executive Singles	£65
117 Doubles/Twins	£75
25 Superior Doubles	£95
19 Suites	£125

Includes full breakfast and VAT

CHARGE/CREDIT CARDS

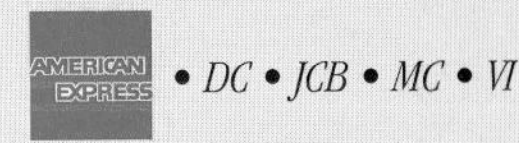

• DC • JCB • MC • VI

ACCOLADES
E.T.B. ♕♕♕♕♕ De Luxe
R.A.C. ★★★★ + Merit Award C
A.A. ★★★★ ❀❀ 75%
Hotel of the Year 94 for Disabled Facilities
Best Restaurant Wine Menu of the Year – Hotel & Restaurant Show

FACILITIES
Health & beauty, gym, jacuzzi, sauna, heli-pad, ice skating rink, dry ski slope
11 meeting rooms/max 350 people
Golf, fishing and riding nearby

RESTRICTIONS
None

ATTRACTIONS
Windsor Castle, Legoland, Ascot Racecourse, Wisley Gardens, Hampton Court Palace

AFFILIATIONS
World Hotels and Resorts
Thames Valley Hotels

NEAREST
MAJOR CITY:
London - 34 miles/45 mins

MAJOR AIRPORT:
London Heathrow - 26 miles/35 mins

RAILWAY STATION:
Bracknell - 2 miles/5 mins

RESERVATIONS
Direct with hotel

ACCESS CODES
Not applicable

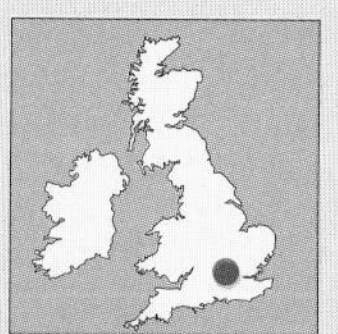

" Danesfield was the highlight of our trip to Europe "

Mrs S Ralston, New York

DANESFIELD HOUSE

Stately country house

Marlow,
Nr Henley-on-Thames,
Buckinghamshire SL7 2EY

Telephone 01628 891010
Fax 01628 890408

GENERAL MANAGER

Brian Miller

ROOM RATES

7 Singles	£125
48 Doubles/Twins	£145
20 Executive Doubles	£175
13 Junior Suites	£195

Includes VAT

CHARGE/CREDIT CARDS

• DC • JCB • MC • VI

ACCOLADES

E.T.B. ♕♕♕♕♕ Highly Commended

R.A.C. ★★★★ + Merit Award C

FACILITIES

Garden, croquet, tennis, outdoor pool, snooker, heli-pad
5 meeting rooms/max 60 people
Golf, fishing and riding nearby

RESTRICTIONS

No dogs

ATTRACTIONS

Windsor Castle, Hughenden Manor, Henley-on-Thames, Oxford

AFFILIATIONS

Small Luxury Hotels

NEAREST

MAJOR CITY:
Maidenhead - 8 miles/12 mins

MAJOR AIRPORT:
London Heathrow - 25 miles/35 mins
London Gatwick - 60 miles/1¼ hrs

RAILWAY STATION:
Maidenhead - 8 miles/12 mins

RESERVATIONS

Toll free in US: 800-525-4800

ACCESS CODES

Access codes applied for

65 acres of magnificent gardens looking down on the River Thames

Danesfield House is set in 65 acres of gardens and parkland overlooking the River Thames and offering panoramic views across the Chiltern Hills. It is the third house since 1664 to occupy this lovely setting and was designed and built in the sumptuous style of the late 19th century. After years of neglect, the house is now fully restored, combining its Victorian splendour with the very best in modern hotel facilities.

Among the many attractions of its 88 luxury bedrooms, all beautifully decorated and furnished, are the extensive facilities they offer. These include two telephone lines (one of which may be used for personal fax), satellite TV, mini bar, trouser press, hair dryer, bath robes and toiletries.

Guests may relax in the magnificent drawing room with its galleried library, or in the sunlit atrium. There is a choice of two restaurants: the Oak Room and the Conservatory Brasserie, both offering a choice of international cuisine with a distinguished wine list.

Leisure facilities include an outdoor pool, croquet, tennis court and jogging and walking trails. Fishing, golf, horseriding, gliding, sailing and shooting can be arranged, as can activities on the River Thames with a picnic hamper from the hotel's kitchens. Major local shopping centres are Henley-on-Thames, Maidenhead and Windsor. Also within easy reach are Windsor Castle, Hughenden Manor, Disraeli's former home Milton's cottage and the Hell Fire Caves of West Wycombe.

LOCATION

M4 Junction 8/9. 3 miles from Marlow on the A4155 travelling towards Henley.

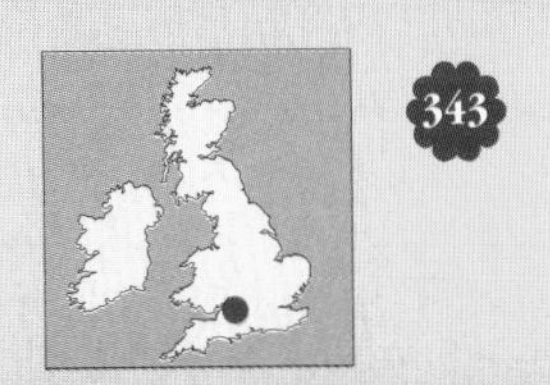

" Having had tea at the Mandarin in Hong Kong, Singapore Slings at Raffles in Singapore and tea at the Ritz, none of them come close to Donnington Valley Hotel "

H S, Newbury

Hotel and golf course

DONNINGTON VALLEY HOTEL

Set in Royal Berkshire with historic cities in every direction

Set in the beautiful countryside of Royal Berkshire and surrounded by an 18-hole golf course, Donnington Valley Hotel blends charm and elegance with the luxury and personal service expected from a privately owned hotel.

As well as having its own 18-hole executive golf course, the hotel is a 40 minute drive from England's top championship courses of Sunningdale and Wentworth.

Inside, uncompromising quality extends to each of the 58 guest rooms and suites which all enjoy peaceful views and ensure total comfort.

The Gallery Restaurant offers an intimate, yet informal atmosphere where guests can enjoy superb cuisine complemented by wines from an excellent cellar, whilst the uniquely designed 'Greens' is the perfect setting for exclusive private parties and gourmet dinners.

A host of activities are available on the 1,000-acre estate offering any combination of golfing, clay pigeon shooting or a day at Newbury Races.

Being at the crossroads of England, you have the perfect touring base for visits to the historic cities of Oxford, Windsor and Bath, and still only an hour's drive from central London.

Whatever the occasion, personal service, and attention to detail will ensure a warm welcome and a memorable stay.

LOCATION

M4/Junction 13. Take A34 southbound to Newbury. Leave A34 at first exit signed Donnington Castle. Turn right then left towards Donnington. Donnington Valley Hotel is one mile on the right.

Old Oxford Road,
Donnington, Newbury,
Berkshire RG14 3AG

Telephone 01635 551199
Fax 01635 551123

GENERAL MANAGER

Ian Leslie

ROOM RATES

53 Doubles £87.50 - £112.50
5 Suites £107.50 - £122.50
Includes VAT

CHARGE/CREDIT CARDS

• DC • MC • VI

ACCOLADES

E.T.B. ♛♛♛♛♛ Highly Commended
R.A.C. ★★★★ + Merit Awards H C & R
A.A. ★★★★ ❀ 74%

FACILITIES

Garden, golf, heli-pad
9 meeting rooms/max 140 people

RESTRICTIONS

None

ATTRACTIONS

Oxford, Bath,
London, Windsor,
Littlecote,
Newbury Racecourse

AFFILIATIONS

Independent

NEAREST

MAJOR CITY:
Oxford - 25 miles/30 mins

MAJOR AIRPORT:
London Heathrow - 50 miles/50 mins

RAILWAY STATION:
Newbury - 2 miles/5 mins

RESERVATIONS

Toll free in US: 800-856-5813

ACCESS CODES

AMADEUS HK EWYDON
APOLLO HT 25903
WORLDSPAN/SAHARA HK DONNI
SABRE HK 30972

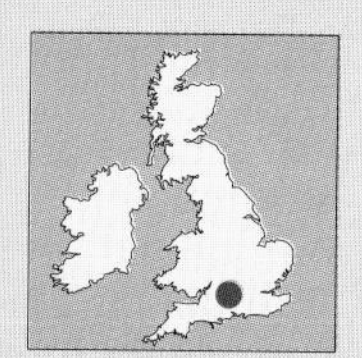

"The immense fun of our stay was second only to the warmth of hospitality"

Mr & Mrs Hollingsworth, California

ESSEBORNE MANOR

Country house hotel

**Hurstbourne Tarrant,
Andover,
Hampshire SP11 0ER**

**Telephone 01264 736444
Fax 01264 736725**

PROPRIETORS
Ian and Lucilla Hamilton

ROOM RATES
Single occupancy £84
10 Doubles/Twins £95 - £120
Includes full breakfast and VAT

CHARGE/CREDIT CARDS

• DC • MC • VI

ACCOLADES
E.T.B. ♛♛♛♛ Highly Commended
A.A. ★★★ ❀❀ 67%

FACILITIES
Garden, croquet, tennis
1 meeting room/max 20 people
Golf and riding nearby

RESTRICTIONS
No young children
No pets

ATTRACTIONS
Stonehenge,
Wolvesey,
Highclere Castle,
Netley Abbey,
Bramber Castle,
Salisbury Cathedral,
Winchester Cathedral

AFFILIATIONS
Pride of Britain

NEAREST
MAJOR CITY:
Andover - 6 miles/10 mins
MAJOR AIRPORT:
London Heathrow - 55 miles/1 hr
RAILWAY STATION:
Andover - 6 miles/10 mins

RESERVATIONS
Toll free in US: 800-98-PRIDE

ACCESS CODES
Not applicable

SOUTH

Close by Stonehenge, arguably the world's "best loved" ancient monument

Esseborne Manor, which carries the name used to record details of the nearby village in the Domesday Book, is small, unpretentious yet stylish. Once referred to as being "invitingly snug" it is set in rich farmland high in the north Wessex Downs, close by the Bourne Valley.

It is difficult to imagine anywhere better placed to tour the south, with Highclere Castle, mystical Stonehenge, Avebury and the Iron Age Danebury Rings but a short drive away, whilst famous gardens, the great cathedrals of Salisbury and Winchester, together with other renowned ancient monuments, are within an easy half day's journey.

Privately owned, the hotel's ten bedrooms, individual in decor, and the comfortable sitting rooms, complement the pretty dining room, which itself reflects the importance placed by the owners on their cuisine and celebrated cellar.

The gardens are for enjoying and lazing and traffic free walks abound. The more energetic may in Summer play croquet on the finely manicured lawns or tennis year round on the all weather court.

Essentially a centre for staying and touring where every comfort is provided by hospitable hosts and caring staff.

LOCATION

Take the M4 to Junction 13 to Newbury. Direction Andover on A343 1½ miles north of Hurstbourne Tarrant on A343 (or M3/A303 to Andover).

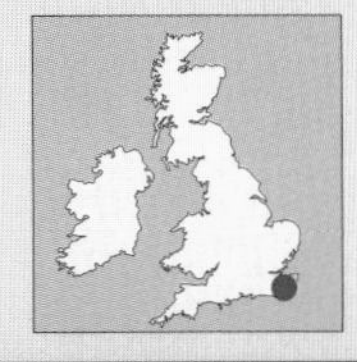

"Wonderful hotel . . . unpretentious, warm and friendly"

Barry D Jones, Singapore

Georgian country house

FLACKLEY ASH HOTEL

A Georgian country home – the perfect place to relax

Deep in the Sussex countryside nestles the pretty village of Peasmarsh near Rye and the delightful Flackley Ash Hotel. A far cry from the hustle and bustle of modern city life, this attractive Georgian country house is the ideal place to enjoy a relaxing holiday.

The fine traditions of comfort and service are retained by Clive and Jeanie Bennett who for twenty years have provided a warm and friendly welcome for their guests. The bedrooms have been individually furnished in the style of a traditional country home and have all the modern facilities. There is a friendly lounge where you can read the morning paper, meet other guests or relax with coffee after a dinner in the award-winning restaurant.

In such a place it is easy to drift back in time. Wander the cobbled streets of medieval Rye with its potteries, antique shops, taverns and tea shops. Discover the enchantingly beautiful Bodiam Castle and Bateman's, the house where Kipling lived. Follow in the footsteps of William the Conqueror, visit the fields where the first 'Battle of Britain' was fought and see the abbey built to mark his victory.

After a busy day enjoy a game of croquet or putting in the pretty gardens. Relax in the indoor swimming pool and leisure centre with its mini-gym, sauna and solarium. Be pampered in the beauty parlour and hair salon.

Clive and Jeanie Bennett, the owners, provide a warm and friendly atmosphere for all their guests. It's the perfect retreat to relax and be pampered.

LOCATION

From M25 exit Junction 5 (signposted A21 Hastings). Turn left on to A268 at Flimwell traffic lights. Proceed through Hawkhurst and Northiam to Peasmarsh.

Peasmarsh, Rye, East Sussex TN31 6YH

Telephone 01797 230651
Fax 01797 230510

PROPRIETORS

Clive and Jeanie Bennett

ROOM RATES

Single occupancy	*£69 - £85*
26 Doubles/Twins	*£98 - £114*
3 Four-posters	*£98 - £114*
2 Suites	*£133*

Includes full breakfast and VAT

CHARGE/CREDIT CARDS

• *DC* • *MC* • *VI*

ACCOLADES

E.T.B. ♛♛♛♛ *Highly Commended*
R.A.C. ★★★
A.A.★★★ ❀ *73%*

FACILITIES

Garden, croquet, snooker, indoor swimming pool, sauna, snooker, gym, health and beauty, heli-pad
2 meeting rooms/max 100 people
Riding nearby

RESTRICTIONS

No facilities for disabled guests

ATTRACTIONS

Cinque Port of Rye, Bodiam Castle, Sissinghurst Castle, Canterbury Cathedral

AFFILIATIONS

Best Western

NEAREST

MAJOR CITY:
London - 60 miles/2 hrs

MAJOR AIRPORT:
London Heathrow - 50 miles/1¾ hrs
London Gatwick - 40 miles/1¼ hrs

RAILWAY STATION:
Rye - 4 miles/10 mins

RESERVATIONS

Direct with hotel

ACCESS CODES

Not applicable

“ The best spit-roasted duck I have ever tasted ”

Kevin Brant, Berkshire

FRENCH HORN HOTEL

Riverside hotel

Sonning on Thames, Berkshire RG4 6TN

Telephone 01734 692204
Fax 01734 442210

PROPRIETOR

M Emmanuel

ROOM RATES

7 Doubles/Twins	£85 - £95
1 Four-poster	£95 - £105
8 Suites	£105 - £130

Includes full breakfast and VAT

CHARGE/CREDIT CARDS

• *DC* • *MC* • *VI*

ACCOLADES

Independent

FACILITIES

Garden, fishing
Golf, health centre and theatre nearby

RESTRICTIONS

No pets
Jacket and tie to be worn by gentlemen in the evening

ATTRACTIONS

Blenheim Palace, Windsor Castle, Mapledurham House, Stratfield Saye House

AFFILIATIONS

Pride of Britain

NEAREST

MAJOR CITY:
London - 36 miles/1 hr

MAJOR AIRPORT:
London Heathrow - 20 mins/45 mins

RAILWAY STATION:
Reading - 4 miles/15 mins

RESERVATIONS

Direct with hotel

ACCESS CODES

Not applicable

SOUTH

Peace and plenty on the banks of the Thames

Nestling at the foot of the Chilterns, beside the tranquil River Thames, is a very special English country house – The French Horn at Sonning. For over 150 years the hotel has provided a riverside retreat from the cares of the world. Today it offers comfortable rooms and outstanding cooking in the most beautiful of settings.

By day the sunny restaurant with its unmatched views of the Thames is the perfect rendezvous for an enjoyable lunch. At night the graceful weeping willows fringing the river are romantically floodlit. The cusine is a traditional mixture of French and English cooking using the freshest ingredients, many of them local. The French Horn's wine list is amongst the finest in Europe and includes many rare and unusual bottles.

In the old panelled bar ducks roast on a spit before an open fire. Upstairs the beautifully decorated suites and rooms look out over landscaped grounds.

The French Horn has four luxury suites in their own grounds, all with full river views. In addition there are 12 well-appointed suites and double rooms. Each has an en suite bathroom, TV, alarm radio and direct dial telephone.

A tradition of family ownership continues at the French Horn; the Emmanuel family ensure that the standard of excellence is maintained throughout.

LOCATION

Leave M4 at Junction 8/9 and follow the A4 to Sonning.

" Gordleton Mill has grown in both its operation and reputation as one of the country's best two red star hotels "

Albert Hampson, Automobile Association

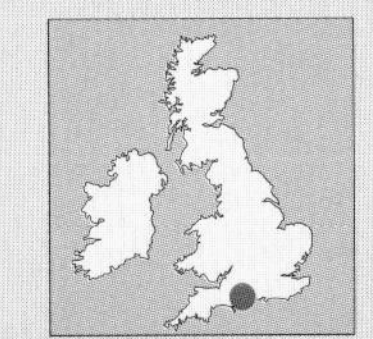

Country residence

THE GORDLETON MILL HOTEL

Spectacularly located and a much-acclaimed hotel and restaurant

Within the New Forest National Park lies the Gordleton Mill Hotel, a privately owned seven bedroomed country residence with its nationally acclaimed 'Provence' Restaurant.

This delightful 17th century water mill house has recently been sympathetically extended and refurbished to an extremely high standard, and since reopening in April 1991, has already established an enviable reputation throughout the country by achieving high ratings from many of the country's leading guides.

Much has been made of the quite spectacular riverside location with views from the classic glazed terrace and adjoining dining room where one may take drinks in the evening and enjoy sumptuous breakfasts in the morning, weather permitting.

The grounds of the hotel extend to 5½ acres with its own mill pond, sluice gates, weir and rustic bridges – surrounded by fields and woods – a sanctuary for wildlife.

This idyllic hotel boasts seven exquisitely furnished bedrooms, most with king-size beds, whirlpool baths and showers. Four rooms are exclusively reserved for non-smokers.

Gordleton Mill is a wonderful place to relax and unwind from the stresses of modern day living.

LOCATION

Exit M27 at Junction 1. Take A337 to Lymington. Just prior to Lymington, straight over mini roundabout and turn right before 'Toll House Inn'. Hotel on right after 1½ miles.

Silver St, Hordle, Lymington, Hampshire SO41 6DJ

Telephone 01590 682219
Fax 01590 683073

OWNER
William F Stone

CHEF/MANAGER
Toby Hill

ROOM RATES

Single occupancy	*£97*
1 Standard Double	*£103 - £112*
5 Superior Doubles	*£116 - £123*
1 Suite	*£129 - £136*

Includes half bottle of champagne on arrival, full breakfast and VAT

CHARGE/CREDIT CARDS

• DC • MC • VI

ACCOLADES
A.A. ★★ ❀❀❀
County Hotel of the Year 1994 - a leading guide

FACILITIES
Garden, fishing, heli-pad, bedrooms with whirlpool baths
1 meeting room/max 30 people
Golf, riding and sailing nearby

RESTRICTIONS
No children under 7 yrs
Lap dogs by arrangement
Kennels opening in 1996

ATTRACTIONS
New Forest, Salisbury, Calshot and Hurst Castles, Beaulieu, Winchester, Exbury and Spinners Gardens

AFFILIATIONS
Independent

NEAREST
MAJOR CITY:
Southampton - 17 miles/30 mins
Bournemouth - 15 miles/25 mins

MAJOR AIRPORT:
London Heathrow - 80 miles/1¾ hrs
Southampton - 17 miles/30 mins

RAILWAY STATION:
Lymington - 2 miles/5 mins

RESERVATIONS
Direct with hotel

ACCESS CODES
Not applicable

“ Steeped in history and set in rolling parklands, Hartwell House is one of the loveliest hotels in the country ”

House and Garden

HARTWELL HOUSE

Stately home

Oxford Road, Nr Aylesbury, Buckinghamshire HP17 8NL

Telephone 01296 747444
Fax 01296 747450

DIRECTOR

Jonathan Thompson

ROOM RATES

6 Singles	*from £115*
23 Doubles/Twins	*from £180*
5 Four-posters	*from £215*
13 Suites	*from £230*

Includes full breakfast, service and VAT

CHARGE/CREDIT CARDS

• *MC* • *VI*

ACCOLADES

R.A.C. Blue Ribbon Award ★★★★
A.A. ★★★★ ❀❀
The Good Hotel Guide

FACILITIES

Garden, croquet, tennis, gym, sauna, indoor pool, health & beauty, whirlpool spa bath, fishing, heli-pad, lake, parkland walks
4 meeting rooms/max 36 people
Golf and riding nearby

RESTRICTIONS

No children under 8 years
Pets allowed in Hartwell Court only

ATTRACTIONS

Waddesdon Manor, Blenheim Palace, Woburn Abbey, Stowe Landscape Gardens, Chiltern Hills, Oxford

AFFILIATIONS

Relais & Châteaux

NEAREST

MAJOR CITY:
London - 50 miles/1¼ hrs

MAJOR AIRPORT:
London Heathrow - 35 miles/45 mins

RAILWAY STATION:
Aylesbury - 2 miles/5 mins

RESERVATIONS

Toll free fax in US: 800-260-8338
(quote Hartwell House)
In Japan: 03-3434-7159

ACCESS CODES

SABRE HK 32002

Once a stately home, now a fine hotel

Hartwell House is a beautifully restored 17th century house, one of the stately homes of Britain, now a superb hotel owned by Historic House Hotels. Situated in rural Buckinghamshire in the Vale of Aylesbury it is only an hour from central London and 20 miles from Oxford.

The house, which is part Jacobean and part Georgian, was from 1809 to 1814 the home in exile of King Louis XVIII of France and his entire court. It is said that in spite of being in exile the King was very happy at Hartwell and it was in the library that he signed the documents that returned him to the throne of France. More recently Hartwell House was visited by President and Mrs Clinton on their D-day trip to Britain.

The house has several magnificent reception rooms furnished with antiques and hung with fine paintings, 47 beautifully decorated and furnished bedrooms and suites, some in the house and some in Hartwell Court, the converted stable block. The Soane and Doric dining rooms are an elegant setting for the excellent food at Hartwell. 90 acres of grounds, landscaped by a pupil of 'Capability' Brown, include a lake, tennis courts, a croquet lawn and a terrace where guests can enjoy drinks or afternoon tea on sunny days. Hartwell House has a health and leisure spa with a large indoor swimming pool, whirlpool spa bath, steam room, saunas, solaria, a well equipped gym, a beauty salon, and the Spa Bar and Buttery overlooking the pool.

LOCATION

In Aylesbury take A418 towards Oxford. Hartwell house is 2 miles along this road on the right hand side.

"Ian and Piera who bought The Hautboy in 1986 have created a monument to 'English Style'"

Jeremy Gates, Daily Express

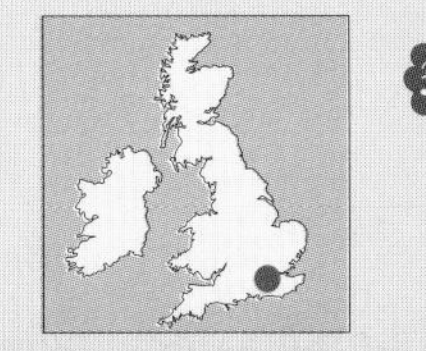

Victorian country mansion

THE HAUTBOY

The small country house hotel with a big reputation

Surprisingly close to motorway links, but nestled in the heart of the English countryside, you will discover a splendid and unique 19th century building – The Hautboy Hotel.

The 1st Earl of Lovelace, a famous architect and engineer in the time of Queen Victoria, used local Ockham bricks and incorporated highly decorative quartre foils to create this marvellous neogothic style building, which overlooks the village cricket green.

Today, the Hautboy is privately owned, and run as a small country house hotel, with a big reputation for service and hospitality. There are five individually designed suites, each delightfully furnished with lovingly collected antiques and pictures.

The hotel has a choice of two restaurants, the Brasserie, originally the Great Hall, has retained its Minstrels gallery, and now offers an ideal setting for an informal lunch or dinner.

The Hautboy Restaurant itself is a delightful blend of sophistication and charm. The exposed mellow brickwork, and the warm welcome guests receive, sets the scene for a meal to remember. The imaginative menu is cooked in traditional English style, and seafood and game are always well represented.

LOCATION

Leave M25 at Junction 10 and take the Guildford road south, turn left into Old Lane and right into Ockham Lane.

Ockham Lane, Ockham, Nr Guildford, Surrey GU23 6NP

Telephone 01483 225355
Fax 01483 211176

PROPRIETOR
Ian and Piera Shier

MANAGER
Enzo Pizzale

ROOM RATES
Single occupancy from £78
5 Doubles/Twins from £98
Includes continental breakfast and VAT

CHARGE/CREDIT CARDS

• DC • MC • VI

ACCOLADES
Independent

FACILITIES
Gardens
Golf and riding nearby

RESTRICTIONS
No pets
No facilities for disabled guests

ATTRACTIONS
Windsor Castle, Wisley Garden Centre, Hampton Court

AFFILIATIONS
Independent

NEAREST
MAJOR CITY:
Guildford - 7 miles/5 mins

MAJOR AIRPORT:
London Heathrow - 20 miles/20 mins
London Gatwick - 20 miles/20 mins

RAILWAY STATION:
East Horsley - 7 miles/5 mins

RESERVATIONS
Direct with hotel

ACCESS CODES
Not applicable

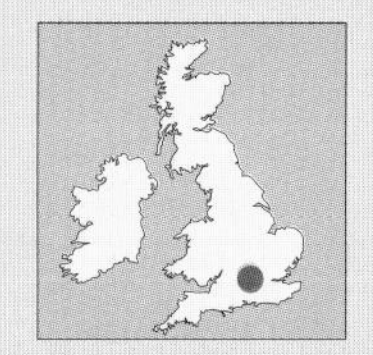

" I came with my wife but took a new woman home "

Mr & Mrs J Torrens, London

HOLLINGTON HOUSE

Edwardian country house

Woolton Hill, Newbury, Berkshire RG20 9XA

Telephone 01635 255100
Fax 01635 255075

PROPRIETORS
John and Penny Guy

ROOM RATES

Single occupancy	*£95 - £155*
7 Deluxe Doubles	*£130 - £150*
12 Spa Deluxe Doubles	*£190 - £275*
1 Suite	*£375*

Includes full breakfast and VAT

CHARGE/CREDIT CARDS

 • *DC* • *MC* • *VI*

ACCOLADES
R.A.C. ★★★ + Merit Awards C & R
A.A. ★★★ ❀❀❀
The Good Hotel Guide
Ackerman Heidsieck Guide

FACILITIES
Garden, croquet, tennis, snooker, outdoor pool, jacuzzi, heli-pad
4 meeting rooms/max 120 people
Golf and riding nearby

RESTRICTIONS
No smoking in dining room
No dogs

ATTRACTIONS
Highclere and Windsor Castles, Oxford, Winchester, Bath, Stonehenge

AFFILIATIONS
Independent

NEAREST
MAJOR CITY:
Newbury - 3 miles/5 mins
Oxford - 25 miles/35 mins

MAJOR AIRPORT:
London Heathrow - 45 miles/1 hr

RAILWAY STATION:
Newbury - 3 miles/5mins

RESERVATIONS
Direct with hotel

ACCESS CODES
Not applicable

The great art of luxury hotelkeeping made perfect by professionals

Hollington House opened in 1992. The Elizabethan-style house built in 1904, is set in 24 acres of mature woodland gardens, adjacent to 800 acres of private parkland and overlooking an unchanged English landscape. Prior to returning to England after an absence of 32 years, John and Penny Guy created and owned Burnham Beeches Hotel near Melbourne, which became Australia's first Relais & Châteaux hotel.

No expense has been spared in their endeavours to achieve similar standards of excellence here. The 20 large individually designed bedrooms, all with king size beds, are furnished with hand-made quilts and wall hangings, many designed and created by Penny. Sumptuous bathrooms with double spa baths (illustrated) are the largest to be found in England. Elegant reception rooms, an oak-panelled galleried hall and private boardroom are among the many splendid features of the house, as are the numerous antiques and paintings.

David Lake is a young and highly motivated chef making a name for himself with country cooking based on local produce and wonderfully tempting dishes.

There is a swimming pool, tennis court and croquet lawn and the surrounding countryside offers opportunities for walking, shooting, hunting and horse riding.

Conference, wedding and weekend packages are available.

LOCATION

Junction 13 of M4, taking the A343 out of Newbury, follow the signs for Hollington Herb Garden. The hotel is next door.

"We felt so at home, we never thought that we were going to have to pay"

Peter Goulandris

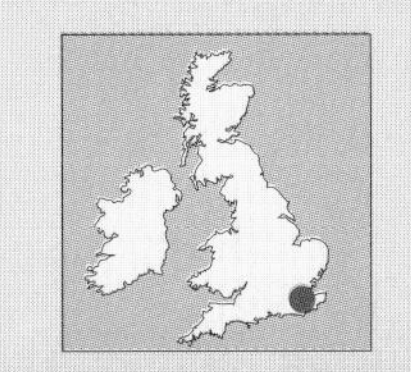

Sporting estate and hotel

HORSTED PLACE

A grand place to indulge your most trivial pursuit or gourmet desire

Horsted Place Sporting Estate and Hotel stands in 1,100 acres including seven acres of beautiful formal gardens, imaginatively designed by Sir Geoffrey Jellicoe – and boasts relaxing woodland walks, hard tennis courts, croquet lawn and helicopter landing area. Plans are also in hand for further outdoor activities – game shooting, ballooning, archery, simulated shooting, motorised pursuits . . . yet indoors, the comfort and tranquillity of Horsted Place encourages relaxation. The peaceful library and open fires beckon; aromatherapy and reflexology are available, wine talks and tastings from local Barkham Vineyard can be arranged – and for the more active, the heated indoor pool awaits.

Accommodation at Horsted Place is spacious, yet intimate with 17 luxury suites and three beautiful double bedrooms, individually and tastefully decorated with views over the gardens and surrounding countryside – an idyllic situation for exclusive use, combining total privacy, efficient unobtrusive service, relaxing and secure surroundings and excellent food and wines.

Indeed, under the direction of Chef de Cuisine Allan Edward Garth, the impressive and elegant Pugin dining room provides the perfect setting, with two further private dining rooms ensuring discreet service in intimate surroundings, thus catering for every occasion.

LOCATION

45 miles from Central London, 2 miles south of Uckfield on A26 to Lewes.

Little Horsted, Uckfield, East Sussex TN22 5TS

Telephone 01825 750581
Fax 01825 750240

GENERAL MANAGER
Jonathan W Ritchie

ROOM RATES

3 The Mews	*£100 - £125*
6 Doubles/Twins	*£130 - £180*
11 Suites	*£200 - £325*

Includes continental breakfast and VAT

CHARGE/CREDIT CARDS

• *DC* • *MC* • *VI*

ACCOLADES
E.T.B. ♛♛♛♛♛ *De Luxe*
A.A. ★★★★ ❀❀❀

FACILITIES
Garden, indoor heated pool, croquet, all weather tennis, reflexology, and holistic massage, golf
5 meeting rooms/max 120 people
Riding and fishing nearby

RESTRICTIONS
Children and pets by arrangement

ATTRACTIONS
Glyndebourne, Sheffield Park, The Bluebell Railway, Wakehurst Place, Lewes Castle

AFFILIATIONS
The European Connection

NEAREST
MAJOR CITY:
London - 45 miles/1½ hrs

MAJOR AIRPORT:
London Gatwick - 25 miles/35 mins

RAILWAY STATION:
Lewes - 7 miles /10 mins

RESERVATIONS
Direct with hotel

ACCESS CODES
Not applicable

"This is perfect"

Al Unser Jr, US racing driver

HOTEL DU VIN & BISTRO

Georgian town house

Southgate Street, Winchester, Hampshire SO23 9EF

Telephone 01962 841414
Fax 01962 842458

PROPRIETORS
Robin Hutson and Gerard Basset

ROOM RATES
13 Doubles/Twins £69 - £99
Includes VAT

CHARGE/CREDIT CARDS

• DC • MC • VI

ACCOLADES
A.A. Townhouse

FACILITIES
Garden, petanque
1 meeting room/max 50 people
Golf, riding and fishing nearby

RESTRICTIONS
No facilities for disabled guests

ATTRACTIONS
Winchester Cathedral, Portsmouth Naval Base, New Forest, Stonehenge, King Alfreds Round Table

AFFILIATIONS
Independent

NEAREST
MAJOR CITY:
Winchester

MAJOR AIRPORT:
London Heathrow - 50 miles/45 mins
Southampton - 10 miles/15 mins

RAILWAY STATION:
Winchester - ½ mile/2 mins

RESERVATIONS
Toll free in US: 800-544-9993

ACCESS CODES
Not applicable

A 'total experience' just minutes away from Winchester Cathedral

In the heart of Winchester, England's ancient capital, and minutes' walk from the Cathedral, is the new Hotel du Vin & Bistro. The red brick Georgian Grade II listed building was built as a private house in 1715; since that time it has been used as the judges' lodgings and was first converted to an hotel about 70 years ago.

After distinguished careers in the world's top hotels, Robin Hutson and Gerard Basset opened Hotel du Vin & Bistro in October 1994. By extensive refurbishment work, they have created a remarkable Town House Hotel. Emphasis is on casual comfort at sensible prices. This is a relaxed establishment with a true warmth of welcome in an unpretentious way. Great attention has been paid to detail and the wine theme is evident throughout. Each bedroom has been sponsored by a wine house including The Veuve Clicquot Room and The Berringer Room. They all feature top quality essentials such as excellent beds, deep baths and power showers. A wonderful collection of drawings, etchings, along with wine memorabilia, adorns the walls.

Basset has been Britain's leading sommelier for many years, and has won countless national and international competitions. The food and wine, which are carefully prepared and chosen, offer really great value for money. The chef has a passion for fresh local produce, which shows in the simple yet innovative style of food. The menu changes daily according to the season. In summer, lunch can be taken in the delightful walled garden.

LOCATION

Drive into centre of Winchester. Follow one way system at top of St George Street, turn left into Southgate Street.

"We couldn't have made a better choice"

Marcia Adams, Gourmet Magazine

Georgian townhouse — LITTLE ORCHARD HOUSE

An informal house party in the medieval town of Rye

Little Orchard House is peacefully yet centrally situated in the medieval hill town of Rye. Rebuilt in 1745 and lovingly renovated, the house retains its original fascinating character. Personal antiques, paintings, books and bears are throughout the house, and owner Sarah Brinkhurst takes care of the small details that ensure guests' comfort and enjoyment. The atmosphere is that of an informal house-party, with guests free to come and go as they please.

The bedrooms have colour TV and hot drinks tray, hairdryer and radio alarm. There are duvets on the beds. One bedroom is named the Lloyd George Room, in honour of the British Prime Minister who stayed in the house some 70 years ago. Guests are welcome to use the large, secluded walled garden with its 18th century Smuggler's Watchtower. You can help feed the hedgehogs or just laze away the summer days in a deckchair with a good book.

Full English breakfast features local organic and free-range products – as much as you can eat, at a time that suits you.

Rye is a totally charming medieval hill town perched on the edge of Romney marsh. There are cobbled streets, art galleries, bookshops and gift shops – and two markets a week. It is within easy reach of Canterbury, Tunbridge Wells, Brighton, Hastings and the channel crossings to France.

LOCATION

From A259 or A268, enter Rye on the one way system. Follow signs for town centre through Landgate Arch into High Street. Take third turn on the left into West Street. Little Orchard House is on the left.

West Street, Rye, East Sussex TN31 7ES

Telephone 01797 223831

PROPRIETOR

Sarah Brinkhurst

ROOM RATES

Single occupancy	*£45 - £60*
1 Double	*£60 - £70*
1 Twin	*£60 - £80*
1 Four-poster	*£70 - £84*

Includes full breakfast and VAT

CHARGE/CREDIT CARDS

• *MC* • *VI*

ACCOLADES

County Hotel for 1995 – a leading guide

FACILITIES

Garden, smugglers' watchtower Beach, windsurfing and cycle hire nearby

RESTRICTIONS

No children under 12 years

ATTRACTIONS

Port of Rye, Sissinghurst Garden, Great Dixter Garden, Henry James House, Bodiam Castle, Canterbury

AFFILIATIONS

Independent

NEAREST

MAJOR CITY: *Canterbury - 35 miles/45 mins*

MAJOR AIRPORT: *London Gatwick - 55 miles/1 hr 20 mins*

RAILWAY STATION: *Rye - ¼ mile/3 mins*

RESERVATIONS

Direct with hotel

ACCESS CODES

Not applicable

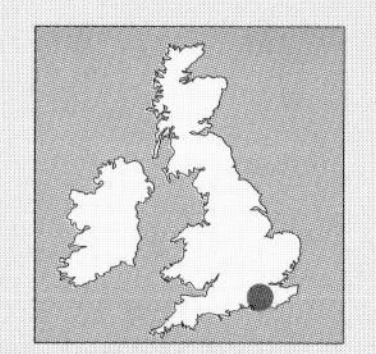

“ J'ai recu le meilleur accueil en Angleterre ”

Valerie Giscard d'Estaing

LITTLE THAKEHAM

Edwardian manor house

Merrywood Lane, Storrington, West Sussex RH20 3HE

Telephone 01903 744416
Fax 01903 745022

PROPRIETORS
Tim and Pauline Ractliff

ROOM RATES
Single occupancy £95
4 Doubles £150
2 Suites £200
Includes full breakfast and VAT

CHARGE/CREDIT CARDS

• DC • MC • VI

ACCOLADES
R.A.C. ★★★ + Merit Awards H C & R
Wendy Arnold Historic Hotels

FACILITIES
Outdoor pool, croquet, tennis, gardens, heli-pad
1 meeting room/max 15 people
Golf and riding nearby

RESTRICTIONS
Children at management's discretion
No facilities for disabled guests
No dogs

ATTRACTIONS
Arundel Castle, Petworth House, Brighton Royal Pavilion

AFFILIATIONS
Pride of Britain

NEAREST
MAJOR CITY:
London - 49 miles/1 hr 20 mins

MAJOR AIRPORT:
London Gatwick - 28 miles/40 mins

RAILWAY STATION:
Pulborough - 3miles/10 mins

RESERVATIONS
Toll free in US: 800-635-3604

ACCESS CODES
Not applicable

Not so much an hotel as a distinguished private house

Little Thakeham is not so much an hotel as the private home of Tim and Pauline Ractliff. Designed and built in 1902 by the foremost English architect Sir Edwin Lutyens, it has, since 1979, been open to the public as a small hotel and restaurant.

Architects, interior designers, antique collectors all appreciate the true art of country house living. Set in orchards and woodlands on Rudyard Kipling's famous South Downs, the house and gardens are a delight.

Nearby, the famous houses of Petworth, Parham and Arundel Castle are all open for viewing. For garden lovers there is nearby Leonardslee, Nymans, Wakehurst Place and Jonathon Brooks charming garden, Denmans.

In the true tradition of the country house, sport is a main feature; racing at Goodwood, polo at Cowdray, golf, tennis and riding are all nearby. During the winter months there are excellent pheasant and partridge shooting opportunities; and, if you wish, hunting to hounds with the Crawley & Horsham Hunt can be arranged.

However, for those who just want to come and relax, there is no better place to be than in the garden or in front of the large log fire at Little Thakeham.

LOCATION

Take the A3 then the A24 towards Worthing. At the roundabout 2 miles south of Ashington, return north up the A24 for 200 yards and turn left into Rock Road for 1 mile. At staggered cross roads, turn right into Merrywood Lane. Little Thakeham is 300 yards on the right.

"It has been a wonderful introduction to unexpected delights"

Peter Ustinov

Tudor country house

LYTHE HILL HOTEL

Poised between past and present, the village green and the city lights

Cradled by the Surrey foothills in a tranquil wealden setting, is the enchanting Lythe Hill Hotel. It is an unusual cluster of ancient buildings, parts of which date from the 14th century.

Five charming rooms in the Tudor house complement a wide choice of more modern rooms across the courtyard, including two luxury garden suites overlooking the lake. In keeping with this style, it is no surprise to find that there is a choice of two restaurants. In the main hotel dining room, the cooking is in the English tradition, whereas superb French cuisine is served in the Auberge de France, the oak-panelled dining room which overlooks the lake and parklands. An exceptional wine list offers over 200 wines from more than a dozen countries.

Its situation, easily accessible from London Heathrow, Gatwick and the Channel Ports makes Lythe Hill the ideal touring centre for south east England.

National Trust hillsides adjoining the hotel grounds provide delightful walking and views over the surrounding countryside. The area is steeped in history with famous country houses and castles to visit. There is horse racing at Goodwood and Fontwell Park and polo at Cowdray Park. Beautiful gardens such as Wisley Royal Horticultural Gardens and Winkworth Arboretum are nearby. Local villages offer all the charms of the village pub and antique shop by the village green. It is an area of truly unspoilt rural England.

LOCATION

Take the A3 and head towards Haslemere. In the town turn left onto the B2131 (Petworth Road). Lythe Hill is 1½ miles on the right.

Petworth Road, Haslemere, Surrey, GU27 3BQ

Telephone 01428 651251
Fax 01428 644131

GENERAL MANAGER

Kevin G Lorimer

ROOM RATES

Single occupancy	*£74 - £84*
26 Doubles/Twins	*£95*
14 Luxury Suites	*£110 - £150*

Includes VAT

CHARGE/CREDIT CARDS

• *JCB* • *MC* • *VI*

ACCOLADES

E.T.B. ♛♛♛♛ *Highly Commended*
R.A.C. ★★★★ + *Merit Awards H C & R*
A.A. ★★★★ ❀❀ *70%*

FACILITIES

Garden, croquet, tennis, fishing, games room, heli-pad
Golf nearby

RESTRICTIONS

None

ATTRACTIONS

Arundel Castle, Petworth House, Uppark, Clandon Park, Chichester Cathedral, Yvonne Arnaud Theatre, Goodwood House and racecourse

AFFILIATIONS

Selected British Hotels

NEAREST

MAJOR CITY:
Guildford - 12 miles/20 mins

MAJOR AIRPORT:
London Heathrow - 35 miles/50 mins
London Gatwick - 35 miles/50 mins

RAILWAY STATION:
Haslemere - local

RESERVATIONS

Toll free in US: 800-323-5463

ACCESS CODES

Not applicable

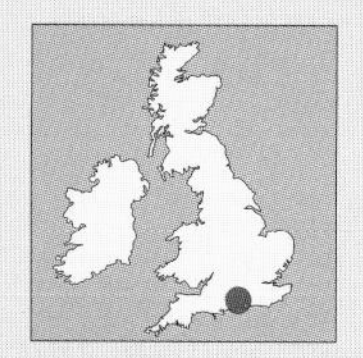

"Many thanks for your kind hospitality during our stay. We all thoroughly enjoyed ourselves and would recommend the hotel to anyone"

Helen Warne & Kathy Meede, Carlton TV

NEW PARK MANOR

16th century hunting lodge

Brockenhurst, Hampshire SO42 7QH

Telephone 01590 623467
Fax 01590 622268

PROPRIETOR

K Van Gelderen

RATES PER PERSON

8 Manor Rooms	£55
13 New Forest Rooms	£65
3 Suites/Four-posters	£75

Includes full breakfast, newspaper and VAT

CHARGE/CREDIT CARDS

• MC • VI

ACCOLADES

E.T.B. ♕♕♕♕ Highly Commended
R.A.C. ★★★ + Merit Award R
A.A. ★★★ ❀❀ 76%

FACILITIES

Garden, croquet, tennis, horse riding, heated outdoor swimming pool (June-Sept)
2 meeting rooms/max 80 people
Golf and fishing nearby

RESTRICTIONS

No children under 7 years
No pets

ATTRACTIONS

New Forest, Exbury Gardens, Beaulieu Motor Museum, Isle of Wight

AFFILIATIONS

Independent

NEAREST

MAJOR CITY:
Southampton - 10 miles/20 mins

MAJOR AIRPORT:
London Heathrow - 80 miles/1½ hrs
London Gatwick - 93 miles/2 hrs

RAILWAY STATION:
Brockenhurst - 1½ miles/5 mins

RESERVATIONS

Direct with hotel

ACCESS CODES

Not applicable

Once King Charles II's favourite hunting lodge

The New Forest is one of England's oldest forests, and New Park's origins go way back to its earliest days. In 1070 William the Conqueror made the Forest his hunting preserve. King Charles II named New Park his favourite hunting lodge on his return from exile in France in 1666, when he used it in the company of Nell Gwyn. His carved Royal Coat of Arms stands proud in the dining room.

New Park Manor brings the romantic past to life. It is one of the New Forest's finest country house hotels. The 24 bedrooms are invididually designed, all with direct-dial telephone and private bathroom, and most overlook forest parklands. The historic, oak-panelled Rufus Bar, with its open fireplace, includes a library stocked with old and rare books. The New Forest Room complements the colours of the New Forest, and conveys the atmosphere of the area. It is available for all functions and conference requirements.

The Stag Head restaurant has upgraded its French-influenced cuisine with excellent table d'hôte and à la carte menus, and a fine wine list. Full afternoon teas are also served during the week.

The hotel has its own stables leading directly into the forest, with BHS trained stablecrew and well-schooled horses. It also has an outdoor swimming pool, tennis court and croquet lawn. There are some marvellous walks into the New Forest. Golf, forest biking, hot air ballooning, helicopter trips and even flying lessons can all be arranged.

LOCATION

From M27, follow A337 for 6 miles south past Lyndhurst. Turn right at sign for New Park Manor: the hotel is ¼ mile into the forest.

"By far the best service we've ever experienced – congratulations!"

Mrs Hanson

Country house hotel

NUTFIELD PRIORY

Great and glorious features with outstanding Surrey views

Nutfield Priory was built with all the embellishments that its then owner could think of, including towers, elaborate carvings, intricate stonework, cloisters, stained glass and mullioned windows. All remain today in wonderfully restored condition to create an unusual and delightful country house hotel that retains a welcoming and friendly ambience still reminiscent of a family home.

Its 40 acres of gardens and parkland combine with elegant lounges, a library, extensive conference facilities, private dining rooms and a cloistered restaurant to create a world far removed from the hectic lifestyle of today. Yet the hotel is still within remarkably easy reach of London, its airports and the motorways.

The new Priory Leisure Club offers guests free use of the indoor pool, sauna, spa and fully-fitted gymnasium. Other facilities available include creche, squash, fitness classes, solarium, Clarins beauty studio and Paul Mitchell hair salon.

All the bedrooms and suites are individually designed and have thoughtful extras such as mineral water, mini safe, a turn down service and unusually, aromatherapy packs. Many rooms have far reaching views over miles of Surrey and Sussex countryside.

In the award-winning restaurant the style of food is modern English with a choice from both à la carte and more conservatively priced set menus.

LOCATION

Leave M25 at Junction 6, take A25 to Redhill. Nutfield Priory is on the left after 5 miles.

Nutfield, Redhill, Surrey RH1 4EN

Telephone 01737 822066
Fax 01737 823321

MANAGER

John Pearmain

ROOM RATES

10 Singles £105
47 Doubles/Twins £120
3 Suites from £200
Includes VAT

CHARGE/CREDIT CARDS

• DC • MC • VI

ACCOLADES

E.T.B. ♛♛♛♛ Highly Commended
R.A.C. ★★★ + Merit Awards H C & R
A.A. ★★★ ❀❀ 74%

FACILITIES

Garden, squash, sauna, indoor pool, jacuzzi, gym, health & beauty, snooker, heli-pad
10 meeting rooms/max 150 people
Golf, riding and fishing nearby

RESTRICTIONS

No facilities for disabled guests

ATTRACTIONS

Hever Castle,
Wisley Gardens,
Chartwell,
Hampton Court

AFFILIATIONS

Arcadian Hotels (UK) Ltd

NEAREST

MAJOR CITY:
London - 25 miles/45 mins

MAJOR AIRPORT:
London Gatwick - 10 miles/15 mins

RAILWAY STATION:
Redhill - 2 miles/5 mins

RESERVATIONS

Direct with hotel

ACCESS CODES

AMADEUS/SYSTEM 1 HK LGWNUT
APOLLO HT41205
SABRE HK 34903
WORLDSPAN HK NUTFI

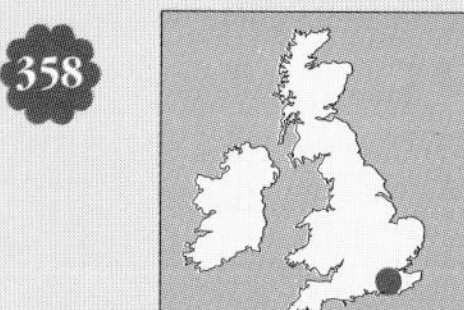

"From the moment I arrived I knew that I would be so glad to have found such a truly beautiful hotel – thank you for not disappointing me!"

D & J Colclough, California

OCKENDEN MANOR

16th century manor house

Ockenden Lane, Cuckfield, West Sussex RH17 5LD

Telephone 01444 416111
Fax 01444 415549

PROPRIETORS

Mr and Mrs H N A Goodman

ROOM RATES

1 Single	£85
16 Doubles/Twins	£115 - £155
3 Four-posters	£160 - £175
2 Suites	£190

Includes continental breakfast and VAT

CHARGE/CREDIT CARDS

• DC • MC • VI

ACCOLADES

E.T.B. ♛♛♛♛ Commended
R.A.C. ★★★ + Merit Awards H C & R
A.A. ★★★ ❀❀ 78%

FACILITIES

Garden, croquet
1 meeting room/max 100 people
Golf, riding and fishing nearby

RESTRICTIONS

No facilities for disabled guests
No pets

ATTRACTIONS

Brighton, Bluebell Railway, Leonardslee Gardens, Chartwell, Wakehurst Place, Hever Castle, Charleston, Penshurst Place, Sheffield Park Gardens

AFFILIATIONS

Pride of Britain
The Celebrated Hotels Collection
Grand Heritage Hotels

NEAREST

MAJOR CITY:
London - 40 miles/35 mins

MAJOR AIRPORT:
London Gatwick - 13 miles/20 mins

RAILWAY STATION:
Haywards Heath - 2 miles/10 mins

RESERVATIONS

Toll free in US: 800-322-2403

ACCESS CODES

AMADEUS HK LGWOCK
APOLLO HK OCKEN
SABRE HK 36354
WORLDSPAN HT 41648

Gastronomic excellence in a 400 year-old family manor

Ockenden Manor is a 16th century manor house set in the tranquil Tudor village of Cuckfield, which is just twenty minutes away from Gatwick Airport. The setting offers peace and quiet but is still within easy reach of major cities such as London and Brighton.

The 22 individually designed and furnished bedrooms, of which five have four poster beds either overlook the splendid nine acre gardens surrounding the manor, or over to the well-known rolling South Downs. The public rooms offer huge log fires in the winter and wonderful views from all the windows all year round. In the summer, it is quite delightful to be able to have meals served outside in the informal garden areas or on the stone terrace.

Ockenden Manor is well known for its Elizabethan oak panelled dining room with its unique gold leaf painted ceiling. Chef, Geoff Welch uses only the finest local produce and ingredients such as fresh crab from Chichester. His cuisine has a delicate but excellent touch and this is borne out by the many return visits from satisfied guests!

The wine cellar is extensive with over 200 bins of both New World and the more traditional French varieties available. There is a wine for every possible taste.

Ockenden Manor is well situated for visits to the opera at Glyndebourne and antique hunting in many of the nearby villages. National Trust properties abound within easy reach, as do golf courses. The seaside is close by, as well as the countryside for walking and outdoor pursuits.

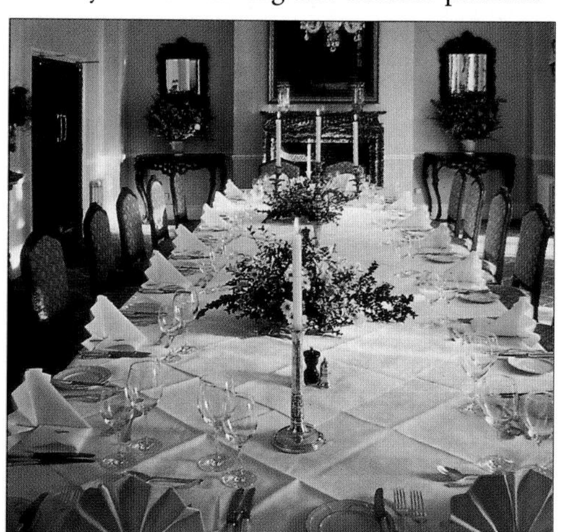

LOCATION

Take A23 south of Crawley towards Brighton. Proceed east at junction B2115 marked Cuckfield. Follow for 3½ miles to village.

“Forest is great: it is true old wild English Nature, and then the fresh heath-sweetened air is so delicious. The Forest is grand”

Alfred Lord Tennyson

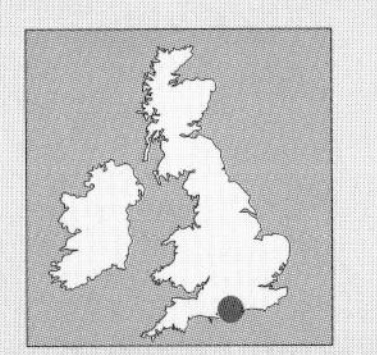

19th century country mansion

PASSFORD HOUSE HOTEL

The hotel on the edge of the picturesque New Forest

Passford House Hotel, the former home of Lord Arthur Cecil, is situated on the edge of the New Forest in nine acres of grounds and beautifully maintained gardens. The hotel boasts a superb leisure centre featuring a spa pool, solarium, gym and indoor and outdoor pools.

The bedrooms, one of which has a four-poster bed, provide every modern comfort and convenience. In addition two suites are available: one is situated across the old stable yard and comprises of two bedrooms, both with en suite facilities, kitchenette and lounge.

The elegant restaurant offers an imaginative and tempting menu complemented by fine wines.

Two miles away, the old Georgian town of Lymington has a good shopping centre, thriving Saturday market, two impressive marinas and superior yachting facilities. Just a short drive away are Beaulieu, the cathedral cities of Winchester and Salisbury, and ferry ports to the Isle of Wight and France.

The New Forest district has five golf courses and, for those interested in riding, there are many stabling and trekking centres.

Why not try a generous helping of Passford's hospitality for yourself.

LOCATION

Leave the M27 at Cadnam (Junction 1) and take the A337 through Brockenhurst for 4 miles. Pass under a railway bridge, cross over a mini roundabout and take the next right. After ¾ mile, bear right into Mount Pleasant Lane. The hotel is ½ mile past a garden centre.

Mount Pleasant Lane, Lymington, Hampshire SO41 8LS

Telephone 01590 682398
Fax 01590 683494

PROPRIETORS

Mr and Mrs Patrick Heritage

ROOM RATES

4 Singles	*£75 - £79*
47 Doubles	*£101 - £135*
1 Four-poster	*£135*
2 Suites	*£175 - £200*

Includes full breakfast and VAT

CHARGE/CREDIT CARDS

• JCB • MC • VI

ACCOLADES

E.T.B. ♛♛♛♛ Highly Commended
R.A.C. ★★★ + Merit Award C
A.A. ★★★ ❀ 74%

FACILITIES

Indoor/outdoor pool, croquet, tennis, gardens, sports complex
4 meeting rooms/max 100 people
Golf, riding, fishing and sailing nearby

RESTRICTIONS

None

ATTRACTIONS

Salisbury, Winchester, Beaulieu, New Forest, Isle of Wight

AFFILIATIONS

Independent

NEAREST

MAJOR CITY:
Southampton - 17 miles/30 mins

MAJOR AIRPORT:
London Heathrow - 80 miles/1¾ hrs
Southampton - 17 miles/30 mins

RAILWAY STATION:
Lymington - 2 miles/5 mins

RESERVATIONS

Direct with hotel

ACCESS CODES

Not applicable

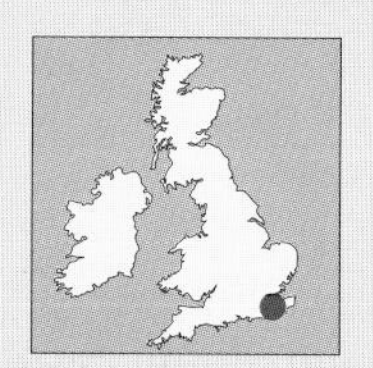

" A style uniquely its own, tremendous hospitality. It's the hosts that make the inn "

General K Israel, US Air Force

POWDERMILLS HOTEL

Country house

Powdermill Lane, Battle, East Sussex TN33 0SP

Telephone 01424 775511
Fax 01424 774540

PROPRIETORS

Douglas and Julie Coupland

ROOM RATES

1 Single	£49 - £75
20 Doubles	£65 - £85
1 Four-poster	£75 - £85
1 Suite	£120

Includes full breakfast and VAT

CHARGE/CREDIT CARDS

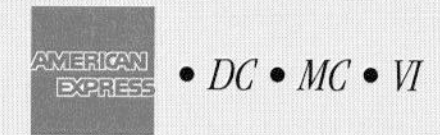

• DC • MC • VI

ACCOLADES

R.A.C. ★★★ + Merit Award H
A.A. ★★★ 68%

FACILITIES

Outdoor pool, gardens, fishing
3 meeting rooms/max 150 people
Golf and riding nearby

RESTRICTIONS

None

ATTRACTIONS

Battle Abbey,
Rye, Hastings,
local antique shops

AFFILIATIONS

Independent

NEAREST

MAJOR CITY:
Hastings - 6 miles/10 mins

MAJOR AIRPORT:
London Gatwick - 48 miles/1 hr

RAILWAY STATION:
Battle - 1 mile/2 mins

RESERVATIONS

Direct with hotel

ACCESS CODES

Not applicable

SOUTH

Many would argue British history started here back in 1066 AD

Powdermills is a stunning 18th century country house hotel set in 150 acres of parks and woodland just outside the historic town of Battle. This is '1066 country' – where William the Conqueror fought and killed King Harold.

A seven-acre specimen fishing lake and three smaller lakes stocked with trout are available to guests. There are plenty of opportunities to relax and wander around the grounds. Proprietors Douglas and Julie Cowpland and their staff are on hand to make you feel at home in warm and friendly surroundings.

The hotel has been richly furnished with antiques from the many local antique shops.

The Orangery Restaurant has received many accolades for its fine classical cooking prepared under the direction of Chef Paul Webbe. It is open to residents and non-residents for lunch, afternoon tea and dinner and, during the summer, dinner may be taken on the terrace overlooking the gardens.

The hotel, with its historic atmosphere and legendary surroundings, is ideally located for exploring the most beautiful and ancient parts of Sussex and Kent.

LOCATION

Through the town of Battle on A2100, direction Hastings. First turning right into Powdermill Lane. Down the lane 1 mile. Hotel on the right hand side after sharp bend.

" It is the best service I have received from any hotel in the UK. Everyone was so accommodating "

Tom Arndt, HFC Bank

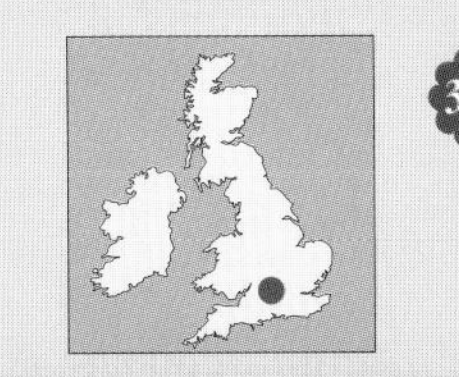

Country house hotel

REGENCY PARK HOTEL

In the heart of Berkshire, a place to come back to time and time again

The Regency Park Hotel at Newbury is a perfect location for those seeking access to the many attractions of Royal Berkshire.

The hotel, set in five acres of gardens, offers all the convenience and comfort of a modern facility whilst maintaining the standards of traditional service and excellence.

The 50 luxury bedrooms, all en suite are quite spacious for a hotel of this size. They incorporate almost every notion of comfort and convenience including many with king size beds, satellite TV (including CNN), mini- bar, trouser press, and refreshment facilities. South facing rooms have private balconies.

Terraces Restaurant is elegant and stylish, possessing an enviable reputation for quality and presentation. Every dish is composed of fresh produce and prepared to order, from the classical cuisine of the à la carte menu through to the light meals served in Fountains Bar.

The management and staff make the Regency Park a particularly enjoyable place to stay and consistently display a courteous and caring attitude to their guests.

Other services include 24 hour room service, valet parking, free baby listening and same day laundry. There is also a purpose-designed business centre and a new fully air conditioned function room called the Orchard Suite, which can accommodate private parties for up to 120 people.

LOCATION

Exit M4 at Junction 13 to Newbury. At roundabout take 2nd exit onto A4, signposted Thatcham/Reading. At 4th set of main traffic lights, turn left into Northfield Road, and then 3rd left into Bowling Green Road. The hotel is located on the right hand side.

**Bowling Green Road,
Thatcham, Newbury,
Berkshire RG18 3RP**

**Telephone 01635 871555
Fax 01635 871571**

PROPRIETOR
Mr P J A Hazlerigg

MANAGER
Meriel Neighbour

ROOM RATES

4 Singles	£85 - £92.50
45 Doubles	£95 - £105
1 Suite	£190 - £255

Includes VAT

CHARGE/CREDIT CARDS

• DC • MC • VI

ACCOLADES
E.T.B. ♛♛♛♛♛ Highly Commended
R.A.C. ★★★★ + Merit Awards H & R
A.A. ★★★★ ❀❀ 74%

FACILITIES
Gardens, all-weather tennis
9 meeting rooms/max 140 people
Golf and riding nearby

RESTRICTIONS
Pets not allowed in public areas

ATTRACTIONS
Ascot and Newbury racecourses, Kennet and Avon canals, Bath, Oxford, Windsor

AFFILIATIONS
Independent

NEAREST
MAJOR CITY:
Reading - 12 miles/30 mins

MAJOR AIRPORT:
London Heathrow - 42 miles/45 mins

RAILWAY STATION:
Newbury - 3 miles/10 mins

RESERVATIONS
Direct with hotel

ACCESS CODES
APOLLO HT 66095
SABRE HK 20685
WORLDSPAN/SAHARA HK REGEP
AMADEUS HK EWYPAR

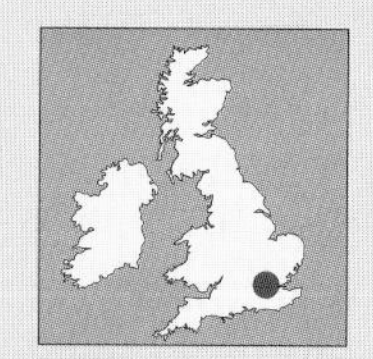

"What a pleasure it was to stay in a country mansion, yet so close to the attractions of London"

James Densham, Monte Carlo

THE ROYAL BERKSHIRE HOTEL

Queen Anne mansion

London Road, Sunninghill, Ascot, Berkshire SL5 0PP

Telephone 01344 23322
Fax 01344 27100

GENERAL MANAGER
Simon Pearce

ROOM RATES

6 Singles	£125
49 Doubles/Twins	£172
2 Four-posters	£295 - £305
4 Suites	£210 - £405

Includes VAT

CHARGE/CREDIT CARDS

• DC • MC • VI

ACCOLADES
E.T.B. ♛♛♛♛♛ *Highly Commended*
R.A.C. ★★★★
A.A. ★★★★ ❀❀ *69%*

FACILITIES
Garden, squash, croquet, tennis, indoor pool, putting green, sauna, jacuzzi, gym, heli-pad
9 meeting rooms/max 100 people
Golf and riding nearby

RESTRICTIONS
No facilities for disabled guests

ATTRACTIONS
Royal Ascot Racecourse, Windsor, London

AFFILIATIONS
Hilton Associate

NEAREST
MAJOR CITY:
London - 25 miles/40 mins

MAJOR AIRPORT:
London Heathrow - 12 miles/25 mins

RAILWAY STATION:
Ascot - 2 miles/7 mins

RESERVATIONS
Direct with hotel

ACCESS CODES
SABRE HL 10159

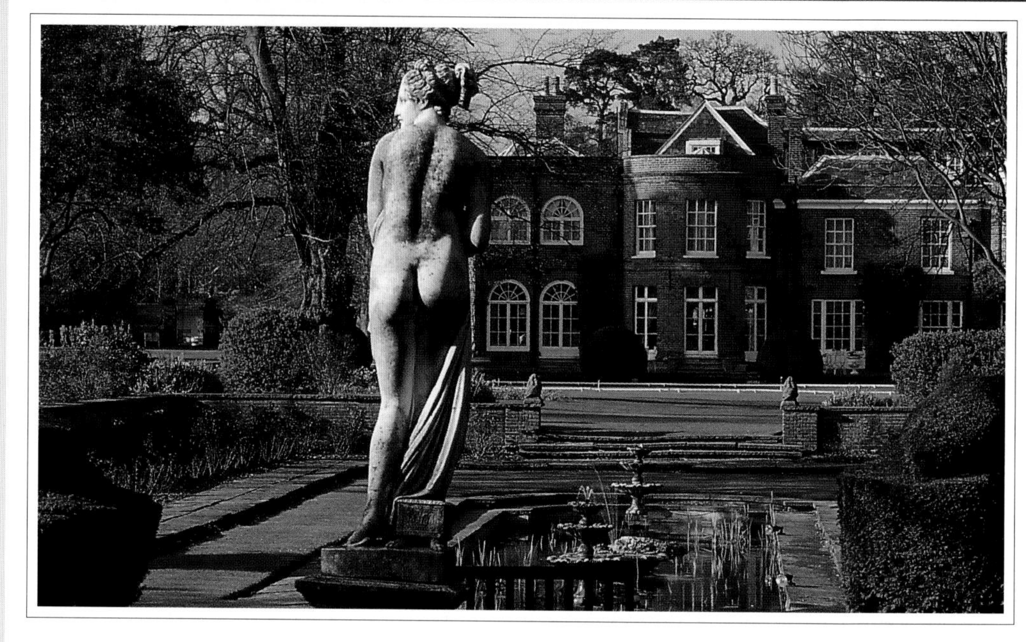

Royal Ascot, Wentworth, Smith's Lawn – the sporting world at your feet

The Royal Berkshire's mellow brick Queen Anne Mansion built in 1705 and set in 15 acres of matured gardens and woodlands is ideally located for Ascot, Wentworth, and polo at Smith's Lawn, yet only 12 miles from London's Heathrow Airport and 40 minutes from the centre of London.

Today, it is a very special hotel indeed. An appealing rural retreat, it is tailor-made for both business and pleasure. A model of comfort and elegance offering exceptional facilities, and a fine tradition of hospitality that other hotels can only dream of.

The hotel boasts a wealth of leisure facilities, including a gym, indoor swimming pool, saunas, whirlpool, and squash court. Outdoors there are two tennis courts, a croquet lawn and putting green.

Tea or drinks can be enjoyed in the drawing rooms or on the terrace with views across the lawns.

For connoisseurs of fine food, the Stateroom Restaurant has established a high reputation for producing a mouth-watering array of contemporary and highly individual dishes. This, together with a fine wine list, makes it a joy to visit this superbly appointed hotel. Weekend rates are available on request.

LOCATION

2 miles from Ascot Station, 12 miles from Heathrow Airport, 6 miles from the M25 and adjacent to A329.

" The experience was unusual in that courtesy, kindness and efficiency was of the highest order "

Eleanor Sanderson, London

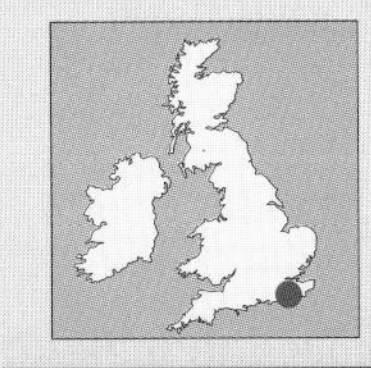

Country manor

SHELLEYS

Wonderfully restored to its former grandeur

Built as an inn in 1526, Shelleys is a Grade II listed building, and a famous local landmark. Converted to a manor house by the Earl of Dorset in 1590, the property took its name from its next occupants, the Shelley family, whose son was Percy Bysshe Shelley. The manor eventually became a hotel in 1932.

Shelleys Hotel is now a Thistle Country House Hotel and Restaurant. A complete refurbishment programme has restored the property to its former historical grandeur.

This includes the 'Drawing Room', and the hotel's elegant banqueting room, which seats 50 people and overlooks the private garden. New soft furnishings decorate Shelleys' deluxe guest rooms, which include the luxurious Earl of Dorset Suite, and the spacious Pelham Room with a four-poster bed overlooking the gardens. All rooms have individual colour schemes with antique furniture and feature televisions with satellite channels, radios, trouser presses, and tea and coffee making facilities.

The hotel is popular with guests visiting the Glyndebourne Opera Season which is located only four miles away and the hotel can provide picnic hampers as well as a limousine service.

Shelleys Hotel is close to London Gatwick airport and is well served by the motorway network, including the M23 link with the M25. The Newhaven ferry is seven miles away and the Channel Tunnel is nearby.

LOCATION

From London take M23/A23 to Brighton. North of Brighton take ring road link to A27. Follow for 4 miles to Lewes. Hotel seen on left approaching town centre.

The High Street, Lewes, East Sussex BN7 1XS

Telephone 01273 472361
Fax 01273 483152

GENERAL MANAGER

Graeme Coles

ROOM RATES

1 Single	*£95*
16 Doubles/Twins	*£120*
1 Four-poster	*£180*
1 Suite	*£150*
1 Deluxe	*£170*

Includes VAT

CHARGE/CREDIT CARDS

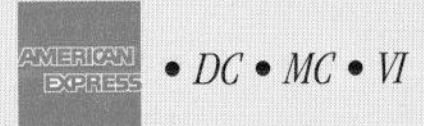

• *DC* • *MC* • *VI*

ACCOLADES

E.T.B. ♛♛♛♛ *Highly Commended*
R.A.C. ★★★
A.A. ★★★ ❀ *76%*

FACILITIES

Garden
3 meeting rooms/max 60 people
Golf and riding nearby

RESTRICTIONS

No facilities for disabled guests

ATTRACTIONS

Charleston Farm House, Brighton Pavilion, Glyndebourne, Beachy Head

AFFILIATIONS

A Thistle Country House Hotel

NEAREST

MAJOR CITY:
Brighton - 7 miles/20 mins

MAJOR AIRPORT:
London Gatwick - 30 miles/40 mins

RAILWAY STATION:
Lewes - 1 miles/5 mins

RESERVATIONS

Toll free in US/Canada: 800-847-4358
Toll free in Australia: 800-062-055

ACCESS CODES

AMADEUS/SYSTEM 1 TI LPLATL
APOLLO TI 18614
SABRE TI 12041
WORLDSPAN TI 4590

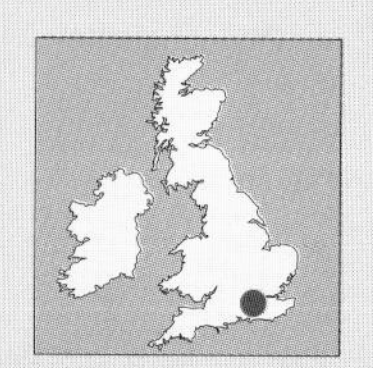

" The Spread Eagle of Midhurst, that oldest and most revered of all the prime inns of this world "

Hilaire Belloc

THE SPREAD EAGLE

15th century coaching inn

South Street, Midhurst, West Sussex GU29 9NH

Telephone 01730 816911
Fax 01730 815668

PROPRIETORS

Sandy and Anne Goodman

ROOM RATES

5 Singles	£75
31 Doubles/Twins	£93 - £120
5 Four-posters	£120 - £175
1 Suite	£175

Includes continental breakfast and VAT

CHARGE/CREDIT CARDS

• DC • MC • VI

ACCOLADES

R.A.C. ★★★ + Merit Awards H C & R
A.A. ★★★ ❀❀ 74%

FACILITIES

Gardens, parking
5 meeting rooms/max 110 people
Golf and riding nearby

RESTRICTIONS

No facilities for disabled guests

ATTRACTIONS

Chawton, Goodwood House, Petworth, Cowdray polo, Arundel town and castle, Uppark Country House

AFFILIATIONS

Independent

NEAREST

MAJOR CITY:
London - 52 miles/1½ hrs

MAJOR AIRPORT:
London Gatwick - 40 miles/50 mins
London Heathrow - 46 miles/1 hr

RAILWAY STATION:
Haslemere - 8 miles/10 mins

RESERVATIONS

Direct with hotel

ACCESS CODES

GH

SOUTH

This famous and historic hotel has been welcoming guests since 1430

The Spread Eagle is one of England's oldest hotels, dating back to 1430. During its considerable history, including its time as a famous coaching inn, influences of successive eras have been reflected both in the architecture and the decorative features. Superb, heavy polished timbers, Flemish stained glass windows and Tudor bread ovens are amongst the many features.

Modern British cooking at its best is served in the candlelit restaurant with its huge coppered inglenook fireplace and dark oak beams, from which hang traditional Sussex Christmas puddings.

Co-ordinated fabrics and antique furnishings are to be found in the individually decorated bedrooms, all with modern facilities.

The 17th century Jacobean Hall is a superb place for meetings or maybe a mediaeval banquet, minstrels and all! There is a secluded courtyard, which in summer is flanked by climbing roses and clematis.

The stately homes of Goodwood, Petworth and Uppark are within a short drive and the Weald, Downland Museum, Chichester Cathedral and Chewton, Jane Austen's home, are among the many local attractions.

LOCATION

Situated in the old and historic town of Midhurst, The Spread Eagle can be found just off the A272 near the old market square.

"As luxurious as we had hoped but much more friendly than we'd ever expected"

Mr & Mrs Poppy, England

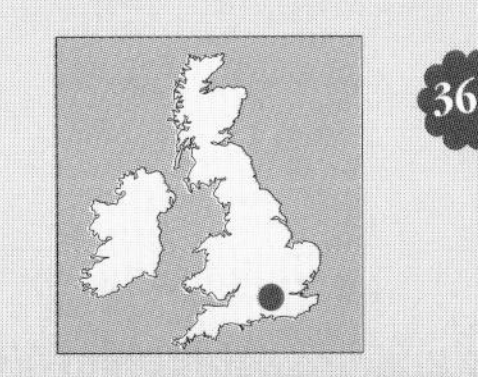

Country mansion

TYLNEY HALL

A luxurious private party awaits all those who enter this stately home

Arriving at Tylney Hall in the evening, you can imagine that you are arriving to a party at a private stately home. This gracious country manor, set in 66 acres of stunning gardens and parkland, typifies the great houses of the past.

Originally built in 1561, the present mansion dates from the beginning of this century when no expense was spared in creating a highly-prized country seat with panelling of Italian walnut and a Rococo ceiling from the Gramini Palace. At the same time, the famous Gertrude Jekyll 'Water Gardens' and Weir Schulz 'arches' transformed the grounds.

Little has changed and today, aperitifs are taken in the oak-panelled library bar and award-winning cuisine is served in the Oak Room restaurant, complemented by fine wines and conscientious service.

An 18-hole golf course borders the hotel and exclusive leisure facilities include indoor and outdoor heated swimming pools, multi-gym, sauna, tennis, croquet and snooker. Hot air ballooning, archery, clay pigeon shooting and horse-riding are offered locally. The wooded trails are ideal for rambling or jogging.

The cathedral town of Winchester, the country home of the Duke of Wellington and the picturesque village of Hartley Wintney, ideal for antiques, are all nearby. London and Windsor are just one hour's drive away.

LOCATION

5 minutes from Junction 5 of the M3.
15 minutes from Junction 11 of the M4.
30 minutes from the M25.

Rotherwick, Hook, Hampshire RG27 9AZ

Telephone 01256 764881
Fax 01256 768141

GENERAL MANAGER
Miss Rita Mooney

ROOM RATES

Single occupancy	*£104 - £114*
65 Doubles/Twins	*£124 - £134*
26 Suites	*£154 - £224*
3 Four-posters	*£274*

Includes full breakfast, newspaper and VAT

CHARGE/CREDIT CARDS

• *DC* • *JCB* • *MC* • *VI*

ACCOLADES
E.T.B. ♛♛♛♛♛ *De Luxe*
R.A.C. Blue Ribbon Award ★★★★
A.A. ★★★★ ❀❀

FACILITIES
Garden, croquet, tennis, indoor and outdoor pools, sauna, snooker, gym, golf, heli-pad
9 meeting rooms/max 100 people
Fishing, riding, clay pigeon shooting, rambling, archery, massage and hot air ballooning nearby

RESTRICTIONS
No facilities for disabled guests
No pets

ATTRACTIONS
Winchester, Windsor Castle, Stonehenge, London, Salisbury

AFFILIATIONS
Small Luxury Hotels

NEAREST
MAJOR CITY:
Winchester - 30 miles/30 mins

MAJOR AIRPORT:
London Heathrow - 35 miles/40 mins
Eastleigh - 35 miles/40 mins

RAILWAY STATION:
Basingstoke - 6 miles/10 mins

RESERVATIONS
Toll free in US/Canada: 800-525-4800

ACCESS CODES
AMADEUS/SYSTEM 1 LX LONTHH
APOLLO LX 21653
AXESS LX 5641
SABRE LX 19817
WORLDSPAN/SAHARA LX SOUTH

AREAS of OUTSTANDING NATURAL BEAUTY

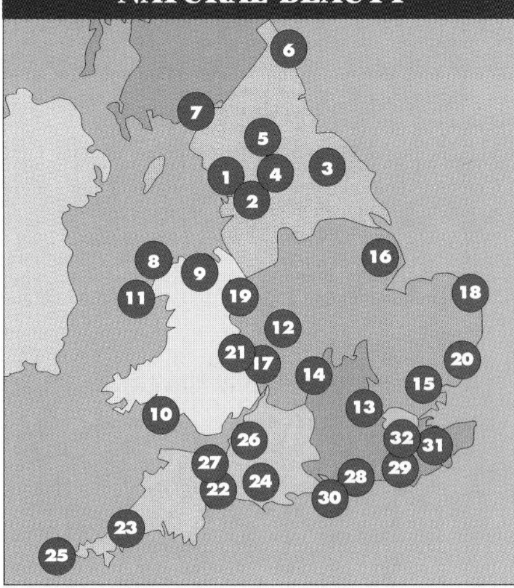

1. Arnside & Silverdale
2. Forest of Bowland
3. Howardian Hills
4. Nidderdale
5. North Pennines
6. Northumberland Coast
7. Solway Coast
8. Angelsey
9. Clwydian Ranges
10. Gower Peninsula
11. Lleyn
12. Cannock Chase
13. Chilterns
14. Cotswolds
15. Constable Country
16. Lincolnshire Wolds
17. Malvern Hills
18. Norfolk Coast
19. Shropshire Hills
20. Suffolk Coast
21. Wye Valley
22. Blackdown Hills
23. Cornwall
24. Cranbourn Chase
25. Isles of Scilly
26. Mendip Hills
27. Quantock Hills
28. Chichester Harbour
29. High Weald
30. Isle of Wight
31. Kent Downs
32. Surrey Hills

NATIVE ANIMALS

Aylesbury's Dormouse *Squirrel-tailed dormouse lives in woods near Aylesbury, Buckinghamshire* ***Midshires***

Belvoir Foxhound *The darkest pure-bred foxhound. Belvoir, Leicestershire* ***Midshires***

Camberwell Beauty *Butterfly visiting the coast near Hull in summer* ***North***

Dartmoor Beast *Legondary cat-like creature said to roam Dartmoor attacking sheep. Many sightings but nothing proved* ***West***

Dartmoor Pony *Small pony, average height five feet, from Dartmoor. Used for breeding riding ponies* ***West***

Feral Goat *On the high mountain screes of Snowdonia* ***Wales***

Golden Eagle *Breeding in the Highlands* ***Scotland***

Kentish Glory *This moth has moved its home to Wyre Forest, near Worcester* ***Midshires***

Large Blue *Butterfly found only in north Cornwall* ***West***

Lulworth Skipper *Small brown and black butterfly lives in Dorset* ***South***

Manx Cat *Tailless cat first bred in the Isle of Man 300 years ago* ***Islands***

Shetland Ponies *Miniature breed of pony once used in coal pits. Height up to 40 inches* ***Islands***

Skomer Vole *Only on Skomer Island, near Pembroke* ***Wales***

Soay Sheep *Britain's only wild sheep live on the island of Soay, Hebrides* ***Scotland***

Yarmouth Bloater *Fish found off the coast of East Anglia* ***Midshires***

Writers' Homes and Heartlands

Jane Austen Chawton, Alton, Hampshire	***South***
Arnold Bennett Around Stoke-on-Trent	***Midshires***
The Brontes The Parsonage, Haworth, West Yorkshire	***North***
John Bunyan Elstow, near Bedford	***Midshires***
Robert Burns Alloway, Ayrshire	***Scotland***
Samuel Taylor Coleridge Nether Stowey, The Quantocks, Somerset	***West***
Charles Dickens Rochester, Kent	***South***
Thomas Hardy Bockhampton, Dorset	***West***
Dr Samuel Johnson Lichfield, Staffordshire	***Midshires***
James Joyce Joyce Museum, Sandycove	***Ireland***
William McGonagall Dundee and "the Silvery Tay"	***Scotland***
Beatrix Potter Hill Top Farm, Cumbria	***North***
William Shakespeare Henley Street, Stratford-upon-Avon,	***Midshires***
George Bernard Shaw Dublin	***Ireland***
Robert Louis Stevenson Edinburgh	***Scotland***
Dylan Thomas Laugharne, Dyfed	***Wales***
William Wordsworth Grasmere, Cumbria	***North***
William Butler Yeats Co Sligo.	***Ireland***

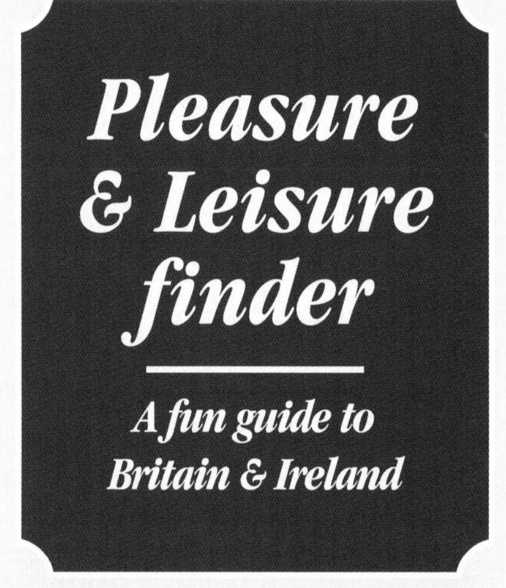
Pleasure
& Leisure
finder
A fun guide to
Britain & Ireland

TOP 10 GARDENS

Hampton Court Gardens	Twickenham	***London***
Tropical World Roundhay Park,	Leeds	***North***
Kew Gardens	Kew	***London***
Royal Botanic Gardens	Edinburgh	***Scotland***
Royal Horticultural Society	Wisley	***South***
Botanic Gardens	Belfast	***Ireland***
Botanic Gardens	Glasgow	***Scotland***
Sir Thomas and Lady Dixon Park	Belfast	***Ireland***
Walsall Arboretum	Birmingham	***Midshires***
Oxford University Botanic Gardens	Oxford	***South***

British Tourist Authority

Some Other Gardens

Blickling Hall	Blickling	***Midshires***
Bodnant Gardens Tal-y-Cafn	Colwyn Bay	***Wales***
Butterstream Garden	Trim, Co Meath	***Ireland***
Coleton Fishacre Garden	Dartmouth, Devon	***West***
Colonsay Sub-tropical Garden	Colonsay	***Islands***
Eric Young Orchid Foundation	Jersey	***Islands***
Japanese Gardens	Tully, Co Kildare	***Ireland***
Kingshayes	Tiverton, Devon	***West***
Mottisfont Abbey Garden	Nr Romsey	***South***
National Botanic Gardens	Dublin	***Ireland***
Botanic Gardens	Isles of Scilly	***Islands***
Sissinghurst	Kent	***South***
Stowe Landscape Gardens	Nr Buckingham	***South***
Wallington	Morepeth,	***North***

NATIONAL SCENIC AREAS of SCOTLAND

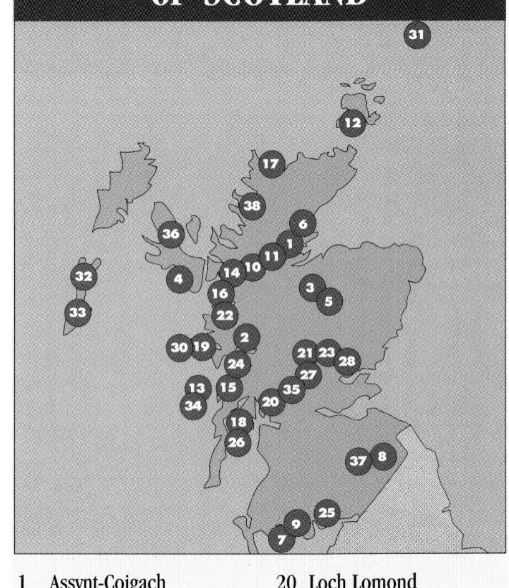

1 Assynt-Coigach
2 Ben Nevis and Glencoe
3 The Cairngorms
4 The Cuillin Hills
5 Deeside and Lochnagar
6 Dornoch Firth
7 East Stewartry Coast
8 Eildon and Leaderfoot
9 Fleet Valley
10 Glen Affric
11 Glen Strathfarrar
12 Hoy and W. Mainland
13 Jura
14 Kintail
15 Knapdale
16 Knoydart
17 Kyle of Tongue
18 Kyles of Bute
19 Loch na Keal, Mull
20 Loch Lomond
21 Loch Rannoch/Glen Lyon
22 Loch Shiel
23 Loch Tummel
24 Lynn of Lorn
25 Nith Estuary
26 North Arran
27 River Earn
28 River Tay (Dunkeld)
29 St Kilda
30 Scarba/Lunga/Garvellachs
31 Shetland
32 S. Lewis/Harris/N.Uist
33 S. Uist Machair
34 The Small Isles
35 The Trossachs
36 Trotternish
37 Upper Tweedale
38 Wester Ross

TOP 10 WILDLIFE CENTRES

London Zoo Regent's Park, NW1	***London***
Chester Zoo	***North***
Sea Life Centre Blackpool	***North***
Edinburgh Zoo	***Scotland***
Whipsnade Wild Animal Park Near Luton	***Midshires***
Twycross Zoo Atherstone, Warwickshire	***Midshires***
Knowsley Safari Park Lancashire	***North***
Bristol Zoo Endangered wildlife conservation. Bristol	***West***
Cotswold Wildlife Park Oxfordshire	***Midshires***
Birmingham Nature Centre	***Midshires***

Source: British Tourist Authority

Other Wildlife Attractions

Birdworld Farnham, Surrey	***South***
Linton Zoo Wildlife Breeding Centre, Cambridgeshire	***Midshires***
Welsh Mountain Zoo Colwin Bay	***Wales***
Jersey Zoological Park Jersey	***Islands***

More on pages 150 and 446

London

Kenwood House, Hampstead, NW3. South front of Georgian mansion rebuilt in 1764-73 by Robert Adam for the Earl of Mansfield. Today it houses the superb Iveagh Bequest art collection (Rembrandt, Gainsborough, Vermeer).

Heritage sites

The following heritage sites can be found on the map overleaf. The key numbers show where they are located.

LONDON

Chiswick House
Eltham Palace
Jewel Tower, Westminster
Kenwood, The Iveagh Bequest
London Wall, Tower Hill
Marble Hill House
Ranger's House
Winchester Palace
Westminster Abbey: Chapter House

SOME OTHER SITES OF INTEREST IN CENTRAL LONDON

Buckingham Palace
St James Palace
Victoria and Albert Museum
National Gallery
National Portrait Gallery
British Museum
Royal Albert Hall
Houses of Parliament
Westminster Cathedral
St Paul's Cathedral
Tower of London
Wallace Collection
The Tate Gallery
Imperial War Museum
Museum of London
Kensington Palace

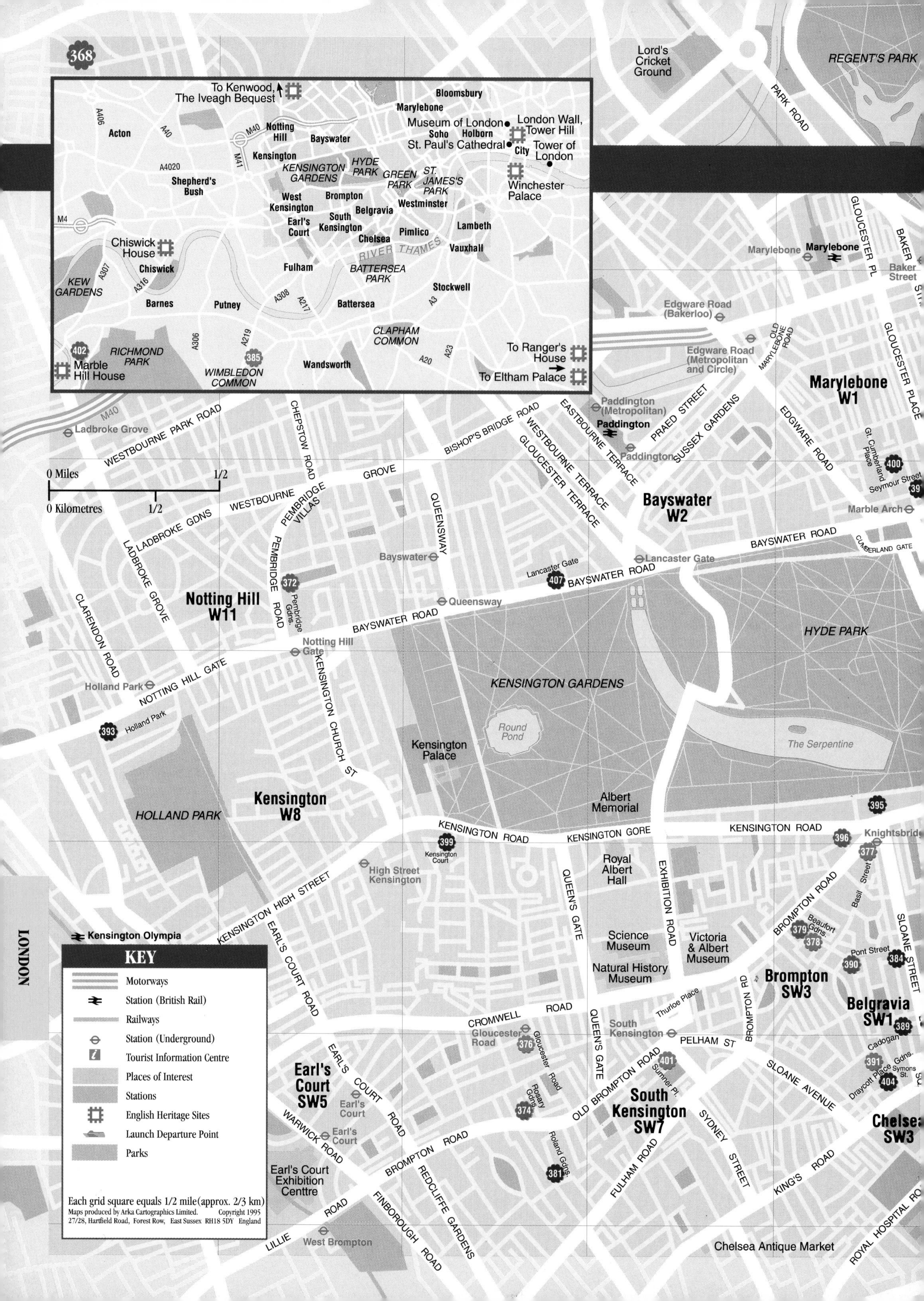
To Kenwood, The Iveagh Bequest
Bloomsbury
Marylebone
Museum of London
London Wall, Tower Hill
Soho
Holborn
St. Paul's Cathedral
City
Tower of London
Winchester Palace
Acton
A406
A40
M40
Notting Hill
Bayswater
M41
Kensington
A4020
Shepherd's Bush
KENSINGTON GARDENS
HYDE PARK
GREEN PARK
ST. JAMES'S PARK
West Kensington
Brompton
Belgravia
Westminster
M4
Earl's Court
South Kensington
Lambeth
Chelsea
Pimlico
Vauxhall
RIVER THAMES
Chiswick House
Chiswick
A307
A316
KEW GARDENS
Fulham
BATTERSEA PARK
Stockwell
Barnes
Putney
A308
A217
Battersea
A3
CLAPHAM COMMON
A306
A219
402
RICHMOND PARK
Marble Hill House
385
WIMBLEDON COMMON
Wandsworth
A20
A23
To Ranger's House
To Eltham Palace
Lord's Cricket Ground
REGENT'S PARK
PARK ROAD
Marylebone
GLOUCESTER PL
BAKER ST
Baker Street
Edgware Road (Bakerloo)
Edgware Road (Metropolitan and Circle)
OLD MARYLEBONE ROAD
GLOUCESTER PLACE
Marylebone W1
M40
Ladbroke Grove
WESTBOURNE PARK ROAD
CHEPSTOW ROAD
BISHOP'S BRIDGE ROAD
WESTBOURNE TERRACE
EASTBOURNE TERRACE
Paddington (Metropolitan)
Paddington
PRAED STREET
SUSSEX GARDENS
EDGWARE ROAD
Gt. Cumberland Place
400
Seymour Street
0 Miles
1/2
0 Kilometres
1/2
WESTBOURNE GROVE
GLOUCESTER TERRACE
Bayswater W2
Marble Arch
LADBROKE GDNS
PEMBRIDGE VILLAS
QUEENSWAY
BAYSWATER ROAD
CUMBERLAND GATE
LADBROKE GROVE
PEMBRIDGE ROAD
Bayswater
Lancaster Gate
Lancaster Gate
407
372
Pembridge Gdns.
CLARENDON ROAD
Notting Hill W11
Queensway
Notting Hill Gate
HYDE PARK
Holland Park
NOTTING HILL GATE
KENSINGTON CHURCH ST
KENSINGTON GARDENS
393
Holland Park
Round Pond
The Serpentine
Kensington Palace
Albert Memorial
Kensington W8
HOLLAND PARK
395
KENSINGTON ROAD
KENSINGTON GORE
KENSINGTON ROAD
396
Knightsbridge
399
Kensington Court
377
Royal Albert Hall
High Street Kensington
QUEEN'S GATE
EXHIBITION ROAD
BROMPTON ROAD
Basil Street
KENSINGTON HIGH STREET
EARL'S COURT ROAD
Science Museum
Victoria & Albert Museum
379
Beaufort Gdns.
378
SLOANE STREET
Kensington Olympia
Natural History Museum
Pont Street
390
384
Brompton SW3
BROMPTON RD
Belgravia SW1
CROMWELL ROAD
Thurloe Place
Gloucester Road
376
Gloucester Road
South Kensington
PELHAM ST
389
Cadogan
QUEEN'S GATE
OLD BROMPTON ROAD
401
Sumner Pl.
SLOANE AVENUE
391
Cadogan Gdns.
Draycott Place
Symons St.
404
Earl's Court SW5
EARL'S COURT ROAD
Earl's Court
Rosary Gdns.
374
South Kensington SW7
SYDNEY STREET
WARWICK ROAD
Earl's Court
Chelsea SW3
BROMPTON ROAD
Roland Gdns.
FULHAM ROAD
KING'S ROAD
Earl's Court Exhibition Centre
381
REDCLIFFE GARDENS
LILLIE ROAD
FINBOROUGH ROAD
West Brompton
Chelsea Antique Market
ROYAL HOSPITAL RO
KEY
Motorways
Station (British Rail)
Railways
Station (Underground)
Tourist Information Centre
Places of Interest
Stations
English Heritage Sites
Launch Departure Point
Parks
Each grid square equals 1/2 mile (approx. 2/3 km)
Maps produced by Arka Cartographics Limited. Copyright 1995
27/28, Hartfield Road, Forest Row, East Sussex RH18 5DY England
LONDON

LONDON

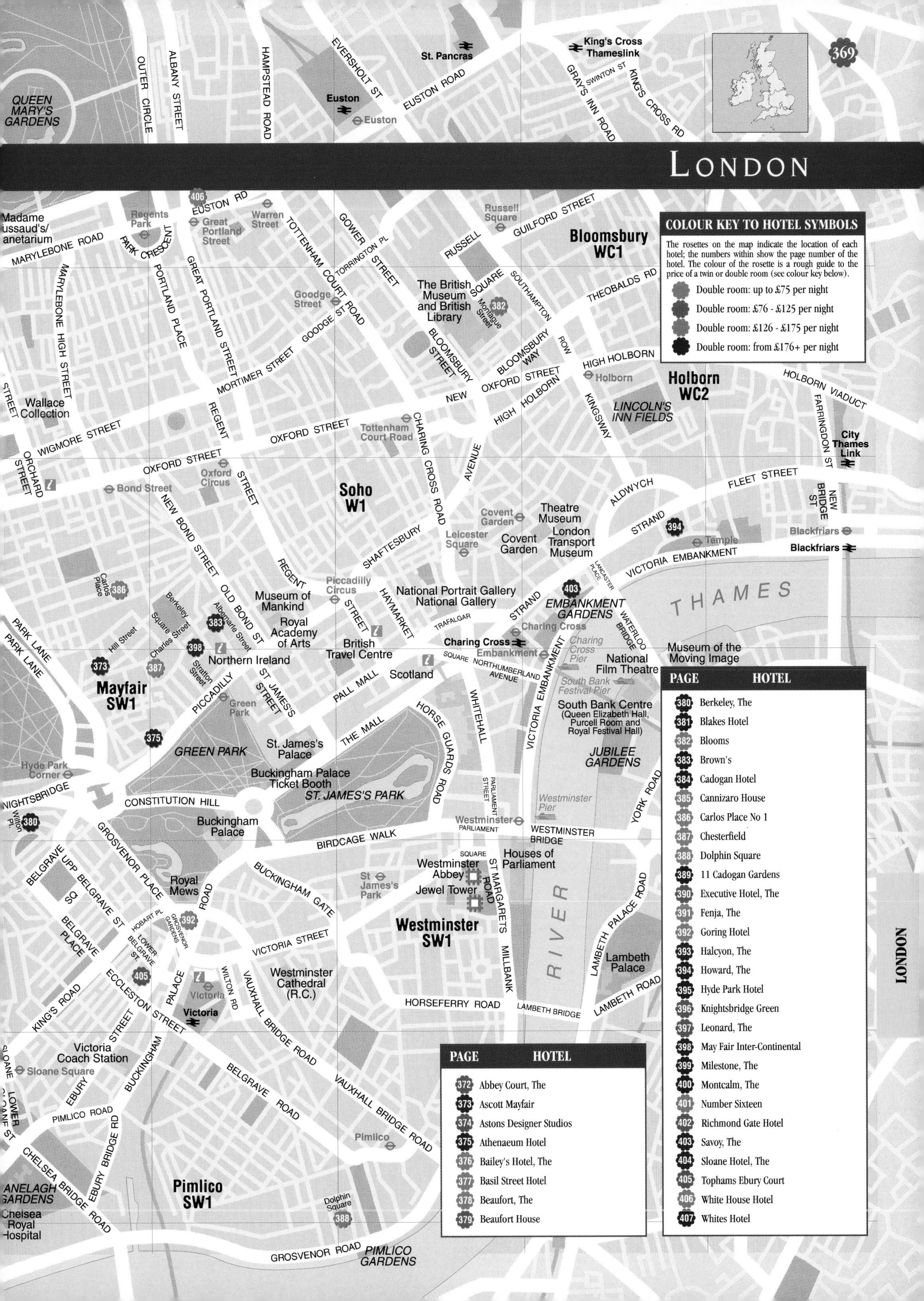
COLOUR KEY TO HOTEL SYMBOLS
The rosettes on the map indicate the location of each hotel; the numbers within show the page number of the hotel. The colour of the rosette is a rough guide to the price of a twin or double room (see colour key below).
Double room: up to £75 per night
Double room: £76 - £125 per night
Double room: £126 - £175 per night
Double room: from £176+ per night
PAGE HOTEL
372 Abbey Court, The
373 Ascott Mayfair
374 Astons Designer Studios
375 Athenaeum Hotel
376 Bailey's Hotel, The
377 Basil Street Hotel
378 Beaufort, The
379 Beaufort House
380 Berkeley, The
381 Blakes Hotel
382 Blooms
383 Brown's
384 Cadogan Hotel
385 Cannizaro House
386 Carlos Place No 1
387 Chesterfield
388 Dolphin Square
389 11 Cadogan Gardens
390 Executive Hotel, The
391 Fenja, The
392 Goring Hotel
393 Halcyon, The
394 Howard, The
395 Hyde Park Hotel
396 Knightsbridge Green
397 Leonard, The
398 May Fair Inter-Continental
399 Milestone, The
400 Montcalm, The
401 Number Sixteen
402 Richmond Gate Hotel
403 Savoy, The
404 Sloane Hotel, The
405 Tophams Ebury Court
406 White House Hotel
407 Whites Hotel
Bloomsbury WC1
Holborn WC2
Soho W1
Mayfair SW1
Westminster SW1
Pimlico SW1
QUEEN MARY'S GARDENS
St. Pancras
King's Cross Thameslink
Euston
Regents Park
Great Portland Street
Warren Street
Russell Square
Goodge Street
The British Museum and British Library
Wallace Collection
Tottenham Court Road
Holborn
LINCOLN'S INN FIELDS
City Thames Link
Oxford Circus
Bond Street
Covent Garden
Theatre Museum
London Transport Museum
Leicester Square
Temple
Blackfriars
THAMES
Piccadilly Circus
Museum of Mankind
Royal Academy of Arts
National Portrait Gallery
National Gallery
EMBANKMENT GARDENS
Charing Cross
Embankment
Northern Ireland
British Travel Centre
Scotland
Museum of the Moving Image
National Film Theatre
South Bank Centre (Queen Elizabeth Hall, Purcell Room and Royal Festival Hall)
Green Park
GREEN PARK
St. James's Palace
Buckingham Palace Ticket Booth
ST. JAMES'S PARK
Hyde Park Corner
JUBILEE GARDENS
Westminster Pier
Westminster
Buckingham Palace
Royal Mews
St James's Park
Westminster Abbey
Jewel Tower
Houses of Parliament
RIVER
Lambeth Palace
Westminster Cathedral (R.C.)
Victoria
Victoria Coach Station
Sloane Square
Pimlico
Dolphin Square
PIMLICO GARDENS
Chelsea Royal Hospital
LONDON

Damask Silk Parlour, Ranger's House, Greenwich, SE10. Built 1700-20 as a 'grace and favour' house for Admiral Francis Hosier. In 1748-9, Philip Earl of Chesterfield added the gallery. The Green Damask Silk Parlour is one of several rooms displaying the art collection donated by Lord and Lady Howard.

For more than a thousand years, London has been the centre of England's government, finance and culture. The list of things to see and do is endless yet growing! Museums, galleries, palaces, parks, department stores and shops. The shopping centres have their own individual styles. High fashion in Sloane Street and Bond Street. Sale bargains in Oxford and Regent Streets. Chelsea and Carnaby Street each have a worldwide reputation. There's Petticoat Lane street market. The restaurants of Soho. Twenty years ago, Covent Garden was the wholesale fruit market where Professor Higgins found Eliza Doolittle. Today Covent Garden bustles with shops, restaurants, museums and street entertainment – all within the original buildings.

London takes on a fresh lease of life every evening. A slice of history comes alive with just about any ticket you buy for a West End Theatre. At the Theatre Royal, Charles II bought oranges from Nell Gwyn. William Terriss was murdered at the stage door of the Adelphi. The Savoy Theatre was purpose-built in 1881 for the Gilbert and Sullivan operas. The Royal Opera House has earned its title. What's on in the West End is shown in the London newspapers. London's equally vast world of alternative music and theatre is detailed in Time Out magazine – gigs, concerts, little theatres and pubs.

There is more to London than its centre. The College Picture Gallery at Dulwich, Camden Passage antique shops in Islington, the Whitgift Shopping Centre in Croydon, the Cutty Sark schooner at Greenwich are just a few of the rich outer circle of attractions. What's mentioned here is necessarily only a tiny sample to whet your appetite. Details, maps and leaflets are available from your hotel, and the information centres are listed on page 480.

Palaces & Historic Houses

Buckingham Palace. Sovereign's principal home. Built in 1703 for the Duke of Buckingham. Changing of the Guard at 11.30 am.

Hampton Court Palace, Hampton Court, Surrey. England's oldest Tudor palace. State apartments, maze, Real Tennis court.

Houses of Parliament, Palace of Westminster, SW1. Site of Edward the Confessor's residence. 14th c Jewel Tower and Westminster Hall.

Kenwood House, Hampstead, NW3. Neo-classical villa by Robert Adam. Paintings, shoe-buckle and jewellery collections.

Osterley Park House, Isleworth, Middlesex. Superb interiors include Adam's plasterwork, carpets and furniture.

St James's Palace, SW1. Built for Henry VIII as sovereign's principal residence. Chapel Royal built c 1532.

Tower of London, EC3. Built 1078. 900 years of British history. Home of the Beefeaters. Crown Jewels. Traitors Gate.

Museums, Galleries & Modern Highspots

Bethnal Green Museum of Childhood, E2. Toys, dolls and houses, games, puppets, toy theatres. Children's costumes.

British Museum, WC1. Civilization! Elgin Marbles, Magna Carta, Sutton Hoo Burial. 6 million books in British Library.

Docklands Visitor Centre, Isle of Dogs, E14. Exhibition of this imaginative development of old London Docks. Canary Wharf.

Imperial War Museum, SE1. Britain and Commonwealth's battles since 1914. Relive the London Blitz!

London Dungeon, SE1. World's first medieval horror museum. The Victorian drama of Jack the Ripper.

Madame Tussauds, Marylebone Road, NW1. Waxed figures in themed settings. Grand Hall, Superstars, Spirit of London.

Museum of London, EC2. Galleries showing 2,000 years of social history. Lunchtime lectures.

National Portrait Gallery, St Martin's Place, WC2. Notable British men and women from middle ages to 20th c.

National Gallery, Trafalgar Square, WC2. Famous artists of all major schools of Britain and Europe.

National Maritime Museum, Greenwich, SE10. Britain's sea heritage. Ships, navigation, astronomy.

Rock Circus, Piccadilly Circus, W1. Personal stereo listening, moving images, models of more than 50 great rock stars.

Science Museum, SW7. Space travel, medicine, industrial machinery. Plenty of visitor participation.

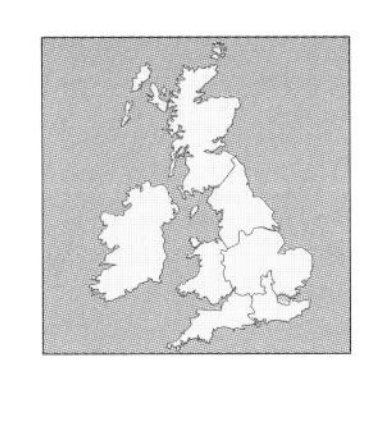

TOURIST OFFICE INFORMATION

Further information about London will be gladly supplied by:

London Tourist Board
26 Grosvenor Gardens
Victoria SW1W 0DU
Tel: 0891 505 465
(Places of Interest)

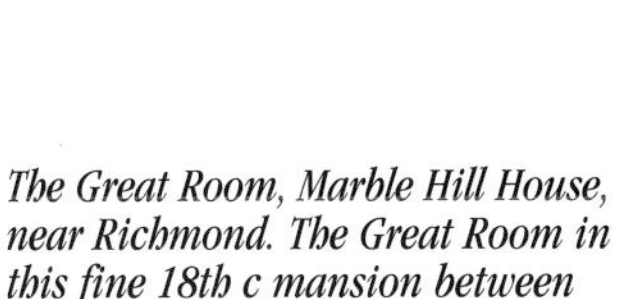

The Great Room, Marble Hill House, near Richmond. The Great Room in this fine 18th c mansion between Richmond Park and the Royal Botanic Gardens, Kew.

Tate Gallery, Millbank, SW1. Built by the sugar magnate. Superb modern art collection including the Chantrey Bequest.

The Red Velvet Room, Chiswick House, W4. Built 1725-9 by the Earl of Burlington in the Palladian style. Features include the octagonal, domed central hall and the white and gold gallery with a frescoed ceiling.

Churches & Cathedrals

All Soul's, Langham Place, W1. Designed by John Nash, built 1824 as pivot of his plan for Regent Street.

Brompton Oratory, SW7. Baroque church in Italian style.

Chapel Royal of St Peter ad Vincula, EC3. Tudor burial place of Anne Boleyn, Catherine Howard, Sir Thomas More.

Clown's Church, Holy Trinity, E8. Commemorating Joseph Grimaldi. Home to Clowns International Gallery.

Southwark Cathedral, SE1. Founded 1106. London's oldest Gothic church. Harvard Chapel, Shakespeare Memorial.

St Paul's Cathedral, EC4. Wren is buried here – "If you want to see his monument, look around". Crypt, ambulatory.

St Margaret's, SW1. Built 16th c. Parish church of House of Commons. Burial place of Sir Walter Raleigh. Notable medieval stained glass.

St George's Cathedral, SE1. Built 1848, the first Catholic cathedral since the Reformation. Rebuilt 1958 after the Blitz.

St James's, Piccadilly, W1. Designed by Sir Christopher Wren, 1684. Frequent concerts and lectures.

St Bartholomew the Great, EC1. 1123, City of London's oldest. Octagonal font, 13th c coffin.

Westminster Abbey, SW1. Scene of Coronations, burial place of monarchs. Poets' Corner, Tomb of Unknown Warrior.

Westminster Cathedral, SW1. Opened 1903. England's principal Catholic church. Fine marbles and mosaics.

Parks & Gardens

Chelsea Physic Garden, SW3. Founded by the Apothecaries in 1673 to grow medicinal plants.

Royal Botanic Gardens, Kew, Richmond. Living collections of over 40,000 plant species.

Syon Park Gardens, Brentford, Middlesex. 55 acres. Miniature steam railway in summer.

Hyde Park/Kensington Gardens, 630 acres of grassland, flowers and trees Henry VIII's royal deer park. Albert Memorial.

St James's Park, SW1. Exquisite royal park. Pelicans and waterfowl.

Regent's Park. Laid out by John Nash in early 19th c. Gardens, boating lake, open-air theatre.

Sport & Outdoors

Wembley Stadium, Middlesex. You can tour this famous venue of Cup Finals and huge pop concerts.

Wimbledon Lawn Tennis Museum, Church Road, SW19. View over the Centre Court. Equipment, trophies, films.

Lord's Cricket Ground, NW8. Home of MCC. Middlesex county plays here.

Rugby Union. Twickenham, Middlesex. HQ of the game, and setting for international matches.

Soccer. Clubs in Premier League are: Arsenal, Chelsea, Crystal Palace, Queens Park Rangers, Tottenham Hotspur, West Ham and Wimbledon.

Music Room, Kenwood House, Hampstead, NW3.

"It's just like being at home – apart from the fact that one doesn't have to do anything"

J Silchenstead, Texas

THE ABBEY COURT

Victorian town house

**20 Pembridge Gardens,
Kensington,
London W2 4DU**

**Telephone 0171 221 7518
Fax 0171 792 0858**

GENERAL MANAGER
Robert Bellhouse

ROOM RATES

6 Singles	£80
11 Doubles/Twins	£120 - £130
3 Four-posters	£160

Includes full breakfast and VAT

CHARGE/CREDIT CARDS

• DC • MC • VI

ACCOLADES
A.A. Town House
The Good Hotel Guide

FACILITIES
Conservatory dining room, jacuzzi
Riding, golf and parks nearby

RESTRICTIONS
Children by prior arrangement
No facilities for disabled guests
No pets

ATTRACTIONS
Kensington Palace, Hyde Park,
Trafalgar Square,
Buckingham Palace

AFFILIATIONS
The Abbey Group

NEAREST
MAJOR CITY:
London

MAJOR AIRPORT:
London Heathrow - 15 miles/40 mins
London Gatwick - 30 miles/1¼ hrs

RAILWAY STATION:
Paddington (British Rail)
Notting Hill Gate (Underground)

RESERVATIONS
Direct with hotel

ACCESS CODES
Not applicable

After a long day's sightseeing, a home that's nothing short of luxurious

The Abbey Court is a beautiful Victorian town house hotel which has been restored to its former elegance. There are 20 bedrooms all individually decorated in hues of deep blue, dusky pink, rust, gold and cream. Carefully chosen antiques make you feel like you are in old England.

After a hard day's travelling, unwind in a sumptuous bathroom featuring Italian marble, gold-plated fittings and heated towel rails. The bathrooms have showers and whirl-pool baths adding luxury to your stay.

Friendly staff welcome visitors into the charming lobby; relax on chintz-covered sofas whilst your luggage is whisked away. Have an early evening drink in the charming conservatory before dining, or going to the theatre. If a light snack is all you need, the efficient 24-hour room service will be happy to oblige.

The Abbey Court is situated within easy walking distance of Portobello Road (famous for its antiques and collectors' market) and two minutes away from Kensington Church Street which has a wealth of antique shops and restaurants. Efficient local transport systems operate to all parts of London. The West End is just ten minutes away by bus, taxi or underground train.

LOCATION

In central London, near Kensington Palace.

" Ascott Mayfair is ranked among the top three serviced apartments in London "

Janet Ho, Sunday Times

Mayfair apartments

ASCOTT MAYFAIR

Your residence in stylish Mayfair

With high quality accommodation, a wide range of facilities and excellent service, the Ascott Mayfair offers a very desirable experience that is unique in London. You will enjoy all the facilities and services of a luxury hotel, with the privacy, comfort and relaxed environment of a home. As a guest, you are invited to think of the Ascott as your residence in London.

The studios and the one, two and three-bedroom apartments are all tastefully and luxuriously furnished. Each has lounge, dining and study area, kitchen and en suite bathroom, satellite TV and computer games, video, music system, and telephone. Complimentary breakfasts, concierge, maintenance and daily maid service are all included. The building's Art Deco heritage is reflected in the design scheme, achieving an elegant and refined style that is welcoming and relaxing. Original artworks in the Ascott's own exclusive Club will delight and amuse you.

With its original Georgian style, prestigious address and proximity to Hyde Park, Mayfair has traditionally had a very special attraction within London. Mayfair is a magnificent place to shop. In its heart are many small specialist shops. It is bordered by Bond Street with its international fashion houses and the department stores of Regent and Oxford Streets. Mayfair maintains its reputation as a good-food centre, with just about every type of cuisine available in the charming Shepherd's Market. Nearby are the West End theatres.

The Ascott Mayfair offers you a unique home welcome, at a most convenient and fashionable London address, in style and splendour.

LOCATION

Between Berkeley Square and Park Lane in Mayfair. NCP car park is in South Audley Street, just around the corner.

49 Hill Street,
Mayfair,
London W1X 7FQ

Telephone 0171 499 6868
Fax 0171 499 0705

GENERAL MANAGER
Colette Langan

APARTMENT RATES

7 Studios	£135 - £140
27 x 1Bedroom Apts	£175 - £195
21 x 2 Bedroom Apts	£275 - £305
1 x 3 Bedroom Apts	£350 - £395

Includes continental breakfast Monday to Friday and full use of the gym, sunbed, sauna and steam room

CHARGE/CREDIT CARDS

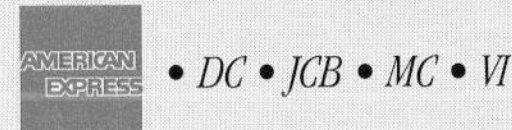

• DC • JCB • MC • VI

ACCOLADES
Independent

FACILITIES
Garden, gym, sauna, sunbeds, steam room
2 meeting rooms/max 16 people
Riding, boating, tennis and squash nearby

RESTRICTIONS
No facilities for disabled guests
No pets

ATTRACTIONS
Hyde Park, Piccadilly Circus, Harrods, Leicester Square, Selfridges, Oxford Street, Covent Garden Market, Buckingham Palace

AFFILIATIONS
Ascott International Management Pte Ltd

NEAREST
MAJOR CITY:
London

MAJOR AIRPORT:
London Heathrow - 15 miles/40 mins

RAILWAY STATION:
Victoria (British Rail) - 2 miles/10 mins
Green Park (U'ground) - ¼ mile/5 mins

RESERVATIONS
Direct with hotel

ACCESS CODES
Not applicable

"Aston's is a fabulous find, it blends Victorian charm with American efficiency. I wouldn't stay anywhere else in London"

Alexis Denicke, Boston

ASTON'S DESIGNER STUDIOS

Serviced apartments

39 Rosary Gardens, South Kensington, London SW7 4NQ

Telephone 0171 370 0737
Fax 0171 835 1419

PROPRIETOR
Mrs Shelagh King

ROOM RATES
20 Single/Double Studios £85 - £105
5 Suites £120 - £152
Includes VAT

CHARGE/CREDIT CARDS

• MC • VI

ACCOLADES
Independent

FACILITIES
Maid service, laundry, dry cleaning, private fax, fully equipped kitchenette, video machines and tapes

RESTRICTIONS
No children under 2 years

ATTRACTIONS
Westminster Abbey, Buckingham Palace, Harrods, Hyde Park, Victoria & Albert Museum, Natural History Museum

AFFILIATIONS
Independent

NEAREST
MAJOR CITY:
London

MAJOR AIRPORT:
London Heathrow - 12 miles/40 mins

RAILWAY STATION:
Victoria (British Rail)
Gloucester Road (Underground)

RESERVATIONS
Toll free in US 800-525-2810

ACCESS CODES
AMADEUS/SYSTEM 1 LON 505/LON 445
WORLDSPAN 4873/5033
AXESS VP1127/VP1128
SABRE 32630/32629

Your own luxury pied-à-terre just minutes from Harrods

Tucked away on a quiet residential street in the centre of London, you'll find Aston's Designer Studios and Suites. A superbly restored, stately Victorian home that offers guests a near-perfect combination of comfort, convenience and exceptional value. You'll feel as if you have your own London residence – with your own personal staff.

Original heavy oak doors and 18th century hunting scenes give Aston's foyer a rich, traditional atmosphere unmatched by so many contemporary hotels.

The opulent Designer Studios and Suites are stunningly decorated and furnished with rich, jewel coloured fabrics. They are fully air-conditioned. Gold-fitted shower and bathrooms are marble-clad and personal bathrobes and hairdryers are provided.

The kitchenettes are fully equipped with the latest cooking technology and have specially designed china. Provisions from Harrods include a continental breakfast to welcome travel weary guests.

The Designer Studios for one or two guests, and the two room Designer Suites for two to four guests, are perfect for visitors enjoying a little longer stay in London. Aston's also has an excellent super-budget range of accommodation available on request.

Since the 18th century, South Kensington has been an exclusive residential area. In 1705, John Bowack described it as "... inhabited by gentry and persons of note". It's still true.

LOCATION
South Kensington, London.

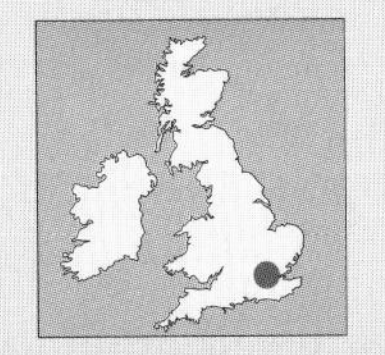

"When I stay at the Athenæum Hotel I know I'm at home with friends"

Victoria Principal

Hotel & apartments

ATHENÆUM HOTEL

A home from home with an elegant yet stylish atmosphere

The Athenæum Hotel and Apartments is not an hotel, it's a home away from home, perfectly located in exclusive Mayfair, overlooking Green Park. With just over 100 guest rooms and suites, and 33 apartments, the Athenæum has a warm and friendly ambience which is evident the moment you step into the tranquil surroundings of the intimate lobby.

The hotel reflects classic English style but is by no means stuffy. Its reputation for discreet and efficient service is a tribute to the dedication of the staff, many of whom have been with the hotel since it opened 23 years ago.

Now under family ownership, a £10 million refurbishment has been completed, transforming the Athenæum into one of London's leading luxury hotels.

A unique feature is the Athenæum Apartments which offer fully serviced one and two bedroom apartments with kitchenette. Located adjacent to the hotel is a row of Edwardian townhouses, the apartments offer a separate street entrance for your own 'front door' in Mayfair, a most exclusive private address in London.

All in all the Athenæum is a must for visitors to London who want to feel as though they are staying with friends yet enjoying the facilities of a top class hotel.

LOCATION

On Piccadilly, in Mayfair overlooking Green Park.

116 Piccadilly, Mayfair, London W1V 0BJ

Telephone 0171 499 3464
Fax 0171 493 1860

GENERAL MANAGER

Jonathan Critchard

ROOM RATES

10 Singles	£198 - £295
101 Doubles/Twins	£230 - £325
12 Suites	£350 - £750
33 Apartments	£299 - £600

Includes VAT

CHARGE/CREDIT CARDS

• DC • MC • VI

ACCOLADES

E.T.B. 5 crowns De Luxe
R.A.C. Blue Ribbon Award ★★★★
A.A. ★★★★ 2 rosettes

FACILITIES

Health & beauty, jacuzzi, gym, sauna
4 meeting rooms/max 100 people
Riding nearby

RESTRICTIONS

No facilities for disabled guests

ATTRACTIONS

Buckingham Palace, Tower of London, Harrods

AFFILIATIONS

Small Luxury Hotels

NEAREST

MAJOR CITY: London

MAJOR AIRPORT: London Heathrow - 15 miles/45 mins

RAILWAY STATION: Victoria (British Rail) Green Park (Underground)

RESERVATIONS

Toll free in US: 800-335-3300

ACCESS CODES

AMADEUS/SYSTEM 1 LX LONATH
SAHARA LX LONTA
SABRE LX 871
WORLDSPAN LX 63196

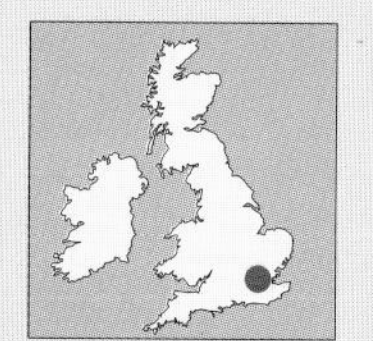

“ Victorian splendour with modern values ”

Richard G Nixon, USA

THE BAILEY'S HOTEL

Victorian mansion

140 Gloucester Road,
South Kensington,
London SW7 4QH

Telephone 0171 373 6000
Fax 0171 370 3760

GENERAL MANAGER
Grant C Wilkins

ROOM RATES

20 Singles	*£140*
183 Doubles/Twins	*£155*
2 Suites	*£200*

Includes VAT

CHARGE/CREDIT CARDS

• DC • MC • VI

ACCOLADES
E.T.B. ♛♛♛♛

FACILITIES
Gym
Riding nearby

RESTRICTIONS
No facilities for disabled guests
No pets

ATTRACTIONS
Royal Albert Hall, Natural History Museum, Science Museum, Victoria and Albert Museum, Knightsbridge, Harrods, Exhibition Centres of Earls Court and Olympia

AFFILIATIONS
Utell International

NEAREST
MAJOR CITY:
London

MAJOR AIRPORT:
London Heathrow - 12 miles/40 mins
London Gatwick - 30 miles/1½ hrs

RAILWAY STATION:
Victoria (British Rail)
Gloucester Road (Underground)

RESERVATIONS
Toll free in US: 800-44-UTELL

ACCESS CODES
SABRE UI 263
APOLLO UI 3852
AMADEUS/SYSTEM 1 UI LONBAI
WORLDSPAN UI 3656
AXESS UI 5745
SAHARA UI LON3656

A grand residence in a fashionable residential area

The Bailey's Hotel, originally opened in 1876, has recently been renovated and carefully restored to its original glory. Complemented by its elegant Victorian façade, the Bailey's Hotel now offers the comforts of a luxurious home with the convenience of modern hotel facilities and traditional service. All 205 bedrooms and suites are decorated in soft, warm colours and include en suite bathrooms, direct-dial telephones, colour television with in-house films and 24-hour room service.

The restaurant and lounge have been tastefully decorated to enhance the grandeur of the Victorian high ceilings and sash windows and a unique feature of the lobby is the original grand staircase with its stained glass windows.

This first class hotel is located in one of London's most favoured residential areas within the Royal Borough of Kensington and Chelsea. It is only a short walk from the world famous Royal Albert Hall, Natural History, Science and Victoria & Albert Museums. Knightsbridge, with its elegant stores, including Harrods, is nearby.

LOCATION

Gloucester Road Underground station is directly opposite where the Circle, District and Piccadilly lines provide a direct link with the West End and the City, as well as with Earl's Court.

"It is so nice to keep seeing familiar faces amongst the staff and to be recognised"

Clare Fellows, Kingston, Ontario

Traditional English hotel

BASIL STREET HOTEL

The Basil – an hotel like hotels used to be

The Basil is an island of hospitality in an increasingly brusque, modern life, and that is why their guests come back again and again. Many of their returning guests have said that The Basil is just like coming home. Tradition is respected, nothing is contrived and there is warmth and friendliness in the air.

The interior is full of English and Oriental antiques, and at every turn there is something to delight the eye. Plants and flowers are in abundance.

Each of the 93 comfortable bedrooms is different in shape and decor and regular visitors are given their favourites whenever possible.

Fully furnished rooms are available for private luncheon or dinner parties. The Basil is large enough to contain all the amenities expected in a cosmopolitan hotel, yet not too large to become impersonal.

General Manager, David Brockett, has recently been appointed and brings a wealth of experience to the hotel. He and his long-serving colleagues will carry on the traditions which have become synonymous with The Basil and will do their utmost to ensure that your visit is an enjoyable one.

LOCATION

In Knightsbridge, a few steps away from Harrods, Harvey Nichols and Knightsbridge Underground Station.

Basil Street, Knightsbridge, London SW3 1AH

Telephone 0171 581 3311
Fax 0171 581 3693

GENERAL MANAGER
David Brockett

ROOM RATES

33 Singles	*£125 - £135*
44 Doubles/Twins	*£175 - £185*
5 Family Rooms	*£250*
1 Suite	*£280*

Includes VAT

CHARGE/CREDIT CARDS

• DC • JCB • MC • VI

ACCOLADES
E.T.B. ♛♛♛♛ Highly Commended
R.A.C. ★★★ + Merit Awards H & R
A.A. ★★★ ❀ 74%
The Good Hotel Guide

FACILITIES
Private dining room
4 meeting rooms/max 100 people
The Parrot Club for women

RESTRICTIONS
No facilities for disabled guests
Pets in bedrooms only

ATTRACTIONS
Harrods, Buckingham Palace, Victoria & Albert Museum, Royal Academy of Art

AFFILIATIONS
Independent

NEAREST
MAJOR CITY:
London

MAJOR AIRPORT:
London Heathrow - 18 miles/45 mins
London Gatwick - 30 miles/1¼ hrs

RAILWAY STATION:
Victoria (British Rail)
Knightsbridge (Underground)

RESERVATIONS
Toll free in US: 800-448-8355

ACCESS CODES
AMADEUS/SYSTEM 1 UI LONBAS
SABRE UI 264
WORLDSPAN UI 3896
APOLLO UI 18513
SAHARA UI LON3896

“If you want to be treated as an individual, stay with the people who know how”

Dyan Cannon

THE BEAUFORT

Private house hotel

**33 Beaufort Gardens,
Knightsbridge,
London SW3 1PP**

**Telephone 0171 584 5252
Fax 0171 589 2834**

PROPRIETOR
Diana Wallis

MANAGER
Jane McKevitt

ROOM RATES

3 Singles	£129.25
5 Superior singles	£152.75
18 Doubles/Twins	£176.25 - £252.63
7 Junior Suites	£282

Includes VAT

CHARGE/CREDIT CARDS

• DC • MC • VI

ACCOLADES
Zaget – Highest Rated Hotel in London for Service (26/30)
The Good Hotel Guide
Courvoisier's Book of the Best

FACILITIES
Guest's private bar
Riding and golf nearby
Pets by arrangement

RESTRICTIONS
Pets by arrangement

ATTRACTIONS
Harrods, Victoria & Albert Museum, Buckingham Palace

AFFILIATIONS
Independent

NEAREST
MAJOR CITY:
London

MAJOR AIRPORT:
London Heathrow - 14 miles/45 mins
London Gatwick - 30 miles/1¼ hrs

RAILWAY STATION:
Victoria (British Rail)
Knightsbridge (Underground)

RESERVATIONS
Toll free fax in US: 800-548-7764

ACCESS CODES
SABRE RW 31342
APOLLO 16376
WORLDSPAN RW 31342

LONDON

Great value, service and much more awaits you in London's Knightsbridge

High quality, individual attention, the best value for money and of course wonderful staff are what makes The Beaufort so successful.

100 yards from Harrods in a quiet tree-lined Victorian square, The Beaufort offers its guests everything it can to make them feel comfortable and at home.

Breakfast is brought to the rooms served on fine bone Wedgwood china with solid silver cutlery – hot croissants and rolls, fresh orange juice and steaming coffee. The rooms are all beautifully decorated in the gentlest colours – and are air-conditioned.

Each room is provided with Swiss chocolates, shortbread, a decanter of brandy and flowers.

Another guest benefit is the hotel's direct dial telephone service where guests can have their own private number, plus the use of a personal fax and answering machine. All rates include service, and there is no tipping. There is CNN, a video and cassette library. For privacy and security, there is a closed front door – only guests have front door keys.

The Beaufort is also home to a now famous and much coveted collection of over 400 original English floral watercolours.

Champagne and cream teas are served free of charge in the drawing room. And in case you need good conversation, Harry the cat can be found there daily.

LOCATION

Quietly situated in the heart of Knightsbridge.

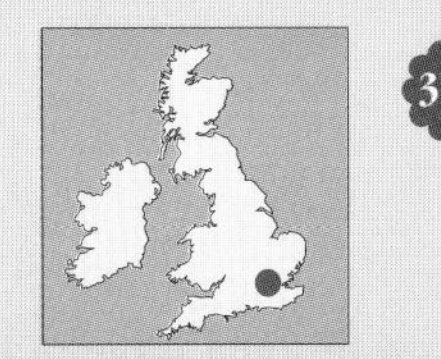

"All the benefits of a first-class hotel are combined with the privacy, discretion and comfort of home"

Johansen's Recommended Hotels

Regency terraced town house

BEAUFORT HOUSE

Fully-serviced traditional apartments just around the corner from Harrods

Beaufort House is situated in the heart of Knightsbridge in a quiet, tree-lined square, just 250 yards from Harrods and the Underground. It is within easy reach of the West End for theatres, restaurants and shopping.

All the benefits of a first class hotel are combined with the privacy, discretion and comfort of home. The self-contained, fully-serviced apartments have each been individually designed in a traditional manner, ranging in size from one to four bedrooms, with spacious lounge and dining rooms and en suite marbled bathrooms. Fitted kitchens complete with modern appliances are an integral feature of each apartment.

Guest services are available 24 hours a day to deal with all personal requests, in addition to a high level of security, daily maid service, dry cleaning and laundry service. Each apartment is full of home comforts with satellite TV and video and a private telephone line.

Complimentary membership to an exclusive health and fitness club is offered to all guests for the duration of their stay. Over the years guests have come to value and enjoy the privacy and space at Beaufort House, whether it be a business or holiday visit, or a short or long term stay.

LOCATION

Knightsbridge, London.

45 Beaufort Gardens, Knightsbridge, London SW3 1PN

Telephone 0171 584 2600
Fax 0171 584 6532

MANAGER
Anne Gledhill

ROOM/APARTMENT RATES

	Daily	Weekly
9 x 1 bdrm	£142-£186	£962-£1300
2 x 2 bdrms	£224-£239	£1538-£1670
9 x 3 bdrms	£296-£317	£2024-£2172
1 x 4 bdrms	£329-£370	£2245-£2543

Includes VAT

CHARGE/CREDIT CARDS

• DC • MC • VI

ACCOLADES
Independent

FACILITIES
Free membership to private health and fitness club

RESTRICTIONS
No facilities for disabled guests
No pets

ATTRACTIONS
Harrods, Hyde Park, Victoria & Albert Museum, Buckingham Palace, Tate Gallery, Tower of London

AFFILIATIONS
Independent

NEAREST
MAJOR CITY:
London

MAJOR AIRPORT:
London Heathrow - 15 miles/45 mins
London Gatwick - 30 miles/1¼ hrs

RAILWAY STATION:
Victoria (British Rail)
Knightsbridge (Underground)

RESERVATIONS
Direct with hotel

ACCESS CODES
Not applicable

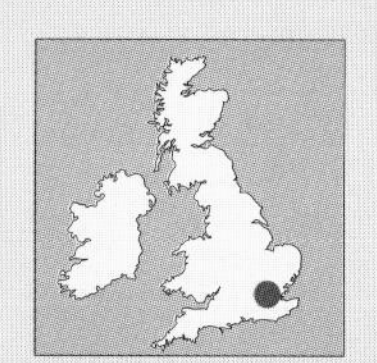

“Not too big to be impersonal, and close to the heart of everything that London has to offer, the hotel meets all of my needs. What more can I say?”

Deborah Kerr, actor

THE BERKELEY

Deluxe hotel

Wilton Place, Knightsbridge, London SW1X 7RL

Telephone 0171 235 6000
Fax 0171 235 4330

GENERAL MANAGER
Jean-Jacques Pergant

ROOM RATES

30 Singles	£211.50 - £246.75
87 Doubles/Twins	£311 - £346
39 Suites	£358 - £799
Conservatory suites	£969

Includes VAT

CHARGE/CREDIT CARDS

• DC • JCB • MC • VI

ACCOLADES
R.A.C. ★★★★★
A.A. ★★★★★ ❀❀

FACILITIES
Indoor pool, sauna, gym, health & beauty
7 meeting rooms/max 450 people

RESTRICTIONS
No facilities for disabled guests
No pets

ATTRACTIONS
Hyde Park, Knightsbridge, Royal Albert Hall, Harrods, Buckingham Palace

AFFILIATIONS
The Savoy Group of Hotels and Restaurants
Leading Hotels of the World
Utell International

NEAREST
MAJOR CITY:
London

MAJOR AIRPORT:
London Heathrow - 16 miles/40 mins
London City - 12 miles/25 mins

RAILWAY STATION:
Victoria (British Rail)
Hyde Park Corner (Underground)

RESERVATIONS
Toll free in US: 800-63-SAVOY

ACCESS CODES
SABRE LW 4768
SAHARA LW LON0404
AMADEUS/SYSTEM 1 LW LON404
WORLDSPAN LW 0404
APOLLO LW 8521

Meticulous attention to detail in elegant Belgravia

The Berkeley is held to be the last truly deluxe hotel to be built in Europe. One of The Savoy Group of Hotels and Restaurants, it moved from its original home in Piccadilly to Knightsbridge in 1972 and still retains the traditional atmosphere of the old hotel, whilst offering every modern amenity.

Overlooking Hyde Park and moments from Knightsbridge and London's finest stores, The Berkeley provides a tranquil meeting place in elegant Belgravia. The Restaurant specialises in the finest French cuisine, and the Foyer Lounge is open throughout the day for cocktails, light snacks and afternoon tea.

The bedrooms and suites are each individually decorated, 100% fresh air-conditioned, (ideal for non-smokers) with fax machines available and CD players in some rooms. A selection of CD's is available.

The newly refurbished banqueting and meeting rooms are ideally suited to every type of business or pleasure occasion and each event is supervised with meticulous detail. The hotel has its own underground garage and a beautiful roof-top swimming pool and health club with views across the park.

LOCATION

Wilton Place is just off Knightsbridge a few hundreds yards from Hyde Park Corner.

“ If ever dreams can become reality, then Blakes is where it will happen ”

Nina Prommer, London

Victorian mansion

BLAKES HOTEL

**33 Roland Gardens,
South Kensington,
London SW7 3PF**

**Telephone 0171 370 6701
Fax 0171 373 0442**

PROPRIETOR
Anouska Hempel

DIRECTOR
Neville Ablitt

ROOM RATES

24 Singles	£127
8 Doubles	£155 - £305
9 Suites	£495 - £600

Includes VAT

CHARGE/CREDIT CARDS

• DC • MC • VI

ACCOLADES
*Andrew Harper's Hideaway Report
The Good Hotel Guide*

FACILITIES
*Membership with local health club
Blakes Restaurant
2 meeting rooms/max 60 people*

RESTRICTIONS
No facilities for disabled guests

ATTRACTIONS
*South Kensington Museums,
Harrods and Knightsbridge,
many antique shops,
Christies Auction Room*

AFFILIATIONS
Independent

NEAREST
*MAJOR CITY:
London*

*MAJOR AIRPORT:
London Heathrow - 12 miles/45 mins
London Gatwick - 30 miles/1¼ hrs*

*RAILWAY STATION:
Victoria (British Rail)
South Kensington (Underground)*

RESERVATIONS
Toll free in US: 800-926-3173

ACCESS CODES
*SABRE PW 21718
APOLLO PW 64952
WORLDSPAN PW 8384
SYSTEM 1 PW LON304
AMADEUS PW LON384
SAHARA PW LON 8384*

Exclusive and stylish – the haunt of the famous

Blakes Hotel was created by Anouska Hempel just over ten years ago out of two Victorian mansions in South Kensington.

Originally built with 28 rooms, it has grown over the past few years as further houses have been added and quickly became accepted as the hotel for fashionable people. Respected for protecting the privacy of its clients, it is the London base of film personalities such as Robert de Niro, Mickey Rourke, Michael Douglas, Jack Nicholson and Ali McGraw. Fashion designers Gianni Versace, Giorgio Armani, Christian Lacroix, Karl Lagerfield, Claude Montana and Issay Miyake are regular residents at Blakes. Regular clients also include leading businessmen from Europe, America and the Far East.

Blakes has achieved international fame and has become the model for ‘the fashionable small hotel’ in London and in many other cities around the world.

Blakes Restaurant, the first in London to provide eclectic dishes on the menu, continues to evolve and develop to critical acclaim as one of the three best restaurants in London – classic cooking with some oriental twists, amusing presentation with spectacular tastes makes Blakes Restaurant the obvious choice.

LOCATION

South Kensington/Brompton Cross.

"We were made to feel so special by everyone at Blooms and this made our stay in London even more enjoyable"

A O'Hanlon, New York

BLOOMS

18th century town house

7 Montague Street,
Bloomsbury,
London WC1B 5BP

Telephone 0171 323 1717
Fax 0171 636 6498

DIRECTOR
Tomas Gronager

ROOM RATES

5 Singles	*£100 - £120*
22 Doubles/Twins	*£150 - £180*

Includes full breakfast and VAT

CHARGE/CREDIT CARDS

• *DC* • *JCB* • *MC* • *VI*

ACCOLADES
E.T.B. ♛♛♛♛ Highly Commended
A.A. Townhouse

FACILITIES
Garden

RESTRICTIONS
No children
No facilities for disabled guests
No pets

ATTRACTIONS
British Museum,
West End, Oxford Street,
Madame Tussauds,
London Planetarium

AFFILIATIONS
Scotland's Commended Hotels

NEAREST
MAJOR CITY:
London

MAJOR AIRPORT:
London Heathrow - 16 miles/40 mins
London Gatwick - 30 miles1¼ hrs

RAILWAY STATION:
Kings Cross/Euston (British Rail)
Russell Square (Underground)

RESERVATIONS
Direct with hotel

ACCESS CODES
SYSTEM 1 EA LONBLO
AMADEUS IA LHRBLO
WORLDSPAN IP 21436
AXESS JL 3644
SABRE AA 23881
APOLLO UA 58898
SAHARA XS LON21436

LONDON

Rich heritage in the cultural heart of London

Blooms is a four-crown town house hotel in an elegant 18th century house close to the British Museum and London University. Blooms is in Bloomsbury, the literary heart of London.

The 27 bedrooms are individually designed to reflect the rich heritage of the hotel. All have private bathroom, satellite TV, telephone, radio, hair dryer, trouser press, tea and coffee making facilities, butler tray and 24-hour room service. The period style lounge combines comfort with the ambience of a bygone era, where guests may relax with the daily papers, select material from the library, or enjoy one of the many board games available.

Overlooking the British Museum is the hotel's own pretty walled garden, where guests can take refreshments during the summer. A breakfast buffet is available each morning, and the famous traditional English breakfast is cooked to order. Throughout the day a selection of light snacks is available in the library or bar.

Bloomsbury is an area of genteel architecture, antiquarian bookshops and the splendid British Museum. It is almost like living in a village, with good local pubs and shops, in the heart of town. Blooms Hotel is ideally situated for shopping in the department stores of Oxford Street, for the historic City of London, the West End, theatreland, Covent Garden and the good food international restaurants of Soho and Charlotte Street.

LOCATION

Blooms is only minutes away from the main railway stations Euston, King's Cross and St Pancras, and Underground stations Russell Square and Holborn, which are on the Piccadilly line direct from Heathrow.

" I don't stay in a hotel, I go to Brown's "

H A J Page, Norwich

Town hotel

BROWN'S

Gracious and discreet service in exquisite surroundings

In 1837, the year Queen Victoria succeeded to the throne, James Brown, a retired gentleman's gentleman, opened a hotel in fashionable Mayfair, a few minutes' walk away from Hyde Park.

Over the years, the hotel became renowned for comfort and elegance, every room furnished and decorated with its own particular style and charm and impeccable service. Victoria herself often came to visit: Napoleon III stayed there following the Franco Prussian war: Theodore Roosevelt married from there, his nephew Franklin and his bride Eleanor made their home at Brown's during their honeymoon.

Today, the style that made Brown's famous is preserved not only in the magnificent furnishings, the richly panelled wood, the original moulded ceilings and elaborate cornices, but in the uniquely English hospitality and service. Beneath this opulence, one has to look closely to observe evidence of a £12.5 million programme of refurbishment. The latest technology has been unobtrusively installed and structural changes made but its sense of continuity has been preserved – and that is perhaps Brown's greatest charm. Whether guests come for the superb location, the food and atmosphere or simply the legendary Brown's teas, staying at Brown's is a reminder of the finer things in life.

Brown's is a centrally positioned for all the attractions London can offer; as Dr Johnson remarked "When you are tired of London, you are tired of life". Perhaps also true of this exquisite hotel.

LOCATION

Between Hyde Park Corner and Piccadilly Circus turn into Albemarle Street from Piccadilly.

Albemarle Street,
Mayfair,
London W1X 4PB

Telephone 0171 493 6020
Fax 0171 493 9381

GENERAL MANAGER
Reto Grass

ROOM RATES

21 Singles	£229
42 Doubles/Twins	£300
15 Triples/Family	£329
28 Executive rooms	£323
4 Four-posters	£347
6 Suites	£535

Includes VAT

CHARGE/CREDIT CARDS

• DC • MC • VI

ACCOLADES
E.T.B. ♛♛♛♛ Highly Commended
R.A.C. Blue Ribbon Award ★★★★
A.A. ★★★★ ❀❀❀

FACILITIES
St Georges Bar, Browns Restaurant, private dining rooms
7 meeting rooms/max 120 people

RESTRICTIONS
No facilities for disabled guests
No pets

ATTRACTIONS
Mayfair, Royal Academy, Buckingham Palace, Green Park, Hyde Park, Tate Gallery, Bond Street

AFFILIATIONS
Forte Exclusive Hotels

NEAREST
MAJOR CITY:
London

MAJOR AIRPORT:
London Heathrow - 15 miles/50 mins
London Gatwick - 30 miles/1¼ hrs

RAILWAY STATION:
Victoria (British Rail)
Green Park (Underground)

RESERVATIONS
Toll free in US: 800-225-5843

ACCESS CODES
SABRE FE 11247
SAHARA FE 5456
WORLDSPAN FE 5929
AMADEUS SYSTEM 1 FE LON225

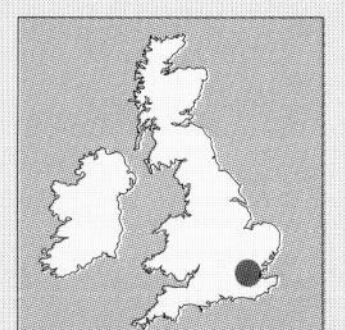

“An ideal place to take someone who likes to be handled with care”

Fay Maschler, Evening Standard

CADOGAN HOTEL

Late Victorian building

75 Sloane Street,
Knightsbridge,
London SW1X 9SG

Telephone 0171 235 7141
Fax 0171 245 0994

DIRECTOR
Malcolm Broadbent

ROOM RATES

27 Singles	£149.50 - £189.50
33 Doubles/Twins	£179.50 - £204.50
5 Suites	£304

Includes breakfast, and VAT

CHARGE/CREDIT CARDS

• MC • VI

ACCOLADES
Independent

FACILITIES
2 meeting rooms/max 40 people
Garden, riding and tennis nearby

RESTRICTIONS
No facilities for disabled guests
No pets

ATTRACTIONS
Harrods, Buckingham Palace, Bond Street, Hyde Park, Victoria and Albert Museum

AFFILIATIONS
Prima Hotels
Utell International

NEAREST
MAJOR CITY:
London

MAJOR AIRPORT:
London Heathrow - 16 miles/30 mins
London Gatwick - 30 miles/1¼ hrs

RAILWAY STATION:
Victoria (British Rail)
Knightsbridge/Sloane Square (Underground)

RESERVATIONS
Toll free fax in US: 800-260-8338 (quote Cadogan Hotel)
In Japan: 03-3434-7159

ACCESS CODES
SABRE UI 23319
AMADEUS UI LONCAD
SAHARA UI LON 2832
AXESS UI 5728
APOLLO UI 22654

The Jersey Lily's home, with Harrods on the doorstep

As the 19th century neared its glittering close, fashionable Londoners flocked to the theatre to admire the beautiful Lillie Langtry, the 'Jersey Lily', favourite of the Prince of Wales who was later to be crowned as King Edward VII. Lillie lived at 21 Pont Street, and she entertained her friends and admirers at the Cadogan Hotel next door. When she moved away, her house became part of the hotel. Lillie continued to be a frequent visitor, sleeping in her original bedroom. One of her close friends was playwright Oscar Wilde and it was from Room 118 of the Cadogan that Oscar Wilde was arrested in 1895 and condemned to Reading Gaol.

The Cadogan remains a place for fashionable people to meet, dine in the air-conditioned restaurant and entertain in Lillie's drawing room. Lillie and Oscar and their friends would be impressed if they visited the Cadogan today. The sumptuous drawing room invites shoppers for morning coffee or afternoon tea, and the 65 bedrooms are furnished and equipped to the highest standards.

The Cadogan, owned and restored by Historic House Hotels, is within walking distance of Harrods and Harvey Nichols, and important London landmarks such as the Victoria and Albert Museum. Taxis and buses pass the door and Underground stations are close by, making West End theatres and cinemas easily accessible. Guests looking for a green oasis in the middle of London can have access to a private garden with its own tennis courts directly opposite the hotel.

LOCATION

In Knightsbridge, one of London's most beautiful and exclusive residential areas.

OVER 3 MILLION AMERICANS WILL VISIT BRITAIN AND IRELAND IN 1997

Here's how to help them and do better business

The Best Loved Hotels of the World Directory has no equal. No other directory pulls together so much detail about so many different kinds of properties in England, Wales, Scotland and Ireland. As one US travel counsellor said:

"... exactly what we need to know without having to review 2 or 3 different reference books."

And - no other directory puts them in the context of tourism like this one.

Keep up-to-date in 1996

Register for FREE confidential information

By registering your copy of the 1996 Best Loved Directory, you will receive the **Best Loved Travel Agent Supplement for 1996** which gives confidential information about travel agent commissions at Best Loved Hotels and their agent discount policies. We have also negotiated special rates at Best Loved Hotels when you visit Britain and Ireland over the coming year.

Keep up-to-date in 1997

Reserve the 1997 edition NOW. Save money.

Information about hotels changes all the time:

- standards change with ownership
- rates go up (come down, too!)
- phone and fax numbers change
- facilities get added (and withdrawn)
- chefs and hotels win awards
- new hotels get added

This year, we welcome 104 new hotel entries to this edition, each the best of its kind within any given area and there will be lots more new ones next year.

The 1997 book is FREE . . . *but*

Over the last two years we have put a copy of this directory on your desk without charge. Next year, in 1997, ***this book (normally $26.95) will still be free of charge*** but we shall be asking for a contribution of $15 per copy to cover postage and handling. As you can see, this book is no lightweight and distribution costs are punitive. It's about the same as the commission on one room night. Here's what a US travel agent said:

"The concise hotel descriptions, special quotes and pertinent information regarding neighboring attractions make selling a breeze".

The $15 could pay for itself within minutes of landing on your desk.

Valuable prizes

Order your 1997 Best Loved Directory now and you could win a 6-day trip visiting some wonderful places to stay (all in this edition), business class tickets to Britain or Ireland and a hundred other prizes too, just see for yourself overleaf ➤➤➤➤➤

Don't delay, send off the reply card below!

REGISTRATION & 1997 BEST LOVED DIRECTORY ORDER CARD

Please fill in this registration/order card and be sure you are on our mailing list to keep abreast of hotel information in Britain and Ireland. All you have to do is fill in the details below and fax this page to the number below. It won't take a minute.

☐ *Tick here* Please register this copy of the 1996 Directory and keep me updated with your **FREE** Confidential 1996 Best Loved Travel Agent Supplement.

☐ *Tick here* Please reserve my **FREE** copy (regular price $26.95) of the **1997 BEST LOVED DIRECTORY.** I agree to pay $15 per copy to cover postage and packing. I understand this qualifies me to be entered in your prize draw to win airline tickets and other wonderful prizes as shown overleaf.

Please bill me ☐ my agency ☐ next December.

Now, please enter my name in the prize draw

Date received ____________

Your name ____________

Title ____________

Agency ____________

Address ____________

____

____

City ____________ State Zip

Telephone ____________ Fax

Fax this card to 800-572-8131

Tear along here

Reserve your 1997 Best Loved Directory
and win one of over a hundred wonderful prizes!

By ordering your 1997 edition of the **Best Loved Hotels of the World Directory** now, you qualify for a draw that could win you any one of these wonderful prizes ...

Grand prize

Two Business Class return tickets

American Airlines

from any US gateway to Britain or Ireland

2 second prizes

A *week touring*

Britain & Ireland

as a guest of

Best Loved Hotels.

Fully inclusive

100 third prizes

A copy of

Historic Castles, Houses and Gardens

A full colour illustrated volume of 1300 places, all rich in heritage and open to the public in Britain and Ireland.

See insert page 320

The Draw takes place on November 29, 1996

Register this copy and order the 1997 Best Loved Hotels of the World Directory by faxing the completed form overleaf to the number below - or tear the card out and post it

800-572-8131

Remember, this is NOT a reservations number

Tear out along this line

Affix stamp here

Best Loved Hotels of the World

c/o DDS
20770 Westwood Drive
Strongsville, OH 44136

“Truly the jewel in the crown of the finest hotels. A visit to the UK without staying would, for us, be unthinkable”

Eloisa Saligado, Madrid

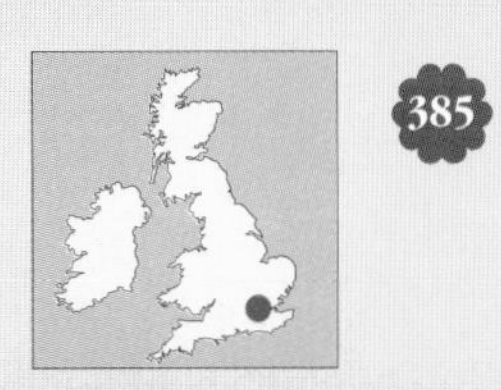

Georgian mansion

CANNIZARO HOUSE

Wimbledon, the home of tennis and Cannizaro House

Cannizaro House, set amidst sweeping lawns, quiet woodland walks and formal gardens, is a delightful Georgian mansion. Situated on the edge of Wimbledon Common, it is proudly and justifiably London's first country house hotel.

Having enjoyed a distinctive and eventful past punctuated with grand names and royal connections, from William Pitt to Oscar Wilde and Tennyson, this gracious residence now plays host to its discerning guests offering all the luxuries expected from a country house hotel.

The award-winning restaurant offers both à la carte and table d'hôte menus together with a wine list that boasts over 200 of the finest wines available.

Each of the 46 bedrooms are individually designed to offer not only luxury and comfort but also the character and atmosphere of country house living.

The drawing room, overlooking the park, with its roaring log fire in the winter months, and the south facing garden terrace during the summer months, both provide the perfect solace for a restful and relaxing stay.

The local area has an abundance of attractions including the famous All England Lawn Tennis Club, Hampton Court Palace, Kew Gardens and being only twenty minutes from the West End, Cannizaro House is ideal for a London weekend break.

Several gracious private dining rooms complete an idyllic residence – whatever the occasion.

LOCATION

From the A3 turn south onto the A219, then turn right into Cannizaro Road. 2nd on the right is West Side Common and Cannizaro House.

West Side, Wimbledon Common, London SW19 4UE

Telephone 0181 879 1464
Fax 0181 879 7338

GENERAL MANAGER
Mr Ray Slade

ROOM RATES

39 Doubles/Twins	£150 - £200
4 Four-posters	£225 - £315
3 Suites	£265 - £375

Includes VAT

CHARGE/CREDIT CARDS

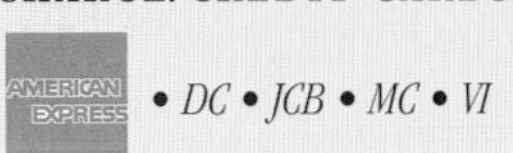

• DC • JCB • MC • VI

ACCOLADES
R.A.C. ★★★★ + Merit Award H
A.A. ★★★★ ❀❀ 70%

FACILITIES
Garden
7 meeting rooms/max 90 people
Golf, riding and fishing nearby

RESTRICTIONS
No children under 8 years
No pets

ATTRACTIONS
London, Wimbledon, Hampton Court, Windsor Castle, Kew Gardens

AFFILIATIONS
A Thistle Country House Hotel

NEAREST
MAJOR CITY:
London - 6 miles/30 mins

MAJOR AIRPORT:
London Heathrow - 12 miles/40 mins

RAILWAY STATION:
Wimbledon - 1 mile/10 mins

RESERVATIONS
Toll free in US/Canada: 800-847-4358
Toll free in Australia: 800-062-055

ACCESS CODES
AMADEUS/SYSTEM 1 TI LONCAN
APOLLO TI 13604
WORLDSPAN TI LONCN
SABRE TI 7578

“ Great to be home again ”

Joan & Marco Weiss, Chicago

NO 1 CARLOS PLACE

Luxury serviced apartments

1 Carlos Place,
Mayfair,
London W1Y 5AE

Telephone 0171 753 0744
Fax 0171 753 0731

GENERAL MANAGER
Patricia Owens

ROOM RATES PER WEEK

4 x 1 Bedroom Apts	*£1410 - £1645*
1 x Small 3 Bedroom Apts	*£2470 - £2705*
3 x Large 3 Bedroom Apts	*£2715 - £3055*
2 x 4 Bedroom Apts	*£3175 - £3525*
1 x Penthouse	*£3290 - £3645*

Includes daily maid service and VAT

CHARGE/CREDIT CARDS

• *MC* • *VI*

ACCOLADES
Independent

FACILITIES
Private fax and direct-dial telephone in each apartment, air-conditioning
Gardens and riding nearby
24-hour security reception

RESTRICTIONS
No facilities for disabled guests
No pets

ATTRACTIONS
Buckingham Palace, Hyde Park, Oxford Street, Piccadilly, Royal Academy of Arts

AFFILIATIONS
Independent

NEAREST
MAJOR CITY:
London

MAJOR AIRPORT:
London Heathrow - 15 miles/45 mins
London Gatwick - 30 miles/1¼ hrs

RAILWAY STATION:
Victoria (British Rail)
Green Park (Underground)

RESERVATIONS
Direct with hotel

ACCESS CODES
Not applicable

A pied-à-terre in Mayfair. For some, it's the only place to stay

For many, the idea of having a pied-à-terre in Central London is a dream which may never be realised. However, miracles do happen and One Carlos Place proves it.

It was built in 1893 and its Flemish-Renaissance style has earned it a Grade II listed building by English Heritage. The interiors have been designed to the highest international standards by a team of talented designers. The style is entirely in keeping with the classic elegance of the building.

There are eleven unusually spacious, fully serviced apartments consisting of living areas, dining rooms, fully fitted and equipped kitchens, luxury bathrooms and a choice of one, three or four bedrooms. There is also a Penthouse with its own roof garden.

You can stay for as little as a night or as long as you can afford your flight of fancy. And, whilst staying at One Carlos Place is an exceptional pleasure, remember there are others close at hand. You will be next door to Berkeley Square, half way between the fashionable shops of Bond Street and the wide open spaces of Hyde Park, a comfortable stroll from Piccadilly and a short taxi ride from London's theatreland.

It comes as no surprise that this is where prominent business executives, leaders and personalities stay – and return to time after time.

LOCATION

Between Grosvenor Square and Berkeley Square in Mayfair.

“I’ve been coming here since the hotel opened and it never fails to please”

Mrs H E Pounds, Illinois

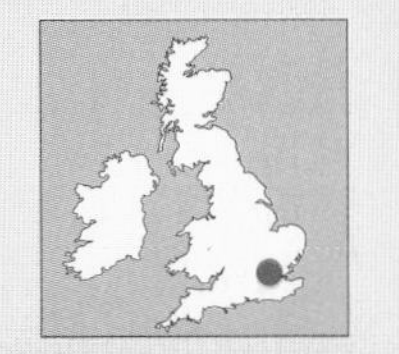

Mayfair hotel

THE CHESTERFIELD

Gracious living just off Berkeley Square

Named after the third Earl of Chesterfield, a noted Mayfair resident in the 18th century, this hotel combines the gracious living standards of an elegant past with every modern comfort, service and convenience.

Traditional fabrics and elegant furnishings have been chosen for each of the 110 suites and guest rooms. Guests are pampered with thoughtful personal comforts that include nightly turndown service, bathrobes, hairdryer, potpourri sachets, bottled mineral water and deluxe toiletries. Plus direct-dial telephone, modem/fax facility, TV with CNN, sports, news and a movie channel, valet and 24-hour room service.

The restaurant features the finest in English and international cuisine. The unobtrusive personal service suggests the ambience of an elegant town house. Menus are seasonally revised, and complemented by a wide selection of fine wines.

The Chesterfield is close to the famous West End theatres and nightlife, a short stroll to elegant shops, museums and landmarks like the Royal Academy of Art and the National Gallery. Piccadilly, and Bond and Regent Streets are nearby. You can jog through Hyde Park and stroll across Green Park to Buckingham Palace. The Chesterfield is the perfect location for your stay in London.

LOCATION

In the heart of Mayfair.

35 Charles Street, Mayfair, London W1X 8LX

Telephone 0171 491 2622
Fax 0171 491 4793

GENERAL MANAGER
Peter Wood

ROOM RATES

24 Singles	£110 - £170
44 Doubles/Twins	£145 - £199
33 King bedded	£160 - £220
5 Deluxe Kings	£210 - £280
4 Executive Suites	£300 - £410

CHARGE/CREDIT CARDS

• DC • JCB • MC • VI

ACCOLADES
R.A.C. ★★★★ + Merit Awards H C & R
A.A. ★★★★ ❀❀ 68%

FACILITIES
6 meeting rooms/max 150 people
Use of leisure facilities nearby

RESTRICTIONS
No pets (guide dogs accepted)

ATTRACTIONS
Buckingham Palace, Bond Street, Regent Street, Piccadilly, Harrods, Royal Academy of Art

AFFILIATIONS
Independent

NEAREST
MAJOR CITY:
London

MAJOR AIRPORT:
London Heathrow - 15 miles/ 45 mins
London Gatwick - 30 miles/1¼ hrs

RAILWAY STATION:
Victoria (British Rail)
Green Park (Underground)

RESERVATIONS
Toll free in US: 800-44-UTELL

ACCESS CODES
AMADEUS/SYSTEM 1 UI LONCHE
WORLDSPAN UI 0327
AXESS UI 5633
SABRE UI 274
APOLLO UI 5219
SAHARA UI LON 0327

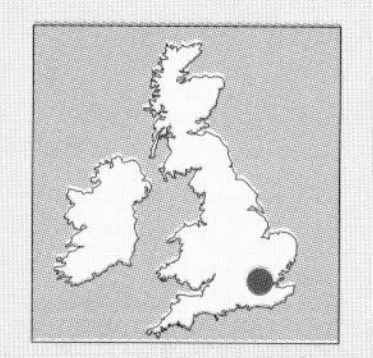

“ The hotel in the square is London’s best kept secret ”

Lord Peter Graves

DOLPHIN SQUARE

Hotel & apartments

Dolphin Square,
Pimlico,
London SW1V 3LX

Telephone 0171 834 3800
Fax 0171 798 8735

MANAGER
John Firrell

ROOM RATES
152 1-3 bedroom suites £99 - £250
Includes service and VAT

CHARGE/CREDIT CARDS

 • DC • MC • VI

ACCOLADES
E.T.B. ♛♛♛♛♛

FACILITIES
Indoor pool, croquet, tennis, gardens, health club, gym, health & beauty, squash, shops, disabled suite
3 meeting rooms/max 100 people
Golf, riding and fishing nearby

RESTRICTIONS
Pets by prior arrangement

ATTRACTIONS
Houses of Parliament, Westminster, Tate Gallery, West End Theatres, Knightsbridge, Royal Parks, Buckingham Palace

AFFILIATIONS
Grand Heritage Hotels

NEAREST
MAJOR CITY:
London

MAJOR AIRPORT:
London Heathrow - 15 miles/45 mins
London Gatwick - 30 miles/1¼ hrs

RAILWAY STATION:
Victoria (British Rail) - 15 mins walk
Pimlico (Underground) - 5 mins walk

RESERVATIONS
Toll free in UK: 0800-616607

ACCESS CODES
GH

A more flexible alternative to a conventional hotel

With five-crown status, Dolphin Square is more than just another hotel. The aim is to provide guests with all the benefits of a high quality central London hotel – and more.

Set in three and a half acres of garden, the fully-serviced suites provide superb space and comfort. Large suites are available in one, two or three bedroom formats and, in addition to a fully fitted kitchen, provide a separate lounge and one, two or three bathrooms. Smaller single or double studio suites have spacious sitting areas, a fully fitted kitchen and bathroom, and unlike most, the hotel’s tariffs are based on suite size not number of guests.

All suites provide television, cable TV, direct-dial telephones, crockery, glasses and cutlery and in-room tea and coffee-making facilities including trouser press and hair-dryers. A disabled person’s suite is available in addition to disabled access.

Comprehensive leisure activities are available for all guests.

Dolphin Square provides a much more flexible alternative to the constraints of a typical hotel when it comes to entertaining, eating and drinking. The cocktail bar is an especially charming place to relax in the evening. The restaurant serves superb and inventive menus in unique surroundings overlooking the pool. In the evening, the varied wine list and the formal and informal menus provide an excellent venue, for business or pleasure.

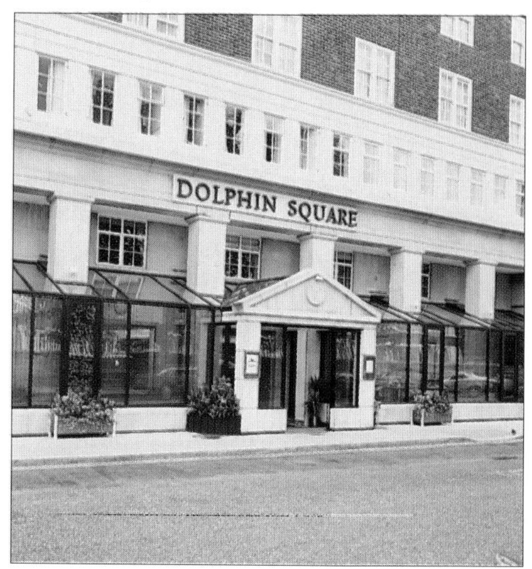

LOCATION

Central London beside the Thames off Grosvenor Road.

“I love your long serving staff, their courtesy and their friendliness. Number Eleven will always be my London home”

Princess ..., Rome (Guest anonymity assured)

Town house

ELEVEN CADOGAN GARDENS

11 Cadogan Gardens,
Sloane Square,
London SW3 2RJ

Telephone 0171 730 3426
Fax 0171 730 5217

PROPRIETOR
Michael Fresson

MANAGER
Mark Fresson

ROOM RATES

25 Singles	£98 - £138
30 Doubles/Twins	£158 - £198
6 Suites	£250 - £385

Includes VAT

CHARGE/CREDIT CARDS

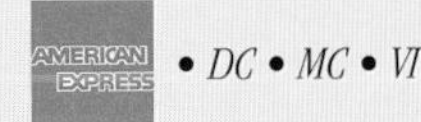

• DC • MC • VI

ACCOLADES
Independent

FACILITIES
In-house gymnasium, beauty room

RESTRICTIONS
No pets
No facilities for disabled guests

ATTRACTIONS
Buckingham Palace, Houses of Parliament, The Tower of London, West End theatres, Harrods

AFFILIATIONS
Independent

NEAREST
MAJOR CITY:
London

MAJOR AIRPORT:
London Heathrow - 15 miles/45 mins
London Gatwick - 30 miles/1¼ hrs

RAILWAY STATION:
Victoria (British Rail)
Waterloo (Eurostar)
Sloane Square (Underground)

RESERVATIONS
Toll free fax in US: 800-359-8361

ACCESS CODES
Not applicable

The classic London town house: a charming synthesis of old and new

Number Eleven Cadogan Gardens was the first of the exclusive private town house hotels in London, and now, with the addition of its in-house gymnasium it continues to take the lead.

Number Eleven remains traditional: there is no reception desk, a butler greets you at the door, you have total privacy and security. It also offers the services you have a right to expect in the 1990's: round-the-clock room service offering excellent light meals, a chauffeur-driven limousine for airport collection and sightseeing, comprehensive concierge service, and a private room which can accommodate twelve people for a meeting and 30 for cocktails. Another attraction is the Garden Suites, one with its own private entrance, and both with large double bedrooms and spacious drawing rooms overlooking the gardens.

The hotel occupies four stately Victorian houses tucked away between Harrods and the King's Road in a quiet tree-lined square. Wood-panelled rooms, hung with oil paintings, are furnished with antiques and oriental rugs in a traditional, understated style. The fashionable shops and first-class restaurants of Knightsbridge and Belgravia are within easy walking distance.

LOCATION

In London's city centre by Sloane Square.

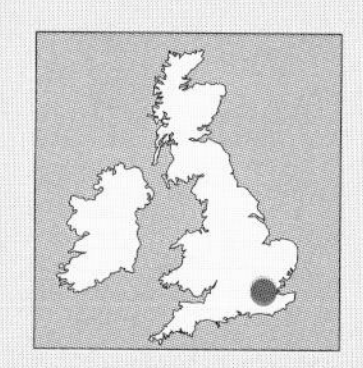

" Exceptional value bed and breakfast accommodation in one of the world's most fashionable neighbourhoods "

Josh Schluerberg, New York

THE EXECUTIVE HOTEL

19th century town house

*57 Pont Street,
Knightsbridge,
London SW1X 0BD*

*Telephone 0171 581 2424
Fax 0171 589 9456*

GENERAL MANAGER
Mr Robert Bellhouse

ROOM RATES

4 Singles	£55 - £75
20 Doubles	£75 - £99
3 Suites	£110

Includes full breakfast and VAT

CHARGE/CREDIT CARDS

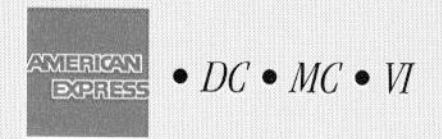

• DC • MC • VI

ACCOLADES
Independent

FACILITIES
Breakfast Room
Golf, riding and fishing nearby

RESTRICTIONS
No pets
No facilities for disabled guests

ATTRACTIONS
Harrods, Sloane Street, West End theatres & shops, Royal Albert Hall, Kensington Palace, Victoria & Albert Museum, Buckingham Palace

AFFILIATIONS
The Abbey Group

NEAREST
MAJOR CITY:
London

MAJOR AIRPORT:
London Heathrow - 15 miles/45 mins
London Gatwick - 30 miles/1¼ hrs

RAILWAY STATION:
Victoria (British Rail)
Knightsbridge/Sloane Sq (Underground)

RESERVATIONS
Direct with hotel

ACCESS CODES
Not applicable

In the heart of London's most exclusive residential and shopping area

A mahogany entrance door opens to a carved staircase leading to the bedrooms, each of which has an en suite bathroom, remote control colour television with satellite channels, direct-dial telephone, and beverage making facilities. Townhouses of this period have a number of floors with lift access.

The Executive Hotel is a listed building, due to its beautiful facade which is in keeping with the architecture of the 1800's and the Knightsbridge area. Pont Street itself has been home to many of Society's fashionable authors and artists.

Situated in the heart of London's most exclusive residential and shopping district. Located just off Sloane Street which is home to Chanel, Gucci and Cartier to name but a few. Harrods itself, is only a five minute walk away.

A buffet-style English breakfast is served 'below stairs' giving a good start to your day of shopping or sightseeing. On a short walk you can visit world-famous museums, such as The Victoria & Albert and the Royal Albert Hall, or stroll in Hyde Park.

The Executive Hotel offers exceptional value for money in a location second to none.

LOCATION

Drive into London on the A4, turn right immediately before Harrods. Proceed down to the traffic lights. Cross over and the hotel is 150 yards on the right.

"I hate to give this one away, it's so special"

Deborah Sussman, Los Angeles

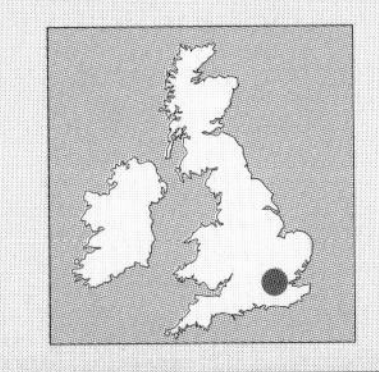

Town house

THE FENJA

**69 Cadogan Gardens,
Nr Sloane Square,
London SW3 2RB**

**Telephone 0171 589 7333
Fax 0171 581 4958**

Once a grand private house, now an exquisite hotel in the heart of London

Escape to the refuge of The Fenja, an elegant town house in the stylish heart of one of the world's busiest cities, only a short stroll from Harrods. A unique small luxurious hotel dedicated to those who appreciate elegance, sophistication and personal, efficient service.

Once a grand private residence, tastefully furnished with antiques and delightful works of art, the 12-room Fenja offers modern amenities but retains a charming intimate atmosphere.

Relax in deliciously comfortable armchairs by an open fire in your generously proportioned superior room, and help yourself to a favourite drink from cut glass decanters.

A traditional breakfast and complimentary newspaper will be served in your room until a decadent 2 p.m. Guests here are made to really feel at home.

Some rooms have four-poster beds – all have pure Irish linen – and many have attractive views of the private gardens, into which all guests are welcomed.

If you wish to stay in trim, make use of the nearby Leisure Club. Enjoy the feeling of being a cherished guest in a luxurious private home – make The Fenja your private address in London.

LOCATION

From Sloane Square, take Symmonds Street, which leads into Cadogan Gardens. The Fenja is 50 yards on the right hand side.

GENERAL MANAGER
Richard G Wentworth

ROOM RATES

11 Doubles	£130 - £195
1 Four-poster	£195

Includes VAT

CHARGE/CREDIT CARDS

• DC • MC • VI

ACCOLADES
Independent

FACILITIES
*Garden,
free membership of fitness club,
1 meeting room/max 12 people
Riding, tennis and fishing nearby*

RESTRICTIONS
*No facilities for disabled guests
No pets*

ATTRACTIONS
*Victoria & Albert Museum,
Buckingham Palace,
Hampton Court, Harrods,
Houses of Parliament,
Westminster Abbey*

AFFILIATIONS
Small Luxury Hotels

NEAREST
*MAJOR CITY:
London*

*MAJOR AIRPORT:
London Heathrow - 15 miles/45 mins
London City - 7 miles/25 mins*

*RAILWAY STATION:
Victoria (British Rail)
Sloane Square (Underground)*

RESERVATIONS
Toll free in US/Canada: 800-525-4800

ACCESS CODES
*AMADEUS LX LONFEN
APOLLO LX 8216
SABRE LX 14795
AXESS LX 5633
WORLDSPAN/SAHARA LX LONTF*

"The Goring is that great rarity, a smart, privately owned one-off hotel

Craig Brown, The Sunday Times

THE GORING HOTEL

Luxury hotel

15 Beeston Place,
London SW1W 0JW

Telephone 0171 396 9000
Fax 0171 834 4393

PROPRIETOR
George Goring

GENERAL MANAGER
William Cowpe

ROOM RATES

24 Singles	*£130*
38 Doubles	*£170*
11 Deluxe Doubles	*£195*
4 Suites	*£250*

Includes service

CHARGE/CREDIT CARDS

• *DC* • *MC* • *VI*

ACCOLADES
E.T.B. ♛♛♛♛♛ *De Luxe*
R.A.C. Blue Ribbon Award ★★★★
A.A. ★★★★ ❀❀
The Good Hotel Guide

FACILITIES
Garden
4 meeting rooms/max 50 people
Golf and riding nearby

RESTRICTIONS
No pets

ATTRACTIONS
Buckingham Palace,
Royal Parks, West End,
Houses of Parliament

AFFILIATIONS
Pride of Britain
Selected British Hotels

NEAREST
MAJOR CITY:
London

MAJOR AIRPORT:
London Heathrow - 16 miles/45 mins
London Gatwick - 30 miles/1¼ hrs

RAILWAY STATION:
Victoria (British Rail/Underground)

RESERVATIONS
Toll free in US: 800-98-PRIDE
800-323-5463

ACCESS CODES
AMADEUS/SYSTEM 1 HK LON GOR
WORLDSPAN HK GORIN
SABRE HK 30136
APOLLO HT 14860
SAHARA LON/GORIN-HK

Charm and efficiency characterise the Goring

For three generations the Goring family has harmonised traditional standards of hotel keeping with progressive management. George Goring, the grandson of the founder and present managing director, is proud to operate one of London's most prestigious hotels.

The 77 bedrooms are individually designed with every modern facility. Many have air conditioning. Marble bathrooms are "in a class of their own".

Two elegant lounges and the Garden Bar overlook The Goring's own private garden and present the perfect rendezvous for lavish bar snacks and afternoon tea. The traditional style and opulence of the lovely restaurant make it popular for both lunch and dinner. Guests can enjoy traditional food, accompanied by some of the best wines in London that have been personally selected by George Goring and William Cowpe.

A quiet haven in the centre of London, The Goring is ideally located. It is adjacent to Buckingham Palace and within walking distance of the Royal Parks, London's principal shopping areas and the heart of the West End and theatreland. The Houses of Parliament and Westminster Abbey are close by.

George Goring, William Cowpe and their faithful, experienced staff will ensure a warm welcome to your London "home from home".

LOCATION

Beeston Place is a small, quiet street off Grosvenor Gardens. It is very close to Victoria British Rail and Underground stations.

“ There are few homes and even fewer hotels that can boast the services of The Halcyon ”

European Travel & Life

Victorian mansion

THE HALCYON

A country house in Holland Park – diplomatic heart of London

The Halcyon, the exclusive Holland Park hotel once dubbed “the city's best kept secret” by the Los Angeles Times, achieves the impossible by fulfilling the role of the ultimate luxurious hideaway, while being located just a couple of miles from the bustle of the West End and the city's most fashionable shopping areas and restaurants.

An elegant stuccoed building, meticulously restored to blend unassumingly with the many imposing ambassadorial residences in the area, The Halcyon is full of surprises. The first is the electrification of the apparently classical doors which swing open as you climb the steps. Entering The Halcyon is like walking into the country house of your dreams, an impression reinforced by the proportions of the rooms and the striking individuality of their furnishings and decor.

The large, beautifully lit rooms offer modern comfort in the best classical traditions. All are individually decorated in superb taste, some have four-poster beds, jacuzzis or corner baths, others gloriously tented ceilings. Everywhere, the colour schemes are impeccably conceived, with well chosen antiques lending a tasteful depth to the decor. Guests, for whom maintaining a low profile is a priority, will be relieved to hear that the entire menu from The Halcyon's upbeat restaurant, The Room, can be served in the comfort of their suite.

LOCATION

Leafy, diplomatic, residential area with easy access to central London (10 minutes).

81 Holland Park,
London W11 3RZ

Telephone 0171 727 7288
Fax 0171 229 8516

MANAGER

Robert Wauters

ROOM RATES

3 Singles	*£165 - £195*
20 Doubles	*£200 - £255*
20 Suites	*£275 - £550*

Includes VAT

CHARGE/CREDIT CARDS

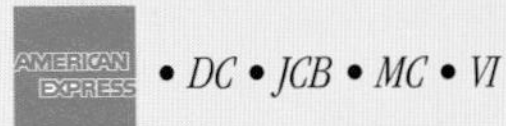

• DC • JCB • MC • VI

ACCOLADES

E.T.B. ♛♛♛♛♛ Commended

FACILITIES

Garden, board room
Private health club, tennis and riding nearby

RESTRICTIONS

None

ATTRACTIONS

Portobello antiques market, Holland Park Estate, Kensington Palace

AFFILIATIONS

Summit International Hotels
Grand Heritage

NEAREST

MAJOR CITY:
London

MAJOR AIRPORT:
London Heathrow - 14 miles/50 mins
London Gatwick - 30 miles/1¼ hrs

RAILWAY STATION:
Paddington (British Rail)
Holland Park (Underground)

RESERVATIONS

Toll free in US/Canada: 800-457-4000

ACCESS CODES

AMADEUS/SYSTEM 1 XL LONHAL
APOLLO XL 24553
WORLDSPAN XL 16458
AXESS UI 5636
SABRE XL 28259
SAHARA XL 24553

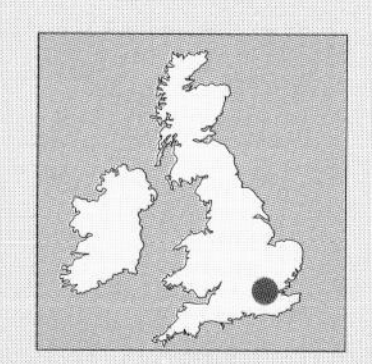

“ You really know how to make a guest feel welcome and special ”

Michael Cunningham, London

THE HOWARD

Luxury hotel

**Temple Place, Strand,
London WC2R 2PR**

**Telephone 0171 836 3555
Fax 0171 379 4547**

DIRECTOR
Michael P Day

GENERAL MANAGER
Nicolino Martini

ROOM RATES

Single occupancy	*£210*
110 Doubles	*£236*
25 Suites	*£255 - £480*

Includes VAT

CHARGE/CREDIT CARDS

• *DC* • *JCB* • *MC* • *VI*

ACCOLADES
E.T.B. ♛♛♛♛♛ *De Luxe*

FACILITIES
*Temple Bar,
Quai d'Or Restaurant,
4 meeting rooms/max 200 people
Health Centre amd riding nearby*

RESTRICTIONS
No pets allowed

ATTRACTIONS
*St Paul's Cathedral,
The Law Courts,
Royal Opera House,
National Theatre*

AFFILIATIONS
*BTH Hotels Inc (USA)
Utell International*

NEAREST
*MAJOR CITY:
London*

*MAJOR AIRPORT:
London Heathrow - 15 miles/45 mins*

*RAILWAY STATION:
Charing Cross - 1 mile/5 mins
Waterloo (Eurostar) - 3 mins*

RESERVATIONS
*Toll free in US: 800-221-1074
Toll free in Canada: 800-344-4034*

ACCESS CODES
*AMADEUS UI LONHOW
APOLLO UI 26955
WORLDSPAN UI 3005
SAHARA UI LON3005*

Riverside opulence where the City meets the West End

The Howard Hotel, where the City meets the West End, has a magnificent riverside view stretching from The Houses of Parliament to St Paul's Cathedral and is only a short walk from Drury Lane, the Royal Opera House and many of London's other key attractions.

Ornate ceilings, classical pillars of marble and glittering chandeliers create a style that is nothing short of regal, a glittering welcome that is a prelude to a most enjoyable stay in central London. The bedrooms feature French marquetry furniture and marble bathrooms, combining modern luxury with traditional design; many have a stunning view of the River. All rooms are fully air-conditioned, offer a 24-hour room service, satellite and CNN channels and direct dial phones.

The opulent Quai d'Or restaurant overlooks an open terrace landscaped with plants and flowers to give a refreshing al fresco atmosphere. It is the perfect setting to savour some of the finest haute cuisine in London.

When it comes to private entertaining, The Howard rises to the occasion; there are four lavishly appointed suites where the service is meticulous and dedicated entirely to you.

The location, splendour, cuisine and comfort provided by The Howard, make this a rare and wonderful experience. Add to all that, a brigade of well-trained staff, attentive to your every need, and you have a world class luxury hotel – not surprising there is a sister hotel in Monte Carlo, the “Hotel Mirabeau”.

LOCATION

On the Embankment overlooking the River Thames. Opposite Temple tube station. Across the river from Waterloo, the new Eurostar terminal. Approximately 2½ miles from The Houses of Parliament.

" I always enjoy my trips to England where you have made the Hyde Park Hotel my 'London home' "

Ronald Reagan

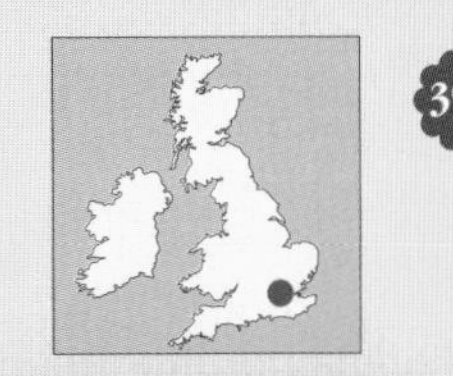

Central hotel

HYDE PARK HOTEL

The relaxed Edwardian country house next to Knightsbridge and Hyde Park

In the heart of fashionable Knightsbridge, overlooking Hyde Park and close to some of London's finest stores including Harrods and Harvey Nichols, stands the Hyde Park Hotel, one of the Exclusive Hotels by Forte. Throughout the century the hotel has been famous for its relaxed Edwardian country house atmosphere and attentive personal service.

The special warmth that is the hallmark of the Hyde Park Hotel starts when you are greeted by the Guest Relations Manager in the lobby. You are then conducted to one of 186 spacious, air-conditioned and double-glazed bedrooms. If you require a sitting room, there is a choice of 19 one or two bedroom suites where butler service and a host of much valued extras are provided. All rooms are as comfortable and restful as any private home.

The hotel's award-winning Restaurant on the Park is famous for its panoramic views of Hyde Park where the Household Cavalry ride by each morning on their way to Buckingham Palace. The Restaurant Marco Pierre White, is one of London's hottest dining venues. As well as being one of the few chefs to achieve this highly acclaimed award, Chef Marco Pierre White is the only British chef and the youngest anywhere in the world to be credited with three Michelin stars.

In short, this discreet and welcoming home from home is as individual as you are.

LOCATION

On Knightsbridge, beside Hyde Park, and close to Knightsbridge underground station.

66 Knightsbridge, London SW1Y 7LA

Telephone 0171 235 2000
Fax 0171 235 4552

EXECUTIVE DIRECTOR

Paolo Biscioni

ROOM RATES

26 Standard Singles	*£241*
138 Doubles/Twins	*£282 - £312*
2 Junior Suites	*£352*
19 Suites	*£705 - £1763*

Includes VAT

CHARGE/CREDIT CARDS

• DC • JCB • MC • VI

ACCOLADES

R.A.C. Blue Ribbon Award ★★★★★
A.A. ★★★★★ ❀❀❀❀❀

FACILITIES

Gym, health & beauty
24 meeting rooms/max 500 people
Tennis and riding nearby

RESTRICTIONS

No pets

ATTRACTIONS

Hyde Park, Harrods, Buckingham Palace, Oxford and Bond Streets, Victoria & Albert Museum

AFFILIATIONS

Forte Exclusive Hotels

NEAREST

MAJOR CITY:
London

MAJOR AIRPORT:
London Heathrow - 17 miles/45 mins
London Gatwick - 30 miles/1¼ hrs

RAILWAY STATION:
Victoria (British Rail)
Knightsbridge

RESERVATIONS

Toll free in US: 800-225-5843
Toll free in Australia/Asia: 008 222 446

ACCESS CODES

SABRE FE 4068
AMADEUS/SYSTEM 1 FE LON232
WORLDSPAN FE 5933
APOLLO FE 5787

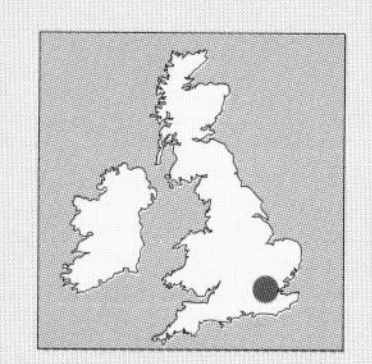

"For more than ten years, Knightsbridge Green has been my 'home' in London . . . it is a very nice place to come back to"

Mr Peter Yeo

KNIGHTSBRIDGE GREEN HOTEL

Town house

159 Knightsbridge, London SW1X 7PD

Telephone 0171 584 6274
Fax 0171 225 1635

PROPRIETOR
The Marler family

MANAGER
Mrs Ann Thomson

ROOM RATES

5 Singles	£80
8 Doubles	£110
12 Suites	£125

Includes VAT

CHARGE/CREDIT CARDS

• DC • MC • VI

ACCOLADES
E.T.B. Commended
Commended past winner of B.T.A London B&B Award Scheme - Certificate of Distinction
The Good Hotel Guide

FACILITIES
Suites with reception rooms
Riding nearby

RESTRICTIONS
No pets

ATTRACTIONS
Harrods, Kensington Palace, Natural History Museum, Victoria & Albert Museum

AFFILIATIONS
Independent

NEAREST
MAJOR CITY:
London

MAJOR AIRPORT:
London Heathrow - 15 miles/45 mins
London Gatwick - 30 miles/1¼ hrs

RAILWAY STATION:
Victoria (British Rail)
Knightsbridge (Underground)

RESERVATIONS
Toll free in US: 800-544-9993

ACCESS CODES
Not applicable

A family-owned hotel with a personal touch

The Knightsbridge Green Hotel is located in the very heart of London, situated adjacent to the beautiful open spaces of Hyde Park, with the world-renowned Harrods just across the street. The hotel offers the business traveller excellent connections to the City, while London's West End, with its world-famous theatres and restaurants, is just minutes away.

The hotel offers a range of accommodation from single rooms to larger suites which include reception rooms to relax in or which could be used for business meetings. All rooms have en suite bathrooms and offer modern conveniences including colour television, telephones, hairdryer, trouser press and tea/coffee making facilities. A full English or continental breakfast is available and is individually prepared to order and served in your room.

The hotel does not have its own restaurant; over the years guests have preferred to explore the vast range of culinary delights that are within easy reach of the hotel.

Being a small hotel, they provide a personal service including help in booking restaurants or theatre tickets.

LOCATION

In Knightsbridge, central London, adjacent to Hyde Park.

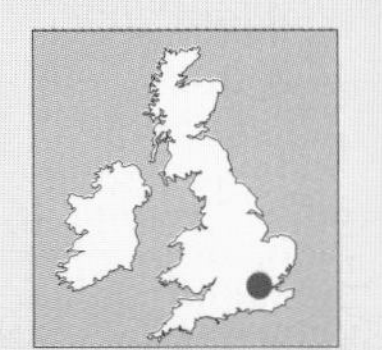

"The scale of the lavishly decorated suites alone means The Leonard offers the ultimate urban luxury – space"

Christine Temin, Boston Globe

Georgian town house

THE LEONARD

15 Seymour Street,
Marylebone,
London W1H 5AA

Telephone 0171 935 2010
Fax 0171 935 6700

GENERAL MANAGER
Andrew Harris

ROOM RATES

6 Doubles	£164 - £210
12 x 1 Bedroom Suites	£235
4 x 2 Bedroom Suites	£258 - £352
4 Grand Suites	£375

Includes VAT

CHARGE/CREDIT CARDS

• DC • MC • VI

Possibly one of the most elegant retreats in the centre of London

Superbly located off Portman Square in central London, The Leonard is ideal for business or pleasure. It is in the heart of the West End close to the famous shopping areas of Oxford Street and Bond Street. The quiet enclosures of Grosvenor Square, Mayfair and Hyde Park are all a short stroll away.

The 26 rooms offer tranquil isolation from city life. It is a haven for those wanting to relax and enjoy London.

From the extraordinary spacious Grand Suites to the bedrooms, the accommodation provides a warm, intimate and luxurious atmosphere. All the twenty suites and six bedrooms are individually decorated with countless details and considerable thought, making them special: exquisite fabrics, antiques, a variety of furnishings and, most importantly, great beds.

Downstairs, on the ground floor, there are marvellous public areas, filled with fresh flowers. There is the Morning Room in which to take a first rate breakfast, or enjoy delightful meals throughout the day.

For conferences there is a fully equipped room with all the facilities. In addition entertaining, dinner parties and canapé receptions can be arranged in the elegant Party Suite.

Professional, friendly and dynamic house staff welcome you, providing help, advice, concierge and 24-hour room service from a refreshingly different menu.

LOCATION

Situated on the south side of Seymour Street, just west of Portman Square. Car parking is available in Bryanston Street.

ACCOLADES
Independent

FACILITIES
Gym
1 meeting room/max 40 people
Riding nearby

RESTRICTIONS
No pets

ATTRACTIONS
Buckingham Palace,
Hyde Park,
Bond Street,
Victoria & Albert Museum,
Wallace Collection

AFFILIATIONS
Grand Heritage Hotels

NEAREST
MAJOR CITY:
London

MAJOR AIRPORT:
London Heathrow - 15 miles/45 mins
London Gatwick - 30 miles/1¼ hrs

RAILWAY STATION:
Paddington (British Rail)
Marble Arch (Underground)

RESERVATIONS
Direct with hotel

ACCESS CODES
GH

"You have made the hotel a compelling part of my life!"

Sir John Harvey-Jones MBE

MAY FAIR INTER-CONTINENTAL

Luxury hotel

Stratton Street,
Mayfair
London W1A 2AN

Telephone 0171 629 7777
Fax 0171 629 1459

GENERAL MANAGER

Ms Dagmar Woodward

ROOM RATES

80 Singles	*£217*
154 Doubles/Twins	*£229 - £317*
51 Suites	*£399 - £1410*

Includes VAT

CHARGE/CREDIT CARDS

• DC • JCB • MC • VI

ACCOLADES

E.T.B. ★★★★★ *De Luxe*

FACILITIES

Indoor swimming pool,
health & beauty, sauna, gym,
voicemail, modem in every room
6 meeting rooms/max 400 people
Squash, golf and riding nearby

RESTRICTIONS

Limited facilities for disabled guests
No pets

ATTRACTIONS

Buckingham Palace,
Tower of London,
Royal Academy of Arts,
The West End

AFFILIATIONS

Inter-Continental Hotels Group

NEAREST

MAJOR CITY:
London

MAJOR AIRPORT:
London Heathrow - 15 miles/45 mins

RAILWAY STATION:
Victoria - 1 mile/5 mins

RESERVATIONS

Toll free in US: 800-327-0200

ACCESS CODES

AMADEUS/SYSTEM 1 IC LONICE
APOLLO IC 19215
SABRE IC 1086
WORLDSPAN IC LONHE

Elegance, style and friendliness in London's most exclusive area

The May Fair was opened in 1927 by King George V and has retained its elegant English character ever since. Lavishly furnished, it is a well-known meeting place for the fashionable and famous, partly due to its historical connections with the entertainment industry.

Situated in London's most exclusive area, between Berkeley Square and Piccadilly, this delightful hotel is ideally placed for shopping, with Bond Street, Oxford Street and Knightsbridge all close by. It is just a few minutes' walk away from Burlington Arcade and Fortnum & Mason, and a short taxi ride from Harrods. The hotel is perfect for arts lovers with the Royal Academy of Arts within walking distance and theatreland easily accessible. For sightseers, Buckingham Palace, the Royal Parks and many other famous landmarks are close by.

Restaurants and bars include the brasserie-style May Fair Cafe, the informal Chateau restaurant, The May Fair Bar, and The Chateau Bar, a sophisticated piano bar where resident pianist Iain Kerr plays every evening. Continental breakfast, morning coffee and afternoon tea are served daily in the delightful lobby lounge, where every afternoon a harpist plays melodies from popular West End shows. The May Fair has a range of luxurious suites, which have recently been refurbished, many with jacuzzi baths, and a modern fitness centre with a plunge pool.

Despite its wonderful facilities, the hotel's most significant asset is without a doubt its staff, who are courteous, friendly, helpful and efficient. It is they who make every guest truly feel at home.

LOCATION

On Stratton Street, just off Berkeley Square.

" How wonderful to find in the heart of Kensington a country house hotel that looks after your every need. Beautiful rooms, wonderful staff . . . fantastic food "

Christopher Biggins, TV presenter

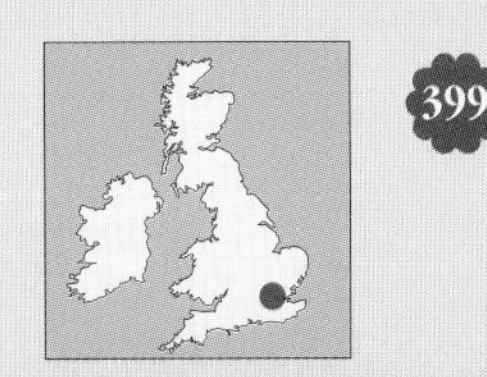

19th century town house

THE MILESTONE

Experience the grace of a former era in 20th century luxury

The Milestone is one of London's most exclusive small hotels. Built in the late 19th century as two private residences, it enjoys unrivalled panoramic vistas overlooking areas of parkland. Visitors have breathtaking views of Kensington Palace, home to the Princess of Wales.

All the hotel's 57 suites and bedrooms, many overlooking the Park, are fully air-conditioned. Each has been individually designed to the highest standards and incorporates two line direct-dial telephones, as well as private fax facilities, satellite television and video recorder. 24-hour room service, same-day laundry and valet parking are also available.

The spacious suites emphasise the fine architectural details of the building; no expense has been spared on the magnificent furnishings and decoration in keeping with the period.

Whether taking advantage of the 24-hour service available in the elegant Park Lounge, relaxing in Stables Bar, or simply unwinding in the health and fitness centre, The Milestone provides the highest standard of personal service in a restful atmosphere.

LOCATION

The Milestone is centrally located, a stone's throw from Knightsbridge and the West End. Within a few minutes walk is Kensington High Street Underground.

1-2 Kensington Court, London W8 5DL

Telephone 0171 917 1000
Fax 0171 917 1010

GENERAL MANAGER
James Caetano

ROOM RATES

Single occupancy	*£200*
45 Doubles/Twins	*£245*
12 Suites (Four-poster)	*From £275*

Children under 2 years free
Includes VAT

CHARGE/CREDIT CARDS

• DC • MC • VI

ACCOLADES
Independent

FACILITIES
Health and Fitness Club Centre
Private facsimile in all rooms
2 meeting rooms/max 25 people
Riding nearby

RESTRICTIONS
No facilities for disabled guests
No pets

ATTRACTIONS
Kensington Palace, Kensington Gardens, Hyde Park, Royal Albert Hall, Victoria & Albert Museum, Knightsbridge shopping

AFFILIATIONS
Preferred Hotels & Resorts Worldwide
Grand Heritage Hotels

NEAREST
MAJOR CITY:
London

MAJOR AIRPORT:
London Heathrow - 15 miles/45 mins
London Gatwick - 30 miles/1¼ hrs

RAILWAY STATION:
Victoria/Paddington (British Rail)
Kensington High Street (Underground)

RESERVATIONS
Toll free in US: 800-323-7500 or 800-HERITAGE

ACCESS CODES
GH
Sabre PH 30954

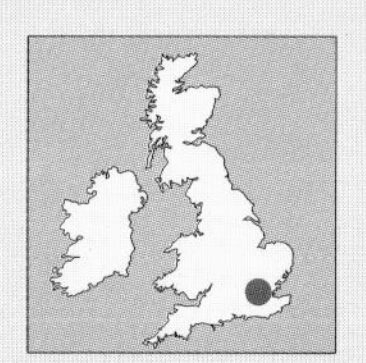

"I have been frequenting The Montcalm for twenty years. It has changed little – it is small, private, discreet and with friendly impeccable service"

Frederick Forsyth, author

THE MONTCALM

Georgian town house

Great Cumberland Place, London W1A 2LF

Telephone 0171 402 4288
Fax 0171 724 9180

MANAGERS

Messrs Gerhard Schaller and Mr Jonathan Orr-Ewing

ROOM RATES

43 Singles	£188 - £211.50
63 Doubles/Twins	£211.50 - £293.75
14 Suites	£293.75 - £587.50

Includes VAT

CHARGE/CREDIT CARDS

• DC • JCB • MC • VI

ACCOLADES

E.T.B. ♕♕♕♕♕

A.A. ★★★★ ❀ 76%

A.A. Courtesy & Care Award 1994

FACILITIES

Bicycles,
Bridal Suite with water bed and jacuzzi
3 meeting rooms/max 80 people
Jogging and horseriding in Hyde Park

RESTRICTIONS

No pets but guide dogs accepted by prior arrangement

ATTRACTIONS

Buckingham Palace, London Diamond Centre, The Wallace Collection, Bond Street, Madame Tussaud's

AFFILIATIONS

Nikko Hotels International

NEAREST

MAJOR CITY:
London

MAJOR AIRPORT:
London Heathrow - 15 miles/50 mins
London Gatwick - 30 miles/1¼ hrs

RAILWAY STATION:
Paddington (British Rail)
Marble Arch (Underground)

RESERVATIONS

Toll free in UK: 0800 282 502
Toll free in US: 800-645-5687

ACCESS CODES

SABRE NK 14527
AXESS JH 4445
AMADEUS/SYSTEM 1 NK LON001
WORLDSPAN NK 14527
SAHARA NK 26211

Make The Montcalm your best-loved address in London

To be in the heart of one of the greatest cities in the world and to be able to offer a quiet restful atmosphere in comfortable, elegant surroundings, is something special. The Montcalm, discreetly located on an elegant Georgian Crescent just two minutes walk from Marble Arch and Oxford Street, is able to make this claim.

A recent refurbishment programme has refreshed and updated the 120 charming bedrooms, including the unique duplex suites. All rooms and public areas are fully air-conditioned, room service is available 24 hours a day and they also offer satellite and CNN channels. The Montcalm provides all the comforts and amenities that one would expect to find in a four-star deluxe hotel, with the personal, friendly service which has become an integral part of the hotel's reputation.

The Crescent Restaurant provides guests with a selection of dishes for luncheon and dinner thoughtfully prepared by Head Chef Gary Robinson and his team. The cuisine is modern British with a variety of dishes to tempt the most discerning palate. They have even prepared a special menu for theatre and concert lovers, allowing them to partake of a starter and main course, returning after the evening performance to enjoy dessert and coffee at their leisure.

Make The Montcalm your best-loved address in London.

LOCATION

Two minutes walk from Marble Arch and Oxford Street.

“Please accept my sincere thanks for a most wonderful stay, and my congratulations on running such a superb hotel”

Ambassador & Mrs Gwyn Morgan, Thailand

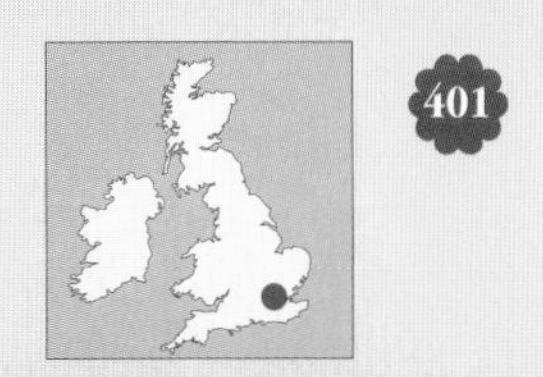

Victorian house

NUMBER SIXTEEN

Personal attention with an atmosphere of total relaxation in the city

A passer-by may wonder what lies behind the immaculate pillared facade of Number Sixteen. Upon entering the hotel, visitors will find themselves in an atmosphere of seclusion and comfort which has remained virtually unaltered in style since its early Victorian origins. The staff are friendly and attentive, regarding each visitor as a guest in a private house. The relaxed atmosphere of the Library is the perfect place to pour a drink from the bar and meet friends or business associates. A fire blazing in the Drawing Room in cooler months creates an inviting warmth, whilst the Conservatory opens on to an award-winning, secluded walled garden where drinks can be taken on summer evenings.

Each spacious bedroom is decorated with a discreet combination of antiques and traditional furnishings. The rooms are fully appointed with every facility that the discerning traveller would expect. A light breakfast is served in the privacy of guests' rooms and tea and coffee service is available throughout the day. Although there is no dining room at Number Sixteen, some of London's finest restaurants are just around the corner.

LOCATION

Drive past South Kensington Underground onto the Old Brompton Road. Sumner Place is first left off the Old Brompton Road.

16 Sumner Place, London SW7 3EG

Telephone 0171 589 5232
Fax 0171 584 8615

GENERAL MANAGER

Jean Branham

ROOM RATES

9 Singles £68 - £99
27 Doubles/Twins £130 - £155
Includes continental breakfast and VAT

CHARGE/CREDIT CARDS

• DC • MC • VI

ACCOLADES

E.T.B. ♛♛ Highly Commended

FACILITIES

Garden, conservatory
Riding nearby

RESTRICTIONS

No children under 12 years
No facilities for disabled guests
No pets allowed

ATTRACTIONS

Buckingham Palace,
West End,
Knightsbridge,
Victoria & Albert Museum

AFFILIATIONS

Independent

NEAREST

MAJOR CITY:
London

MAJOR AIRPORT:
London Heathrow - 15 miles/45 mins
London Gatwick - 30 miles/1¼ hrs

RAILWAY STATION:
Victoria (British Rail)
South Kensington (Underground)

RESERVATIONS

Direct with hotel

ACCESS CODES

Not applicable

"Delicious food, excellent service, wonderful atmosphere"

Donna Dawson, Boston

RICHMOND GATE HOTEL

Georgian mansion

Richmond Hill,
Richmond-upon-Thames,
Surrey TW10 6RP

Telephone 0181 940 0061
Fax 0181 332 0354

MANAGER
Niklaus V Kaiser

ROOM RATES

20 Singles	£105
26 Doubles	£125
15 Luxury & Four-posters	£145

Includes VAT
Quote 'Best Loved' on arrival for possible room upgrade

CHARGE/CREDIT CARDS

• DC • MC • VI

ACCOLADES
E.T.B. ♛♛♛♛ Highly Commended
R.A.C. ★★★★ + Merit Awards C & R
A.A.★★★★ 68%

FACILITIES
Croquet, gardens, indoor pool, gym, sauna, jacuzzi, steam room, aerobics, health & beauty, crèche
6 meeting rooms/max 80 people
Boating, golf, riding and fishing nearby

RESTRICTIONS
No facilities for disabled guests
No pets

ATTRACTIONS
Hampton Court Palace, Kew Palace & Botanical Gardens, Richmond Royal Park, Twickenham, Wimbledon

AFFILIATIONS
Securicor Hotels
Utell International

NEAREST
MAJOR CITY:
London - 7 miles/30 mins
MAJOR AIRPORT:
London Heathrow - 7 miles/30 mins
RAILWAY STATION:
Richmond - 1 mile/5 mins

RESERVATIONS
Toll free in US: 800-544-9993
Toll free fax in UK: 0800 387546

ACCESS CODES
SABRE UI 25533
APOLLO UI 22152

Richmond – where kings chose to live

A Georgian country house, The Richmond Gate Hotel stands on the crest of Richmond Hill close to the Royal Park and Richmond Terrace with its commanding views of the River Thames.

The 64 stylishly furnished, en suite bedrooms combine every comfort of the present with the elegance of the past. Several luxury four-poster rooms with a traditional ambience add the perfect touch to any stay.

Imaginative cuisine is presented in the 'Gates On The Park Restaurant', where diners have an impressive choice of menus in relaxed and sophisticated surroundings. During the week the less formal Bistro offers an equally appetizing alternative in the Victorian style conservatory which opens out on to the hotel's walled garden. Guests can also enjoy an English afternoon tea here or in the Club Lounge.

'Cedars Health and Leisure Club' offers a wide range of facilities: 20-metre pool, spa, gym, aerobics studio, sauna, steam, health and beauty suite.

Richmond is close to central London and the West End yet in a pleasant country setting. Visitors can enjoy a wide range of activities, such as shopping for antiques in the narrow lanes, visiting the Victorian theatre, taking a boat along the Thames or walking through the Royal Park with its herds of deer.

Health and Beauty Weekends and Heritage Breaks including one attraction are available from £110. Central London is a simple journey by Underground or Britrail.

LOCATION

7 miles from London Heathrow Airport. From the M25, via the M4 motorway and Kew Bridge (or M3 and A316), into Richmond. First left up Richmond Hill.

“ The Savoy, as always, is happy, and able, to deliver ”

Peter Chapman, Business Traveller

Deluxe hotel

THE SAVOY

The guilded legacy of D’Oyly Carte, César Ritz and Escoffier

Mention “The Savoy” and the mind conjures a picture of consummate luxury, but behind the guilded images are a few surprises, all of which add lustre to this unique establishment.

Built on the site of the medieval Palace of Count Peter of Savoy, the hotel was created in 1889 by Richard D’Oyly Carte, the legendary impresario. In the early days César Ritz became its manager and engaged Escoffier as the Maître Chef des Cusines. The famous names associated with the hotel are legion: Strauss conducted in the Thames Foyer, Caruso sang and Pavlova danced here, to name but a few.

The Savoy has a very English tradition of service and individuality. Bedrooms are decorated and furnished in a variety of styles – traditional, art deco and contemporary – and all share a standard of unrivalled comfort.

In the Restaurant, with its stunning views of the Thames, classic dishes by Escoffier are recreated, while The Savoy Grill is the meeting place for leading lights in the arts, media and the City.

And there is a paradox: the classic Savoy style contrasts with all the latest technologies that contribute to the quality of life at The Savoy.; nothing exemplifies this better than The Savoy Fitness Gallery with its roof-top swimming pool and state-of-the-art fitness facilities.

LOCATION

On Strand, halfway between Charing Cross and Aldwych.

Strand,
London WC2R 0EU

Telephone 0171 836 4343
Fax 0171 240 6040

GENERAL MANAGER

Duncan Palmer

ROOM RATES

51 Singles	*£217 - £247*
102 Doubles/Twins	*£299 - £376*
49 Suites	*£358 - £764*

Includes service and VAT

CHARGE/CREDIT CARDS

• DC • JCB • MC • VI

ACCOLADES

R.A.C. Blue Ribbon Award ★★★★★
A.A. ★★★★★ ❀❀❀
Best Business Hotel 1995 - ‘Business Traveller’
Courvoisier’s Book of the Best

FACILITIES

Indoor pool, sauna, gym, health & beauty
11 meeting rooms/max 800 people
Complimentary golf nearby

RESTRICTIONS

No pets

ATTRACTIONS

Buckingham Palace, St Pauls Cathedral, Covent Garden, Westminster Abbey, Houses of Parliament

AFFILIATIONS

The Savoy Group of Hotels & Restaurants
Leading Hotels of the World
Utell International

NEAREST

MAJOR CITY:
London

MAJOR AIRPORT:
London Heathrow - 18 miles/40 mins
London City - 9 miles/25 mins

RAILWAY STATIONS:
Charing Cross (British Rail/Underground)

RESERVATIONS

Toll free in US: 800-63-SAVOY

ACCESS CODES

SABRE LW 4710
AMADEUS/SYSTEM 1 LW LON403
APOLLO LW 8522
WORLDSPAN LW 00403
AXESS LW 8400

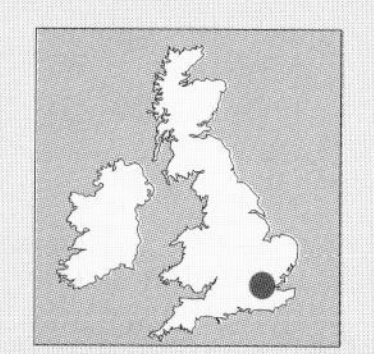

“Superb decor, excellent staff, my home away from home in London”

Jim Kent, Florida

THE SLOANE HOTEL

Central location

29 Draycott Place,
Chelsea,
London SW3 2SH

Telephone 0171 581 5757
Fax 0171 584 1348

GENERAL MANAGER
Rebecca Maxwell

ROOM RATES

2 Doubles	£141 - £152.75
7 Deluxe Doubles	£205
3 Four-poster Suites	£264

Includes VAT

CHARGE/CREDIT CARDS

• DC • MC • VI

ACCOLADES
Independent

FACILITIES
Roof-top reception room, technical and secretarial support

RESTRICTIONS
No pets allowed
No facilities for disabled guests

ATTRACTIONS
Harrods, Hyde Park, Buckingham Palace, Christies, Victoria & Albert Museum

AFFILIATIONS
Independent

NEAREST
MAJOR CITY:
London

MAJOR AIRPORT:
London Heathrow - 15 miles/40 mins
London Gatwick - 30 miles/1¼ hrs

RAILWAY STATION:
Victoria (British Rail)
Victoria (Underground)

RESERVATIONS
Toll free in US: 800-324-9960

ACCESS CODES
APOLLO HT 25927
SABRE HK 32477

Small, intimate and beautifully furnished

A small, intimate hotel set in the heart of London's Chelsea, a part of a Royal borough and with strong artistic connections. The Sloane is as luxurious as any of its larger five-star contemporaries.

Stunning designs and individual themes are features of the twelve fully air-conditioned bedrooms, which range from the contemporary to the traditional and neo-classical. Beautiful furnishings include vibrant silks, muted tapestries and lace bedspreads. Antique treasures are complemented by modern amenities to ensure maximum comfort. Guests who appreciate fine decor will be pleased to know that all items furnishing the rooms can be purchased. A 24-hour full room service is available.

Breakfast, light meals or traditional afternoon tea are all available in a roof-top reception room, featuring a terrace and views across Chelsea. The Sloane's business centre provides full technical and secretarial support. The Sloane is situated within walking distance of The Royal Albert Hall and many of London's great museums and shops, including Harrods. At the same time The Sloane has easy access to the City and West End.

LOCATION

Off Sloane Square on Draycott Place, running north parallel to the Kings Road, on the left side when coming from Sloane Square.

" An oasis of calm in Belgravia's palm "

Major Hugh Holmes, author

Town house

TOPHAMS EBURY COURT

The charm of an English country house in fashionable Belgravia

Tophams Ebury Court evokes the charm of a country house, yet is situated in the heart of Belgravia – one of London's most exclusive residential areas.

Nick and Marianne Kingsford, the second generation of the same family to own and run Tophams for more than half a century, have made many improvements and refurbishments without in any way denying the character of the original style. A variety of accommodation is offered, from compact single rooms to four-poster bedrooms.

The new garden rooms can be used for private lunch or dinner parties, for cocktail parties and receptions or for business meetings. Tophams Ebury Court is named after its founders, Romer and Diana Topham, a family of artists whose paintings hang in the restaurant for your added pleasure.

The location of Tophams makes it an ideal centre for shopping, sightseeing, visiting any of London's famous theatres and restaurants, and for walking in St James's and Hyde Parks.

The hotel has a worldwide reputation for caring for its guests who return year after year. You will be encouraged to join them.

LOCATION

Belgravia, central London. Three minutes' walk from the Underground, bus and rail services of Victoria Station.

28 Ebury Street, Belgravia, London SW1W 0LU

Telephone 0171 730 8147
Fax 0171 823 5966

PROPRIETORS
Marianne Topham and Nick Kingsford

GENERAL MANAGER
Charlie Hutchings

ROOM RATES

16 Singles	*£70 - £100*
24 Doubles	*£95 - £125*
2 Luxury Four-posters	*£135*

Includes full breakfast and VAT

CHARGE/CREDIT CARDS

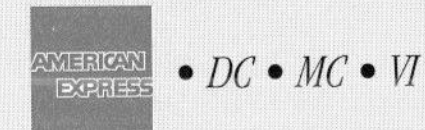

• *DC* • *MC* • *VI*

ACCOLADES
The Good Hotel Guide

FACILITIES
Garden rooms for social events
3 meeting rooms/max 100 people
Golf nearby

RESTRICTIONS
No facilities for disabled guests
Pets by arrangement

ATTRACTIONS
Buckingham Palace, Knightsbridge, Houses of Parliament, Rotten Row, Hyde Park

AFFILIATIONS
Independent

NEAREST
MAJOR CITY:
London

MAJOR AIRPORT:
London Heathrow - 15 miles/50 mins
London Gatwick - 30 miles/1¼ hrs

RAILWAY STATION:
Victoria (British Rail)
Victoria (Underground)

RESERVATIONS
Direct with hotel

ACCESS CODES
Not applicable

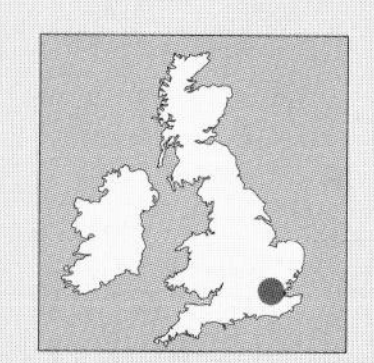

"My wife and I continue to think of a London vacation as synonymous with the White House Hotel"

Louis G Lesce, New York

WHITE HOUSE

Luxury apartments

Albany Street, Regents Park, London NW1 3UP

Telephone 0171 387 1200
Fax 0171 388 0091

GENERAL MANAGER
Gordon S Smith

ROOM RATES

48 Singles	£126 - £137
249 Doubles	£132 - £159
26 Triples	£147
206 Executive Doubles	£148
27 Executive Triples	£163
23 Suites	£180 - £350

Includes VAT

CHARGE/CREDIT CARDS

• DC • JCB • MC • VI

ACCOLADES

E.T.B. ♛♛♛♛ Commended
A.A. ★★★★ ❀ 66%

FACILITIES
Gym, sauna, business centre, 'Reserve Club'
7 meeting rooms/max 120 people
Golf driving range, pool, tennis and riding nearby

RESTRICTIONS
No pets

ATTRACTIONS
Madame Tussauds, London Zoo, Regents Park, Oxford Street

AFFILIATIONS
Utell International
Flag International
Abela Hotels

NEAREST
MAJOR CITY:
London

MAJOR AIRPORT:
London Heathrow - 17 miles/45 mins
London City - 10 miles/40 mins

RAILWAY STATION:
Euston (British Rail/Underground)
Great Portland Street (Underground)

RESERVATIONS
Toll free in US: 800-44-UTELL
Toll free in UK: 0800 243 953

ACCESS CODES
AMADEUS/SYSTEM 1/WORLDSPAN UI LONWHH
AXESS UI 5706
SABRE UI 873
APOLLO UI 49588
SAHARA UI LON3562

Cuisine, comfort and everything you need for your visit to London

The White House holds a special place among London hotels. Built in the district where Charles Dickens and Hector Berlioz had their homes, the White House was originally the private apartments of prominent socialites. It was considered to be one of London's most exclusive addresses. Today, after an extended conversion, it offers a standard of comfort that still sets it apart.

High levels of refinement are to be seen in the 584 bedrooms and suites. All have private bath and shower, colour TV, trouser press, hair dryer, dual voltage for international travellers, mini bar and 24-hour room service.

Everything guests may need is on the premises. The restaurant is spacious, air-conditioned and has won acclaim for its classical cuisine and wine list. The cocktail lounge is an elegant setting for pre-meal drinks. The Garden Café, open all day, offers light meals and traditional afternoon tea. Services include theatre and travel bookings, car hire, sight-seeing tours, valet, laundering, and fitness and sauna suite.

Close to Regent's Park (home of London Zoo), to Oxford Street shops and to West End theatres, the White House is ideally situated for your visit to London. Madame Tussauds and Sherlock Holmes' Baker Street are within seven minutes' walk. Piccadilly Circus is ten minutes by Underground or taxi.

LOCATION

Directly opposite Great Portland Street Underground station. A2 (Euston) air bus from Heathrow.

"We truly felt at home . . . fine food, great accommodations. We miss you all"

Gloria Green, California

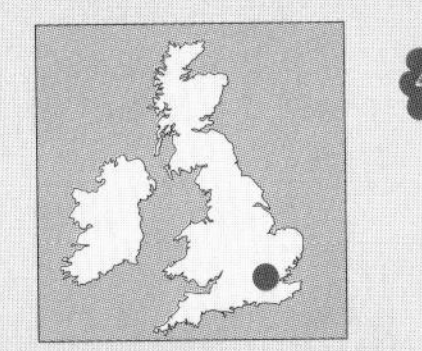

19th century private house

WHITES HOTEL

Gracious living in a 'country house in town' atmosphere

Built in 1866 as fine private houses Whites was internally reconstructed in the 1980's to reflect its Victorian architecture. It is a Grade II listed building.

Whites overlooks the green and peaceful Royal Kensington Gardens on Bayswater Road. The attractions of the West End and Knightsbridge are close by.

From the charming cobbled forecourt, pass beneath Whites unique glass canopies and you will discover a Victorian town house of style and distinction. The hallmark of Whites – rare luxury and caring personal service – offers a home from home to the discerning guest. Here guests can recapture the bygone era of gracious living and extravagant luxury in a 'country house in town' atmosphere. Whites bedrooms are unique, each with its own design, swagged silk moire drapes, deep pile carpets and marble bathrooms imported from Italy.

Fine cuisine is served in the hotel's intimate dining room where soft shades of old rose and white, gleaming silver place settings, and crystal chandeliers richly blend to create the perfect atmosphere. James's Bar offers a club style feeling, serving cocktails and afternoon teas, with a view from the terrace to the wooded Kensington Gardens.

Whites Hotel is a Thistle Country House Hotel.

LOCATION

From Bayswater Road, midway between Queensway and Lancaster Gate Underground stations.

90 Lancaster Gate, London W2 3NR

Telephone 0171 262 2711
Fax 0171 262 2147

GENERAL MANAGER

Michael Wills

ROOM RATES

19 Singles	*£155*
32 Doubles/Twins	*£190 - £230*
1 Four-poster	*£210*
2 Suites	*£350 - £395*

Includes VAT

CHARGE/CREDIT CARDS

 • *DC* • *JCB* • *MC* • *VI*

ACCOLADES

R.A.C. Blue Ribbon Award ★★★★
A.A. ★★★★ 70%

FACILITIES

2 meeting rooms/max 50 people
Riding and health club nearby

RESTRICTIONS

No facilities for disabled guests
No pets

ATTRACTIONS

Buckingham Palace,
Tower of London,
Kensington Palace,
Hyde Park

AFFILIATIONS

A Thistle Country House Hotel

NEAREST

MAJOR CITY:
London

MAJOR AIRPORT:
London Heathrow - 15 miles/45 mins
City Airport - 9 miles/40 mins

RAILWAY STATION:
Paddington - (British Rail/Underground)

RESERVATIONS

Toll free in US/Canada: 800-847-4358
Toll free in Australia: 800-062-055

ACCESS CODES

AMADEUS/SYSTEM 1 TI LONWHE
APOLLO TI 22279
SABRE TI 21353
WORLDSPAN TI 4598

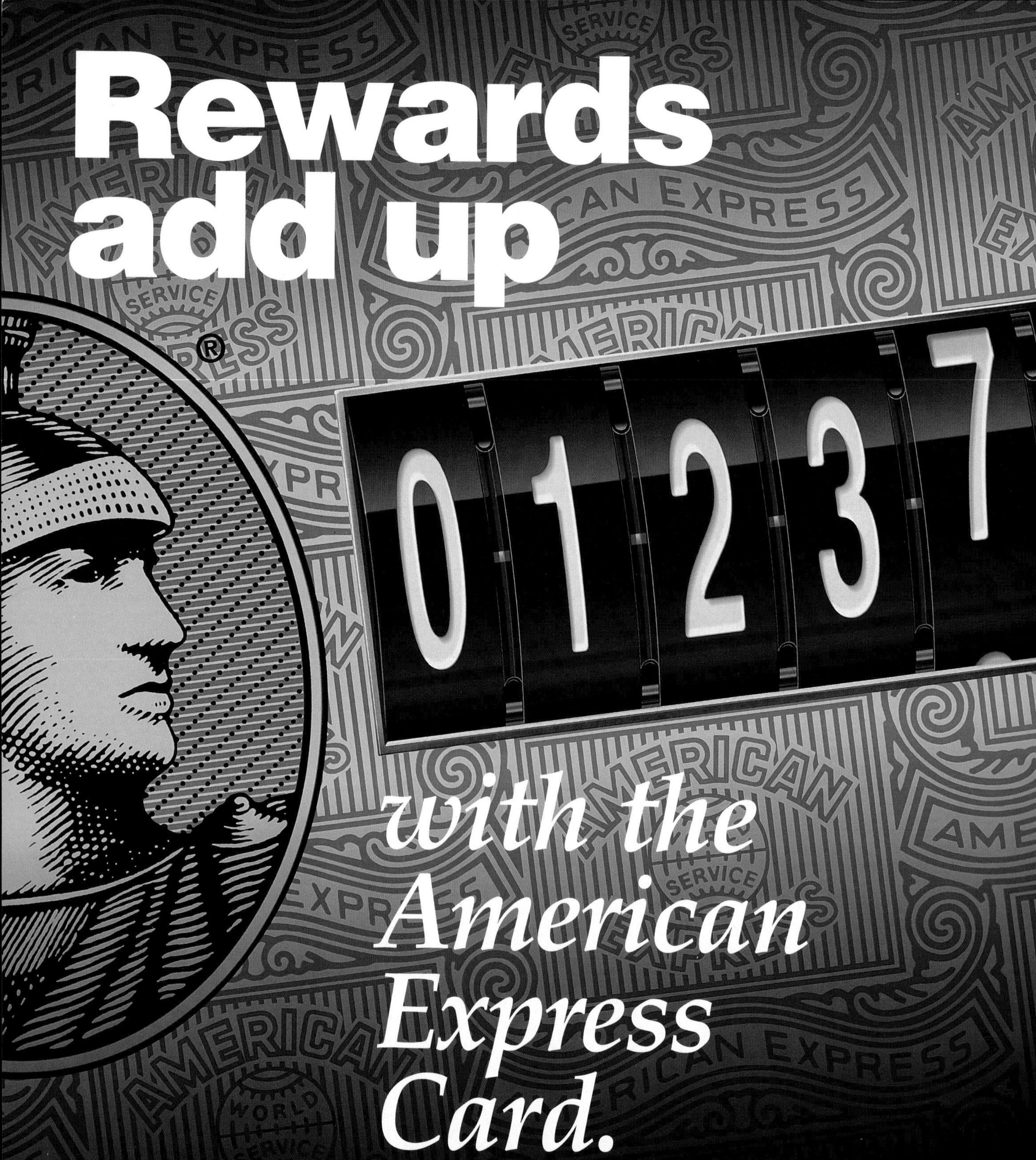
Rewards add up®
01237
with the American Express Card.
Join Membership Rewards™ and earn points every time you use the Card. To enrol call your local Customer Service Representative.

AMERICAN EXPRESS
3745
6892
01009
CHARLES FROST
Membership Rewards

Ireland

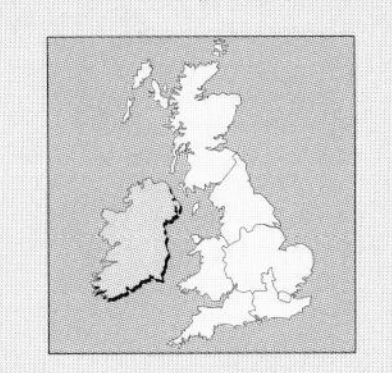

The Giant's Causeway, part of the beautiful coast of Co Antrim, consists of some 40,000 polygonal rock columns rising in steps up to 20 feet or more above the water. This remarkable phenomenon was caused by the even cooling of volcanic lava and the erosion by the sea.

Heritage sites

The following heritage sites can be found on the map overleaf. The key numbers show where they are located.

Ardgillan Castle	1
Ayesha Castle	2
Drimnagh Castle	3
James Joyce Tower	4
Malahide Castle	5
Newbridge House	6
Newman House	7
Russborough,	8
Killruddery House	9
Johnstown Castle, Demesne	10
Bantry House	11
Blarney Castle & Rock Close	12
Blarney House & Gardens	13
Riverstown House	14
Dunloe Castle Hotel Gardens	15
Muckross House & Gardens	16
Castle Matrix	17
King John's Castle	18
Bunratty Castle & Folk Park	19
Cratloe Woods House	20
Knappogue Castle	21
Lissadell House	22
Castletown House	23
Castle Leslie Estate & Gardens	24
Dunguaire	25
Kylemore Abbey	26
Thoor Ballylee	27
Birr Castle, Demesne	28
Charleville Forest Castle	29
Clonalis House	30
Carrigglas Manor	31
Giant's Causeway	32
Dunluce Castle	33
Carrickfergus Castle	34
Navan Fort	35
Castle Coole	36
Florence Court	37
Marble Arch Caves	38
Walls of Derry	39
Beaghmore Stone Circles	40
Ulster American Folk Park	41

Scotland
see pages 14,15

COLOUR KEY TO HOTEL SYMBOLS

The rosettes on the map indicate the location of each hotel; the numbers within show the page number of the hotel. The colour of the rosette is a rough guide to the price of a twin or double room (see colour key below).

- Double room: up to £75 per night
- Double room: £76 - £125 per night
- Double room: £126 - £175 per night
- Double room: from £176+ per night

PAGE	HOTEL
414	Adare Manor
415	Ahernes
416	Ard na Sidhe
417	Assolas Country House
418	Barberstown Castle
419	Bushmills Inn, The
420	Cahernane Hotel, The
421	Caragh Lodge
422	Castle Grove
423	Cromleach Lodge
424	Dunadry Hotel
425	Dunloe Castle
426	Galgorm Manor
427	Glassdrumman Lodge
428	Gregans Castle
429	Hibernian Hotel
430	Hunters Hotel
431	Kinnitty Castle
432	Liss Ard Lake Lodge

PAGE	HOTEL
433	Longfields
434	Markree Castle
435	Marlfield House
436	Moyglare Manor
437	Muckross Park Hotel
438	Nuremore Hotel
439	Park Hotel Kenmare
440	Rosleague Manor
441	Sand House Hotel
442	Sheen Falls Lodge
443	Tinakilly House
444	Tyrella House
445	Waterford Castle

MALIN HEAD
Rathlin Island
Aran Island
Donegal Bay
Achill Island
Dundalk Bay
STRATHCLYDE
Stranraer
To Douglas (Summer Only)
NORTHERN IRELAND
DONEGAL
SLIGO
MAYO
LEITRIM
ROSCOMMON
CAVAN
MONAGHAN
LOUTH
LONGFORD
CONNEMARA NATIONAL PARK
LOUGH NEAGH
Moville
Portballintrae
Portstewart
Bushmills
Ballycastle
COLERAINE
Cushendall
Buncrana
Eglinton
Milford
Limavady
LONDONDERRY
Ballymoney
Garvagh
Glenarm
Dungloe
Letterkenny
Dungiven
Portglenone
BALLYMENA
LARNE
Glenties
Ballybofey
Strabane
Maghera
Magherafelt
Toome
Ballyclare
Glencolumbkille
Carrick
Killybegs
Donegal
Moneymore
Antrim
Templepatrick
Whitehead
Carrick-fergus
Rossnowlagh
Ballyshannon
Bundoran
Omagh
Cookstown
Belfast (International)
BELFAST
Belfast City
BANGOR
Donaghadee
Millisle
Kesh
Dromore
Dungannon
Coalisland
LISBURN
Newtownards
Irvinestown
Comber
Belmullet
Dromore West
Manorhamilton
Enniskillen
Aughnacloy
Craigavon
LURGAN
Hillsborough
Dromore
SLIGO
Ballysadare
Belcoo
Fivemiletown
PORTADOWN
Ballynahinch
Bangor Erris
Collooney
ARMAGH
Banbridge
Strangford
Portaferry
Downpatrick
Monaghan
Crossmolina
Ballina
Newtown Butler
Clones
Newtownhamilton
Rathfriland
Castlewellan
Newcastle
Castlebaldwin
Tobercurry
Belturbet
Castleblayney
NEWRY
Warrenpoint
Annalong
Kirkeel
Mallaranny
Foxford
Charlestown
Boyle
Carrick-on-Shannon
Cavan
Castlebar
Connaught Regional
Ballaghaderreen
Mohill
Carrickmacross
DUNDALK
Westport
Louisburgh
Knock
Ballyhaunis
Tulsk
Castlerea
Strokestown
Virginia
Ardee
Castlebellingham
Claremorris
Granard
Longford
Ballymoe
Ballinrobe
Meathas Troim (Edgeworthstown)
Ceanannus Mór (Kells)
DROGHEDA
Letterfrack
Clifden
Dunmore
Lanesborough
Roscommon
Slane
Athleague
Navan
Recess
Maam Cross
Headford
Tuam
Ballymahon
Athboy
Balbriggan

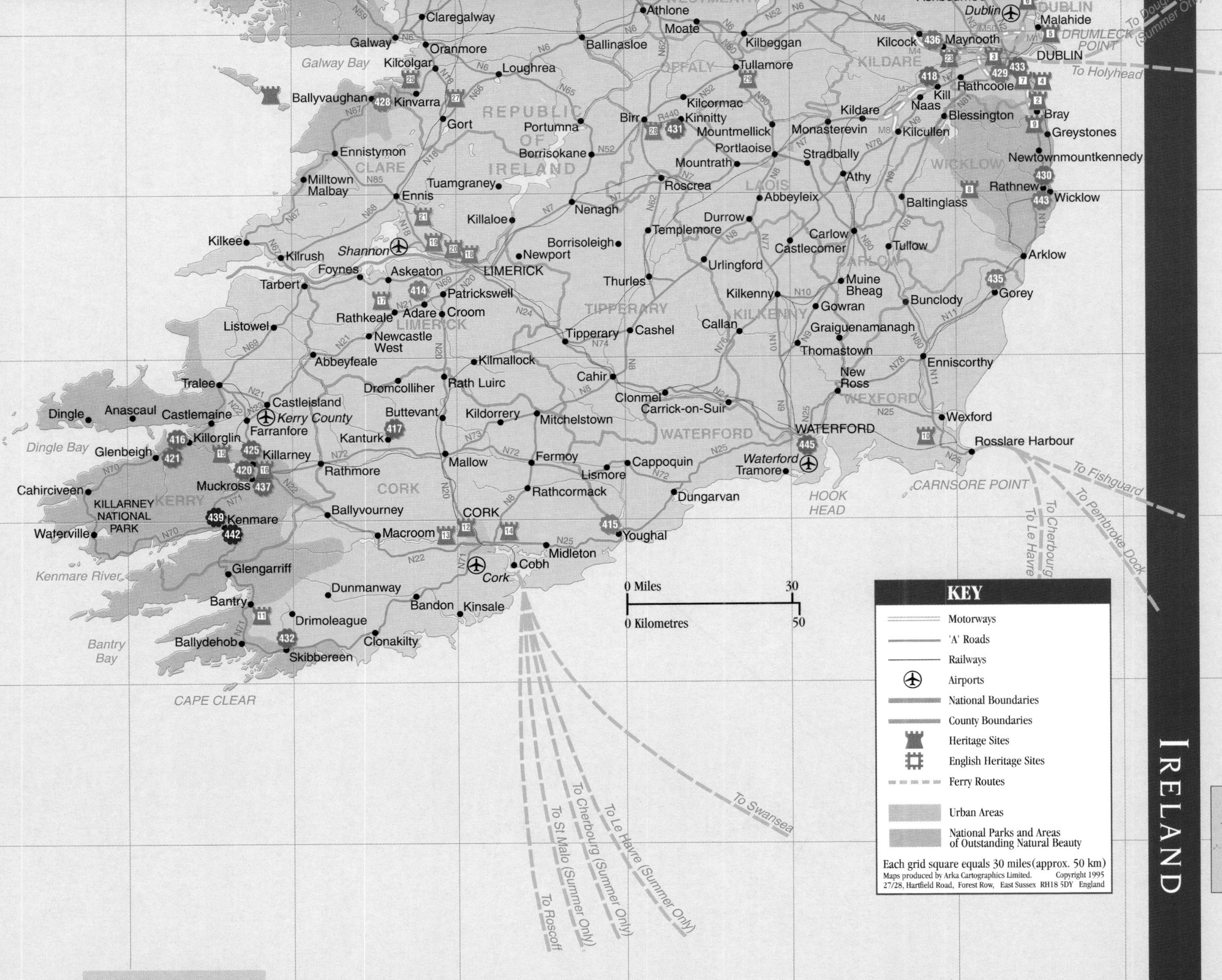
KEY
Motorways
'A' Roads
Railways
Airports
National Boundaries
County Boundaries
Heritage Sites
English Heritage Sites
Ferry Routes
Urban Areas
National Parks and Areas of Outstanding Natural Beauty
Each grid square equals 30 miles (approx. 50 km)
Maps produced by Arka Cartographics Limited. Copyright 1995
27/28, Hartfield Road, Forest Row, East Sussex RH18 5DY England
0 Miles 30
0 Kilometres 50
REPUBLIC OF IRELAND
DUBLIN
Dublin
Malahide
DRUMLECK POINT
To Holyhead
Maynooth
Kilcock
Ashbourne
KILDARE
Rathcoole
Kill
Naas
Blessington
Bray
Greystones
Newtownmountkennedy
Kildare
Monasterevin
Kilcullen
WICKLOW
Rathnew
Wicklow
Baltinglass
Arklow
Athlone
WESTMEATH
Moate
Kilbeggan
Tullamore
OFFALY
Ballinasloe
Kilcormac
Kinnitty
Birr
Mountmellick
Portlaoise
Mountrath
Stradbally
Athy
LAOIS
Abbeyleix
Roscrea
Durrow
Templemore
Carlow
Castlecomer
Tullow
CARLOW
Urlingford
Thurles
Borrisoleigh
Kilkenny
KILKENNY
Muine Bheag
Gowran
Bunclody
Gorey
Callan
Graiguenamanagh
Thomastown
Enniscorthy
New Ross
WEXFORD
Wexford
Rosslare Harbour
CARNSORE POINT
To Fishguard
To Pembroke Dock
To Cherbourg
To Le Havre
Claregalway
Galway
Oranmore
Galway Bay
Kilcolgar
Loughrea
Ballyvaughan
Kinvarra
Gort
Portumna
Borrisokane
Ennistymon
CLARE
Milltown Malbay
Tuamgraney
Ennis
Killaloe
Nenagh
Kilkee
Kilrush
Shannon
Newport
LIMERICK
Foynes
Askeaton
Tarbert
Patrickswell
Adare
Croom
Rathkeale
LIMERICK
Listowel
Newcastle West
Abbeyfeale
Kilmallock
TIPPERARY
Tipperary
Cashel
Cahir
Clonmel
Carrick-on-Suir
WATERFORD
Tralee
Dromcolliher
Rath Luirc
Castleisland
Kerry County
Farranfore
Dingle
Anascaul
Castlemaine
Buttevant
Kildorrery
Mitchelstown
Dingle Bay
Glenbeigh
Killorglin
Killarney
Kanturk
Rathmore
Mallow
Fermoy
Lismore
Cappoquin
WATERFORD
Waterford
Tramore
HOOK HEAD
Cahirciveen
KILLARNEY NATIONAL PARK
KERRY
Muckross
Kenmare
CORK
Rathcormack
Dungarvan
Ballyvourney
CORK
Waterville
Macroom
Youghal
Midleton
Cork
Cobh
Kenmare River
Glengarriff
Dunmanway
Bantry
Bandon
Kinsale
Drimoleague
Bantry Bay
Ballydehob
Skibbereen
Clonakilty
CAPE CLEAR
To Swansea
To Le Havre (Summer Only)
To Cherbourg (Summer Only)
To St Malo (Summer Only)
To Roscoff

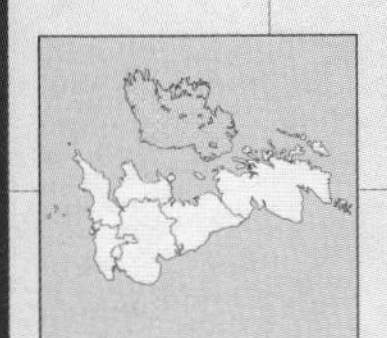

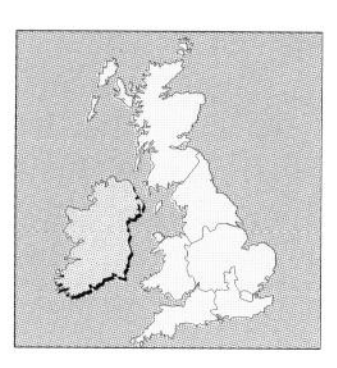

Ross Castle, Killarney, Co Kerry

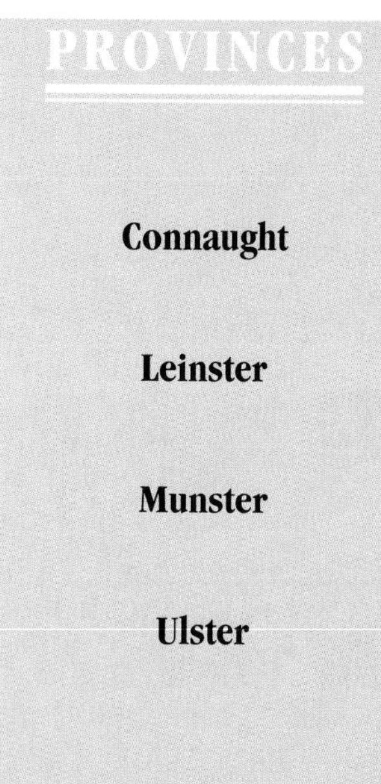

PROVINCES

Connaught

Leinster

Munster

Ulster

The island of Ireland has a special place in the hearts of people throughout the English-speaking world. Today it is easier than ever to come from the United States to the land of your ancestors and your dreams. Flights from the major British airports arrive nearly every hour, and there are excellent ferry services from six British ports.

Dublin traces its history back to Ptolemy in 140 AD. In the 9th century, the conquering Vikings named it Dubh Linn, meaning Dark Pool. Today in Dublin you can marvel at Georgian beauty, follow the Cultural Heritage Trail, or the Ulysses journey from Joyce Tower in Sandycove. In Belfast, look out for Queen's University, the marbled City Hall, framed against Ben Madigan and the distant blue hills. Admire the town's fine linen. Mile for mile, these cities give you so much enjoyment in walking, talking, eating, drinking and shopping.

From the Mountains of Mourne and the Giant's Causeway of Finn MacCoul in the North to the Ring of Kerry in the far Southwest, you will find ancient towns and unspoiled hills and countryside. There are magnificent varied landscapes, rugged mountains, lush green fields, deep blue lakes and uncrowded sandy beaches. Because the air is pure and clean, your eye and your camera will see it all clearly. You can trace the history from monuments older than the Pyramids, through ancient Celtic earthen castles, to Roman forts, to medieval churches and towers.

Above all, Ireland is a place to enjoy on holiday. The food is made with wholesome, good fresh local ingredients, and served in generous portions. The people are interested in their visitors, and enjoy meeting them. The country is proud of its reputation as "Ireland of the Welcomes" and does its utmost to deserve it.

Castles, Stately Homes, Historic Houses

Avondale Forest Park, Co Kildare. Built in 1777, this was the home of Charles Stewart Parnell.

Belfast City Hall, Donegal Street. Rectangular classical Renaissance style, huge copper dome. Completed 1906.

Belfast, Stormont Parliament Building, Upper Newtonards Road. Erected 1928. Guided tours.

Carra Castle, Co Antrim. Here Sean the Proud O'Neill was slain by the MacDonnells in 1567.

Castletown House, Co Kildare. This impressive Palladian mansion was built in 1722.

Charleville Castle, Co Offaly. Designed by Francis Johnson in 1798. The first and finest Gothic house in Ireland.

Clonalis House, Castlerea. Ancestral home of the O'Conor clan, Europe's oldest family. Since Feredach the Just in 75 AD, the O'Conors have provided 24 kings to Connacht, 11 high kings to Ireland and one US presidential candidate (in 1872).

Dublin Castle. Built 1208-1220 on a Viking stronghold site. 13th century Record Tower. Guided tours of State Apartments.

Custom House, Dublin. James Gandon's first Georgian masterpiece in Dublin. Built 1791, re-opened to the public in 1991.

Guinness Brewery, James Street, Dublin. Brewing Ireland's most famous beverage since 1759.

Tailors Hall, off Christchurch Place, Dublin. Built 1706, the last surviving guild hall in Dublin.

Kilkenny Castle. The first stone castle was built in 1204. Main seat of the Butler family from 1391.

Lismore Castle, Co Waterford. Overlooking the River Blackwater, this is the Irish seat of the Duke of Devonshire.

Roscommon Castle. Built in 1269, destroyed by fire in 1273, rebuilt in 1280.

Slayne Castle, Co Meath. George IV's writing desk is here in the home of his mistress, Lady Conyngham.

Tullynally Castle, Co Westmeath. Home of the Earls of Longford since the 17th c. Woods and walled gardens.

Museums, Galleries & Modern Highspots

Carrowmere Megalithic Tombs, nr Sligo. Considered to be Europe's greatest concentration of megalithic tombs.

Celtworld, Tramore, Co Waterford. Three-dimensional images are used to tell the stirring story of Ireland's past.

Doll Museum, Leamybrien, Co Waterford. Antique dolls and toys dating back to 1820.

Civic Museum, South William Street, Dublin. Dublin life from Vikings to modern times.

Marsh's Library, Dublin, beside St Patrick's Cathedral. The oldest public library in Ireland.

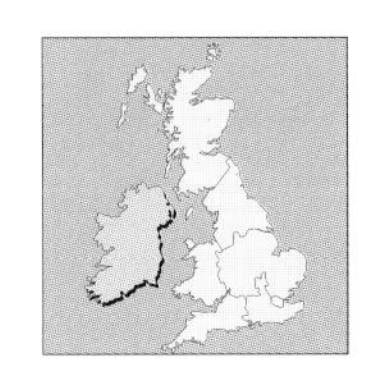

TOURIST OFFICE INFORMATION

Further information about Ireland will be gladly supplied by:

Bord Failte (Irish Tourist Board)
Baggot Street Bridge, Dublin 2

Tel: 1 676 5871

150 New Bond Street, London W1Y 0AQ

Tel: 0171 493 3201
Fax: 0171 493 9065

Northern Ireland Tourist Board
St Anne's Court, 59 North Street, Belfast BT1 1NB

Tel: 01232 231221

For international offices, please turn to page 480

Fine stone carvings of clergymen, warriors and sacrificial animals, some with distinctly pagan motifs dating back from the 8th or 9th century. These figures are part of a 12th century ruined church on White Island off the coast of Fermanagh.

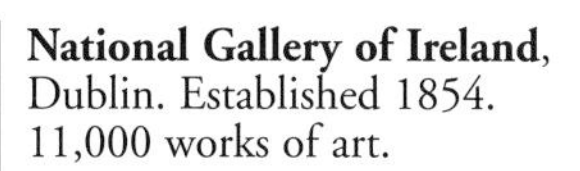

National Gallery of Ireland, Dublin. Established 1854. 11,000 works of art.

National Museum of Ireland, Dublin. Great treasures of early Irish art include the Tara Brooch and the Ardagh Chalice.

Royal Irish Academy, Dublin. Irish manuscript library contains Psalter of St Columcille and Vulgate version of the Psalms.

Shaw Birthplace, Dublin, 33 Synge Street. Preserved as a small Victorian house and garden.

Galway City Museum. Contains many ancient artefacts.

Roth House, Co Kilkenny. A museum in a Tudor merchant's house.

Irish National Heritage Park, Ferrycarrig, Co Wexford. A creation of settlements from pre-history to Vikings and into the Middle Ages.

Russborough, Co Wicklow. This noble house is the home of the famous Beit art collection.

Ulster Museum, Botanical Gardens, Belfast. Celtic finds from 200 B.C. Paintings by Breughel, Turner, Gainsborough.

Westgate Medieval Experience. The town's ancient history presented audio-visually within an early 13th c gate tower.

Churches, Cathedrals, Abbeys & Monasteries

St Patrick's Cathedral, Dublin. Built in 1191, on the site of a church dating from 450 AD. Jonathan Swift was Dean 1713 to 1745. See his tomb and epitaph.

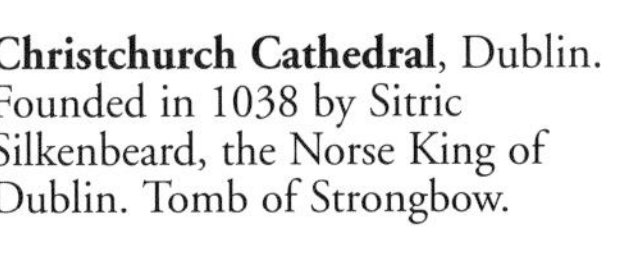

Armagh City, Cathedral of St Patrick. Burial place of Ireland's High King Brian Boru.

Belfast, St Anne's Cathedral. Built in 1898 in neo-Romanesque basilican style. Magnificent marbled nave. Fine carvings.

Belfast, St Patrick's Church, Donegall Street. Late Victorian church with pre-Raphaelite triptych.

Black Abbey, Kilkenny. A Dominican friary founded in 1225.

Downpatrick, Co Down. Church of Ireland Cathedral. Burial place of St Patrick. 10th c high cross, 11th c Celtic font.

Mellifont Abbey, Co Louth. Ireland's first Cistercian Abbey, founded in 1142.

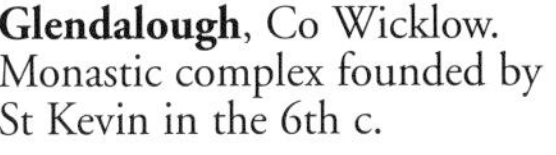

Christchurch Cathedral, Dublin. Founded in 1038 by Sitric Silkenbeard, the Norse King of Dublin. Tomb of Strongbow.

St Mary's Pro-Cathedral, Dublin. The main Catholic church in Dublin, dedicated in 1825.

Glendalough, Co Wicklow. Monastic complex founded by St Kevin in the 6th c.

Knock. In 1879, several local people saw a vision of the Blessed Virgin Mary. Pilgrims visit.

St Olave's, Waterford. 9th c church.

St Canice's Cathedral, Kilkenny. Completed in 1285 and still in use.

St Brigid's, Co Kildare. Medieval cathedral beautifully restored to former splendour.

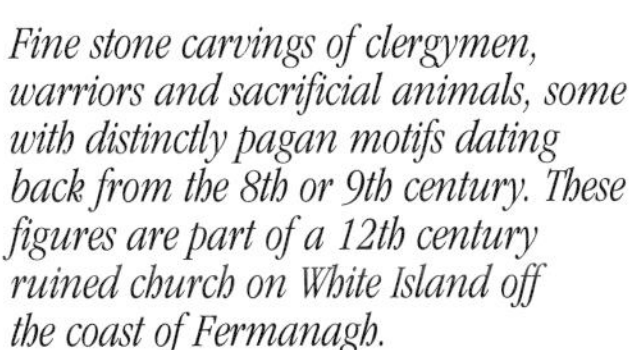

Megalithic site on the Carrowmore Islands, Co Donegal.

Sport & Outdoors

Angling. Come and match your wits against wild fish in some of Europe's cleanest rivers, lakes and seas. Salmon and trout abound.

Curragh Racecourse, Newbridge. The Irish Derby is run here each year.

Golf. Magnificent courses, challenging yet uncrowded throughout Ireland.

Hurling. This ancient, traditional sport is a fast, exciting spectacle played in many towns and villages.

Racehorse breeding and training. This is centred on Co Kildare, with many racecourses throughout the country.

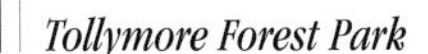

Tollymore Forest Park

“ Lovely escape – we both loved our stay here in paradise – will return ”

Mary Harkins, Texas

ADARE MANOR

18th century manor

Adare,
Co Limerick
Republic of Ireland

Telephone +353 (0)61 396566
Fax +353 (0)61 396124

GENERAL MANAGER

Stephen Quinn

ROOM RATES

16 Standard Doubles/Twins Ir£110 - £195
35 Deluxe Doubles/Twins Ir£124 - £225
8 State Rooms Ir£144 - £265
5 Dunraven State Rooms Ir£160 - £295
Includes VAT

CHARGE/CREDIT CARDS

• DC • MC • VI

ACCOLADES

R.A.C. ★★★★★
A.A. ★★★★ ❀

FACILITIES

Garden, indoor pool, gym, health & beauty, sauna, snooker, limousine service, fishing, riding, golf, clay pigeon shooting, heli-pad

RESTRICTIONS

None

ATTRACTIONS

Adare village, Bunratty Castle and Folk Park, Curraghchase Forest Park, Ring of Kerry, Cliffs of Moher

AFFILIATIONS

Small Luxury Hotels

NEAREST

MAJOR CITY:
Limerick - 8 miles/20 mins

MAJOR AIRPORT:
Shannon - 22 miles/45 mins

RAILWAY STATION:
Limerick - 8 miles/20 mins

RESERVATIONS

Toll free in US: 800-462-3273

ACCESS CODES

AMADEUS/SYSTEM 1 LX SNNADA
WORLDSPAN/SAHARA LX SNNAM
AXESS LX 5590
SABRE LX 30170
APOLLO LX 8211

Internationally renowned hotel set in a picturesque thatched village

The former family seat of the Earls of Dunraven, this 18th century manor stands along the meandering river Maigue amid 840 acres of formal gardens and lush parklands. Professional staff will pamper you in old world style. Candlelight dinners, afternoon teas, or a sing-along in the manor's Tack Room pub are sure to create fond memories.

Adare Manor, a rare RAC five-star hotel, was recently listed in Conde Nast Traveller's Top 100 of the World's Best and ranked fourth among the Top 20 Foreign Resorts in their annual readers choice awards.

Encompassing 64 elegant bedrooms and over 50 individually carved fireplaces, the manor resembles a museum of architecture.

The hotel has entered a new era with the opening of Adare Golf Club. The 18 hole championship golf course designed by Robert Trent Jones Sr measures 7138 yards off the championship tees.

The indoor pool and fitness centre as well as the outdoor pursuits of horseback riding, fishing and clay pigeon shooting are sure to meet your needs for rest and relaxation.

Located only 22 miles from Shannon airport, Adare Manor offers the finest of Irish hospitality with plenty of excitement for the experienced traveller.

LOCATION

Adare Manor is located on the Killarney road (N21) south of Limerick city.

"They are surrounded by the finest fish in the sea"

The Guardian

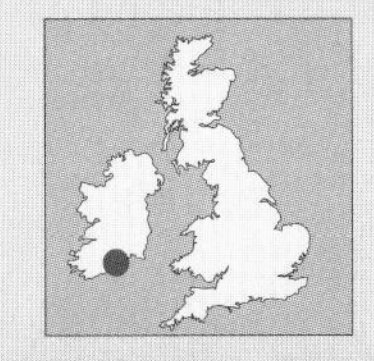

Restaurant with accommodation

AHERNES

Luxury rooms with a "seafood view"

Aherne's, in the heart of the picturesque Youghal (pronounced Yawl), the old historic walled port at the mouth of the River Blackwater. Aherne's is a family pub that the Fitzgibbons (3rd generation) have changed into an internationally renowned restaurant that specialises in the freshest locally landed seafood. Lobsters, crab, sole, salmon, monkfish, crab, mussels, clams all feature on menus that change daily.

The ten luxurious en suite bedrooms, generous in size, have been tastefully decorated and furnished. They combine modern features (six-foot beds, hairdryer, TV, direct-dial telephone and trouser press) with carefully chosen antiques that blend perfectly together.

East Cork is a primary tourist area on the splendid south coast of Ireland. Ancient historic buildings include the still used 12th century Collegiate Church, the unique Clock Tower and Ireland's first post-Norman University, founded in 1464.

There is a wide range of leisure pursuits in the immediate area: 18-hole golf course, deep sea and river angling, riding and other equestrian activities, two Blue Flag beaches and superb walks through beautiful countryside. From the moment you are first greeted by the family, you will find Aherne's is a marvellous place to relax and enjoy yourself.

LOCATION

On the N25, on Youghal's main street.

163 North Main Street,
Youghal, Co Cork
Republic of Ireland

Telephone +353 (0)24 92424
Fax +353 (0)24 93633

PROPRIETORS

The Fitzgibbon Family

ROOM RATES

Single occupancy	*Ir£55 - £60*
10 Doubles	*Ir£40 - £50*

Includes full breakfast and VAT

CHARGE/CREDIT CARDS

• *DC* • *MC* • *VI*

ACCOLADES

R.A.C. ★★ + Merit Awards H C & R
A.A. QQQQ Selected
The Good Hotel Guide

FACILITIES

1 meeting room/max 20 people
Golf and fishing nearby

RESTRICTIONS

No pets

ATTRACTIONS

Jamieson Heritage Centre,
Cork,
Waterford Crystal,
Blarney Castle

AFFILIATIONS

Ireland's Blue Book
Robert Reid & Associates

NEAREST

MAJOR CITY:
Cork - 30 miles/45 mins

MAJOR AIRPORT:
Cork - 30 miles/45 mins

RAILWAY STATION:
Cork - 30 miles/45 mins

RESERVATIONS

Direct with hotel

ACCESS CODES

Not applicable

"The days at Ard-na-Sidhe are the highlight of our visit in Ireland"

Hans Jürgen Linschind

ARD NA SIDHE

Victorian country house

Caragh Lake, Killorglin,
Co Kerry
Republic of Ireland

Telephone +353 (0)66 69105
Fax +353 (0)66 69282

RESIDENT MANAGER

Kathleen Dowling

ROOM RATES

2 Singles Ir £68
15 Doubles/Twins Ir £102 - £118
3 Superiors Ir £132
Includes full breakfast and VAT

CHARGE/CREDIT CARDS

• DC • MC • VI

ACCOLADES

I.T.B. ★★★★
R.A.C. ★★★★ + Merit Award H
National Garden Competition Winner

FACILITIES

Garden, fishing, boating
Golf nearby

RESTRICTIONS

No children under 10 years
No pets
Closed 1 October – 30 April

ATTRACTIONS

Ring of Kerry,
Caragh Lake,
Killarney National Park,
Dingle Peninsula

AFFILIATIONS

Killarney Hotels Ltd

NEAREST

MAJOR CITY:
Cork - 91 miles/2 hrs 10 mins

MAJOR AIRPORT:
Shannon - 95 miles/2½ hrs
Cork - 70 miles/2¼ hrs

RAILWAY STATION:
Killarney - 17 miles/40 mins

RESERVATIONS

Toll free in US: 800-221-1074

ACCESS CODES

Not applicable

The house of your dreams in an award-winning garden

Ard na Sidhe translates as "the Hill of the Fairies". This 20-bedroom mansion hotel on the edge of Caragh Lake at Killarney has no lack of the modern facilities you would expect from Killarney Hotels, one of Ireland's leading leisure groups. It offers high standards of cuisine and service. It stands in an award-winning garden, on the shores of a stunningly beautiful lake. Yet it also has a mystic history that reaches deep into the country's distant and magical past.

Lady Gordon, a lady of titled Irish lineage, built the house in 1913. She enlisted the help of a contractor from Killorglin, using local workmen. All the materials were of Irish origin, except the greeny-grey Westmorland roof slates. The house is long and low and gabled, with casement windows set in stone mullions, "and never", said Lady Gordon, "looked new." The ghost of her ancestor, Bess Stokes, is said to haunt the grounds, but it was "The Hill of the Fairies" long before Bess.

The house fits harmoniously into superbly romantic scenery, beside Ireland's highest mountain, McGillicuddy's Reeks. All around is magnificently beautiful countryside for fishing, cycling and boating on the lakes. Several of the country's finest golf courses are within easy driving range.

At the Ard na Sidhe you will enjoy the full range of holiday leisure and historical touring attractions that have made Killarney one of the best-loved places in the world. And there is an extra special something in the unique and mystical history of The Hill of the Fairies.

LOCATION

Right at the edge of the beautiful Caragh Lake at Killarney.

" Exceptional, food and service of this quality in such delightful surroundings is a rare treat "

Georgina Campbell

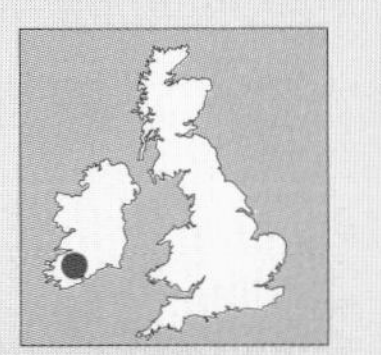

17th century manor

ASSOLAS COUNTRY HOUSE

A prize-winning guest house with a chef and gardens of distinction

Assolas is a small 17th century manor set in prize winning gardens, with its own stretch of river complete with swans. The house has belonged to the Bourke family for several generations, and is now run as a guest house by Joe and Hazel Bourke.

It is very much the family home where guests are warmly welcomed to afternoon tea in the garden, pre-dinner drinks in the drawing room and coffee beside the fire.

Hazel is internationally recognised as a chef of distinction. She uses herbs, vegetables and soft fruit from the walled garden, combined with local ingredients. She cooks without over-elaboration to emphasise the intensity of the natural fresh flavours.

Assolas has nine guest bedrooms. Six of the rooms are standard, three of which are in the main house, and the other three in a restored stone building in the courtyard. They have three superior rooms, which are the largest and command the finest views.

You really don't want to go beyond the garden gates, but if you wish to, one of the family will be there with maps, suggestions and routes to see the best of the south west. Gardens, castles, lakes and mountain walks are all to be explored in the vicinity. Hidden away in the rolling country side, Assolas forms a central residence from which to visit Killarney and the peninsulas, Blarney, Cork and Kinsale.

LOCATION

Off the N72, 8 miles west of Mallow.

Kanturk,
Co Cork
Republic of Ireland

Telephone +353 (0)29 50015
Fax +353 (0)29 50795

PROPRIETORS

Joe, Hazel and the Bourke Family

ROOM RATES

Single occupancy	*Ir £50 - £75*
6 Doubles/Twins	*Ir £80 - £110*
3 Superior	*Ir £110 - £150*

Includes full breakfast and VAT

CHARGE/CREDIT CARDS

• *DC* • *MC* • *VI*

ACCOLADES

I.T.B. ★★★★ Guest House
A.A. QQQQQ
The Good Hotel Guide

FACILITIES

Garden, croquet, tennis, boating, fishing
1 meeting room/max 28 people
Riding and complimentary golf course nearby

RESTRICTIONS

Children - Special rate sharing with adult accommodation
Pets welcome but not allowed in the house

ATTRACTIONS

Annesgrove Gardens, Blackwater Valley, Rock of Cashel, Donnervaile Park, Blarney, Cork, Kinsale, Lakes of Killarney

AFFILIATIONS

Ireland's Blue Book

NEAREST

MAJOR CITY:
Cork - 30 miles/1 hr

MAJOR AIRPORT:
Cork - 30 miles/1 hr
Shannon - 65 miles/1½ hrs

RAILWAY STATION:
Mallow - 10 miles/15 mins

RESERVATIONS

Toll free in US: 800-223-6510

ACCESS CODES

Not applicable

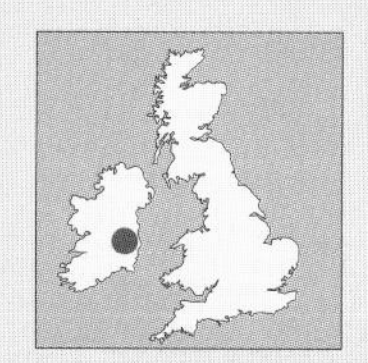

" Barberstown Castle will be remembered by one and all as living up to our reputation – Ireland of the Céad Míle Fáilte "

Mary Petrie, Kildare

BARBERSTOWN CASTLE

13th century castle

Straffan,
Co Kildare
Republic of Ireland

Telephone +353 (0)1 628 8157
Fax +353 (0)1 627 7027

PROPRIETORS
Kenneth and Catherine Healy

ROOM RATES
Single Occupancy Ir £65
10 Doubles Ir £110
Includes full breakfast and VAT
Plus service charge 10%

CHARGE/CREDIT CARDS

• MC • VI

ACCOLADES
I.T.B. ★★★
R.A.C. ★★★ + *Merit Awards H C & R*
A.A. ★★★ ❀❀ 75%
A.A. Courtesy & Care Award 1995

FACILITIES
Gardens
Golf, riding and fishing nearby

RESTRICTIONS
No children under 12 years
No facilities for disabled guests
No pets
(Exceptions to every rule)

ATTRACTIONS
Dublin, Racing,
National Stud Farm,
Castletown House,
Kildare Country Club

AFFILIATIONS
Ireland's Blue Book

NEAREST
MAJOR CITY:
Dublin - 15 miles/35 mins

MAJOR AIRPORT:
Dublin - 20 miles/45 mins

RAILWAY STATION:
Maynooth - 4 miles/10 mins

RESERVATIONS
Direct with hotel

ACCESS CODES
Not applicable

750 years of Irish history and as individual as they come

Barberstown Castle is one of the first great Irish country houses to open up its splendour to the outside world. The castle keep was built in the early 13th century by Nicholas Barby. The Elizabethan Wing, built in the second half of the 16th century, is one of the few houses in this area that has been in continuous occupation for over 400 years. The Victorian House, built in the 1830's by Hugh Barton, completes a heritage that embraces over 750 years of Irish history, inviting you to discover the unique attractions of this Irish castle.

The restaurant at Barberstown is renowned for its creative food. Each of the en suite bedrooms has been decorated in an individual style and dedicated to the ordinary and extraordinary people who have lived within its walls.

Golf can be arranged at the Kildare Country Club and at several other courses nearby. Expert equestrian tuition as well as hunting, racing, tennis, gym, squash and clay pigeon shooting are all available in the area as are coarse, trout and salmon fishing on the River Liffey with ghillies available. For the less active, relax in an atmosphere of pure calm and tranquillity, deep in the heart of County Kildare, yet only 30 minutes from the centre of Dublin.

LOCATION

Travelling south on N7, take the turn for Straffan at Kill. Travelling west on N4 take the turn for Straffan at Maynooth.

"It's one of those places where you hope it rains all day so you have an excuse to snuggle indoors"

Ian Cruikshank, Canada

Coaching inn and restaurant

THE BUSHMILLS INN

In the village that is home to the world's oldest distillery

The Giant's Causeway Coast boasts the most spectacular coastline in the British Isles – wide sandy beaches are washed by Atlantic rollers, neat fishing harbours nestle between craggy cliffs and grassy dunes provide a superb environment for wildlife. The area is truly a golfer's paradise with no less than seven courses, including Royal Portrush, nearby, while for anglers the River Bush is almost within casting distance of the courtyard.

The cosy glow of a turf fire is the first of many features such as the gas lamps and the circular library, with its intriguing secret room, which give the inn a unique character. Bedrooms, all en suite, are individually decorated in comfortable cottage style. Each day the finest fresh foods are served in the restaurant. Created from the old stables it features stripped pine, white-washed walls and intimate snugs. The inn's double stairway leads to a pine panelled gallery where the beauty of the Causeway coast is uniquely displayed in oils and water colours with a permanent exhibition by the acclaimed local artist James McKendry.

For its tasteful restoration in 1988 the hotel was honoured with the British Airways Tourism Award. Bushmills has come to epitomise the true spirit of Ulster hospitality.

LOCATION

On the A4 Antrim coast road. From Ballymoney take the B62 turning right on to the B17 from Coleraine. Follow the Giant's Causeway signs. Main hotel entrance and car park is through arch.

25 Main Street, Bushmills,
Co Antrim BT57 8QA
Northern Ireland

Telephone +44 (0)12657 32339
Fax +44 (0)12657 32048

OWNERS

Roy Bolton and Richard Wilson

ROOM RATES

1 Single	*£48 - £52*
9 Doubles	*£78 - £85*

Includes full breakfast and VAT

CHARGE/CREDIT CARDS

ACCOLADES

N.I.T.B. ★★★
R.A.C. ★★★
Taste of Ulster

FACILITIES

Garden patio
2 meeting rooms/max 100 people
Golf, riding, fishing and walking nearby

RESTRICTIONS

No facilities for disabled guests

ATTRACTIONS

Giant's Causeway,
Dunluce Castle,
Old Bushmills Distillery,
Carrick-a-Rede rope bridge

AFFILIATIONS

Independent

NEAREST

MAJOR CITY:
Belfast - 60 miles/1 hr 10 mins

MAJOR AIRPORT:
Belfast International - 48 miles/1 hr
Londonderry - 32 miles/45 mins

RAILWAY STATION:
Coleraine - 9 miles/15 mins

RESERVATIONS

Direct with hotel

ACCESS CODES

Not applicable

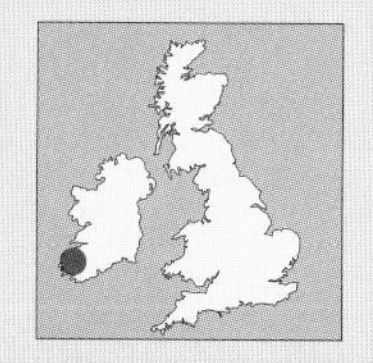

" Fits like a favourite old slipper "

H R Prince

THE CAHERNANE HOTEL

Victorian country house

Muckross Road, Killarney,
Co Kerry
Republic of Ireland

Telephone +353 (0)64 31895
Fax +353 (0)64 34340

MANAGER/DIRECTOR
Conor O'Connell

ROOM RATES

4 Singles	Ir £75 - £85
35 Doubles/Twins	Ir £97.50 - £125
10 Suites	Ir £125 - £160

Includes full breakfast and VAT

CHARGE/CREDIT CARDS

• DC • MC • VI

ACCOLADES
I.T.B. ★★★★
R.A.C. ★★★ + Merit Awards H C & R
A.A. ★★★ ❀❀ 75%

FACILITIES
Croquet, tennis, gardens, conservatory, private fishing
1 meeting room/max 50 people
Golf, riding and walks nearby

RESTRICTIONS
No facilities for disabled guests
Pets must be under control

ATTRACTIONS
Kenmare,
Gap of Dunloe,
Lakes of Killarney,
Sneem,
Ring of Kerry,
Dingle Peninsula

AFFILIATIONS
Manor House Hotels of Ireland

NEAREST
MAJOR CITY:
Cork City - 60 miles/1 hr

MAJOR AIRPORT:
Shannon - 95 miles/3 hrs
Kerry - 10 miles/20 mins

RAILWAY STATION:
Killarney -1 mile/5 mins

RESERVATIONS
Toll free in US: 800-55-CONSORT

ACCESS CODES
CN

As mellow and welcoming as an old friend

The Cahernane Hotel, built in 1877, was once the grand home of the Herbert family who were the Earls of Pembroke. In the last few years the house has been restored and renovated to its former glory.

Pine and blond oak woodwork, over the years worn to a lovely patina, gives a warm feeling to the elegant old house. A blazing log fire and deep sofa in the spacious entrance hall beckons a country house welcome.

At the top of the grand staircase are several comfortable, old-fashioned bedrooms offering superb views of the estate through their tall windows. As a direct contrast to this mellow scene, a wing of modern bedrooms and suites has been added to one side of the house, bridged by a large glass sun lounge. Here, the bright white rooms are tastefully decorated with vibrant purple, blue and mauve curtains and drapes. The bathrooms are spacious, deluxe modern affairs, with luxurious black and brass fittings.

The hotel has two award-winning restaurants, the Herbert and Pembroke rooms, which have been recommended by leading guides, and there are over 270 wines in the wine cellar, including their very own Italian house wine.

LOCATION

From Killarney town centre, take the road to Kenmare and Muckross House/Gardens for 1 mile. The hotel is on the right hand side.

" Paradise on earth, can't wait 'til next time "

Captain John Pettit, Senior Training Captain, British Airways

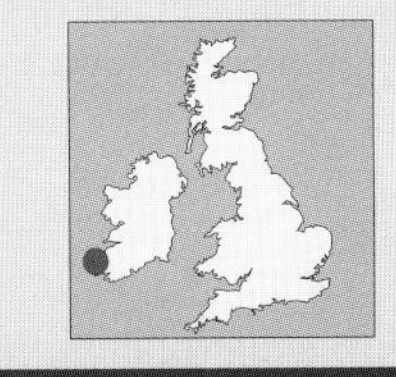

Country house

CARAGH LODGE

A gracious house a stone's throw from the spectacular Ring of Kerry

Less than one mile from the spectacular Ring of Kerry and four miles from the golden beaches of Dingle Bay, Caragh Lodge sits on the shore of Caragh Lake, looking towards the breathtaking slopes of the McGillycuddy Reeks, Ireland's highest mountains.

The en suite rooms are sumptuously decorated with period furnishings and antiques. The converted garden rooms offer guests spectacular views. Each looks on to stunning displays of magnolias, rhododendrons, azaleas, camelias and many rare and sub-tropical shrubs. Exquisite furnishings and welcoming log fires of the main house's lounges provide the perfect place to end the day.

Overlooking the lake, the dining room features only the finest Irish cuisine, freshly caught wild salmon, succulent Kerry lamb, garden grown vegetables and home baked breads, all personally prepared by Mary Gaunt.

Golfers will find Caragh Lodge the perfect base. With no less than eight courses nearby, tee-off times can be easily arranged or organised prior to your stay.

Salmon and brown trout fishing are on the doorstep and two boats are available for guests. Ghillies or any necessary permits for fishing in the two local rivers can be arranged.

LOCATION

Caragh Lodge is situated just off the N70. Travelling from Killorglin towards Glenbeigh, take the road signposted "Caragh Lodge 1 mile". Turn left at the lake, the lodge is on the right.

Caragh Lake, Co Kerry Republic of Ireland

Telephone +353 (0)66 69115
Fax +353 (0)66 69316

OWNER
Mary Gaunt

ROOM RATES
2 Singles Ir £60
8 Doubles/Twins Ir £80 - £95
Includes full breakfast and VAT

CHARGE/CREDIT CARDS

• MC • VI

ACCOLADES
I.T.B. ★★★★
The Good Hotel Guide

FACILITIES
Garden, tennis, sauna, fishing
Golf, riding and beaches nearby

RESTRICTIONS
No children under 7 yrs
No facilities for disabled guests
No pets

ATTRACTIONS
Ring of Kerry, Dingle Peninsula, Killarney, Skelligs Rock

AFFILIATIONS
Ireland's Blue Book

NEAREST
MAJOR CITY:
Cork - 70 miles/2 hrs
MAJOR AIRPORT:
Shannon/Cork - 70 miles/2 hrs
RAILWAY STATION:
Killarney - 16 miles/30 mins

RESERVATIONS
Toll free in US: 800-223-6510

ACCESS CODES
Not applicable

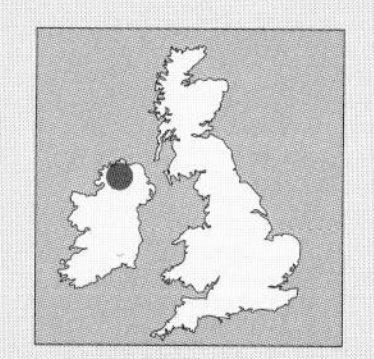

"A sample of world-renowned 'Irish welcome' – combined with excellent cuisine and professional service"

European Diplomat

CASTLE GROVE COUNTRY HOUSE

Georgian house

Ramelton Road,
Letterkenny,
Co Donegal
Republic of Ireland

Telephone +353 (0)74 51118
Fax +353 (0)74 51384

PROPRIETOR
Mary Sweeney

ROOM RATES
Single occupancy Ir £45
7 Doubles/Twins Ir £60 - £90
Includes full breakfast and VAT

CHARGE/CREDIT CARDS

• *DC* • *MC* • *VI*

ACCOLADES
I.T.B. ★★★★

FACILITIES
Garden
1 meeting room/max 20 people
Golf, riding and fishing nearby

RESTRICTIONS
No facilities for disabled guests
No pets

ATTRACTIONS
Glen Veagh National Park,
Atlantic Drive,
Fanad Peninsular,
Giants Causeway

AFFILIATIONS
Independent

NEAREST
MAJOR CITY:
Dublin - 200 miles/4 hrs

MAJOR AIRPORT:
Belfast International - 100 miles/2 hrs
Eglinton - 30 miles/1 hr

RAILWAY STATION:
Derry - 30 miles/1 hr

RESERVATIONS
Direct with hotel

ACCESS CODES
Not applicable

The reward of a stay here is geniality and delicious food

Castle Grove is a fine example of Georgian country house architecture. It stands imperiously in its own parkland estate overlooking Lough Swilly and approached by a mile-long avenue leading up to its classic portico.

First impressions of a grand old home are amply justified; the spacious rooms are well furnished and warmed in winter by great log fires. The reward of a stay here, however, is the geniality of the company and a comfortable informality one would expect of a family home.

Donegal, romanticised in poetry and song for its beauty, is rich in its harvest of good things to eat. The local produce benefits from the rich Irish soil and the seafood from some of the cleanest waters in the world. All this is deliciously placed before you with all the panache to satisfy the exacting taste of the gourmet or as simply as you like.

The en suite bedrooms are large and comfortable with facilities that are entirely up-to-date: direct-dial telephone, hairdryer and so on.

Castle Grove is also a perfect base for field sports. Fishing can be arranged on the river or the lough with boats and ghillie supplied. Shooting, too, but this time the ghillie provides the dogs. And, of course, there is golf nearby.

So where better to enjoy the fruits and pleasures of Donegal than Castle Grove where a 'Céad Míle Fáilte' always awaits you.

LOCATION

From Letterkenny N245 on Ramelton Road. Pick up sign about 4 km from town – it indicates exit to the right. Entrance gates 600 yards to right.

" Cromleach Lodge is undoubtedly one of Ireland's finest restaurants (with accommodation to match) and well worth a special journey "

Georgina Campbell, food critic

Modern country house hotel CROMLEACH LODGE HOTEL

Unsurpassed views across the lake to the mountains

Cromleach Lodge is set in the hills just above Lough Arrow, with the Carrowkeel Cairns meeting the ever-changing sky beyond – a spectacular vista of mountains, lake and valley.

Justly renowned for its fine cuisine, splendid accommodation and the beauty of its surroundings, this modern hotel and restaurant is the discerning traveller's perfect choice.

Resident proprietors Moira and Christy Tighe, along with their dedicated staff, insist on the utmost comfort for all their guests. The en suite bedrooms/mini suites are exceptionally spacious – each is decorated in its own colour scheme, and each overlooks the beautiful views across the lake to the mountains.

Cromleach Lodge's pièce de resistance is its restaurant, where dishes created by Moira Tighe are a gastronomic delight, rivalled only by the views from the table. Food critic Helen Lucy Burke described her pudding of white chocolate mousse thus: "it was like 24-carat white gold creamed or liquidised magnolias" – an indication of the standards that diners can anticipate.

Ramble carelessly through fields and woodlands and absorb the tranquil silence broken only by the song of a thrush or a twig falling from a tree.

LOCATION

Take the N4 to Castlebaldwin, 17 miles east of Sligo. Then follow signs.

Castlebaldwin, Boyle,
Co Sligo
Republic of Ireland

Telephone +353 (0)71 65155
Fax +353 (0)71 65455

PROPRIETORS

Christy and Moira Tighe

ROOM RATES

Single occupancy Ir £60 - £100
10 Doubles/Twins Ir £90 - £130
Includes full breakfast and VAT

CHARGE/CREDIT CARDS

• DC • MC • VI

ACCOLADES

I.T.B. ★★★★
The Good Hotel Guide

FACILITIES

Garden, heli-pad, fishing
1 meeting room/max 14 people
Walking and hill climbing nearby

RESTRICTIONS

No children under 7 years allowed in dining rooms after 7 pm
No facilities for disabled guests
No pets

ATTRACTIONS

Lough Arrow - fishing,
Carrowkeel Passage Grave Cemetery,
Lough Gill, Yeat's Country,
Lissadell House

AFFILIATIONS

Independent

NEAREST

MAJOR CITY:
Dublin - 120 miles/2 ½ hrs

MAJOR AIRPORT:
Dublin - 120 miles/2 ½ hrs

RAILWAY STATION:
Boyle - 10 miles/20 mins

RESERVATIONS

Direct with hotel

ACCESS CODES

Not applicable

"Her Royal Highness greatly enjoyed the evening, and thought that the setting was wonderful"

John McCaffrey, Director, ABSA

THE DUNADRY HOTEL

Country inn and leisure centre

2 Islandreagh Drive,
Dunadry,
Co Antrim BT41 2HA
Northern Ireland

Telephone +44 (0)1849 432474
Fax +44 (0)1849 433389

GENERAL MANAGER
John Mooney

ROOM RATES

Single occupancy	*£90*
45 Doubles/Twins	*£112*
8 Executive Singles	*£110*
14 Executive Doubles	*£138*

Includes full breakfast, country club facilities, and VAT

CHARGE/CREDIT CARDS

• *DC* • *MC* • *VI*

ACCOLADES
N.I.T.B. ★★★★

FACILITIES
Garden, croquet, gym, jacuzzi, indoor pool, health & beauty, solarium, crazy golf, bowling green, fishing
12 meeting rooms/max 350 people
Golf and riding nearby

RESTRICTIONS
No pets

ATTRACTIONS
The Antrim coast, Giants Causeway, Carrickfergus Castle, Dunluce Castle

AFFILIATIONS
Independent

NEAREST
MAJOR CITY:
Belfast - 16 miles/20 mins

MAJOR AIRPORT:
Belfast - 5 miles/10 mins

RAILWAY STATION:
Antrim - 4 miles/10 mins

RESERVATIONS
Direct with hotel

ACCESS CODES
Not applicable

Good food and leisure facilities, close to the heart of Belfast

Formerly a linen mill, the original buildings have been tastefully converted into a four-star hotel situated on ten acres of gardens in the beautiful northern Ireland countryside. All 67 bedrooms are extremely spacious and distinctive in design, many having French windows that lead on to the garden or inner courtyard. Eleven executive rooms are also available providing facsimile machines, personal computer points and ample working space.

Guests have the chance to relax in The Dunadry Country Club with facilities including a 12.5 metre swimming pool, spa pool, steam room, fitness conditioning suite and relaxation room. Alternatively, for those who prefer the open air, outdoor activities include a croquet lawn, crazy golf and mountain biking. Fishing is also available on site. The river, Six Mile Water, is a good trout river and it also enjoys a late season run of Dollaghan (Lough Neagh Salmon). Four miles away, you will find the championship Massereene 18 hole golf course.

The Dunadry's restaurant boasts one of the finest reputations in the province. With its wood panelling and open fire, it creates an atmosphere of total relaxation and well-being. The superb menu offers many Ulster specialities and seasonal dishes. You can have a buffet lunch in the Copper Bar and take tea in the afternoon sunshine of the Conservatory.

LOCATION

From Belfast, take M2 northwards to A57. Follow signs for Belfast International Airport, Ballyclare and Templepatrick. Take A6 after Templepatrick – follow signs for Antrim. The Dunadry is 1 mile along A6, on the left.

"Your property is outstanding; its pastoral setting, magnificent"

Lynn Dixson, North Carolina

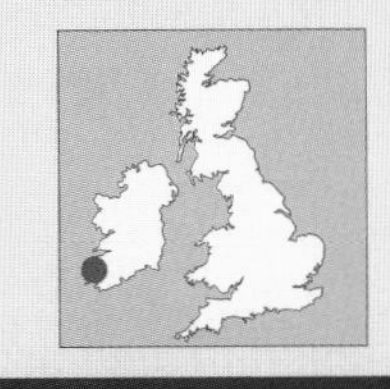

Luxury hotel

DUNLOE CASTLE

Peace and birdsong in a historic Killarney setting

The five-star Hotel Dunloe Castle is located in the midst of a fascinating park landscape. The Green Isle's magic is reflected in the hotel park, a botanic collection of international renown which has won several awards. An unbelievable assortment of flowers and plants flourishes here, and there are Haflinger horses grazing nearby. The park looks out to the famous Gap of Dunloe, and the beauties of unspoilt nature. All smells fresh, the birds sing and time seems to stand still.

For many visitors, the empty shell of the castle keep with its dense clinging ivy has a wild and romantic air which echoes the dark chapters of its past. Today the hotel is a member of the Historic Houses and Gardens Association.

The hotel's furnishings are elegant and comfortable. Its decor is stylish with exquisite details. The 120 rooms and mini-suites, have each been designed to include world class deluxe appointments.

In the most beautiful natural settings, you can enjoy the best of international and Irish cuisine in the gourmet restaurant. A magnificent list of wines is there to complement your meal, and you can have a Guinness, an Irish whiskey or anything else you fancy in the cocktail bar.

There are countless opportunities for leisure activities. Within easy reach there are no fewer than ten golf courses.

LOCATION

Close to the beautiful Lakes of Killarney.

Killarney, Co Kerry, Republic of Ireland

Telephone +353 (0)64 44111
Fax +353 (0)64 44583

RESIDENT MANAGER

Philip Hennessey

ROOM RATES

17 Singles Ir £68
75 Doubles/Twins Ir £98
27 Superior Ir £122
1 Suite Ir £200
Includes full breakfast and VAT

CHARGE/CREDIT CARDS

• DC • MC • VI

ACCOLADES

I.T.B. ★★★★★
R.A.C. ★★★★ *+ Merit Award H*

FACILITIES

Garden, tennis, outdoor pool, sauna, riding, putting green, fishing
4 meeting rooms/max 250 people
Golf nearby

RESTRICTIONS

No facilities for disabled guests
No pets
Closed 2 October – 16 April

ATTRACTIONS

Gap of Dunloe, Dunloe Castle, Ring of Kerry, Dingle Peninsula

AFFILIATIONS

Killarney Hotels Ltd
Historic Houses & Gardens Association

NEAREST

MAJOR CITY:
Cork - 57 miles/1 hr 20 mins

MAJOR AIRPORT:
Cork - 60 miles/1 hr 20 mins

RAILWAY STATION:
Killarney - 7 miles/20 mins

RESERVATIONS

Toll free in US: 800-221-1074

ACCESS CODES

Not applicable

“Above all expectations, wonderful stay”

Elyse Wright, Pennsylvania

GALGORM MANOR

Country residence

Ballymena,
Co Antrim BT42 1EA
Northern Ireland

Telephone +44 (0)1266 881001
Fax +44 (0)1266 880080

PROPRIETORS

Paul and Nicholas Hill

ROOM RATES

Single occupancy	*£79 - £89*
12 Doubles	*£95 - £110*
2 Four-posters	*£115 - £120*
3 Suites	*£105 - £115*
6 Family rooms	*£115 - £125*
6 S/C cottages	*£250 - £400 pw*

Includes full breakfast and VAT

CHARGE/CREDIT CARDS

• DC • MC • VI

ACCOLADES

N.I.T.B. ★★★★ Luxury
R.A.C. ★★★★
A.A. ★★★★ ❀ 71%

FACILITIES

Garden, archery, riding, clay pigeon shooting, fishing
4 meeting rooms/max 500 people
Golf and watersports nearby

RESTRICTIONS

No pets

ATTRACTIONS

Arthur Cottage,
Giant's Causeway,
Bushmills Distillery,
Glens of Antrim,
Royal Portrush Links Golf Course

AFFILIATIONS

Manor House Hotels of Ireland

NEAREST

MAJOR CITY:
Belfast - 25 miles/30 mins

MAJOR AIRPORT:
Belfast International - 16 miles/20 mins
Belfast City - 25 miles/30 mins

RAILWAY STATION:
Ballymena - 2 miles/5 mins

RESERVATIONS

Toll free in US: 800-55-CONSORT

ACCESS CODES

CN

A deluxe hotel with cottages in an 85-acre country estate

This converted gentleman's residence is set amidst some of Northern Ireland's most beautiful lush scenery, with the River Maine running less than 100 yards from the main entrance.

Most of the comfortable en suite bedrooms offer spectacular views of the surrounding countryside. The dining room offers a choice of table d'hôte or à la carte menus with local produce used wherever possible. For lighter eating there is a full bar menu in the Gillies Bar. There are six self-catering chalets available in the grounds which are perfect for weekend breaks or the longer stay.

The Manor offers a varied choice of meeting rooms, all with the most modern facilities.

Its estate includes 12 stables, a show jumping course and an eventing cross country practice area, so there is plenty of scope for the equestrian enthusiast. Clay pigeon shooting is also available and there are opportunities to play golf on some of the best links courses in Ireland.

Galgorm Manor is perfectly located for touring Northern Ireland. The lovely Antrim coast, including the Giant's Causeway, is only a short drive away.

LOCATION

Follow A42 towards Ballymena. Take the road to the left before Ballymena for Galgorm County Hall. At Galgorm village turn right and follow the hotel signs.

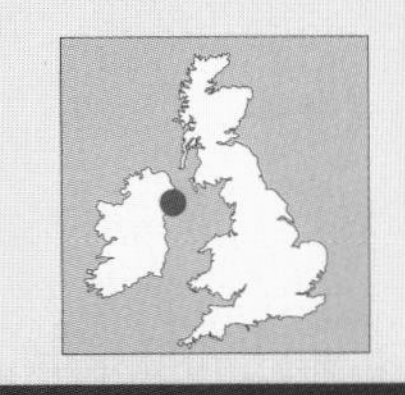

“ This is the finest place I have ever stayed in! I truly felt I was a guest in your home ”

Will Holm, Illinois

Country house — GLASSDRUMMAN LODGE

Simple excellence 'where the Mountains of Mourne sweep down to the sea'

Set in the dramatically beautiful landscape where "the Mountains of Mourne sweep down to the sea", Glassdrumman Lodge combines the luxury and seclusion of a country house with the warmth and hospitality of a family home. The lodge is owned by Graeme and Joan Hall whose philosophy is "simple excellence". Guests will find a friendly Irish welcome and a unique and restful atmosphere.

The eight well-appointed bedrooms and two suites, each named after a peak in the Mournes, have panoramic views of the mountains and the Irish Sea. Each has en suite bathroom, laundry service and 24-hour room service.

Dinner at the lodge is always an occasion. Seated around the 20-foot long pitch pine dining table, guests enjoy the highly acclaimed cuisine inspired by a great variety of local produce, much of which is grown on the lodge farm.

The surrounding area offers all manner of possibilities, providing peaceful walks at Silent Valley, Spelga Dam and Tollymore Forest Park or golf at the famous Royal County Down Golf Course. Horse riding is also available at the lodge's equestrian centre.

Glassdrumman Lodge aptly fits old Brillat-Savarin's aphorism: "To invite someone is to take charge of his happiness during the time he spends under your roof".

LOCATION

From Dublin: to Newry, then A2 coast road to Warrenpoint, Kilkeel, Annalong. Turn left at Halfway House. From Belfast: to Newcastle, then A2 coast road to Annalong. Turn right at Halfway House.

85 Mill Road, Annalong,
Co Down BT34 4RH
Northern Ireland

Telephone +44 (0)13967 68451
Fax +44 (0)13967 67041

PROPRIETOR
Joan Hall

ROOM RATES

10 Singles	£75 - £85
5 Doubles/Twins	£95 - £110
2 Suites	£120 - £135
2 Deluxe Doubles	£110 - £120

Includes breakfast and VAT

CHARGE/CREDIT CARDS

• DC • MC • VI

ACCOLADES
A.A. ★★ ❀❀
The Good Hotel Guide

FACILITIES
Garden, tennis, riding
1 meeting room/max 20 people
Golf, fishing and health club nearby

RESTRICTIONS
No facilities for disabled guests
No pets indoors

ATTRACTIONS
Silent Valley,
Giant's Causeway,
Navanfort, Armagh,
Mournes

AFFILIATIONS
Ireland's Blue Book

NEAREST
MAJOR CITY:
Belfast - 40 miles/1 hr

MAJOR AIRPORT:
Belfast - 55 miles/1 hr 30 mins

RAILWAY STATION:
Newry - 25 miles/30 mins

RESERVATIONS
Toll free in US: 800-223-6510
Toll free in Canada: 800-424-5500

ACCESS CODES
Not applicable

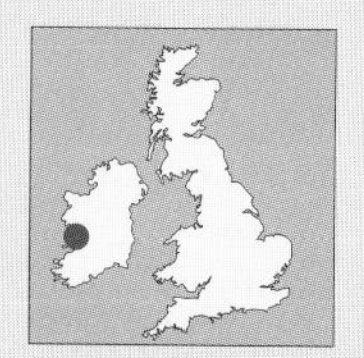

"Ireland is my place and The Burren speaks for itself. Add to this Gregans Castle Hotel, yourselves and your staff, and what can I say?"

June & John Freeman, Hampshire

GREGANS CASTLE

18th century country house

Ballyvaughan,
Co Clare
Republic of Ireland

Telephone +353 (0)65 77005
Fax +353 (0)65 77111

E Mail gregans@iol.ie

PROPRIETORS
The Haden Family

MANAGER
Simon P Haden

ROOM RATES

Single occupancy	*Ir £49 - £76*
14 Doubles	*Ir £79 - £140*
4 Suites	*Ir £119 - £200*

Includes full breakfast and VAT
Excludes service charge 15%

CHARGE/CREDIT CARDS

• *MC* • *VI*

ACCOLADES
I.T.B. ★★★★
R.A.C. Blue Ribbon Award ★★★
A.A. ★★★ ❀❀

FACILITIES
Croquet, gardens
Golf, riding and fishing nearby

RESTRICTIONS
No pets

ATTRACTIONS
The Burren, Cliffs of Moher,
Galway Bay, The Aran Islands

AFFILIATIONS
Ireland's Blue Book

NEAREST
MAJOR CITY:
Galway - 33 miles/45 mins

MAJOR AIRPORT:
Shannon - 36 miles/1 hr

RAILWAY STATION:
Gort - 22 miles/25 mins

RESERVATIONS
Toll free in US: 800-223-6510

ACCESS CODES
Not applicable

A solitaire in The Burren's majestic wilderness

Travelling through the more remote parts of the West of Ireland, Gregans Castle Hotel is one of those surprises so welcome to discerning travellers. Nestling at the foot of the Corkscrew Hill with majestic views of bare limestone mountains and Galway Bay, this country house offers warmth, welcome and every possible comfort.

This area of only ten miles square is called The Burren and is known worldwide for its wild flowers and distinctive scenery. A rich legacy of ancient monuments tells the story of inhabitants as far back as 5,000 years.

The seascapes are dramatic: Atlantic Ocean, Galway Bay, the famous Cliffs of Moher, two golden beaches and several small local fishing harbours of character.

Gregans Castle Hotel was built as a private house more than 150 years ago for the Martyn family to replace their home in the old castle nearby. Recently converted into an hotel, it is now one of the most comfortable hostelries on the west coast of Ireland. All the suites and bedrooms are individually decorated, with different views of the local scenery.

Dinner is an essential part of the day and a special emphasis is placed on local produce. The expert cooking has earned the hotel many accolades in all the better travel guide books.

Gregans Castle Hotel is owner-managed by the Haden family, and is an elected member of the prestigious "Ireland's Blue Book".

LOCATION

On the west coast of Ireland, near the village of Ballyvaughan in County Clare.

“ The quantity of service was only exceeded by the personal charm of the staff ”

Lord Wedgwood of Barlaston

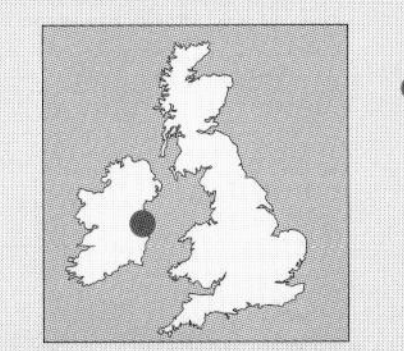

Victorian town house

HIBERNIAN HOTEL

Like Dublin: classical, enchanting and a very good place to eat

Tucked away in bustling downtown Dublin, the Hibernian Hotel is a magnificent architectural feat constructed just before the turn of the century in the commercial heart of the city. A grand 30-bedroomed townhouse hotel, the Hibernian prides itself on the elegance, style and warmth of service it can offer visitors to this vibrant metropolis.

David Butt is ably assisted by a young professional and energetic team for which nothing is too much trouble, to make your stay memorable. Pampering is abundant at the Hibernian with treats such as liquorice allsorts and candy bars to make you feel special.

The hotel's chef David Foley, has brought a unique style that is becoming synonymous with the Hibernian. His marrying together of fresh natural produce creates a dining experience that is hard to match in any other city hotel. Dishes such as corn-fed chicken filled with Clonakilty Black Pudding will have you screaming for more!

Like Dublin, this hotel is both classical and enchanting, offers an excellent choice for discerning diners and is a wonderful option for visitors to the Irish Capital.

LOCATION

Turn right from Mespil Road into Baggot Street Upper; then left into Eastmoreland Place. The Hibernian is at the end on the left.

Eastmoreland Place,
Ballsbridge, Dublin 4
Republic of Ireland

Telephone +353 (0)1 668 7666
Fax +353 (0)1 660 2655

MANAGER

David Butt

ROOM RATES

Single occupancy	*from Ir £95*
Standard Doubles/Twins	*Ir £120 - £135*
Superior Doubles/Twins	*Ir £142 - £157*
1 Suite	*from Ir £160*

Includes full breakfast and VAT

CHARGE/CREDIT CARDS

• *DC* • *MC* • *VI*

ACCOLADES

R.A.C. ★★★ + Merit Awards H C & R
A.A. ★★★ ❀❀❀ 73%
The Good Hotel Guide

FACILITIES

Restaurant
1 meeting room/max 50 people
Golf nearby

RESTRICTIONS

No pets

ATTRACTIONS

National Art Gallery,
National Library, Trinity College

AFFILIATIONS

Small Luxury Hotels
The Celebrated Hotels Collection
The Small Hotel Company
Manor House Hotels of Ireland

NEAREST

MAJOR CITY:
Dublin

MAJOR AIRPORT:
Dublin - 7 miles/30 mins

RAILWAY STATION:
Connolly - 2 miles/15mins

RESERVATIONS

Toll free in US/Canada: 800-525-4800

ACCESS CODES

AMADEUS/SYSTEM 1 LX DUBTHH/DUB100
AXESS 1054
SABRE LX 3582
APOLLO 58480
SAHARA/WORLDSPAN LX DUBHH

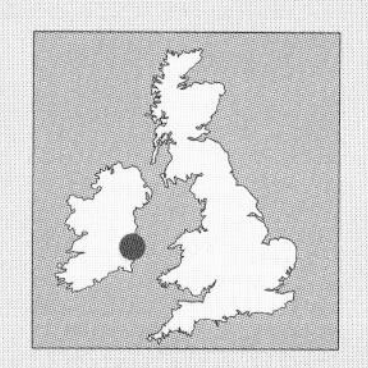

"I have been to many places in the south of Ireland but I find this lovely spot the most peaceful and charming of them all"

W D Doherty FRCS, London

HUNTERS HOTEL

18th century coaching inn

Newrath Bridge, Rathnew,
Co Wicklow
Republic of Ireland

Telephone +353 (0)404 40106
Fax +353 (0)404 40338

PROPRIETORS
The Gelletlie Family

ROOM RATES
2 Singles Ir £45 - £62.50
14 Doubles Ir £90
Includes full breakfast and VAT

CHARGE/CREDIT CARDS

• *DC* • *MC* • *VI*

ACCOLADES
I.T.B. ★★★
A.A. ★★ *65%*

FACILITIES
Garden
1 meeting room/max 30 people
Golf, riding and fishing nearby

RESTRICTIONS
None

ATTRACTIONS
Mount Usher Gardens, Powerscourt Gardens and Waterfall, Glendalough, Russborough House

AFFILIATIONS
Ireland's Blue Book

NEAREST
MAJOR CITY:
Dublin - 28 miles/45 mins

MAJOR AIRPORT:
Dublin - 40 miles/1¼ hrs

RAILWAY STATION:
Wicklow - 3 miles/5 mins

RESERVATIONS
Toll free in US: 800-223-6510

ACCESS CODES
Not applicable

Good food and old-world charm – a family tradition of five generations

Hunter's Hotel, one of Ireland's oldest coaching inns, has been established for over 270 years, since the days of post horses and carriages. Run by the same family for five generations, the hotel has built up a strong tradition based on good food, comfortable surroundings and unique, old world charm.

Set in one of Ireland's most beautiful counties, the hotel stands in gardens bordering the River Vartry. All the rooms retain the character of bygone days, with antique furniture, open fires, fresh flowers and polished brass. Most of the 16 attractive bedrooms overlook the gardens.

Golf (12 courses within 30 minutes drive), sea angling, riding, hunting, tennis, swimming and hiking – are all available in the immediate locality. The beautiful Wicklow countryside, which has earned for the county the title 'Garden of Ireland', lies at your doorstep. Lovely sandy beaches, breathtaking mountain scenery, quiet glens and well known beauty spots such as Mount Usher Gardens, Powerscourt, Russborough House, Avondale House, Glendalough, the Devil's Glen and Roundwood are all within easy reach.

Whether you want a country base from which to visit Dublin, a peaceful rural holiday or just a pleasant overnight stop after the Fishguard to Rosslare ferry, en route to Dublin, Hunter's Hotel is the ideal location.

LOCATION

Take N11 to Rathnew village. Turn left just before the village on Dublin side.

" Simply splendid – history reborn "

G Hetherington, New Zealand

20th century castle

KINNITTY CASTLE

A neo-gothic castle with a 20,000-acre sporting heritage

The story of Kinnitty Castle is almost as eventful as the tumultuous history of Ireland and, like Ireland, has its roots in fable. It was rebuilt three times: in 1213 after Dhorrough O'Brien destroyed it; in 1630, it ascended over the ruins of an Augustinian abbey and in 1929, after it had been raised to the ground by Republican forces, it took its present form.

The estate, which lies right in the centre if Ireland, has changed little, however, and remains as it always has, a rich area for field sports. The hotel's 20,000 acres of forest and woodland on the slopes of the Slieve Bloom hills beckon ramblers and equestrians alike. Indeed, riding is a special feature of a stay at Kinnitty Castle. For fishermen, the hotel provides fishing in the neighbouring rivers, Little Brosna and the Camcor or, less than 30 minutes away, the legendary waters of Lough Ennel or the Shannon.

You can play tennis or croquet in the well-tended garden or try your hand at archery.

The wonderful neo-gothic style of the castle is splendidly followed through in the choice of fabrics, furniture, fitments and fittings. In a word, the interiors are *grand*. And, though the present castle may be a newcomer to the scene, you are constantly aware of Kinnitty's noble antecedents. Definitely a most rewarding place to stay for those who enjoy an active life.

LOCATION

Situated 1½ hrs from Dublin, Galway and Limerick in the village of Kinnitty.

Kinnitty, Birr, Co Offaly Republic of Ireland

Telephone +353 (0)509 37318
Fax +353 (0)509 37284

PROPRIETORS

Con and Kathleen Ryan

GENERAL MANAGER

Michelle Brooks

ROOM RATES

Single occupancy £80
16 Doubles £120
Includes full breakfast and VAT

CHARGE/CREDIT CARDS

• DC • MC • VI

ACCOLADES

Awards pending

FACILITIES

Garden, croquet, tennis, shooting, riding, walking, heli-pad
2 meeting rooms/max 20 people
Golf and fishing nearby

RESTRICTIONS

None

ATTRACTIONS

Cadamstown, Kinnitty Cross, St Finbarrs Abbey, Lockes Distillery, Birr Castle and gardens

AFFILIATIONS

Independent

NEAREST

MAJOR CITY:
Galway - 60 miles/1½ hrs

MAJOR AIRPORT:
Shannon - 70 miles/1½ hrs

RAILWAY STATION:
Tullamore - 16 miles/20 mins

RESERVATIONS

Direct with hotel

ACCESS CODES

Not applicable

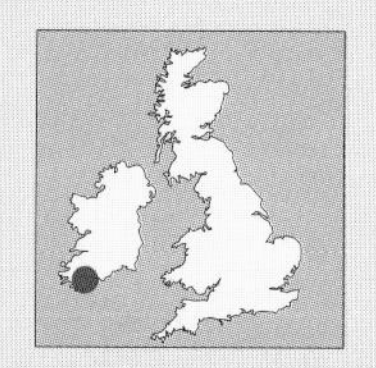

“ I don’t mind now if I never get to Heaven – I’ve already been there ”

Audrey Haas, Zurich

LISS ARD LAKE LODGE

Victorian manor

Skibbereen,
Co Cork,
Republic of Ireland

Telephone +353 (0)28 22365
Fax +353 (0)28 22839

MANAGING DIRECTOR
Delwyn Klevenow

RATES PER PERSON
Single occupancy £75 - £180
1 Double £50 - £60
7 Luxury Doubles £80 - £100
2 Junior Suites £90 - £120
Includes full breakfast and VAT

CHARGE/CREDIT CARDS

• *DC* • *MC* • *VI*

ACCOLADES
Independent

FACILITIES
Garden, tennis, gym, sauna, lake, fishing, sky garden
1 meeting room/max 20 people
Golf, beaches and riding nearby

RESTRICTIONS
Children under 12 on request
No facilities for disabled guests
No pets

ATTRACTIONS
Sherkin Island, Mizen Head, Ring of Bearra, Cape Clear, Blarney Castle

AFFILIATIONS
Small Hotel Company
Romantik Hotels & Restaurants

NEAREST
MAJOR CITY:
Cork - 50 miles/1 hr 10 mins

MAJOR AIRPORT:
Cork - 44 miles/1 hr

RAILWAY STATION:
Cork - 50 miles/1 hr 10 mins

RESERVATIONS
Direct with hotel

ACCESS CODES
Not applicable

Style, imagination and stunning scenery in County Cork

Liss Ard Lake Lodge is a small luxury hotel set in the midst of an inspiring contemporary 50-acre park, overlooking the beautiful Lough Abisdealy. It is a fine old manor house designed and decorated with absolute simplicity. The only decorations on the walls are mounted specimens of the 249 different species of butterfly that have been discovered within the grounds.

The two junior suites and seven double bedrooms are designed to maximise views of the superb scenery. Clean-lined simplicity combines with luxury: TV units with video and hi-fi, and mini-bars. The distinctive bathrooms have Japanese screens, and are finished to a very high standard.

Elegantly appointed tables in the restaurant offer superb views of the lake, and imaginative non-dairy menus by Claudia Meister. Typical main courses include turbot en papillote or lacquered duck. Accompanying vegetables are of highest quality and freshness. Desserts follow that are so rich, it is unbelievable they are made without dairy products. Butter does, however, play its part in the delicious breakfasts.

Skibbereen is the headquarters of West Cork, and its main market town. The coast is a delight of beaches, bays, harbours and quiet seaside villages. Within easy reach are Bantry House, former seat of the Earls of Bantry where hang four panels of Aubusson tapestry made for Marie Antoinette. Don’t miss the massive keep and stepped battlements of 15th century Blarney Castle, once a fortress of the MacCarthys and still the home of the famous Stone with its oratorical properties.

LOCATION

From Skibbereen, take the Tragumna road. The house is sign-posted and easily distinguished by its tower gates, a folly.

“An oasis of tranquillity in the heart of Dublin's Georgian quarter”

Irish Times

Georgian house

LONGFIELD'S

One of Dublin's most distinguished small hotels

The Georgian “Doors of Dublin” are an established visual attraction in souvenir poster form no less than in situ. A prime example is No. 10 Fitzwilliam Street, part of the longest unbroken line of authentic Georgian houses in these islands – and home of Longfield's, one of Dublin's most distinguished small hotels. A quiet haven for the discerning visitor, Longfield's makes an ideal base for forays into the capital's prime, fashionable shopping streets for bargain hunting in antique and curio shops. Also, cinemas, theatres and art galleries are situated within easy walking distance of St Stephen's Green, Grafton Street, Trinity College, the city's many cultural attractions and the burgeoning “bohemian” quarter of Temple Bar.

Attention to detail and impeccable service are the hallmarks at Longfield's. This is seen to good effect in the elegantly furnished bedrooms and reception area and is perhaps best exemplified in the restaurant, affectionately known as “No. 10” to Dubliners dining out. Apart from creating favourable impressions on today's restaurant reviewers, the proximity of No. 10 to Government buildings is an irony of nomenclature not lost on native politicians nor on visitors from Britain.

LOCATION

500 yards from Stephens Green, take the Baggot Street exit off the Green. Longfield's is on the junction with Fitzwilliam Street.

Fitzwilliam Street Lower,
Dublin 2
Republic of Ireland

Telephone +353 (0)1676 1367
Fax +353 (0)1676 1542

GENERAL MANAGER

G Finnegan

ROOM RATES

2 Singles	*Ir £90*
13 Twins	*Ir £115*
13 Doubles	*Ir £115*

Includes full breakfast and VAT

CHARGE/CREDIT CARDS

• *DC* • *MC* • *VI*

ACCOLADES

R.A.C. ★★ *+ Merit Awards H C & R*
A.A. ★★ ❀❀ *73%*

FACILITIES

“No 10” Restaurant
Theatres, galleries, museums and golf nearby

RESTRICTIONS

No children
No pets

ATTRACTIONS

Christchurch Cathedral,
Trinity College,
Stephens Green,
National Museum,
House of Parliament

AFFILIATIONS

Manor House Hotels of Ireland

NEAREST

MAJOR CITY:
Dublin

MAJOR AIRPORT:
Dublin - 4 miles/30 mins

RAILWAY STATION:
Dublin - ½ mile/5 mins

RESERVATIONS

Toll free in US: 800-223-6510

ACCESS CODES

Not applicable

“ Ireland's finest castle of its period ”

Lord Clark, Civilisation television programme

MARKREE CASTLE

17th century castle

Collooney,
Co Sligo
Republic of Ireland

Telephone +353 (0)71 67800
Fax +353 (0)71 67840

PROPRIETORS

Charles and Mary Cooper

ROOM RATES

Single occupancy Ir £58.50 - £62.50
24 Doubles Ir £93 - £105
5 Suites Ir £103 - £115
Includes full breakfast and VAT

CHARGE/CREDIT CARDS

• DC • MC • VI

ACCOLADES

I.T.B.★★★
R.A.C. ★★★
Bewley's Best Coffee Award
Ireland's 100 Best Hotels
Ireland's 100 Best Restaurants

FACILITIES

Croquet, gardens, horse riding

RESTRICTIONS

Children's menu not provided
No facilities for disabled guests

ATTRACTIONS

Yeats Country,
Carrowmore megalithic remains
Lough Gill,
Parke's Castle

AFFILIATIONS

Independent

NEAREST

MAJOR CITY:
Galway - 80 miles/2 hrs

MAJOR AIRPORT:
Dublin/Belfast - 125 miles/3 hrs
Shannon - 125 miles/3 hrs

RAILWAY STATION:
Collooney - 1 1/2 miles/5 mins

RESERVATIONS

Toll free in US: 800-221-1074
or 800-223-6510

ACCESS CODES

Not applicable

The Coopers have lived here for 350 years – the welcome is as warm as ever

Home of the Cooper family for over 350 years, Markree Castle is now run as a small family hotel by Charles and Mary Cooper, the 10th generation of the Coopers to live at Markree.

Set in a large estate with lovely gardens, the original house has been altered many times over the years, with the main addition being built in 1802 by the architect Francis Johnston. The enormous oak staircase is overlooked by a stained glass window depicting the Cooper family tree going back 20 generations, and the Louis Philippe style plasterwork in the dining-room makes it one of the most spectacular rooms in Ireland.

Charles Cooper worked in hotels in many other countries before returning to Markree in 1989. Since then he has restored much of the splendid interior and created a family hotel of great character. The bedrooms all have private bathrooms, telephones, and efficient heating, yet great care has been taken to retain the character of the old building and the family atmosphere, rather than the formal impersonal atmosphere of more luxurious hotels.

The restaurant has also become well known for carefully prepared meals of the highest standard.

LOCATION

8 miles south of Sligo town, just off N4 and N17 junction.

" Yet again a marvellous combination of sumptuous cuisine and graceful surroundings with a standard of service that has all but vanished elsewhere "

Dr Ray Raymond, New York

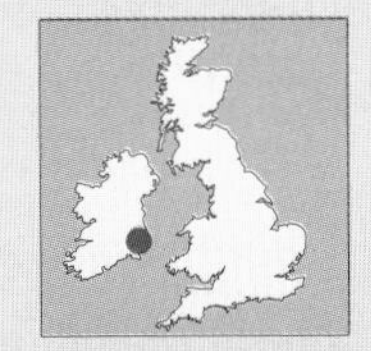

Regency country house

MARLFIELD HOUSE

One of the treasures of Ireland's countryside heritage

Marlfield House is a fine Regency house set in 35 acres of woodlands and gardens and was the residence in Ireland of the Earl of Courtown. Just an hour from Dublin, it provides an ideal setting for touring the beauty spots of Wicklow and the south east of Ireland.

There are 19 bedrooms, including five State Rooms and one magnificent Master Suite. The whole house is lavishly decorated with sumptuous fabrics, period fireplaces and numerous antiques. Bathrooms feature highly polished marble, free-standing bathtubs – some with jacuzzis.

Eating in the impressive curved Turner conservatory dining room is a memorable experience; modern French cooking is served with a strong classical influence. The gardens provide the vegetables, herbs and fruits necessary for a kitchen to maintain its excellent reputation which has earned it numerous awards, including the Relais & Châteaux Worldwide Best Breakfast Award. It was also listed in the Hideaway Report "Best 24 Hotels in the World" in 1988 and 1990.

The house has been converted by its present owners, Ray and Mary Bowe, whose aim is to meet the demands of the more discerning guest looking for the best country house atmosphere.

LOCATION

The hotel is situated 57 miles south of Dublin Ferry Port; 63 miles south of Dublin Airport; 50 miles south of Dun Laoghaire Ferry Port; 39 miles north of Rosslare Ferry.

Gorey,
Co Wexford
Republic of Ireland

Telephone +353 (0)55 21124
Fax +353 (0)55 21572

PROPRIETORS

Ray and Mary Bowe

ROOM RATES

2 Singles	*Ir £85*
11 Doubles/Twins	*Ir £138 - £144*
5 State Rooms	*Ir £190 - £310*
1 Master Suite	*Ir £421*

Includes full breakfast and VAT

CHARGE/CREDIT CARDS

• DC • MC • VI

ACCOLADES

I.T.B. ★★★★
R.A.C. Blue Ribbon Award ★★★
A.A. ★★★ ❀❀❀
The Good Hotel Guide - 1996 César Award

FACILITIES

Tennis, croquet, jacuzzi, sauna heli-pad, 36 acres of gardens and woodland with Wildlife Reserve
2 meeting rooms/max 90 people
Golf and fishing nearby

RESTRICTIONS

Pets by prior arrangement

ATTRACTIONS

Co Wicklow - Powerscourt Demesne and Mount Usher Gardens, Devil's Glen, beaches

AFFILIATIONS

Relais & Châteaux
Ireland's Blue Book

NEAREST

MAJOR CITY:
Dublin - 57 miles/1 hr 20 mins

MAJOR AIRPORT:
Dublin - 63 miles/1¾ hrs

RAILWAY STATION:
Gorey - 1½ miles/5 mins

RESERVATIONS

Toll free in US: 800-223-6510

ACCESS CODES

Not applicable

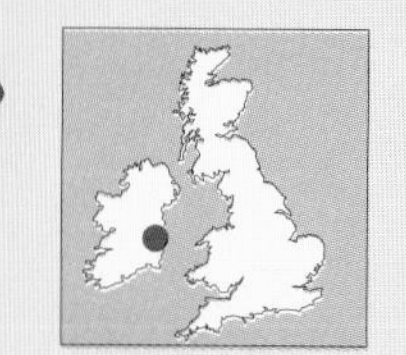

" One of the best hotels I will always remember "

Gene Autry, USA

MOYGLARE MANOR

Georgian mansion

Maynooth,
Co Kildare
Republic of Ireland

Telephone +353 (0)1 628 6351
Fax +353 (0)1 628 5405

PROPRIETOR
Norah Devlin

MANAGER
Shay Curran

ROOM RATES

1 Single	Ir £95
14 Doubles	Ir £130
1 Four-poster	Ir £130
1 Suite	Ir £350

Includes full breakfast and VAT

CHARGE/CREDIT CARDS

• DC • MC • VI

ACCOLADES
I.T.B.★★★★
R.A.C. ★★★ + Merit Awards H & C

FACILITIES
Gardens, tennis, heli-pad
3 meeting rooms/max 40 people
Golf, riding and fishing nearby

RESTRICTIONS
No children under 12 years
No pets

ATTRACTIONS
Maynooth College,
Castletown House,
National Stud Farm,
Carton House,
Russborough House

AFFILIATIONS
Irish Country Houses

NEAREST
MAJOR CITY:
Dublin - 25 miles/30 mins

MAJOR AIRPORT:
Dublin - 25 miles/30 mins

RAILWAY STATION:
Maynooth - 3 miles/10 mins

RESERVATIONS
Direct with hotel

ACCESS CODES
Not applicable

Luxury and award-winning cuisine in an area famed for horse breeding

Moyglare Manor is a Georgian house set in beautiful parkland and evokes a splendid era of Irish country house living and hospitality.

At the top of an imposing Georgian staircase each bedroom, equipped with spacious en suite bathroom, is individually styled. Period furniture blends perfectly with tasteful modern decor and conveniences, creating an aura of elegance and old world charm. Cosy log fires in the lounges give an extra touch of warmth which is part of the hospitality that is Moyglare Manor.

Good food is an integral part of the concept of gracious living that Moyglare imparts, and their award-winning chef ensures that the cuisine is both varied and excellent, with fresh vegetables and fruit from the hotel's own gardens and orchards.

Moyglare Manor is situated a mile and a half from the university town of Maynooth and is only 20 miles from Dublin city. The great limestone plain on which the town stands has been the breeding ground for some of the world's best horses and the area has many stud farms and race tracks where meetings occur on a regular basis. Castletown House is nearby and the area is rich in archeological remains.

LOCATION

From Dublin, travel west on N4 through Maynooth. Keep right at church for 2 km.

"It is unusual to find such considerate and personal service as we have experienced here. A 'gem' of a hotel!"

Helen Young, UK

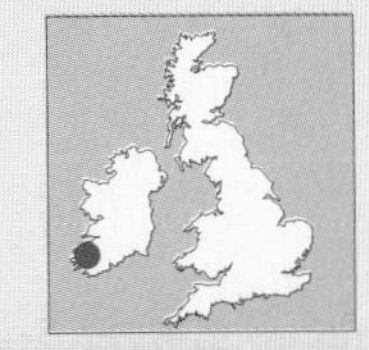

Country house — MUCKROSS PARK HOTEL

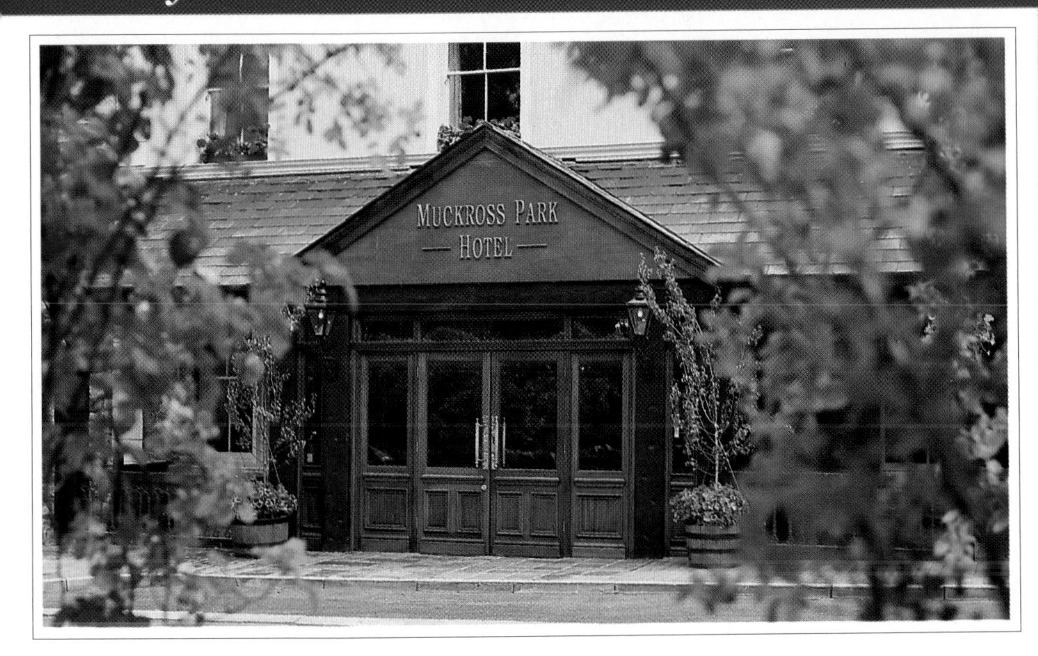

A luxury hotel with an award-winning traditional pub and restaurant

Set in the heart of Killarney's world famous National Park, in the village of Muckross, the Muckross Park Hotel is a redevelopment of the oldest hotel in Killarney. Welcoming visitors since 1795, the hotel retains the luxurious ambience of a traditional Irish country house, but with the comfort and convenience of a modern four-star hotel.

All of their 25 guest bedrooms are exceptional by any standard and both of the suites are simply unique. The Bluepool Restaurant, where one can savour the delights from the country kitchen, overlooks two acres of landscaped gardens leading down to the hotel's river frontage and forest walks.

Adjacent to the hotel, you will find Molly's, an award-winning traditional Irish pub and restaurant, which was voted 'All Ireland Pub of the Year 1992' and 'Pub of the Year' for both Kerry and Munster for three successive years. Its stone walls, wooden floors, beamed ceilings, open fires and live entertainment recreate the pleasures of bygone days.

Situated only 2½ miles outside Killarney town, the hotel is only minutes away from Muckross House and Gardens, Muckross Abbey and Killarney's world famous lakes. Golfing, hill walking, boating, fishing, tennis, clay pigeon shooting and horseriding can all be arranged through the hotel during your visit.

You will be welcomed by a friendly yet professional staff who will ensure your stay is an enjoyable and memorable one.

LOCATION

2½ miles outside Killarney town on road to Kenmare.

Muckross Village, Killarney,
Co Kerry
Republic of Ireland

Telephone +353 (0)64 31938
Fax +353 (0)64 31965

MANAGER
Tony Lynch

ROOM RATES

Single occupancy	*Ir £65 - £80*
25 Doubles	*Ir £80 - £120*
2 Suites	*Ir £150 - £250*

Includes full breakfast and VAT

CHARGE/CREDIT CARDS

• *DC* • *MC* • *VI*

ACCOLADES
I.T.B. ★★★★
A.A. ★★★★ *70%*

FACILITIES
Landscaped gardens, fishing
3 meeting rooms/max 200 people
Forest walks, golf, riding and boating nearby

RESTRICTIONS
No pets
No facilities for disabled guests

ATTRACTIONS
Killarney National Park,
Muckross House and gardens,
Ross Castle,
Torc Waterfall

AFFILIATIONS
Utell International

NEAREST
MAJOR CITY:
Cork - 50 miles/1 hr

MAJOR AIRPORT:
Shannon - 80 miles/2 hrs
Cork - 55 miles/1½ hrs
Kerry - 10 miles/20 mins

RAILWAY STATION:
Killarney - 2½ miles/5 mins

RESERVATIONS
Toll free in US: 800-223-6510

ACCESS CODE
UI

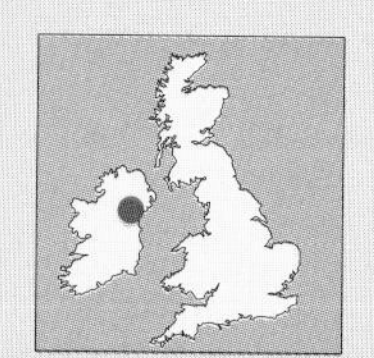

" Outstanding surroundings and accommodation, magic golf plus the magic of Ireland "

Paul Clark, Woodstock

NUREMORE HOTEL & COUNTRY CLUB *Victorian house*

Carrickmacross,
Co Monaghan
Republic of Ireland

Telephone +353 (0)42 61438
Fax +353 (0)42 61853

PROPRIETOR

Julie Gilhooly

ROOM RATES

1 Single Ir £70 - £90
63 Doubles/Twins Ir £110 - £120
5 Suites Ir £120 - £130
Includes full breakfast and VAT

CHARGE/CREDIT CARDS

• DC • MC • VI

ACCOLADES

I.T.B. ★★★★

A.A. ★★★★ ❀❀ 71%

FACILITIES

Indoor swimming pool, tennis, gardens, 18-hole golf course, steam room, sauna, gymnasium, squash, snooker room
Riding and fishing nearby

RESTRICTIONS

No pets

ATTRACTIONS

Newgrange, Co Meath, Navan Fort, Co Armagh, Carlingford Lough, Co Louth

AFFILIATIONS

Independent

NEAREST

MAJOR CITY:
Dublin - 50 miles/1 ½ hrs

MAJOR AIRPORT:
Dublin - 50 miles/1 ½ hrs

RAILWAY STATION:
Dundalk - 14 mile/25 mins

RESERVATIONS

Direct with hotel

ACCESS CODES

Not applicable

A luxury hotel and country club with superb facilities in a magnificent setting

The Nuremore Hotel and Country Club is beautifully situated within its own 18-hole championship golf course in the rolling countryside of County Monaghan.

Originally a Victorian country house, the Nuremore has, over the years, been skilfully converted into a magnificent luxury hotel. Each of its 70 bedrooms has been individually designed and beautifully appointed to create a generous sense of personal space. The lounges are both warm and spacious and furnished with huge sofas, striking floral arrangements, open fires and deep windows, giving brilliant views of the sparkling lake below.

A vast array of leisure features is available for residents' use, including an 18-metre swimming pool, whirlpool, steam room, sauna, gymnasium, and facilities for squash, tennis and snooker.

The golf course (6,833 yards par 72), nestles snugly among the drumlins and lakes for which this part of Ireland is justly famous. The course designer has managed to carve out of the Monaghan hillside, a layout that is both challenging and scenically fascinating. Golf tuition is available from resident PGA professional, Maurice Cassidy.

Situated just over an hour's drive from Dublin Airport, the Nuremore Hotel is an ideal venue for a relaxing holiday.

LOCATION

50 miles northwest of Dublin off the N2.

“ Set fair to become the outstanding hotel in Ireland ”

Travel & Leisure

Victorian country hotel

PARK HOTEL KENMARE

Step back in time beyond the cares of today

The building was constructed in 1897 by the Great Southern and Western Railway Company to facilitate passengers travelling to Parknasilla 17 miles away. In those days the train stopped at Kenmare and here the gentry stayed overnight before continuing their journey to Parknasilla. Ownership continued in the hands of GS&W Company until 1977 when the hotel was sold.

In 1980, refurbishment began and the hotel was re-opened in late 1980 under its new name 'The Park Hotel Kenmare'. Since then, it has become renowned for its splendid collection of antiques and interior furnishings.

In 1985, Mr. Francis Brennan, the manager, took complete control becoming the proprietor and managing director.

In the quest for superior guest comfort, a refurbishment programme was undertaken to double the size of the bedrooms. This latest development has firmly established the hotel as one of Ireland's most luxurious. The hotel lays special emphasis on personalised service and has won many accolades to date.

An abundance of outdoor activities are available, including an 18-hole golf course, fishing (sea and lake), horse riding, and many scenic walks.

The pressures of modern living can easily be forgotten at the Park Hotel Kenmare where the staff are waiting to make your stay – whether for a holiday or on business – most memorable.

LOCATION

Southwest Ireland, off the N70 from Killarney on the 'Ring of Kerry'.

Kenmare,
Co Kerry
Republic of Ireland

Telephone +353 (0)64 41200
Fax +353 (0)64 41402

PROPRIETOR

Mr Francis Brennan

RATES PER PERSON

8 Singles	Ir £87 - £104
27 Doubles	Ir £71 - £87
6 Four-posters	Ir £87 - £107
9 Suites	Ir £131 - £160

Includes VAT
Excludes service charge of 15%

CHARGE/CREDIT CARDS

• DC • MC • VI

ACCOLADES

I.T.B. ★★★★★ De Luxe
R.A.C. Blue Ribbon Award ★★★★
A.A. ★★★★ ❀❀
The Good Hotel Guide
Hideaway Report 'Hotel of the Year'

FACILITIES

Croquet, tennis, gardens, workout room
18 hole golf course adjoining hotel
Fishing, cycling and riding nearby

RESTRICTIONS

No pets

ATTRACTIONS

Ring of Kerry,
Lakes of Killarney,
World renowned gardens

AFFILIATIONS

Relais & Châteaux
Small Luxury Hotels
Ireland's Blue Book

NEAREST

MAJOR CITY:
Cork - 60 miles/1½ hrs

MAJOR AIRPORT:
Cork - 60 miles/1½ hrs

RAILWAY STATION:
Killarney - 20 miles/45 mins

RESERVATIONS

Toll free in US: 800-223-6510
Toll free in US: 800-223-6764

ACCESS CODES

AMADEUS/SYSTEM 1 LX KIRPHK
APOLLO LX 32328
SAHARA LX KIRPH
SABRE LX 30949

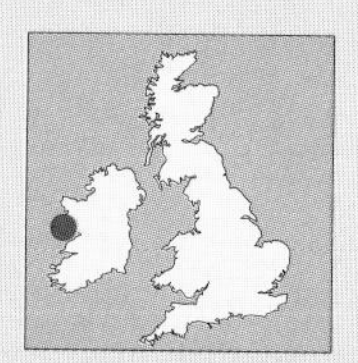

" Thank you once more and most heartily for the unforgettable experience of your hospitality at Rosleague Manor "

Richard Weiszäcker, President of German Federal Republic, 1987

ROSLEAGUE MANOR

Country house

Letterfrack,
Co Galway,
Republic of Ireland

Telephone +353 (0)95 41101
Fax +353 (0)95 41168

PROPRIETORS

Patrick and Anne Foyle

RATES PER PERSON

Single occupancy	*Ir £65 - £75*
16 Doubles/Twins	*Ir £45 - £60*
4 Suites	*Ir £70 - £80*

Includes full breakfast and VAT

CHARGE/CREDIT CARDS

• MC • VI

ACCOLADES

The Good Hotel Guide
100 Best Places to Stay

FACILITIES

Garden, tennis, sauna, snooker
Sea, river and lake fishing and riding nearby

RESTRICTIONS

Pets by prior arrangement

ATTRACTIONS

Connemara National Park,
Kylemore Abbey,
Cliffs of Moher,
scuba diving,
hill walking

AFFILIATIONS

Ireland's Blue Book

NEAREST

MAJOR CITY:
Galway - 50 miles/1¼ hrs

MAJOR AIRPORT:
Shannon - 110 miles/2½ hrs
Knock - 70 miles/1½ hrs

RAILWAY STATION:
Galway - 50 miles/1¼ hrs

RESERVATIONS

Direct with hotel

ACCESS CODES

Not applicable

Character and charm in rugged Connemara

Rosleague is a Regency manor now run as a first class country house hotel by sister and brother Anne and Patrick Foyle. It overlooks a sheltered bay that is surrounded by mountains and forests. The original house is almost 200 years old, with later additions sympathetically treated to retain the character and charm of the 1800s, and yet to provide all the amenities expected by today's discerning guest.

Acclaimed by top food guides, Rosleague's cuisine is personally supervised by the owners. All the food is produced locally and prepared by them, with the help of a skilled and experienced staff. The menus are based on the freshest and finest ingredients available. Fresh seafood and Connemara lamb are specialities. There is a fully licensed cocktail bar and two delightful drawing rooms in which to relax.

The hotel has an all-weather tennis court and a sauna. There are short walks through the gardens and a path to the ocean's edge. The famous Connemara Golf Course is close by. Some of the most beautiful beaches in the world are within a few miles. Boats from the harbour at Cleggan make daily fishing trips and excursions to the island of Inisboffin. Other activities at hand include scuba diving, hill walking, horse riding and superb salmon and trout fishing.

LOCATION

Letterfrack is 7 miles north of Clifden, the capital of Connemara off the N59.

“ One of Ireland’s west coast treasures ”

Pat Tunison, US Travel writer

Seaside resort hotel

SAND HOUSE HOTEL

Whatever inspired Yeats, you'll find it around here

The Sand House, described as “one of Ireland’s west coast treasures”, is magnificently situated on the sandy shores of the Atlantic Ocean overlooking Donegal Bay. It is a haven of comfort and tranquillity amidst the beauty of rural Ireland.

The hotel is located in the small resort of Rossnowlagh, known as ‘the heavenly cove’, where the surfing is said to be the best in the country. A few miles south of historic Donegal town and north of Sligo, Yeats country, the hotel is half way between the wild beauty of Connemara and the North Donegal Highlands. It is an ideal touring location.

The Sand House, a converted 19th century fishing lodge, now transformed into a gracious and tastefully-appointed hotel, combines the highest standards of luxurious accommodation, superb cuisine and friendly, efficient service with the old world charm and the leisurely ambience of its country house origins.

Enjoy award-winning cuisine enhanced by a carefully chosen and imaginative wine list. The menus are designed around the wonderful natural produce which thrives in the unpolluted waters and hinterland. Seafood specialities include Donegal Bay salmon, trout, scallops, crab, mussels and fresh oysters from their own oyster beds.

For outdoor enthusiasts, there are a wealth of facilities and is a golfer’s paradise at the centre of three 18-hole championship golf courses.

LOCATION

30 miles north of Sligo and 10 miles south of Donegal town. From Dublin follow N3 via Cavan or N4 via Sligo. From Galway N17 via Sligo. From Belfast M1 and A4 via Enniskillen.

Rossnowlagh, South Co Donegal Republic of Ireland

Telephone +353 (0)72 51777
Fax +353 (0)72 52100

PROPRIETORS
Mary and Brian Britton

MANAGER
Paul Diver

RATES PER PERSON

6 Singles	*Ir £55 - £65*
22 Doubles/Twins	*Ir £45 - £55*
4 Four-posters	*Ir £45 - £60*
3 Suites	*Ir £60 - £75*

Includes full breakfast and VAT

CHARGE/CREDIT CARDS

• DC • MC • VI

ACCOLADES
I.T.B. ★★★★ Highly Commended
A.A. ★★★ ❀❀ 73%
National Hygiene Awards

FACILITIES
Tennis, mini-golf, croquet, watersports Golf, walking, hill climbing and watersports nearby

RESTRICTIONS
No facilities for disabled guests
No dogs in public rooms

ATTRACTIONS
Donegal Highlands, Yeats country & Lough Gill, Glenveagh Castle and Gardens, Donegal Championship Golf course

AFFILIATIONS
Manor House Hotels of Ireland

NEAREST
MAJOR CITY:
Dublin - 140 miles/3½ hrs
Sligo - 30 miles/45 mins
MAJOR AIRPORT:
Dublin - 140 miles/3½ hrs
Shannon - 165 miles/4 hrs
Sligo - 30 miles/45 mins
RAILWAY STATION:
Sligo - 30 miles/45 mins

RESERVATIONS
Toll free in US/Canada: 800-55-CONSORT

ACCESS CODES
CN

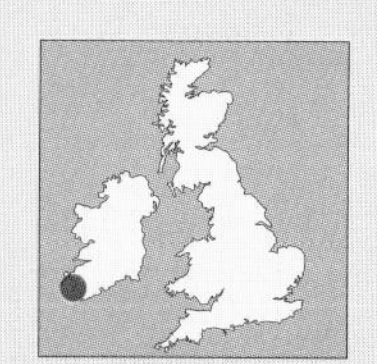

"Elegance in a country setting, what more could the soul ask for?"

Nancy & Harold Winch, Ohio

SHEEN FALLS LODGE

Luxury resort hotel

Kenmare,
Co Kerry
Republic of Ireland

Telephone +353 (0)64 41600
Fax +353 (0)64 41386

PROPRIETOR
Mr B Hoyer

MANAGER
Mr P Mac Cann

ROOM RATES

Single occupancy	Ir £135 - £185
25 Deluxe Doubles/Twins	Ir £160 - £240
6 Superior Doubles/Twins	Ir £205 - £305
9 Suites	Ir £255 - £360

Includes VAT

CHARGE/CREDIT CARDS

• DC • MC • VI

ACCOLADES
I.T.B. ★★★★★ De Luxe
R.A.C. Blue Ribbon Award ★★★★
A.A. ★★★★ ❀❀
The Good Hotel Guide

FACILITIES
Garden, croquet, gym, sauna, jacuzzi, 18 hole golf course, tennis, riding, private fishing, clay shooting, health spa, snooker, heli-pad
3 meeting rooms/max 140 people

RESTRICTIONS
No dogs in hotel
(facilities can be arranged)

ATTRACTIONS
Beara Peninsula and The Healy Pass, The Ring of Kerry, Killarney National Park

AFFILIATIONS
Relais & Châteaux
The Small Hotel Company

NEAREST
MAJOR CITY:
Cork - 60 miles/1½ hrs
MAJOR AIRPORT:
Cork - 60 miles/1½ hrs
Kerry - 35 miles/1 hr
RAILWAY STATION:
Killarney - 21 miles/45 mins

RESERVATIONS
Toll free in US: 800-221-1074

ACCESS CODES
Not applicable

Waterfalls, moon-lit woods . . . a thousand miles from the cares of today

A masterfully transformed 17th century country retreat presiding over a dramatic 300 acre estate above the Sheen Waterfalls and the Kenmare Bay.

Nestled in the beautiful award winning gardens at the base of the Caha Mountains, Sheen Falls Lodge offers luxury and comfort, hospitality and natural beauty. Stay in one of the 40 guestrooms and dine in their highly rated restaurant overlooking the waterfalls.

Guests wishing to pursue outdoor activities may try their hand at salmon and trout fishing along 15 miles of the Sheen River. All equipment is provided and tuition is available on request. For the more active, there is horse riding at Sheen Falls Lodge, clay target shooting clinic, 18-hole golf course and numerous walking and jogging routes.

The Health and Fitness Centre provides specialist health and beauty treatments. One can also enjoy the state of the art jacuzzi, steamroom, sauna, plunge pool, and fully equipped gymnasium.

Sheen Falls Lodge is just outside the town of Kenmare, within easy reach of airports and ferries and has its own heli-pad. Despite this, it still seems a thousand miles from the cares of the world. Sheen Falls is truly the perfect setting for pure relaxation. Discover a little southwestern hospitality and magic at Sheen Falls Lodge.

LOCATION

The hotel is 1 mile outside Kenmare. Follow the Glengarriff road, take first turn on left and hotel is ½ mile on the left.

“ William Power was the perfect host. The atmosphere was gracious and cultured, the food exceptional and interesting ”

Hilary Rubinstein, The Good Hotel Guide

Country house hotel and restaurant

TINAKILLY HOUSE

Splendid fresh food in elegant Victorian surroundings

In the Garden of Ireland, a stone's throw from Dublin, stands Tinakilly House, nestling in seven acres of gardens that sweep down to the Irish Sea. Built for Captain Robert Halpin, Commander of the “Great Eastern” which laid the transatlantic telegraph cables, the house exhibits ornate interiors rich in period furnishings, oil paintings and seafaring memorabilia.

Tinakilly House a country manor, is now the home of the Power family who, together with their friendly staff, bid you a warm welcome.

Each of the 29 bedrooms is a perfect blend of Victorian splendour and modern comfort. The Admirals Suites and Junior Suites enjoy breathtaking sea views.

The award-winning kitchen is famed for its fresh country house cuisine. The fish and lamb are local and embellished with vegetables and herbs from the kitchen garden. Bee Power bakes delicious brown bread daily and the wines have been carefully selected to complement house specialities. The most valued tribute comes from the many guests who return again and again.

Nearby are some excellent equestrian and golfing facilities; in addition to the enchanting gardens of Wicklow, its mountains, lakes, valleys and historic sites.

Tinakilly offers special sporting packages and evening entertainment.

LOCATION

Follow the main Dublin-Wexford road, the N11/M11 to Rathnew village and the R570 towards Wicklow town. Entrance is on left hand side 500 metres outside of Rathnew village.

Rathnew, Co Wicklow
Republic of Ireland

Telephone +353 (0)404 69274
Fax +353 (0)404 67806

PROPRIETORS

William and Bee Power

ROOM RATES

Single occupancy	*Ir £85- £110*
10 Doubles/Twins	*Ir £110 - £126*
4 Four-posters	*Ir £140 - £160*
12 Junior Suites	*Ir £140 - £160*
3 Admirals Suites	*Ir £180 - £200*

Includes full breakfast and VAT

CHARGE/CREDIT CARDS

• *DC* • *JCB* • *MC* • *VI*

ACCOLADES

I.T.B. ★★★★
R.A.C. Blue Ribbon Award ★★★
A.A. ★★★ ❀❀
The Good Hotel Guide
Top Wine List in Ireland Award 1994
Hotel Breakfast of the Year 1994/95

FACILITIES

Garden, croquet, tennis, putting green, heli-pad
3 meeting rooms/max 100 people
Riding and fishing nearby

RESTRICTIONS

No pets

ATTRACTIONS

Glendalough Monastic Site, Powerscourt Gardens & Waterfall, Mount Usher Gardens, Trinity College Dublin and Book of Kells

AFFILIATIONS

Ireland's Blue Book
The Celebrated Hotels Collection

NEAREST

MAJOR CITY:
Dublin - 29 miles/45 mins
MAJOR AIRPORT:
Dublin - 40 miles/1¼ hrs
RAILWAY STATION:
Wicklow - 2 miles/5 mins

RESERVATIONS

Toll free in US: 800-233-6510
Toll free fax in US: 800-426-5096

ACCESS CODES

AMADEUS IA DUBTIN
SYSTEM 1 EA DUBTIN
AXESS JL 3917
APOLLO UA 63871
SAHARA XS DUB 19868
SABRE AA 24203
WORLDSPAN IP 19868

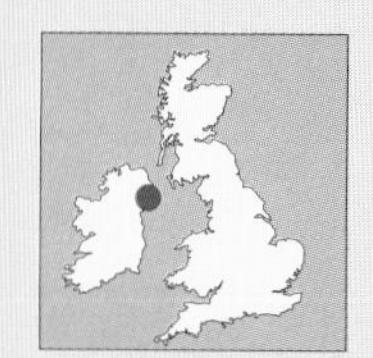

" I loved your beautiful house and you made us warm, welcome and well fed "

Valerie Singleton, television presenter

TYRELLA HOUSE

Family home

Downpatrick,
Co Down BT30 8SU
Northern Ireland

Telephone +44 (0)1396 851422
Fax +44 (0)1396 851422

OWNERS

David and Sally Corbett

ROOM RATES

1 Single £37.50 - £42.50
2 Doubles/Twins £65 - £76
Includes full breakfast and VAT

CHARGE/CREDIT CARDS

• *VI*

ACCOLADES

Independent

FACILITIES

Garden, Japanese water garden croquet, tennis, mini-golf, riding, polo and walking
Golf, hill climbing and fishing nearby

RESTRICTIONS

No children under 8 yrs
No facilities for disabled guests
No dogs in house

ATTRACTIONS

Castle Ward, Donegal Highlands, Castlewellan Arboretum, Mount Stewart, Yeats country, Strangford Lough, Lough Gill, Downpatrick Museum and Steam Railway, Glenreagh Castle and Gardens

AFFILIATIONS

Independent

NEAREST

MAJOR CITY:
Belfast - 30 miles/1 hr

MAJOR AIRPORT:
Belfast - 30 miles/1 hr 10 mins
Dublin - 100 miles/2¼ hrs

RAILWAY STATION:
Newry - 25 miles/40 mins

RESERVATIONS

Direct with hotel

ACCESS CODES

Not applicable

Tyrella's farmlands sweep down to a private beach

Hidden away under the Mourne Mountains and sheltered from the sea breezes by woods of tall beech, Tyrella's grasslands sweep down to a private sandy beach.

Not so much an hotel, more of a family home open for visitors, Tyrella is a wonderful place to relax after a day discovering some of Ulster's little known delights. You can unwind in front of a log fire and contemplate a delicious dinner of perhaps home grown lamb and vegetables from the garden. In season there may be locally caught lobster or wild salmon. For those with energy to spare there is lawn tennis or croquet or a walk in the woods to explore the Victorian Japanese Water Garden.

Riding on the powerful Irish Hunters for which Ireland is famous, let them take you over one of their cross country courses (there are small jumps as well as more advanced ones spread over the 300 acre working farm) or gallop on the sandy beach that stretches for miles in either direction. Up the mountain tracks of Mourne you will be on some of the best riding country in Ireland. Visitors with their own horses are welcome.

For garden and architecture lovers there is the National Trust's Mountstewart, Castleward and Rowellen. Try sea or lake fishing or play golf at Newcastle. Tyrella House is also well placed for racing at Downpatrick or the Maze (stables and gallops are available here too).

For those that prefer, there are some well equipped self catering cottages.

LOCATION

From Clough to Ardglass take the A2 for 4 miles until reaching stone wall and follow for ½ mile until gates with wooden name plaque.

" I came tired and left relaxed. One of the best hotels in the world "

Michael & Irene Dowd, New York

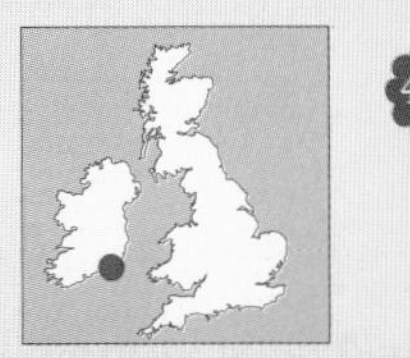

11th century castle

WATERFORD CASTLE

A castle with its own 18-hole golf course set on a 310-acre island

Waterford Castle dates back to the 11th century and is former home to the Fitzgerald family. It is located two miles from Waterford city and is uniquely situated on its own private 310 acre island surrounded by woodlands and an 18-hole golf course in the estuary of the River Suir.

Proceed to the water's edge and the island's ferry waits to take you across a channel of centuries, for here is both retreat and refuge, sanctuary and seclusion. A stone arched doorway leads to the castle's main entrance hall where a crackling log fire welcomes to all its guests.

Dinner is served each evening in the award winning Elizabethan oak-panelled dining room using fresh local produce where possible prepared by the castle's head chef Paul McCluskey. Last year the castle was awarded Bridgestone's top 100 restaurants in Ireland and the restaurant has also been awarded two AA rosettes.

The castle offers accommodation of a very high standard. It includes superb four-poster suites and deluxe twin and double rooms. All rooms are individually decorated to reflect the quality throughout.

Leisure facilities on the island include an 18 hole championship golf course, Ireland's only true island golf designed by Irish professional Des Smyth. Within the grounds is an indoor heated swimming pool, tennis courts, croquet and garden walks.

LOCATION

From the city of Waterford, cross bridge and keep left along river for 1 mile. Left at traffic lights and travel for 2 miles towards ferry. Castle is on the left.

The Island, Ballinakill, Waterford, Republic of Ireland

Telephone +353 (0)51 78203
Fax +353 (0)51 79316

PROPRIETOR

E J Kearns

RATES PER PERSON

14 Doubles/Twins Ir£75 - £100
5 Deluxe Four-Posters Suites Ir£135 - £175
Includes VAT

CHARGE/CREDIT CARDS

• DC • MC • VI

ACCOLADES

R.A.C. ★★★★ + Merit Awards H C & R
A.A. ★★★★ ❀❀ 75%

FACILITIES

Garden, croquet, tennis, indoor pool, 18-hole championship golf course, heli-pad
2 meeting rooms/max 28 people
Fishing and riding nearby

RESTRICTIONS

Dogs in kennels only

ATTRACTIONS

Waterford Crystal, Kilkenny and Lismore Castles, local beaches

AFFILIATIONS

Independent

NEAREST

MAJOR CITY:
Waterford - 3 miles/5 mins

MAJOR AIRPORT:
Dublin - 109 miles/2½ hrs

RAILWAY STATION:
Waterford - 3 miles/5 mins

RESERVATIONS

Toll free in US: 800-221-1074

ACCESS CODES

Not applicable

Pleasure & Leisure finder

A fun guide to Britain & Ireland

MOTOR MUSEUMS

SCOTLAND

Myreton Motor Museum, Aberlady, East Lothian. Tel: 01875 7288/01875 53117

Glenluce Motor Museum, Glenluce, Wigtownshire. Tel: 01572 767280/01572 767386

The Motor Museum, Mill Two, New Lanark Mills, Lanark

Melrose Motor Museum, Annay Road, Melrose, Borders Tel: 0189 6822624

Moray Motor Museum, Lossibank Woollen Mills, Bishopmill, Elgin, Moray. Tel: 01343 44933

Doune Motor Museum, Carse of Cambus, Doune, Perthshire Tel: 01786 841203

Highland Motor Heritage Centre, Bankfoot, Perthshire Tel: 01709 558701

NORTH COUNTRY

Mouldsworth Motor Museum, The Balcony House, Erindale Crescent, Frodsham, Cheshire. Tel: 01923 831781

Hebden Bridge. Automobilia, Billy Lane, Old Town, Hebden Bridge, West Yorkshire. Tel: 01422 844775

Cars of the Stars, Standish Street, Keswick, Cumbria. Tel: 017687 73757/017687 72810

Lakeland Motor Museum, Holker Hall, Cark in Cartmel, Cumbria. Tel 0153 9558509

Newburn Hall Motor Museum, 35 Townfield Gardens, Newburn, Tyne and Wear. Tel: 0191 2642977

Yorkshire Car Collection, Grange Street, Keighley, West Yorkshire. Tel: 01535 690499

WALES

Betws-y-Coed Motor Museum, Betws-y-Coed, Caerns, North Wales. Tel: 01690 710632.

Llangollen Motor Museum, Petrefelin, Llangollen, Clwyd. Tel: 01978 860324

Pembrokeshire Motor Museum, Keeston Hill, Haverfordwest, Pembrokeshire. Tel: 01437 710950

Amguedda Madog Motor Museum, Portmadog, North Wales. Tel: 01758 712308

MIDSHIRES

Cotswold Motor Museum, The Old Mill, Bourton on the Water, Gloucestershire. Tel: 01451 821225

Midland Motor Museum, Stanmore Hall, Stourbridge Road, Bridgnorth, Shropshire Tel: 01746 761761

Bugatti Trust, Prescott, Cotherington, Cheltenham, Gloucestershire Tel: 01242 677201

Jaguar/Daimler Heritage, Jaguar Cars Ltd, Coventry. Tel: 01203 402102

Donington Collection (Racing Cars), Donington Park, Castle Donington, Derby. Tel: 01332 810048

Caister Castle Motor Museum, Caister on Sea, Great Yarmouth, Norfolk. Tel: 0157 284251

Sandringham Museum (Royal Cars), The Estate Office, Sandringham, Norfolk. Tel: 01553 772675

WEST COUNTRY

Atwell-Wilson Motor Museum, Downside, Stockley, Calne, Wiltshire. Tel: 01249 813119.

The Motor House, Christchurch Ski & Leisure Centre, Matchams Lane, Hurn, Christchurch, Dorset. Tel: 01202 488100

Automobilia, The Old Mill, St Stephen, St Austell, Cornwall. Tel: 01726 823092

Totnes Motor Museum, Steamer Quay, Totnes, Devon. Tel: 01803 862777

Weston-super-Mare Motoring & Memorabilia Museum, Chestnut House, 4 Chestnut Chase, Nailsea, Avon Tel: 01275 857855

Haynes Motor Museum, Sparkford, Near Yeovil, Somerset. Tel: 01963 440804

SOUTH

Beaulieu. National Motor Museum, Beaulieu, Hampshire. Tel: 01590 612345

Canterbury Motor Museum, 11 Cogans Terrace, Canterbury, Kent. Tel: 01227 464272

Bentley Wildfowl & Motor Museum, Halland, Near Lewes, East Sussex. Tel: 01825 840711

Vauxhall Heritage Centre, Luton, Bedfordshire. Tel: 01582 21122

Filching Manor Motor Museum, Wannock, Near Polegate, Sussex. Tel: 01323 487838

Ramsgate Motor Museum, Westcliff Hall, Ramsgate, Kent. Tel: 01843 581948

West Wycombe Motor Museum, Cockshoot Farm, Chorley Road, West Wycombe, Buckinghamshire. Tel: 01494 443329

Brooklands Museum, The Clubhouse, Brooklands Road, Weybridge, Surrey. Tel: 01932 857381

IRELAND

National Museum of Irish Transport, Scotts Garden, Killarney, County Kerry. Tel: 01103 5364 32638

Ulster Folk and Transport Museum, Cultra, Hollywood Tel: 01232 428428

ISLANDS

Jersey Motor Museum, St Peter's Village, Jersey, Channel Islands.

Murrays Motor Cycle Museum, Bungalow Corner TT Course, Snaefell Mountain, Isle of Man. Tel: 0162 486719

Manx Motor Museum, Crosby, Isle of Man. Tel: 01624 851236

TOP 20 ATTRACTIONS & PLEASURE PARKS

Alton Towers	*Midshires*
Madame Tussaud's	*London*
Tower of London	*London*
St Paul's Cathedral	*London*
Natural History Museum	*London*
Chessington World of Adventures	*South*
Thorpe Park	*South*
Science Museum	*London*
Blackpool Tower	*North*
Drayton Manor Park	*Midshires*
Edinburgh Castle	*Scotland*
Flamingo Land	*North*
Kew Gardens	*London*
Royal Academy	*London*
Roman Baths and Pump Room	*West*
London Zoo	*London*
Chester Zoo	*North*
Windsor Castle	*The South*
American Adventure	*Midshires*
Jorvik Viking Centre	*North*

British Tourist Authority

More on pages 150 and 446

Some Specialist Museums

Big Pit Mining Museum	Blaenafon, near Abergavenny, South Wales	*Wales*
Boot and Shoe Collection	Central Museum & Art Gallery, Northampton	*Midshires*
Centre for Alternative Technology	Environmental solutions, Machynlleth, Powys	*Wales*
Corinium Museum	Roman antiquities. Cirencester, Gloucestershire	*Midshires*
The Cutty Sark	World famous tea clipper, Greenwich	*London*
Eurotunnel Exhibition Centre	Folkestone, Kent	*South*
Flag Fen Excavations	3,000-year-old Bronze Age site, Fengate, Nr Peterborough	*Midshires*
Gilbert White's House	Home of the great naturalist, Selborne, Nr Alton	*South*
Highland Folk Museum	Kingussie, near Aviemore	*Scotland*
Housesteads Roman Fort	Britain's most complete surviving Roman fort	*North*
Ironbridge Gorge Museum	250-year-old works of the Shropshire ironmasters	*Midshires*
Maritime Museum	Collection of ancient and modern model ships, Greenwich	*London*
Merchant Adventurers' Hall	Medieval guild hall, York	*North*
Museum of Childhood	Edinburgh	*Scotland*
Museum of the Moving Image	Movies and TV, South Bank, Waterloo	*London*
National Horseracing Museum	Newmarket, Suffolk	*Midshires*
HMS Victory	Nelson's flagship at the Battle of Trafalgar, Portsmouth	*South*
Welsh Industrial & Maritime Museum	Cardiff Bay	*Wales*
William Grant Distilleries	Scotch Whisky, Dufftown	*Scotland*
Wimbledon Lawn Tennis Museum	All England Club, Wimbledon	*London*

Islands

Mont Orgueil Castle that overlooks St Helier, the capital of Jersey. The island has its own government, its own currency and its own language, French Patois.

Heritage sites

The following heritage sites can be found on the map overleaf. The key numbers show where they are located.

ISLE OF SKYE

Dunvegan Castle	1

ISLE OF MULL

Mull Duart Castle	2

IONA

St Columba's Abbey & St Oran's Cemetery	3

ORKNEYS

St Magnus Cathedral	4

ISLE OF MAN

The Laxey Wheel	5
Castle Rushen	6

HOLY ISLAND

Lindisfarne Priory	7

ARAN ISLANDS

St Benan's Church	8

GUERNSEY

Castle Cornet	9

ISLE OF WIGHT

Osborne House	10
Carisbrooke Castle	11

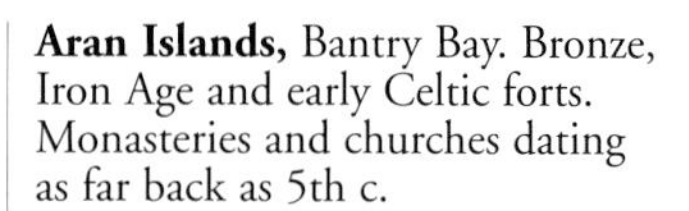

Sailing off the Isles of Scilly is 'Genesis', a 45ft Bermudan cutter exclusively available to guests of St Martins Hotel (see page 462).

Aran Islands, Bantry Bay. Bronze, Iron Age and early Celtic forts. Monasteries and churches dating as far back as 5th c.

Arran. 'Scotland in miniature'. Streams, glens, lochs and the Goat Fell mountain. Bronze Age cairns. King's Caves sheltered Robert the Bruce in the 14th c. Brodick port and holiday village.

Colonsay, Inner Hebrides. Beautiful and unspoilt.

Fair Isle. Midway between Orkneys and Shetlands. Over 300 species of birds, from Atlantic swift to osprey.

Farne Islands. Swarming bird colonies, and seals.

Guernsey, Channel Islands, South. Town and harbour St Peter Port. French and English languages. Guernsey and UK coinages.

Hebrides, Outer. Ferries from Oban sail to magic seascapes. Iona was the cradle of Christianity in Scotland. On Staffa, Fingal's Cave has not changed since it inspired Mendelssohn.

Hebrides, Outer, Wild rugged colourful islands, stretching over 130 miles. Harris gave its name to the tweed. Benbecula saw the escape of Bonnie Prince Charlie in 1746.

Holy Island. Linked to mainland by three-mile causeway. Bishop Eadfrith compiled the Lindisfarne Gospels c AD 700. Vikings invaded in 793.

Islay, Inner Hebrides. Malt whiskies, Celtic crosses. Monument on the Oa commemorates 650 US sailors lost at sea in 1918.

Jersey, Channel Isles. Largest Channel Island. A treasury of flowers. Jersey cows and potatoes.

Around the mainland islands of Britain and Ireland are many smaller islands to visit. You can get away from it all, and even stay in a Best Loved Hotel. You can spend time free from hustle and bustle, yet enjoy active facilities and events. You can live close to rare animals, birds, wild plants and flowers and special island breeds like Shetland ponies, Manx cats, Jersey and Guernsey cows. You can climb rugged mountains, walk through peaceful gardens, and you are always close to the sea.

The independent character of the islands shows in practical things: the Isle of Man mints its own coins; Lundy prints its own stamps; the Channel Islands set their taxes on beers and wines and cigarettes much lower than on the mainland. Nowhere else in the world are scenes like the sea-sculpted rocks of the Orkneys, the magnificent cliffs of Mull, the multi-coloured sandstone layers at Alum Bay on the Isle of Wight. Several islands have their own languages: Manx on Man, French patois on the Channel Islands, old Norse was spoken by Orcadians and Shetlanders until the 18th century and lives on in place-names.

Never think that history passed the islands by. Norsemen and Vikings marauded on the Orkneys, Shetlands and Farne Islands in the first millennium. The Isle of Man's Tynwald Parliament was established long before the one at Westminster. Queen Victoria had her summer residence on the Isle of Wight. The Channel Islands were the only part of Britain occupied during the Second World War.

The islanders are proud of the beauty and traditions of their islands. They are eager to share them with visitors. The islands become ever easier to reach, with ferries, airports, road and rail crossings. If you have never visited one of the islands, now is a good time to start. It could become your Best Loved holiday ever.

Jura. Rugged and mountainous. Three high peaks and its own loch.

Lundy. Two-hour steamer trip from Ilfracombe. Famous for its puffins, and its own stamps.

Man, Isle of. The island has its own Celtic language, Parliament, laws, taxes . . . Peel kippers and tail-less Manx cats. Robert the Bruce landed at Ramsey in 1313.

Mull, Inner Hebrides. Forest, mountain and Rannoch Moor setting of Stevenson's *Kidnapped*. Spanish treasure galleon Florida was blown up in Tobermory Bay in 1588.

Orkneys. 65 islands. The capital Kirkwall on Mainland is a busy harbour town. Nine RSPB nature reserves.

Sark, Channel Islands. Caves and rock-worn bays. Car-free.

Scilly Isles, West. Spring flowers bloom on these mild islands as early as November. Seabirds, seals, porpoises, dolphins.

Shetlands. Over 100 islands. 15 are inhabited. Britain's most northerly islands stretch further north than Alaska, yet the Gulf Stream keeps the climate mild. Shetland ponies. RSPB nature reserves. More prehistoric sites per acre than anywhere else in Britain. Midnight sun in June.

Skye, Isle of. Castles, weapons and relics of heroes. 4,000 years of bravery and magic. A rich treasury of wildlife and flowers. Fishing and climbing in the Cullin mountains. Pony trekking.

Wight, Isle of. High chalk downs and chines beside the sea. When Queen Victoria established her summer residence here, it became the holiday Mecca of Victorian Britain.

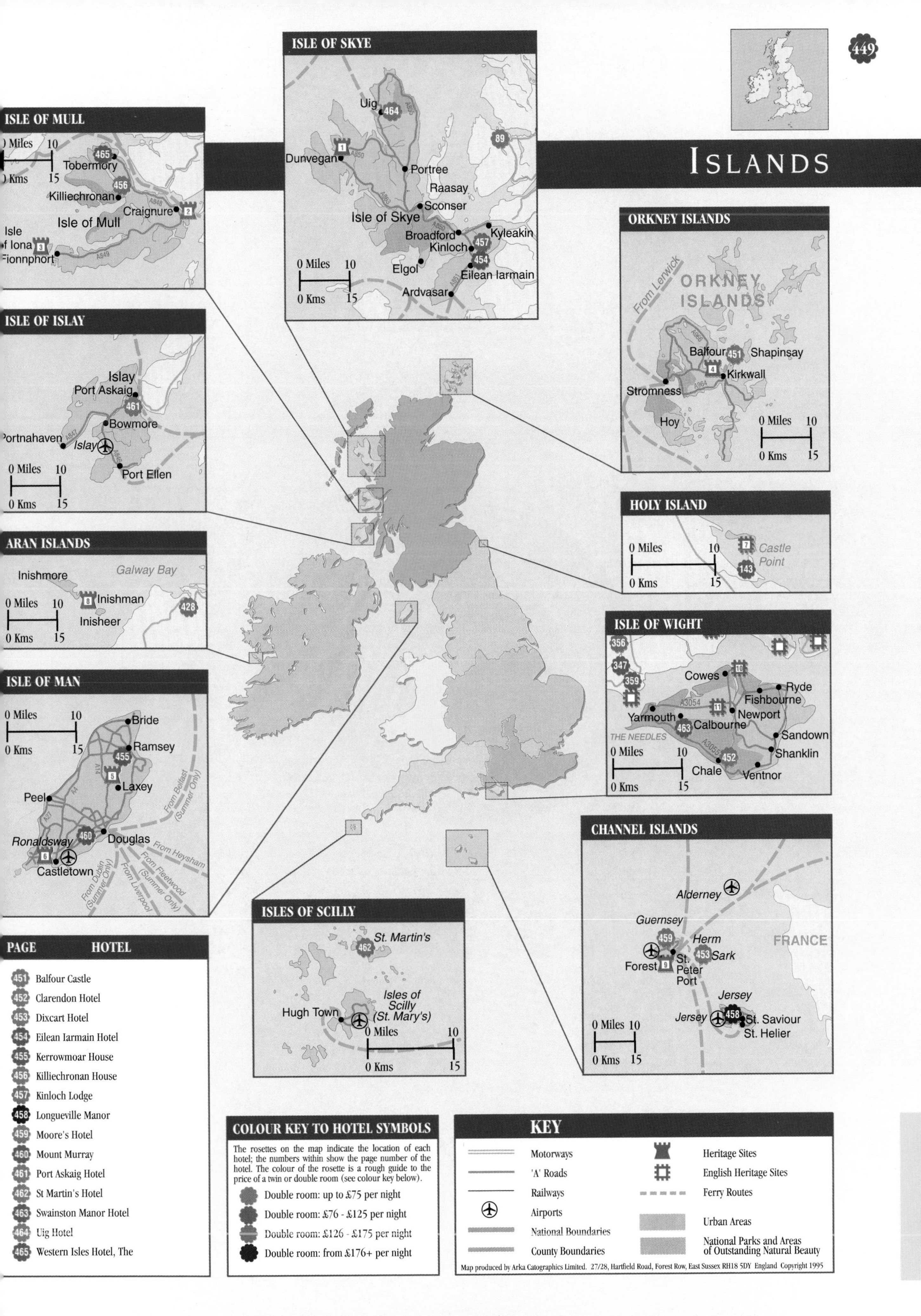

449
ISLANDS
ISLE OF SKYE
Uig
464
A855
89
Dunvegan
1
A850
Portree
Raasay
A863
Sconser
Isle of Skye
A850
Broadford
Kyleakin
457
Kinloch
454
Eilean Iarmain
Elgol
A851
Ardvasar
0 Miles 10
0 Kms 15
ISLE OF MULL
0 Miles 10
0 Kms 15
465
Tobermory
456
Killiechronan
A848
Craignure
2
Isle of Mull
Isle of Iona
3
Fionnphort
A849
ISLE OF ISLAY
Islay
Port Askaig
461
Bowmore
Portnahaven
A847
Islay
A846
Port Ellen
0 Miles 10
0 Kms 15
ARAN ISLANDS
Inishmore
Galway Bay
0 Miles 10
0 Kms 15
8
Inishman
Inisheer
428
ISLE OF MAN
0 Miles 10
0 Kms 15
Bride
Ramsey
455
A14
5
Laxey
Peel
A4
A21
460
Douglas
Ronaldsway
6
Castletown
From Belfast (Summer Only)
From Heysham
From Fleetwood (Summer Only)
From Liverpool
From Dublin (Summer Only)
ORKNEY ISLANDS
From Lerwick
ORKNEY ISLANDS
A966
Balfour
451
Shapinsay
4
Kirkwall
A964
Stromness
Hoy
0 Miles 10
0 Kms 15
HOLY ISLAND
0 Miles 10
0 Kms 15
7
Castle Point
143
ISLE OF WIGHT
356
347
359
Cowes
10
Ryde
Fishbourne
A3054
11
Newport
Yarmouth
463
Calbourne
THE NEEDLES
Sandown
A3055
0 Miles 10
0 Kms 15
452
Shanklin
Chale
Ventnor
CHANNEL ISLANDS
Alderney
Guernsey
459
Herm
FRANCE
453
Sark
Forest
9
St. Peter Port
Jersey
Jersey
458
St. Saviour
St. Helier
0 Miles 10
0 Kms 15
ISLES OF SCILLY
St. Martin's
462
Isles of Scilly (St. Mary's)
Hugh Town
0 Miles 10
0 Kms 15
PAGE HOTEL
451 Balfour Castle
452 Clarendon Hotel
453 Dixcart Hotel
454 Eilean Iarmain Hotel
455 Kerrowmoar House
456 Killiechronan House
457 Kinloch Lodge
458 Longueville Manor
459 Moore's Hotel
460 Mount Murray
461 Port Askaig Hotel
462 St Martin's Hotel
463 Swainston Manor Hotel
464 Uig Hotel
465 Western Isles Hotel, The
COLOUR KEY TO HOTEL SYMBOLS
The rosettes on the map indicate the location of each hotel; the numbers within show the page number of the hotel. The colour of the rosette is a rough guide to the price of a twin or double room (see colour key below).
Double room: up to £75 per night
Double room: £76 - £125 per night
Double room: £126 - £175 per night
Double room: from £176+ per night
KEY
Motorways
'A' Roads
Railways
Airports
National Boundaries
County Boundaries
Heritage Sites
English Heritage Sites
Ferry Routes
Urban Areas
National Parks and Areas of Outstanding Natural Beauty
Map produced by Arka Catographics Limited. 27/28, Hartfield Road, Forest Row, East Sussex RH18 5DY England Copyright 1995
ISLANDS

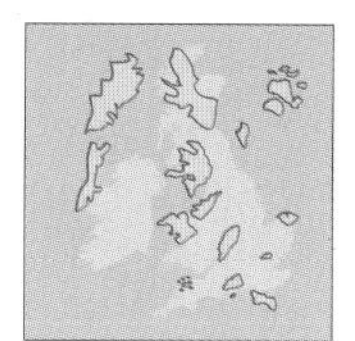

These dramatic stones were erected over 4000 years ago at Callanish on the island of Lewis, one of the Outer Hebrides.

TOURIST OFFICE INFORMATION

Further information about the Islands will be gladly supplied by:

Channel Islands
Jersey: ***Tel*** 01624 686766
Guernsey: ***Tel*** 01481 72 6611

Isle of Man
Douglas: ***Tel*** 01624 686766

Isle of Wight
Newport: ***Tel*** 01983 524 343

Scilly Isles
St Marys: ***Tel*** 01720 422 536

Isle of Mull
Tobermory: ***Tel*** 01688 2182

Isle of Islay
Bowmore: ***Tel*** 0149 681 254

Isle of Skye
Portree: ***Tel*** 01478 2137

Orkney Islands
Stromness: ***Tel*** 01856 850716

Fishing village of Cregheash on the Isle of Man.

CASTLES, STATELY HOMES, HISTORY & PRE-HISTORY

Aran Islands. Inisheer. Ruined 15th c castle of the O'Briens, who ruled the islands from 11th to 16th c.

Arran. Brodick Castle, built in 1456, former home of the Dukes of Hamilton.

Jersey. Hougue Bie chamber tomb dates from Stone Age (2000 BC).

Man, Isle of. Castle Rushen, one of Britain's finest medieval castles.

Mull. Duart Castle, 13th century stronghold of the Lord of the Isles, now home of the Chief of the Clan MacLean. Moy Castle on Loch Buie has a water-filled dungeon.

Orkneys. Earl's Palace, Kirkwall. Built for the 2nd Earl of Orkney, Patrick Stewart, hanged as a tyrant in 1614.

Orkneys. Maes Howe, near Finstown on Mainland, is the finest Stone Age tomb in Britain.

Skye. Dunvegan Castle, ancestral home of the clan MacLeod of Macleod. They here for over 700 years. Here, in 1577, they asphyxiated 395 members of the neighbouring clan MacDonald.

Wight, Isle of, near Cowes. **Osborne House**, built as an Italian villa by Cubitt for Queen Victoria. Visit the private and State apartments.

Wight, Isle of. Carisbrooke Castle. Mighty 12th c Norman castle, built on site of Roman fort. Charles I imprisoned here in 17th c.

MUSEUMS, GALLERIES & ATTRACTIONS

Jersey. German Occupation Museum

Jersey. Jersey Museum. The story of the island from earliest times to present day.

Man, Isle of. Castletown Nautical Museum. Manx National Museum, Douglas. Motorcycle Museum, Snaefell.

Shetlands. Lerwick celebrates old Norse fire festival of '**Up-Helly-Aa**', burning a 30-ft model of a Viking ship.

CHURCHES, CATHEDRALS, ABBEYS

Anglesey, Isle of. Cruciform church of **St Cybi,** with 13th c chapel.

Holy Island. Ruins of 11th c **Benedictine chapel**.

Iona. 8th c **St Oran's chapel**. Benedictine Abbey with unique 'Street of the Dead'. Reilig Odhrain, the kings' graveyard: four Irish, eight Norwegian and 48 Scottish kings including Macbeth.

Orkneys. Kirkwall. **St Magnus's Cathedral.** Founded in 1137 in memory of Norse ruler Magnus, murdered by a rival Earl. St Magnus's skull was discovered during renovations in 1919.

WILDLIFE & GARDENS

Colonsay. Sub-tropical garden at **Colonsay House.**

Jersey. Gerald Durrell's **Jersey Zoological Park.**

Jersey. Eric Young Orchid Foundation.

Scilly Isles. Sub-tropical **Botanic Gardens** on island of Tresco.

SPORT & OUTDOORS

Man, Isle of. Motor cycle Tourist Trophy races in June, car rally in September – all on public roads.

Skye. Highland games. August.

Wight, Isle of. Cowes Week. One of the world's great international regattas. August.

Wight, Isle of. Round-The-Island sailing race. June.

The Needles, huge chalk stacks on the western tip of the Isle of Wight. A familiar sight to yachtsmen and women taking part in the Admiral's Cup, the Round the Island Race and to many round-the-world sailors.

“ There is much doubt whether one should reveal this lovely place to a living soul ”

Hugo Jensen, Norway

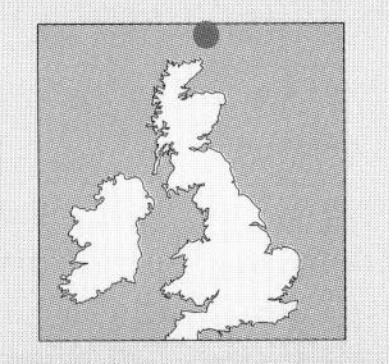

Island castle

BALFOUR CASTLE

Shapinsay,
Orkney Islands KW17 2DY

Telephone 01856 711282
Fax 01856 711283

OWNERS
Catherine A Zawadski,
Patricia and Andrew Lidderdale

RATES PER PERSON

3 Doubles	£68
2 Four-posters	£68
2 Suites	£68

Includes full breakfast, dinner and VAT
30% discount for under 12's

CHARGE/CREDIT CARDS

• MC • VI

ACCOLADES
The Good Hotel Guide

FACILITIES
Garden, snooker, fishing, hotel speedboat
3 meeting rooms/max 80 people
Golf, fishing and birdwatching nearby

RESTRICTIONS
No facilities for disabled guests
No pets

ATTRACTIONS
The Orkney Islands, archaeological sights, wildlife, St Magnus Cathedral, Skara Brae, Music Festival

AFFILIATIONS
Independent

NEAREST
MAJOR CITY:
Aberdeen - 200 miles/50 mins

MAJOR AIRPORT:
Inverness - 140 miles/35 mins
Kirkwall - 4 miles/30 mins

FERRY PORT:
Kirkwall - 4 miles/30 mins
Scabster/John O'Groats - 45 mins

RESERVATIONS
Direct with hotel

ACCESS CODES
Not applicable

Still a family home after 146 years – now open to just a few

The seven spires of Balfour Castle and the 12th century Norwegian tower of St Magnus Cathedral are the landmarks of Shapinsay, one of the rugged islands of the Orkneys, small enough to walk across and back in a day. The Mor Stone, dating back some 5000 years and a fort or broch predating the Vikings are evidence of man's ancient tenure of the island.

The clean, sandy beaches and cliff walks make for invigorating walks with plenty of wildlife, notably a great variety of seabirds, to be seen. The hotel's private motor boat will take you fishing or to the nearby islands, uninhabited except for colonies of seals.

Balfour Castle, built in 1848 in the Victorian Gothic style, still retains the original carpets and furniture. The en suite bedrooms have been updated to provide every comfort and facility. Your stay will be very much en famille.

The Victorian walled garden and the home farm provide an abundance of fresh meat, fruit and vegetables while the local fishermen harvest a catch of excellent fish and shellfish. The result: wonderful home cooking to be relished and remembered.

Getting to the Orkneys is easier than you may think. The air connection with mainland Scotland is good and the ferry to Kirkwall takes 25 minutes.

LOCATION

From Kirkwall to Shapinsay, 2 minutes from the harbour.

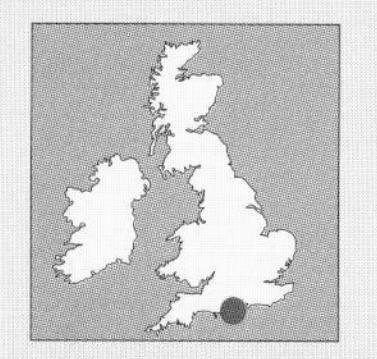

"Came for a day, stayed for four. Will definitely be back for more"

Colin & Maureen Banks, Hatfield

CLARENDON HOTEL & WIGHT MOUSE INN — *19th century inn*

Chale,
Isle of Wight PO38 2HA

Telephone 01983 730431
Fax 01983 730431

PROPRIETORS
John and Jean Bradshaw

RATES PER ROOM
13 Doubles/Twins £58 - £66
2 luxury suites available
Includes full breakfast and VAT

CHARGE/CREDIT CARDS
MC • VI

ACCOLADES
E.T.B. ♛♛♛ Highly Commended
R.A.C. ★★ + Merit Awards H & C
A.A. ★★ 65%
UK Family Pub of the Year Award 1995/96
UK Whisky Pub of the Year 1994

FACILITIES
Garden, pool table, riding, walking, live entertainment nightly
Fishing nearby

RESTRICTIONS
No facilities for disabled guests
No pets in dining room

ATTRACTIONS
Blackgang Chine,
The Needles,
Osborne House,
Carisbrooke Castle

AFFILIATIONS
Independent

NEAREST
MAJOR CITY:
Portsmouth - 1 hr/20 mins (by ferry)

MAJOR AIRPORT:
London Gatwick - 78 miles/2¾ hrs

RAILWAY STATION:
Shanklin - 10 miles/15 mins

FERRY PORT:
Yarmouth - 15 miles/20 mins
Cowes - 15 miles/30 mins
Fishbourne - 15 miles/30 mins

RESERVATIONS
Direct with hotel

ACCESS CODES
Not applicable

The perfect holiday hotel, whatever your pleasure, whatever your age

How do you rate an hotel? If its location is paramount, The Clarendon Hotel would be hard to beat. It stands on the south west slopes of the Isle of Wight overlooking Chale Bay, one of the finest areas in the country for beaches.

If you are interested in history, look no further: The great oak beams in the property came from the wreck that sank in Chale Bay in 1836; nearby Blackgang Chine was once the haunt of pirates; a short drive will take you to Carisbrooke Castle where King Charles was imprisoned; Tennyson was inspired to write "Idylls of a King" on Tennyson Downs; and Queen Victoria's, Osborne House, is just across the island.

If it is comfort and hospitality you seek, you will find it here in generous proportions: John and Jean Bradshaw have won all kinds of awards and many new friends who 'discover' this hotel. The rooms are comfortable, prettily furnished and well-appointed for your convenience.

If it's sport you're after, this is the place for you: golf, fishing (freshwater and sea), shooting and riding can all be arranged for you. There is excellent surfing at Compton Bay and sailing at Bembridge or watching it at Cowes.

If a good drink is important, the Wight Mouse Inn (see below) is an absolute find! There are six splendid, well-kept real ales and a selection of 365 malt whiskies that could blind you to all else!

And if you happen to be a child, this place *is* heaven: there are facilities indoors and out, on the premises or nearby, guaranteed to fill your days with endless pleasure.

LOCATION

From Yarmouth travel along the A3054/5. From Cowes/Fishbourne travel to Newport, taking the A3020 signposted Chale.

" A quiet state of grace "

Marianne Curphey, The Times

16th century farmhouse

DIXCART HOTEL

An old fashioned welcome to peaceful life on the feudal island of Sark

Family owned and managed, Dixcart is the oldest established hotel on the Isle of Sark. It played an important part in the island's history. Dixcart still has its own seat in Sark Parliament. Prince Henry, Edward VII, and writers Victor Hugo and A C Swinburne all stayed at Dixcart, then Sark's only hotel. It is the original 16th century farm "longhouse" of La Jaspellerie Tenement. It has 40 acres of land with medieval hand-terraced gardens, fields, a densely wooded valley and Dixcart Bay, a sheltered beach and landing place in use since Roman times.

All the single, double and family bedrooms are en suite and centrally heated. There are three comfortable lounges and a residents/diners bar with log fires. The candlelit restaurant offers beautifully presented food and wines with the emphasis on "value for money". The Public Bar serves a wide range of snacks and seafood dishes.

Sark is the smallest independent state in the British Commonwealth. Cars are banned. The magical, feudal island is almost untouched by the 20th century. Your luggage arrives by tractor, you on foot, bike or horse and cart. You smell and touch beautiful wild flowers, see wild animals as they were on Sark a thousand years ago. You experience peace and quiet as nowhere else in the world, yet you also receive the warmest of welcomes from the people at Dixcart and Sark's 600 other residents.

LOCATION

Left at end of main avenue, past old prison on outskirts of the village.

Isle of Sark
Channel Islands GY9 0SD

Telephone 01481 832015
Fax 01481 832164

PROPRIETORS
Mr and Mrs J Brannam

RATES PER PERSON
3 Singles £25 - £35
12 Doubles/Twins £25 - £35
Includes full breakfast

CHARGE/CREDIT CARDS

• DC • MC • VI

ACCOLADES
Independent

FACILITIES
1 meeting room/max 20 people
Garden, snooker, fishing
caving, cycling, walking and swimming nearby

RESTRICTIONS
No facilities for disabled guests
Pets from UK only
No cars

ATTRACTIONS
La Seigneurie Gardens, Woodturner, glassblower, potters, silversmith, Venus pool, La Coupée Isthmus, Horse and cart travel, VAT exempt

AFFILIATIONS
Logis of Great Britain
Les Routiers

NEAREST
MAJOR CITY:
St Peter Port - 9 miles by boat

MAJOR AIRPORT:
Guernsey - 15 miles by boat and taxi

FERRY PORT:
Guernsey - 9 miles by boat

RESERVATIONS
Direct with hotel

ACCESS CODES
Not applicable

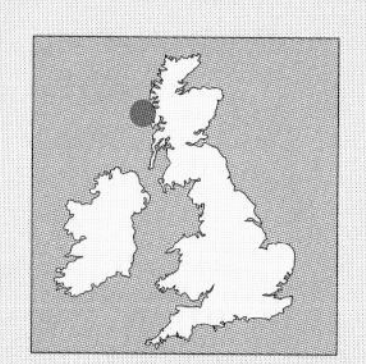

“ Still a great pleasure to stay at the best hotel in Skye, lovely welcome, gorgeous food ”

Lady Christian Innes, Ross-shire

HOTEL EILEAN IARMAIN

Victorian house

Sleat,
Isle of Skye IV43 8QR

Telephone 01471 833332
Fax 01471 833275

OWNERS
Sir Iain and Lady Noble

GENERAL MANAGER
Effie Kennedy

ROOM RATES

Single occupancy	£60
10 Doubles	£85 - £90
1 Triple	£115 - £120
1 Four-poster	£95

Includes full breakfast and VAT

CHARGE/CREDIT CARDS

• MC • VI

ACCOLADES
S.T.B. ♛♛♛ Commended
R.A.C. ★ + Merit Awards H & R
A.A.★ ❀ 70%
A.A. Courtesy & Care Award 1995
Taste of Scotland

FACILITIES
Garden, shooting, fishing, heli-pad
2 meeting rooms/max 150 people

RESTRICTIONS
No facilities for disabled guests

ATTRACTIONS
Clan Donald Centre,
Dunvegan Castle,
Aros Heritage Centre,
Talisker Distillery,
Hotel Eilean Iarmain Art Gallery

AFFILIATIONS
Independent

NEAREST
MAJOR CITY:
Glasgow - 148 miles/4½ hrs

MAJOR AIRPORT:
Inverness - 93 miles/2½ hrs

RAILWAY STATION:
Kyle of Lochalsh - 14 miles/30 mins

FERRY PORT:
Mallaig/Armadale - 8 miles/15 mins

RESERVATIONS
Direct with hotel

ACCESS CODES
Not applicable

An enchanted atmosphere reflecting the legends and romance of Skye

Built in 1888, this small, privately owned hotel has retained its Victorian charm and old-world character.

Hotel Eilean Iarmain is situated on the small rocky bay of Isle Ornsay in the south of Skye, with expansive views over the Sound of Sleat to the Knoydart hills.

The twelve bedrooms, which have views of the hills or sea, are decorated and furnished in traditional style. Each bedroom has its own charm: “The Tower Room”, panelled in old pine, and “The Leabaidh Mhor”, with a canopied bed from nearby Armadale Castle, to name two of them.

There are log fires in the reception rooms, and a panelled dining room where candlelit dinners can be enjoyed overlooking the bay.

In the award-winning restaurant, the dinner menu, of four courses, combines imaginative cooking with the variety of fresh local produce, including fish and shellfish landed at the old stone pier, oysters and game from the estate, home baked bread and oatcakes. The extensive and interesting wine list has been selected by the proprietors with the aim of offering some unusual wines with fascinating historical provenances, as well as a very good range of more famous wines.

Hotel Eilean Iarmain is open year round.

LOCATION

From Armadale follow the A851 for 15 minutes, then on right-hand side follow sign for A852 to Eilean Iarmain.

"I'd surrender my molars to live there permanently!"

Hilary Ivory, Esquire Magazine

Georgian house

KERROWMOAR HOUSE

Welcome to a magnificent Georgian home on the Isle of Man

Kerrowmoar House is a magnificent Georgian house in the north of the Isle of Man, the home of Fred and Di Parkes. Visitors from all around the world and "locals" in search of a quiet break much enjoy this old country house, surrounded by paddocks and gardens.

The three delightful bedrooms in the house provide towelling dressing gowns and hair dryers, the two large bathrooms and shower room have fragrances, shampoo, body lotions, talcs, and other pampering ingredients. There is a charming mews apartment adjacent to the stables.

Kerrowmoar is ideally placed for a wonderful exploration of the island, fortified by magnificent breakfasts using locally and home grown produce. Not to mention the famous Manx Kipper!

Walk up through the gardens on to the Millennium way, established in 1979, to celebrate one thousand years of Tynwald, the Manx Parliament. This stretches for 28 miles over mountain and vale, from Ramsey to Castletown. Only for the wildly energetic! For the less serious, descend after three or four miles!

In the best of traditions, afternoon tea consisting of home baked everything, including scrumptious chocolate cake, fruit cake and other temptations, can be taken on the sun patio or if the weather deters around the log fire in the drawing room.

Kerrowmoar House offers an unusual and most enjoyable way to see the island way of life. Its guest book abounds with quotes such as: "Just like staying with old friends" and "I'm counting the days till next time!"

LOCATION

At Sulby on the A3 from Ramsey.

Sulby, Lezayre,
Ramsey,
Isle of Man IM7 2AX

Telephone 01624 897543
Fax 01624 897927

PROPRIETOR

Mrs Diana Parkes

ROOM RATES

Single occupancy £45 - £55
4 Doubles £70 - £85
Includes full breakfast

CHARGE/CREDIT CARDS

ACCOLADES

I.O.M.T.B. De Luxe

FACILITIES

Garden, tennis,
indoor swimming pool, heli-pad
Golf, fishing and riding nearby

RESTRICTIONS

No children under 10 years
No facilities for disabled guests
Pets by prior arrangement

ATTRACTIONS

Castle Rushen, Laxey Wheel, Manx Museum, Cregneash Village, Peel Castle and Odin's Raven, Nautical Museum, Steam Railway

AFFILIATIONS

Independent

NEAREST

MAJOR CITY:
Ramsey - 3 miles/10 mins

MAJOR AIRPORT:
Ronaldsway - 22 miles/45 mins

RAILWAY STATION:
Ramsey - 3 miles/10 mins

FERRY PORT:
Douglas - 18 miles/30 mins

RESERVATIONS

Direct with hotel

ACCESS CODES

Not applicable

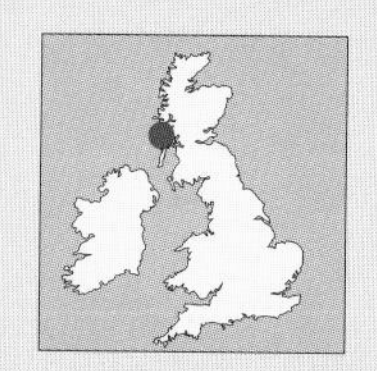

"Warm hospitality and delectable food, beautiful rooms, perfect!"

Robert & Sue Armstrong, Herefordshire

KILLIECHRONAN HOUSE

Former estate lodge

Killiechronan, Isle of Mull PA72 6JU

Telephone 01680 300403
Fax 01680 300463

OWNER
John L Leroy

MANAGERS
Margaret and Patrick Freytag

RATES PER PERSON
1 Single from £60
5 Doubles/Twins from £52
Includes dinner, full breakfast and VAT

CHARGE/CREDIT CARDS

• *MC* • *VI*

ACCOLADES
S.T.B. ♛♛♛♛ Highly Commended
A.A. ★★ ❀ 71%

FACILITIES
Garden, croquet, fishing, pony trekking, sailing
Golf nearby

RESTRICTIONS
No children under 14 years occupying own rooms
No facilities for disabled guests
No pets in public rooms
Hotel closed 31 Oct - 1 March

ATTRACTIONS
Tobermory, Torosay, Duart Castle, Calgary Sands, Iona, Staffa and Ulva Islands

AFFILIATIONS
Logis of Great Britain

NEAREST
MAJOR CITY:
Glasgow - 107 miles/3 hrs
MAJOR AIRPORT:
Glasgow - 107 miles/3 hrs
RAILWAY STATION:
Oban - 14 miles/1 hr
FERRY PORT:
Craignure - 14 miles/30 mins
Oban - 1 hr 20 mins (via ferry)

RESERVATIONS
Direct with hotel

ACCESS CODES
Not applicable

Sheer inspiration set within 6000 acres

Beautifully situated at the head of Loch na Keal in the centre of the Isle of Mull, Killiechronan, together with its estate of over 6,000 acres, offers hospitality in its original Highland Lodge, built in 1846. Killiechronan is the family home of owners Mr and Mrs J Leroy who are known in Scotland for their fine hotels at Oban and Port of Menteith. It contains a magnificent collection of antiques and pictures.

All six bedrooms are now transformed so that each one has its own bathroom, radio, direct dial telephone and all the little extras that make guests feel at home.

Chef Patrick Freytag had already established a fine reputation for his cuisine at the Manor House, Oban. He prepares mouthwatering dinners, complemented by a fine wine list. Patrick's wife Margaret manages the rest of Killiechronan's facilities. You can rely on the expert and careful attention of Margaret and her staff to make sure you enjoy your stay.

Mull and the neighbouring mainland are renowned for their outstanding scenic beauty. Like Mendelssohn, you can visit Fingal's Cave. For less musical inspiration, you can also see the white beach at Calgary, Duart Castle, Moy Castle on Loch Buie and its water-filled dungeon, the herring and treasure-seeking village of Tobermory, and Torosay with its Italianate gardens.

LOCATION

Mull is reached by ferry from Oban or Lochalin. Take A849 to Salen. Left onto B8035. Turn right after 2 miles.

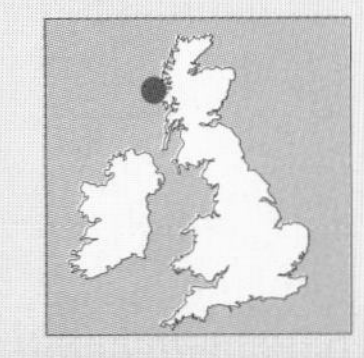

" Kinloch is unique! It combines the very best of modern living while allowing you to feel the history of this great family in every part "

John Abler, Memorable Scottish Journeys

Lochside island hotel

KINLOCH LODGE

At home with the High Chief of the Clan Donald

Kinloch dates back to the early 1600's and is the home of Lord and Lady Macdonald. Lord Macdonald is the High Chief of Clan Donald, the oldest and largest of the Highland clans. Kinloch is full of paintings of his ancestors, old furniture, family ornaments and photographs – very much a family home with two comfortable drawing rooms log fires and the most spectacular views. The ten bedrooms, all comfortably appointed and individually decorated, vary in size and this is reflected in the tariff.

The decor throughout, like the bedrooms, is the choice of Lady Macdonald, as is the food, for Claire Macdonald is one of the most renowned cooks and food enthusiasts in Scotland. An award-winning journalist and author of twelve best selling cookbooks, Claire has for the last twenty years produced the most delicious food seasonal to Scotland. Everything is homemade and accounts for Kinloch's enviable international reputation over two decades.

The house itself is a mile from the main road, at the head of a sea loch amidst an area famous for its flora and fauna. Otters inhabit the sea shore and eagles soar in the mountains behind. Kinloch is unique in every way – from the tranquillity of its surroundings, the clean, pure air through to the delicious peaty water which comes from the spring behind the house.

LOCATION

1 mile off A851. 6 miles south of Broadford and 10 miles north of Armadale.

Sleat, Isle of Skye
Highland IV43 8QY

Telephone 01471 833214
Fax 01471 833277

PROPRIETORS

Lord and Lady Macdonald

ROOM RATES

10 Doubles/Twins £90 - £180
Includes full breakfast and VAT

CHARGE/CREDIT CARDS

MC • VI

ACCOLADES

S.T.B. ♛♛♛♛ Highly Commended
A.A.★★ ✿✿ 73%
Courvoisier's Book of the Best

FACILITIES

Gardens,
heli-pad,
fishing, stalking

RESTRICTIONS

No facilities for disabled guests
Pets by prior arrangement

ATTRACTIONS

Isle of Skye,
Clan Donald Centre,
Inverewe Gardens,
Dunvegan Castle

AFFILIATIONS

The Celebrated Hotels Collection

NEAREST

MAJOR CITY:
Inverness - 100 miles/3½ hrs

MAJOR AIRPORT:
Inverness - 100 miles/3½ hrs

FERRY PORT:
Kyle of Lochalsh - 12 miles/45 mins

RAILWAY STATION:
Kyle of Lochalsh - 12 miles/45 mins

RESERVATIONS

Toll free in US: 800-322-2403

ACCESS CODES

Not applicable

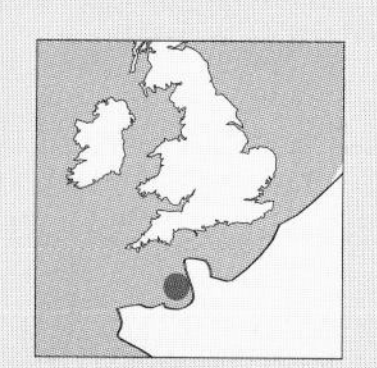

" The loyal staff are renowned for their friendliness and efficiency and the smart but homely atmosphere has reached the ideal mix "

Harpers & Queen

LONGUEVILLE MANOR

13th century manor house

Longueville Road, St Saviour, Jersey JE2 7SA

Telephone 01534 25501
Fax 01534 31613

PROPRIETORS

Lewis and Dufty Families

ROOM RATES

Single occupancy	*£120 - £180*
30 Doubles/Twins	*£150 - £230*
2 Suites	*£270 - £320*

Includes full breakfast and newspaper

CHARGE/CREDIT CARDS

• DC • MC • VI

ACCOLADES

J.T.B. 5 Suns
R.A.C. Blue Ribbon Award ★★★★
A.A. ★★★★ ❀❀❀
The Good Hotel Guide

FACILITIES

Outdoor swimming pool, croquet, tennis, gardens, 3 meeting rooms/max 100 people Golf, riding, sailing, windsurfing, beaches and fishing nearby

RESTRICTIONS

None

ATTRACTIONS

Gerald Durrel Wildlife Preservation Park, Eric Young Orchid Foundation, German occupation relics, Jersey Museum, VAT exempt

AFFILIATIONS

Relais & Châteaux

NEAREST

MAJOR CITY:
Southampton - 50 miles/45 mins by air

MAJOR AIRPORT:
Jersey - 7 miles/15 mins

FERRY PORT:
St Helier - 4 miles/10 mins

RESERVATIONS

Direct with hotel

ACCESS CODES

Not applicable

An award-winning hotel on the island of flowers

Guests are assured of a very warm welcome from the Lewis and Dufty families who, over the past 40-odd years, have converted this 13th century manor house into one of the most prestigious small hotels in Europe, recently awarded the ultimate accolade of 'Hotel of the Year' by a renowned guide book.

In the comfort of the exquisitely decorated rooms and surrounded by floral displays, fine antique furnishings and elegant fabrics, you will be pampered by the courteous and attentive hand-picked staff who strive to make your stay a most pleasing and memorable experience.

The quality of service is carried through into each of the two dining rooms where, in the ancient oak-panelled room, there is an array of silver trophies awarded for the excellence of the cuisine. The second dining room is light, spacious and equally comfortable. Many of the fruits and vegetables, as well as the herbs and flowers, are grown in the walled kitchen gardens and hot houses to provide fresh produce that would otherwise be out of season.

There are 30 bedrooms and two suites, all individually furnished and decorated with flair and imagination. Separate seating areas are provided with books, magazines, flowers and fresh fruit, whilst the bathrooms are luxuriously equipped and include thick, oversize towels and robes.

LOCATION

10 minutes from the capital, St Helier in the centre of the eastern part of the island.

“ Tout a été parfait ”

Salmon Yvah, Rennes, France

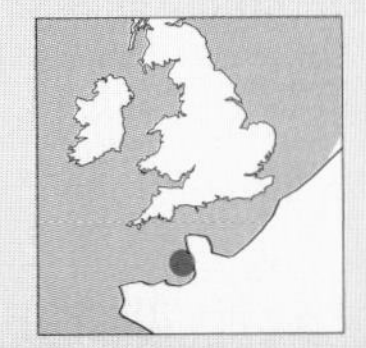

19th century townhouse

MOORE'S HOTEL

Le Pollet, St Peter Port,
Guernsey GY1 1WH
Channel Islands

Telephone 01481 724452
Fax 01481 714037

PROPRIETORS
André and Sheila Sendlhofer
Karel and Mike Harris

RATES PER PERSON

2 Singles	£35 - £60
46 Doubles/Twins	£31 - £42.50
2 Suites	£45 - £65

Includes full breakfast

CHARGE/CREDIT CARDS

• DC • MC • VI

ACCOLADES
G.T.B. ♛♛♛♛
R.A.C. ★★★
A.A. ★★★ 67%

FACILITIES
Terrace garden
2 meeting rooms/max 20 people
Golf, fishing, riding, sailing, surfing, windsurfing and waterskiing nearby

RESTRICTIONS
No facilities for disabled guests
Pets at management's discretion

ATTRACTIONS
St Peter Port, Military Museum, Guernsey Museum, Castle Corner, Maritime Museum, Victor Hugo's house, VAT exempt

AFFILIATIONS
Consort Hotels

NEAREST
MAJOR CITY:
Southampton - 120 miles/40 mins by air

MAJOR AIRPORT:
Guernsey - 5 miles/15 mins

FERRY PORT:
St Peter Port - ½ mile/3 mins

RESERVATIONS
Direct with hotel

ACCESS CODES
Not applicable

Where too much of a good thing can be simply wonderful

In the heart of St Peter Port stands Moore's Central Hotel, an elegant blue granite building which was once the home of the de Saumarez's, one of Guernsey's oldest families. Parts of the building date back to the middle of the 18th century, and during the years it has been carefully added to and restored. Moores lives up to its slogan that “Too much of a good thing can be simply wonderful.”

The 48 bedrooms each have private bathroom and toilet. All rooms have colour TV with teletext, radio, tea-making facilities, trouser press, hair-dryer and direct-dial telephone.

The main restaurant is the Conservatory, part of which is under glass. Full English breakfast is served here each morning. In the evening you can select from a five-course dinner menu, or from an extensive à la carte menu where the specialities are fresh fish and seafood. The Austrian-style Patisserie offers home-baked gateaux and light lunches and there is also a Library Bar and Carvery. The cocktail bar has a blazing log fire on winter days, but spring and summer come early to Guernsey.

The almost traffic-free shopping streets of Guernsey's capital are near at hand. Just a few minutes' stroll brings you on to the sea front with its picturesque marinas full of colourful yachts. From here ferries frequently depart to St Malo, Jersey and the smaller islands. If you enjoy exploring on foot, St Peter Port offers plenty of pleasant surprises, with its narrow lanes, and spectacular views of the harbour.

LOCATION

In the town centre of St Peter Port.

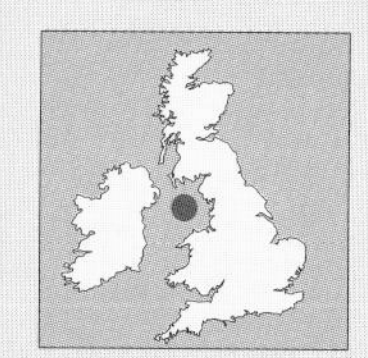

"Highly impressed with the efficient and friendly service . . . undoubtedly the most successful event ever"

Keith Watson, British Airways Organiser BA Millionaires' Club

MOUNT MURRAY HOTEL & COUNTRY CLUB *Resort*

Santon,
Isle of Man IM4 2HT

Telephone 01624 661111
Fax 01624 611116

MANAGING DIRECTOR
Jeremy P Leeds

GENERAL MANAGER
Jonathan Dawson

ROOM RATES

Single occupancy	*£72.50 - £75*
18 Executives	*£80 - £90*
68 Doubles/Twins	*£112 - £115*
4 Four-posters	*£120 - £140*

Includes full breakfast and VAT

CHARGE/CREDIT CARDS

• *DC* • *MC* • *VI*

ACCOLADES
I.O.M.T.B. ♛♛♛♛♛ *Highly Commended*
R.A.C. ★★★★
A.A. ★★★★ ❀ *71%*

FACILITIES
Indoor swimming pool, squash, indoor and outdoor tennis, golf, snooker, sauna, gym, health & beauty, driving range and bowling green
3 meeting rooms/max 300 people
Riding and fishing nearby

RESTRICTIONS
No pets

ATTRACTIONS
Laxey Wheel, Manx Museum, Folk Museum

AFFILIATIONS
Independent

NEAREST
MAJOR CITY:
Douglas - 3 miles/10 mins

MAJOR AIRPORT:
Ronaldsway - 6 miles/15 mins

RAILWAY STATION:
Douglas - 4 miles/15 mins

FERRY PORT:
Douglas - 4 miles/15 mins

RESERVATIONS
Direct with hotel

ACCESS CODES
Not applicable

Sophisticated leisure on the beguiling Isle of Man

By any standards, Mount Murray is a most unusual place; to call it a hotel is to understate its wealth of facilities for golf, swimming, tennis, squash . . . the list seems endless. And its an excellent venue for conferences.

Even Mount Murray's appearance belies its status as an hotel: it looks more like a village set in 202 acres of rolling hills and woodlands. And it even looks out over its own lake.

The 90 en suite rooms include deluxe four-poster rooms. Not much is left to chance: there is a professionally managed crèche in addition to a fashion and sportswear shop, hair, beauty and massage salon, sports and juice bar.

Besides the impressive array of Mount Murray's facilities, there is the magic of the Isle of Man itself: heather-clad hills, dramatic coastline and wooded glens. A scenic railway will take you to the islands peak where you can see Ireland, Scotland, England and Wales from the same spot. The Isle of Man is rich in history and richer still in quaint and curious folklore.

Mount Murray is easy to get to, just six miles from the airport on the road to Douglas, the island's busy seaside capital. And if you think all this would have to cost the earth, just cast a glance at the tariff panel.

LOCATION

Take the A25 out of Douglas and join the A5 to Castletown. Mount Murray is signposted on the right hand side as you enter Santon.

“ I know you are proud of your employees and we truly enjoyed their excellent service and friendly personalities ”

Douglas Murdock, Clan Donald

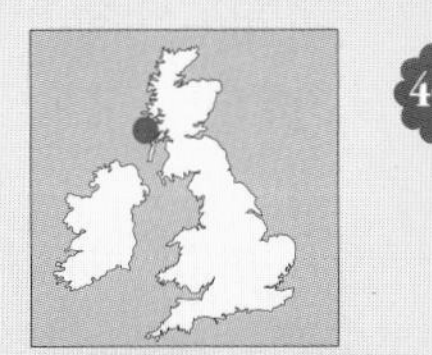

Highland inn PORT ASKAIG HOTEL

Whisky galore and much, much more on Islay

Often described as one of the most picturesque spots on the west coast of Scotland, Port Askaig can hardly aspire to the title “village” having a total resident population of five.

Port Askaig Hotel was originally an old drove inn, a haven for the cattlemen who would regularly escort their herds away from island to the mainland via Jura – now only a few minutes away by car ferry.

The hotel is well regarded, having been recommended by most major guides. There are two bars, the “Snug” bar and the public bar which is reckoned to be about 400 years old. All the local malt whiskies are available and food is served all day.

The dining room menu features a comprehensive selection of Islay produce – venison, pheasant, salmon, oysters and other shellfish complemented by a moderately priced wine list. Salads and vegetables are grown in the hotel garden.

All the double bedrooms have private facilities with colour TV, radio and hospitality tray.

The Islay lifeboat is moored in the hotel bay, closely guarded by a cannon!

Mavis and Frank Spears have been resident proprietors since 1958 and since then the hotel has seen a few changes, all of them for the better.

LOCATION

Opposite Port Askaig pier at which daily car ferry arrives from Kennacraig, near Tarbert.

Isle of Islay,
Argyll PA46 7RD

Telephone 01496 840245
Fax 01496 840295

PROPRIETORS

Mavis and Frank Spears

ROOM RATES

2 Singles	*£30 - £38*
6 Doubles	*£60 - £76*

Includes full breakfast and VAT

CHARGE/CREDIT CARDS

• DC • MC • VI

ACCOLADES

S.T.B. ♛♛♛ Commended

A.A. ★★ 63%

FACILITIES

Garden
Fishing nearby

RESTRICTIONS

No children under 5 years
No facilities for disabled

ATTRACTIONS

Distilleries,
Museums,
Finlaggan,
Kildalton Cross

AFFILIATIONS

Scotland's Commended Hotels
Select Hotels of Argyll

NEAREST

MAJOR CITY:
Bowmore - 10 miles/30 mins

MAJOR AIRPORT:
Glasgow - 120 miles/2¼ hrs
Islay - 15 miles/35 mins

FERRY PORT:
Port Askaig - opposite/1 min

RESERVATIONS

Direct with hotel

ACCESS CODES

Not applicable

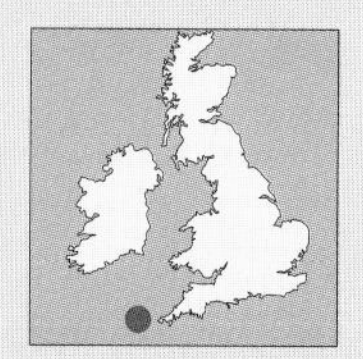

"In 1492 Columbus discovered America, in 1992 my husband and I discovered the Isles of Scilly"

Denise & Frank Lucibello, Paramus, New Jersey

St Martin's Hotel

Island hotel

Lower Town, St Martins, Isles of Scilly TR25 0QW

Telephone 01720 422092
Fax 01720 422298

OWNER
Peter Sykes

GENERAL MANAGER
Keith Bradford

ROOM RATES

16 Doubles/Twins	£50 - £90
2 Four-posters	£50 - £90
2 Suites	£95 - £130
4 Superior	£75 - £110

Includes full breakfast and VAT

CHARGE/CREDIT CARDS

• DC • MC • VI

ACCOLADES
E.T.B. ♛♛♛♛ Highly Commended
A.A. ★★★ ❀❀ 75%

FACILITIES
Gardens, indoor pool, snooker, fishing, sailing Watersports, golf, riding and tennis nearby

RESTRICTIONS
No facilities for disabled guests

ATTRACTIONS
Uninhabited islands, 45ft Bermudan Cutter, The Botanical Gardens, Tresco Abbey

AFFILIATIONS
Pride of Britain

NEAREST
MAJOR CITY:
Penzance: 40 miles/2½ hrs (ferry) (15 mins Skybus/20 mins helicopter)

MAJOR AIRPORT:
London Heathrow - 2 hrs by air via Newquay or Plymouth

RAILWAY STATION:
Penzance - 40 miles/2½ hrs (ferry)

RESERVATIONS
Toll free in UK: 0800-834056

ACCESS CODES
Not applicable

The first and only hotel in this idyllic setting

An island two miles by a half, 28 miles southwest of Lands End in the Duchy of Cornwall, warmed by the Gulf stream, is the breathtaking setting for this stunning hotel.

When you arrive at the St Martin's Hotel private quay by launch from the main island of St Marys, you will already have been exposed to the beauty and tranquillity of these "Fortunate Isles".

The pleasures of these islands are varied and unique. Glorious uncrowded beaches and crystal clear waters for safe swimming, fascinating diving and snorkelling with Atlantic grey seals. 'Genesis', their 45ft Bermudan cutter, is exclusively available to guests for island hopping, sailing and picnics on remote islands, and then there is fishing and stunning scenic walks with birdlife and flora galore.

The hotel at the water's edge has fabulous panoramic views over uninhabited islands, a heated swimming pool and an award winning restaurant specialising in local seafood. This combination of a first class hotel, great food and outstanding beauty is seldom found, as such promises a great vacation.

LOCATION

Located just off the coast of Cornwall in southwest England. A short trip by sea, plane or helicopter and then by launch to the hotel's own quay.

“ My wife, Mary, and I travel all over the world and I can honestly say that we have never stayed in a more comfortable hotel and with such a welcoming atmosphere ”

Dick Francis, author

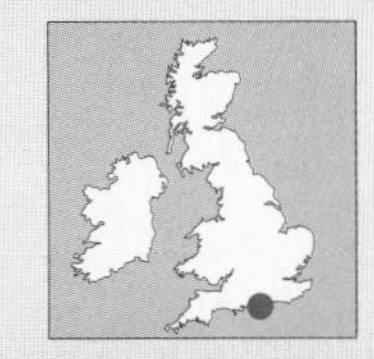

Manor house

SWAINSTON MANOR HOTEL

High standards, following a distinguished list of previous owners

Set in thirty-two acres of unspoilt countryside, Swainston Manor Hotel is a very special place to visit and has a fascinating history stretching back to AD735. During the reign of Edward I, the Charter granting the Parish of Newtown to the Bishops of Winchester was served here at Swainston. Through the ages, ownership has been a distinguished list including Richard, Earl of Warwick; George, Duke of Clarence; Sir William Barrington and Sir John Simeon.

Swainston Manor Hotel offers the highest standards of comfort and hospitality. All the en suite bedrooms are spacious and airy, well-appointed and individually furnished, and all have the most wonderful views. The atmosphere of the old world is combined with comfort of modern amenities, such as central heating, TV, radio, telephone, trouser press and courtesy facilities for tea and coffee making.

The indoor heated pool has an interesting wall painting and the beautiful 12th century chapel, adjoining the main building, is the ideal venue for musical evenings and wedding receptions.

The owners are justifiably proud of the elegant Fitzwilliam Restaurant at the heart of the manor which is open to both residents and non-residents and offers a menu with a wide choice of high quality dishes. The service here is attentive and unfussy, making your meal a relaxing and really pleasurable experience. An excellent wine cellar completes the gastronomic delights.

LOCATION

On arrival at the Island Ferry Terminal, head for the B3401 Newport to Freshwater Road. Swainston is 4 miles west of Newport and 1 mile east of Calbourne.

Calbourne, Isle of Wight PO30 4HX

Telephone 01983 521121
Fax 01983 521406

RESIDENT DIRECTOR

Fred Woodward

ROOM RATES

3 Singles	*£54*
7 Doubles/Twins	*£83.60 - £101*
3 Four-posters	*£83.60 - £101*
1 Suite	*£140*

Includes full breakfast and VAT

CHARGE/CREDIT CARDS

• MC • VI

ACCOLADES

E.T.B. ♕♕♕♕♕ Highly Commended

FACILITIES

Garden, indoor pool, fishing, heli-pad
4 meeting rooms/max 180 people
Golf and riding nearby

RESTRICTIONS

None

ATTRACTIONS

Carisbrooke Castle, Brickfields Horse Country, Osborne House, Godshill

AFFILIATIONS

Paragon Group

NEAREST

MAJOR CITY:
Southampton - 24 miles/1¼ hrs

MAJOR AIRPORT:
London Heathrow - 90 miles/2¼ hrs
Eastleigh - 26 miles/1¼ hrs

RAILWAY STATION:
Ryde - 12 miles/20 mins

FERRY PORT:
Yarmouth - 7 miles/15 mins
Cowes - 10 miles/20 mins

RESERVATIONS

Toll free in UK: 0500-131257

ACCESS CODES

Not applicable

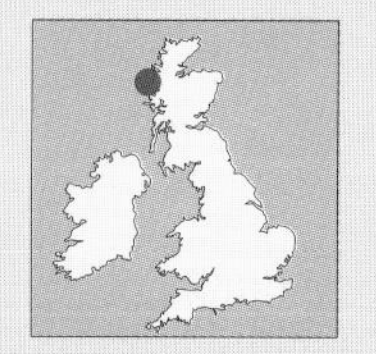

"After 46 years our favourite hotel just gets better"

Jim & Dorothy Reid, Kirkcudbright

UIG HOTEL

Coaching inn

Uig, Portree,
Isle of Skye IV51 9YE

Telephone 01470 542205
Fax 01470 542308

PROPRIETOR

David Taylor

ROOM RATES

5 Singles £28 - £45
12 Doubles/Twins £56 - £90
Includes full breakfast and VAT

CHARGE/CREDIT CARDS

• DC • MC • VI

ACCOLADES

S.T.B. Commended
The Good Hotel Guide

FACILITIES

Garden, riding, helipad
Fishing nearby

RESTRICTIONS

Dogs by arrangement

ATTRACTIONS

Quairang,
Cuillins,
Outer Hebrides,
Dunvegan Castle

AFFILIATIONS

Independent

NEAREST

MAJOR CITY:
Inverness - 138 miles/3¾ hrs

MAJOR AIRPORT:
Inverness - 138 miles/3¾ hrs

FERRY PORT:
Kyle of Lochalsh - 50 miles/1 hr

RAILWAY STATION:
Kyle of Lochalsh - 50 miles/1 hr

RESERVATIONS

Direct with hotel

ACCESS CODES

Not applicable

Over the sea to artistic flair and comfort

Built in the early 1800's Uig Hotel is an old coaching inn on a hillside overlooking Uig Bay with views westwards over Loch Snizort.

Grace Graham took over the hotel in 1946 and 50 years later still plays an active role while her son David Taylor is responsible for the day to day running of the hotel. An artistic flair is much in evidence in the tasteful decor and furnishings. Original paintings by William Carrick, depicting the Scottish west coast and islands hang in the public rooms.

The bedrooms, mostly with a westward view are comfortable, well-appointed, and all en suite. Equally pleasing are the converted farm steadings.

Uig is a good base from which to explore the island. A network of excellent traffic free roads makes access easy and most parts of the island are within an hour's drive. The Outer Isles ferry leaves Uig three times a day in summer and the timetable allows a variety of excursions to Harris and Lewis and North Uist. Caledonian Macbrayne offer Hopscotch and Rover tickets, giving discounted travel within the islands. Skye is particularly famous for the Cuillin Mountains, one of the premier climbing areas in the British Isles. There are also considerable hillwalking opportunities and in Spring the island is a paradise for flower and bird lovers. The hotel has its own pony trekking centre and offers short break holidays throughout the summer.

LOCATION

From Portree, the hotel is on the right hand side of the road beside a white painted church and opposite the round tower.

"What a super place. We shall return to this lovely hotel"

Earl & Countess Grey

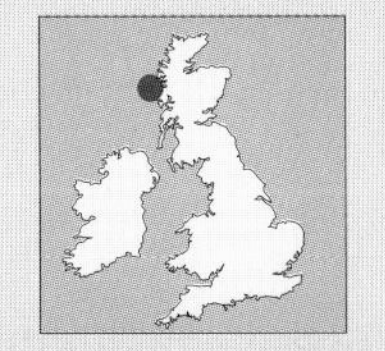

THE WESTERN ISLES HOTEL

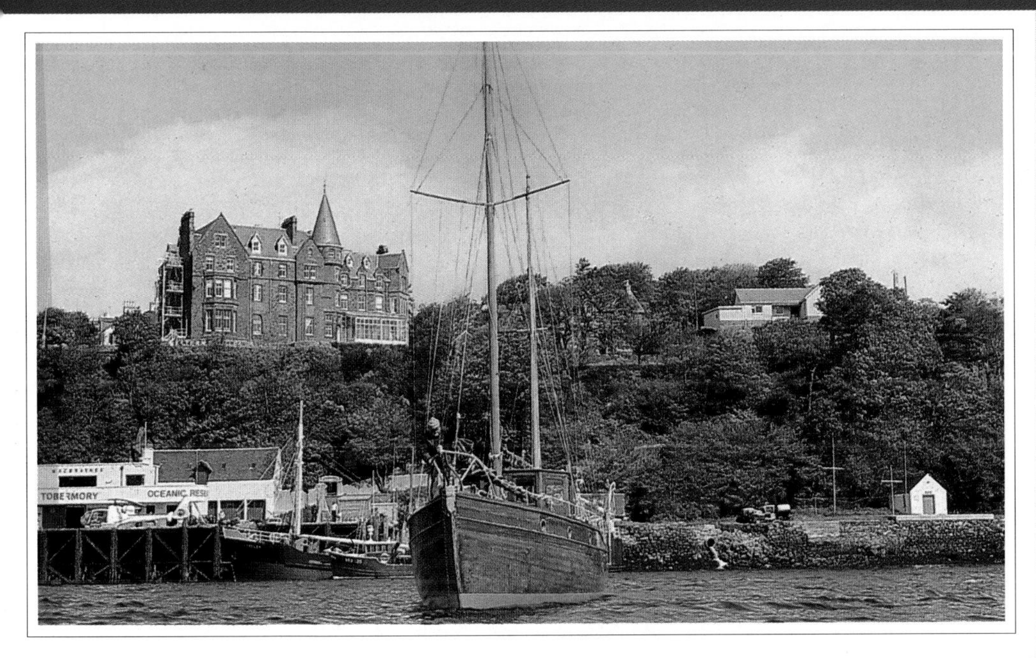

See The Sound of Mull change from fiery orange to rippled silver

The imposing Western Isles Hotel, set above the picturesque fishing village of Tobermory, occupies one of the finest positions in the beautiful Hebridean Isles. From most vantage points in the hotel you will be thrilled by an ever-changing and breathtaking panoramic view that simply cannot be ignored.

The hotel's lounge offers an atmosphere of grace and comfort, perfect for tea-time recuperation or a fireside liqueur after dinner, whilst the conservatory is for romantic hearts on scented summer evenings. Here you can share the experience of watching the sun set amongst the hills and see The Sound of Mull changing from fiery orange to rippled silver as the night welcomes the coming moon.

The bar is the stage for many a story of past adventures – treasure ships, ones that got away, and other folklore. Whilst exchanging stories around the open fire, why not try one of the wide range of malt whiskies on offer.

Dine in the elegant restaurant which overlooks The Sound of Mull. Choose your meals from an imaginative and varied menu – the chef will present you with fare that is carefully selected, skilfully prepared and certain to please. A good choice of fine wines, spirits and liqueurs is available to complement your meal.

Each bedroom is spacious, comfortable and attractive, and is equipped with all the items that help to make a holiday so special.

LOCATION

From Oban allow 40 mins on ferry to Craignure. Turn right on leaving ferry, then 40 mins drive to Tobermory. The hotel is signposted.

Tobermory, Isle of Mull, Argyllshire PA75 6PR

Telephone 01688 302012
Fax 01688 302297

PROPRIETORS

Sue and Michael Fink

ROOM RATES

2 Singles £36 - £43
23 Doubles/Twins £72 - £163
Includes full breakfast and VAT

CHARGE/CREDIT CARDS

• MC • VI

ACCOLADES

S.T.B. ♛♛♛♛ Highly Commended
R.A.C. ★★★ + Merit Award H
A.A. ★★★ 72%

FACILITIES

Gardens
Golf, riding and fishing nearby

RESTRICTIONS

No facilities for disabled guests

ATTRACTIONS

Iona, Staffa (Fingals Cave), Torosay Castle, Duart Castle

AFFILIATIONS

Scotland's Commended

NEAREST

MAJOR CITY:
Glasgow - 90 miles/2½ hrs
Edinburgh - 100 miles/3 hrs

MAJOR AIRPORT:
Glasgow - 90 miles/2½ hrs

FERRY PORT:
Craignure - 22 miles/40 mins
Oban - 1 hr 20 mins (via Ferry)

RESERVATIONS

Direct with hotel

ACCESS CODES

Not applicable

A - Z index of hotels

Berwick-on-Tweed

A - Z index by region

Hotel facilities

SWIMMING POOL

Definition: *Hotels reporting that they have either outdoor, indoor or heated swimming pools on their premises*

HEALTH & BEAUTY

Definition: *Hotels reporting that they have either indoor/outdoor or all-weather tennis courts.*

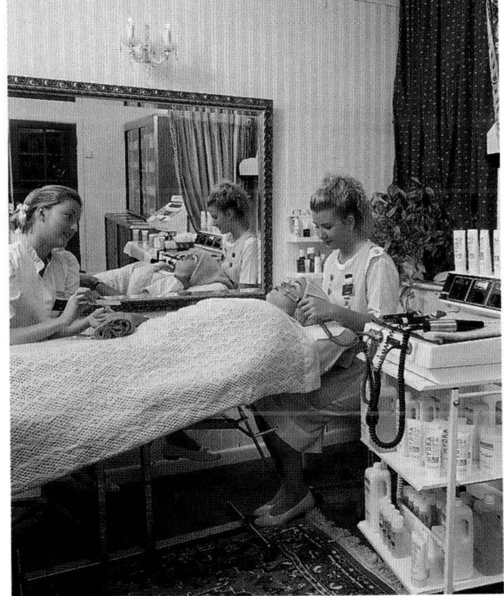

TENNIS

Definition: *Hotels reporting that they have either indoor/outdoor or all-weather tennis courts.*

FISHING

Definition: *Hotels reporting fishing on, or adjacent to, their premises.*

Hotel facilities

RIDING

Definition: *Hotels who report they have horse-back riding available on site.*

BEST LOVED HOTELS OF THE WORLD

Bibliography

More information

Listed below are various guides which have been helpful in our travels and in researching this book. All are available in good bookshops throughout the United Kingdom and abroad. Please see the special offer for *Historic Houses Castles & Gardens in Great Britain and Ireland* located between pages 320 and 321.

Hotel Ratings

We have used the tourist board, RAC and AA ratings whenever any hotel featured in this book has merited them. As indicators of quality and value, they speak for themselves but for more details, please refer to the appropriate tourist board listed in the introduction to every region in this book or the RAC and AA addresses below.

Historic Houses Castles & Gardens in Great Britain and Ireland

United States:
Reed Information Services,
200 Clearwater Drive,
Oak Brook, IL 60521-8806

The Good Hotel Guide 1996

Hilary Rubenstein Books Ltd
61 Clarendon Road London W11

Published in the US as:
Europe's Wonderful Little Hotels & Inns

RAC Publications

RAC Hotel Guide Great Britain & Ireland
RAC Bartholomews Road Atlas
RAC Motoring Atlas of Great Britain & Ireland
RAC Road Atlas Britain 1995 Perfect

United Kingdom:
RAC Book Point Ltd,
39 Milton Park, Abingdon,
Oxford OX14 4TD

AA Publications

AA Hotels in Britain and Ireland
Great Britain Road Atlas
Road Atlas of the British Isles
The Big Road Atlas of Britain
The Maxi Scale Atlas of Britain

United Kingdom:
Automobile Association Developments Limited,
Fanum House, Basingstoke, Hampshire RG21 2EA

United States:
Hunter Publishing Inc.,
300 Raritan Center, Parkway,
Edison, NJ 08818

Our grateful thanks

A project of this scale could not come together without the support and help of many organizations especially the following, of which many of the hotels in this book are affiliated. Many of the hotels refer to these organizations in their page's Fact Column under "Affiliations" and "Reservations".

The Celebrated Hotels Collection • The Cotswolds Collection • Fine Individual Hotels
Ireland's Blue Book • Pride of Britain • Relais & Châteaux • Selected British Hotels
Scotland's Commended Hotels • The Small Hotel Company
Small Luxury Hotels of the World • Welsh Rarebits

Golf guide

Best Loved Hotels with a golf course on site

	Page
Scotland	
Balbirnie House Hotel	24
North	
Aldwark Manor Hotel	97
Wales	
Celtic Manor Hotel	161
Soughton Hall	183
Midshires	
Hintlesham Hall	217
Stocks Hotel	243
Welcombe Hotel	247
West Country	
Cedar Falls Health Farm	268
Chedington Court	269
South	
Chewton Glen	338
Donnington Valley	343
Horsted Place	351
Tylney Hall	365
Ireland	
Adare Manor	414
Nuremore Hotel	438
Waterford Castle	445
Islands	
Mount Murray C. C.	460

Hotel	Course	Miles Away	Page
SCOTLAND			
Achray House Hotel	Crieff	12	18
Allt-Chaorain House Hotel	Loch Lomond	23	19
Ardanaiseig	Glencruitten	24	20
Arisaig House	Fort William	32	21
Atholl Hotel	Royal Aberdeen	3	22
Auchen Castle Hotel	Moffat	3	23
Balgonie Country House	Ballater	1	25
Ballathie House Hotel	Rosemount	5	26
Baron's Craig Hotel	Southerness-Dumfries	7	27
Braemar Lodge	Braemar	½	28
Bunchrew House Hotel	Nairn	13	29
Channings	Braid Hills	3	30
Chapeltoun House Hotel	Royal Troon	14	31
Colin House	Kirkcudbright	12	32
Corsemalzie House Hotel	Wigtownshire County	12	33
Coul House Hotel	Royal Dornoch	¾	34
Craigellachie Hotel	Kingussie	10	35
Cringletie House Hotel	Peebles	2½	36
Cromlix House	Dunblane New	4	37
Cross, The	Kingussie	½	38
Culdearn House	Grantown-on-Spey	1	39
Culloden House Hotel	Nairn Championship	13	40
Dalmunzie House	Blairgowrie	18	41
Darroch Learg	Ballater	½	42
Devonshire Hotel, The	Douglaston	7	43
Dornoch Castle	Royal Dornoch	1	44
Dunain Park Hotel	Nairn	12	45
Enmore Hotel	Cowal	¼	46
Farleyer House	Taymouth	5	47
Fernhill Hotel	Dunskey	½	48
Gean House, The	Alloa (Schawpark)	½	49
Glenfeochan House	Glencruitten	15	50
Golf View Hotel, The	Nairn	½	51
Greywalls	Muirfield	½	52
Hazlehurst Lodge	Aboyne	½	53
Howard, The	Mussleburgh	8	54
Invercauld Arms Hotel	Braemar	½	55
Invercreran Hotel	Oban	18	56
Inverlochy Castle	Fort William	½	57
Johnstounburn House	North Berwick West	15	58
Kildrummy Castle	Alford	9	59
Kilfinan Hotel	Port Bannatyne	6	60
Kirkton House	Cardross	1	61
Knockinaam Lodge	Creachmore-Stanraer	7½	62
Knockomie Hotel	Forres	2	63
Ladyburn	Brunston Castle	3	64
Lake Hotel, The	Aberfoyle	2	65
Leslie Castle	Insch	4	66
Loch Melfort Hotel	Oban	19	67
Loch Torridon Hotel	Gairloch	10	68
Lodge on the Loch	Fort William	10	69
Manor House, The	Glencruitten	5	70
Mansion House Hotel	Elgin	1	71
Montgreenan Mansion House	Gailes	6	73
Muchalls Castle	Royal Aberdeen	12	74
Nivingston House	Canmore	6	75
Old Library Lodge, The	Traigh	2	76
Old Manor Hotel	Lundin Links	¼	77
Old Mansion House	Downfield	5	78
Peat Inn, The	St Andrews	6	79
Philipburn House Hotel	Selkirk	1	80
Polmaily House Hotel	Nairn	¾	81
Roman Camp House	Callander	⅓	82
Royal Marine Hotel	Brora	⅓	83
St Andrews Golf Hotel	St Andrews	⅓	84
Shieldhill Hotel	Lanark	7	85
Sunlaws House Hotel	Dalmahoy East	38	87
Taychreggan	Glencruitten	20	88
Tigh-an-Eilean Hotel	Gairloch	14	89
Udny Arms Hotel	Cruden Bay	8	90
NORTH			
Alderley Edge Hotel, The	Wilmslow	2	96
Appleton Hall Hotel	Kirkbymoorside	3	98
Armathwaite Hall Hotel	Keswick	6	99
Aynsome Manor	Ulverston	12	100
Borrowdale Gates, The	Keswick	6	101
Broxton Hall	Carden Park	3	102
Burgoyne Hotel, The	Richmond	10	103
Crabwall Manor	Curzon Park	2	104
Crosby Lodge	Eden	½	105
Dale Head Hall	Keswick	5	106
Devonshire, The	Skipton	5	107
Dower House	Knaresborough	1	108
Farlam Hall Hotel	Brampton	2½	109
Feversham Arms Hotel, The	Kirkbymoorside	6	110
Frogg Manor	Carden Park	2	111
Gilpin Lodge Hotel	Windermere	½	112
Grange Hotel, The	Fulford	3	113
Grants Hotel	Rudding Park	3	114
Graythwaite Manor Hotel	Grange	1½	115
Hipping Hall	Kirkby Lonsdale	3	116
Holbeck Ghyll Hotel	Windermere	4	117
King's Arms Hotel	Masham	10	118
Lakeside Hotel	Grange	6	119
Linthwaite House	Windermere	1	120
Manor House, The	Beverley	2	121
Michaels Nook	Keswick	10	122
Middlethorpe Hall	Pike Hills	2	123
Miller Howe Hotel	Windermere	2	124
Monk Fryston Hall	Selby	6	125
Mount Royale	Fulford	2	126
Nanny Brow Hotel	Windermere	7	127
Nidd Hall	Knaresborough	5	128
Northcote Manor	Wilpshire	2	129
Old Vicarage, The	Grange	4	130
Pheasant Hotel	Kirkbymoorside	4	131
Redworth Hall Hotel	Oakleaf	3	132
Rookery Hall	Portal	9	133
Rothay Manor	Windermere	5	134
Royal Oak Inn, The	Appleby	1	135
Sharrow Bay Hotel	Penrith	6	136
Studley Hotel	Pannal	3	137
Swinside Lodge Hotel	Keswick	6	138
Temple Sowerby House	Penrith	7	139
Tillmouth Park Hotel	Goswick	15	140
Underscar Manor	Keswick	4	141
Victoria & Albert Hotel	Worsley	5	142
Waren House Hotel	Bamburgh Castle	2	143
Wateredge Hotel	Windermere	7	144
White Moss House	Windermere	5	145
Willington Hall	Portal	3	146
Woodland Park Hotel	Altrincham	¼	147
Wordsworth Hotel, The	Keswick	10	148
Worsley Arms Hotel	Malton & Norton	8	149
WALES			
Bodidris Hall	Ruthin Pwllglas	8	156
Bodysgallen Hall	Maesdu	2	157
Bontddu Hall Hotel	Royal St David's	10	158
Bryn Tirion Hotel	Bull Bay	13	159
Cawdor Arms, The	Glynhir	4	160
Conrah Country House Hotel	Aberystwyth	3	162
Crown at Whitebrook, The	Monmouth Rolls	5	163
Dolmelynllyn Hall	Royal St David's	12	164
Edderton Hall	Welshpool	3	165
Empire, The	North Wales	1	166
Fairyhill	Pennard	8	167
George III Hotel	Royal St David's	16	168
Hand Hotel, The	Oswestry	8	169
Lake Country House, The	Builth Wells	6	170
Lake Vyrnwy Hotel	Builth Wells	10	171
Llangoed Hall	Cradoc	11	172
Maes-y-Neuadd, The	Royal St David's	3	173
Milebrook House	Knighton	1½	174
Miskin Manor	Vale of Glamorgan	2	175
Old Rectory, The	Conwy	3	176
Palé Hall Country House	Bala Lake	1½	177
Penally Abbey	Tenby	2	178
Penmaenuchaf Hall	Dolgellau	2	179
Peterstone Court	Cradoc	5	180
Plas Penhelig Hotel	Aberdovey	10	181
Soughton Hall	Northop	¼	183
St Brides Hotel	Tenby	3	182
Tan-y-Foel Country House	Betws-y-Coed	2	184
Three Cocks Hotel	Cradoc	10	185
Trearddur Bay Hotel	Holyhead	1	186

Hotel	Course	Miles Away	Page
Tyddyn Llan Country House	Llangollen	18	187
Ty'n Rhos Country House	Caernarfon	9	188
Warpool Court Hotel	Haverfordwest	16	189
Ynyshir Hall	Borth and Ynyslas	8	190
MIDSHIRES			
Angel Hotel, The	Fornham Park	1	196
Barnsdale Lodge Hotel	Greetham	8	197
Bedford Arms	Moor Park	5	198
Bretforton Manor	Broadway	5	199
Brockencote Hall	Ombersley	6	200
Brookhouse, The	Bretby	4	201
Burleigh Court	Minchinhampton	1½	202
Calcot Manor	Cotswold Edge	3	203
Charingworth Manor	Broadway	7	204
Cotswold House Hotel	Broadway	3	205
Cottage of Content	Belmont Lodge	10	206
Crown Inn & Hotel, The	Naunton Downs	6	207
Dinham Hall	Oldfield	4	208
Dormy House	Broadway	½	209
Ettington Park Hotel	Stratford-upon-Avon	10	210
Fallowfields	Frilford Heath	1	211
Feathers, The	Chesterton	5	212
Glewstone Court Hotel	Rolls of Monmouth	5	213
Grafton Manor	Bromsgrove	6	214
Greenway, The	Lilley Brook	3	215
Halewell	Lilley Brook	8	216
Hotel on the Park	Lilley Brook	3	218
Le Manoir Aux Quat' Saisons	Waterstock	3	219
Lords of the Manor	Naunton Downs	4	220
Lovells at Windrush Farm	Burford	5	221
Lygon Arms, The	Broadway	1	222
Mallory Court Hotel	Leamington & County	1	223
Mill at Harvington, The	Evesham	4	224
Nailcote Hall	Forest of Arden	4	225
New Hall	Belfry	3	226
Normanton Park	Greetham Valley	8	227
Nuthurst Grange	Shirley	2	228
Old Beams	Leek	7	229
Old Parsonage	The Oxfordshire	8	230
Old Rectory, The	Royal West	17	231
Old Vicarage Hotel	Worfield Golf Club	1	232
Painswick Hotel, The	Painswick	1	233
Peacock Hotel at Rowsley, The	Matlock	8	234
Peterstow Country House	Ross-on-Wye	5	235
Redfern Hotel, The	Wharton Park	6	236
Regent Hotel, The	Leamington & County	2	237
Royalist, The	Naunton Downs	5	238
Seckford Hall	Seckford	½	239
Seymour House	Broadway	3	240
Shaven Crown, The	Burford	5	241
Springs Hotel, The	Mapledurham	10	242
Studley Priory	Studley Wood	2	244
Thatcher's Inn	Waterstock	8	245
Washbourne Court Hotel	Naunton Downs	2	246
Wentworth Hotel	Aldeburgh	1½	248
Weston Manor Hotel	Chesterton	3	249
White Hart Hotel, The	Frilford Heath	12	250
Wild Duck, The	Cirencester	5	251
Woodlands Manor	Bedford & County	½	252
Wroxton House Hotel	Rye Hill Golf Club	5	253
Ye Olde Salutation Inn	The Hereford	3	254
WEST COUNTRY			
Alston Hall	Bigbury	10	260
Alverton Manor	Truro	2	261
Bath Spa Hotel	Cumberwell Park	4	262
Beechleas Hotel	Parkstone	6	263
Bolt Head	Dartmouth	12	264
Boscundle Manor	Carlyon Bay	½	265
Buckland-Tout-Saints	Dartmouth	5	266
Carpenters Arms, The	Farrington	3	267
Cedar Falls Health Farm	Tiverton	20	268
Combe Grove Manor	Bath Sham Castle	1	270
Combe Park Hotel	Saunton	18	271
Court Barn	Holsworthy	3½	272
Crown Hotel, The	Minehead	15	273
Downrew House Hotel	Saunton	10	274
Eagle House	Cumberwell	2	275
Easton Court Hotel	Moretonhampstead	3	276
Ebford House	Woodbury	4	277
Floyd's Inn	Dartmouth	1	278
Gabriel Court Hotel	Dainton Park	4	279
Garrack Hotel, The	West Cornwall	3	280
Haydon House	Bath	2	281
Heddon's Gate Hotel	Saunton	15	282
Holly Lodge	Bath Sham Castle	3	283
Holne Chase Hotel	Stover	6	284
Hunstrete House	Stockwood Vale	5	285
Kittiwell House Hotel	Saunton Golf Club	2	286
Langley House Hotel	Taunton Vale	20	287
Langtry Manor	Queens Park	1	288
Leusdon Lodge	Wrangaton	12	289
Lewtrenchard Manor	Hurdwick	6	290
Lugger Hotel, The	Truro	12	291
Manor Hotel, The	Bridport/West Dorset	5	292
Manor House Hotel	Isle of Purbeck	2	293
Mansion House Hotel, The	Parkstone	4	294
Masons Arms	Axe Cliff	6	295
Mill End Hotel	The Manor House	5	296
Mortons House Hotel	Isle of Purbeck	3½	297
Nare Hotel, The	Truro	12	298
Old Bell, The	Bowood	10	299
Old Success Inn, The	Cape Cornwall	5	300
Oxenham Arms, The	Okehampton	4	301
Periton Park Hotel	Minehead/W Somerset	2½	302
Priory Hotel	Weymouth	6	303
Priory Hotel, The	Bath Sham Castle	½	304
Queens Hotel, The	Cape Cornwall	8	305
Queensberry Hotel	Bath Sham Castle	2	306
Rising Sun Hotel, The	Saunton	18	307
Riviera, Hotel	Sidmouth	6	308
Royal Castle, The	Dartmouth	5	309
Royal Oak Inn, The	Minehead	10	310
St Olaves Court Hotel	Woodbury Park	10	311
Salterns Hotel	Parkstone	½	312
Simonsbath House Hotel	Saunton	25	313
Soar Mill Cove Hotel	Dartmouth	8	314
Summer Lodge	Dorchester	10	315
Talland Bay Hotel	St Mellion	5	316
Thornbury Castle	Thornbury	1½	317
Tides Reach Hotel	Thurlestone	5	318
Trengilly Wartha Inn	Falmouth	5	319
Watersmeet Hotel	Saunton	7	320
Well House, The	St Mellion	10	321
Whatley Manor	Chippenham	12	322
Whitechapel Manor	Royal North Devon	25	323
Woodbridge Inn, The	R.A.F. Upavon	1	324
Woolacombe Bay Hotel	Saunton	5	325
Woolley Grange Hotel	Bowood	8	326
SOUTH			
Amberley Castle	Cowdray Park	5	332
Ashdown Park Hotel	Royal Ashdown	3	333
Audleys Wood	Dummer	5	334
Bailiffscourt Hotel	Littlehampton	3	335
Buxted Park Hotel	East Sussex National	5	336
Chequers Hotel	West Sussex	2	337
Chewton Glen	Barton-on-Sea	2	338
Chilston Park	Chart Hills	7	339
Cisswood House Hotel	Mannings Heath	2	340
Coppid Beech Hotel	Blue Mountain	1½	341
Danesfield House	Temple	4	342
Esseborne Manor	Andover	10	344
Flackley Ash Hotel	Rye	6	345
French Horn Hotel	Castle Royale	½	346
Gordleton Mill Hotel, The	Brockenhurst Manor	5	347
Hautboy, The	Drift	2	349
Hollington House	Newbury	3	350
Hotel du Vin & Bistro	South Winchester	3	352
Little Orchard House	Rye	3	353
Little Thakeham	West Sussex	5	354
Lythe Hill Hotel	Chiddingfold	2	355
New Park Manor	Brockenhurst Manor	1½	356
Nutfield Priory	Betchworth Park	5	357
Ockenden Manor	East Sussex National	15	358
Passford House Hotel	Brockenhurst Manor	3	359
Powdermills Hotel	Aldershaw	3	360
Regency Park Hotel	Newbury & Crookham	5	361
Royal Berkshire Hotel, The	Wentworth	2	362
Shelleys	Cooden Beach	20	363
Spread Eagle, The	Cowdray Park	5	364
LONDON			
Abbey Court, The	Ealing	7	372
Ascott Mayfair	Wentworth	10	373
Aston's Designer Studios	Wentworth	10	374
Athenaeum Hotel	Hampstead	7	375
Bailey's Hotel, The	Richmond Park	6	376
Basil Street Hotel	Highgate	9	377
Beaufort House	Royal Mid Surrey	8	379
Beaufort, The	Ealing	7	378
Blakes Hotel	Wentworth	10	381
Blooms	Hampstead	7	382
Brown's	Stockley Park	17	383
Cadogan Hotel	Wentworth	10	384
Cannizaro House	London & Scottish	½	385
Carlos Place, No 1	Wentworth	10	386
Chesterfield, The	Royal Mid Surrey	6	387
Dolphin Square	Dulwich/Syndenham	2	388
Eleven Cadogan Gardens	Royal Mid Surrey	8	389
Executive Hotel, The	Ealing	7	390
Fenja, The	Wentworth	10	391
Goring Hotel, The	Royal Mid Surrey	5	392
Halcyon, The	Wentworth	22	393
Howard, The	Highgate	6	394
Hyde Park Hotel	Wentworth	10	395
Knightsbridge Green Hotel	Ealing	7	396
Leonard, The	Wentworth	10	397
May Fair Inter-Continental	Wentworth	10	398
Milestone, The	Royal Mid Surrey	5	399
Montcalm, The	Hendon	10	400
Number Sixteen	Wentworth	22	401
Richmond Gate Hotel	Royal Mid Surrey	1	402
Sloane Hotel, The	Royal Mid Surrey	5	404
Topham's Ebury Court	Royal Mid Surrey	12	405
Whites Hotel	Wentworth	25	407
White House Hotel	Hampstead	6	406
IRELAND			
Ahernes Seafood Restaurant	Youghal	2	415
Ard na Sidhe Hotel	Killorglin	2	416
Assolas Country House	Kanturk	4	417
Barberstown Castle	Hermitage	8	418
Bushmills Inn, The	Royal Portrush	5	419
Cahernane Hotel, The	Killarney	3	420
Caragh Lodge	Dooks	4	421
Castle Grove Country House	Otway	2	422
Cromleach Lodge Hotel	Rosses Point	25	423
Dunadry Hotel	Massereene	5	424
Dunloe Castle, Hotel	Killarney	1	425
Galgorm Manor	Ballymena	3	426
Glassdrumman Lodge	Royal County Down	8	427
Gregans Castle	Lahinch	15	428
Hibernian Hotel	Royal Dublin	4	429
Hunters Hotel	Druid's Glen	6	430
Kinnitty Castle	Birr	8	431
Liss Ard Lake lodge	Skibbereen	3	432
Longfields	Portmarnock	4	433
Markree Castle	County Sligo	10	434
Marlfield House	Courtown	3	435
Moyglare Manor	Knockanally	4	436
Muckross Park Hotel	Killarney	5	437
Park Hotel Kenmare	Kenmare	¼	439
Rosleague Manor	Connemara	15	440
Sand House Hotel	Donegal	6	441
Tinakilly House	European Club	6	443
Tyrella House	Royal County Down	8	444
ISLANDS			
Balfour Castle	Kirkwall	4	451
Clarendon Hotel	Shanklin/Sandown	10	452
Kerrowmoar House	Ramsey	3	455
Killiechronan House	Craignure	12	456
Longueville Manor	Royal Jersey	2	458
Moore's Hotel	L'Ancresse	4	459
Port Askaig Hotel	Machrie	18	461
Swainston Manor Hotel	Freshwater Bay	6	463
Uig Hotel	Sconser	25	464
Western Isles Hotel, The	Tobermory	½	465

Meeting facilities

Castle Stalker, Argyll

MOST BEST LOVED HOTELS have facilities for meetings, conferences, receptions and weddings, some small and comfortable, some large and sophisticated. Take your choice from this list, get full details from the page on which your choice appears and telephone to find out more.

Definition: Hotels reporting the maximum number of individuals they could accommodate for a cocktails reception and the number of meeting and reception rooms they maintain.

CAPACITY: UP TO 25 PEOPLE

HOTEL	REGION	MEETING ROOMS	PAGE
Ahernes Seafood Restaurant	Ireland	1	415
Arisaig House	Scotland	1	21
Ascott Mayfair	London	2	373
Aston's Designer Studios	London	2	374
Baron's Craig Hotel	Scotland	1	27
Beaufort, The	London	1	378
Beechleas Hotel	West Country	1	263
Bodidris Hall	Wales	2	156
Brookhouse, The	Midshires	1	201
Broxton Hall	North	1	102
Burgoyne Hotel, The	North	1	103
Burleigh Court	Midshires	1	202
Castle Grove Country House	Ireland	1	422
Chedington Court	West Country	1	269
Chequers Hotel	South	1	337
Cotswold House Hotel	Midshires	1	205
Cromleach Lodge Hotel	Ireland	1	423
Crosby Lodge	North	2	105
Crown at Whitebrook, The	Wales	1	163
Dalmunzie House	Scotland	1	41
Dixcart Hotel	Islands	1	453
Dolmelynllyn Hall	Wales	1	164
Dunain Park Hotel	Scotland	1	45
Esseborne Manor	South	1	344
Fairyhill	Wales	1	167
Farlam Hall Hotel	North	1	109
Fenja, The	London	1	391
Frogg Manor	North	2	111
Gabriel Court Hotel	West Country	1	279
George III Hotel	Wales	1	168
Gilpin Lodge Hotel	North	2	112
Glassdrumman Lodge	Ireland	1	427
Grafton Manor	Midshires	1	214
Greywalls	Scotland	1	52
Hand Hotel, The	Wales	1	169
Hipping Hall	North	1	116
Hotel on the Park	Midshires	1	218
Kilfinan Hotel	Scotland	1	60
Kinnitty Castle	Ireland	3	431
Knockinaam Lodge	Scotland	1	62
Langley House Hotel	West Country	1	287
Leusdon Lodge	West Country	1	289
Liss Ard Lake lodge	Ireland	1	432
Little Thakeham	South	1	354
Loch Melfort Hotel	Scotland	1	67
Loch Torridon Hotel	Scotland	1	68
Lovells at Windrush Farm	Midshires	1	221
Maes-y-Neuadd,Hotel	Wales	1	173
Mallory Court Hotel	Midshires	2	223
Manor House, The	North	1	121
Milestone, The	London	2	399
Minmore House	Scotland	2	72
Mount Royale	North	2	126
Old Beams	Midshires	1	229
Old Vicarage Hotel	Midshires	2	232
Peacock Hotel at Rowsley, The	Midshires	2	234
Penally Abbey	Wales	1	178
Periton Park Hotel	West Country	1	302
Philipburn House Hotel	Scotland	1	80
Priory Hotel	West Country	1	303
Queensberry Hotel	West Country	1	306
Redfern Hotel, The	Midshires	1	237
Rothay Manor	North	1	134
Royal Oak Inn, The	North	1	135
Royal Oak Inn, The	West Country	1	310
Sharrow Bay Country House Hotel	North	1	136
Studley Hotel	North	1	137
Summer Lodge	West Country	1	315
Talland Bay Hotel	West Country	1	316
Taychreggan	Scotland	2	88
Temple Sowerby House	North	3	139
Underscar Manor	North	1	141
Washbourne Court Hotel	Midshires	1	246
Well House, The	West Country	1	321
Willington Hall	North	3	146
Woodbridge Inn, The	West Country	1	324
Woodlands Manor	Midshires	3	252

CAPACITY: 26 TO 50 PEOPLE

HOTEL	REGION	MEETING ROOMS	PAGE
Amberley Castle	South	3	332
Assolas Country House	Ireland	1	417
Auchen Castle Hotel	Scotland	2	23
Bailiffscourt Hotel	South	2	335
Bedford Arms	Midshires	1	198
Brockencote Hall	Midshires	2	200
Buckland-Tout-Saints	West Country	2	266
Cadogan Hotel	London	2	384
Cahernane Hotel, The	Ireland	1	420
Carpenters Arms, The	West Country	2	267
Cawdor Arms, The	Wales	1	160
Channings	Scotland	2	30
Conrah Country House Hotel	Wales	1	162
Craigellachie Hotel	Scotland	3	35
Cromlix House	Scotland	3	37
Devonshire Hotel, The	Scotland	2	43
Dinham Hall	Midshires	1	208
Downrew House Hotel	West Country	1	274
Eagle House	West Country	1	275
Ebford House	West Country	2	277
Empire, The	Wales	1	166
Enmore Hotel	Scotland	2	46
Farleyer House	Scotland	2	47
Feversham Arms Hotel, The	North	1	110
Garrack Hotel, The	West Country	1	280
Glewstone Court Hotel	Midshires	3	213
Gordleton Mill Hotel, The	South	1	347
Goring Hotel, The	London	4	392
Grange Hotel, The	North	3	113
Graythwaite Manor Hotel	North	2	115
Greenway, The	Midshires	2	215
Hartwell House	South	4	348
Hibernian Hotel	Ireland	1	429
Holbeck Ghyll Hotel	North	2	117
Howard The	Scotland	2	54
Invercreran Country House Hotel	Scotland	1	56
Knockomie Hotel	Scotland	3	63
Le Manoir Aux Quat' Saisons	Midshires	1	219
Leonard, The	London	1	397
Lewtrenchard Manor	West Country	2	290
Linthwaite House	North	1	120
Llangoed Hall	Wales	2	172
Lodge on the Loch	Scotland	1	69
Lords of the Manor	Midshires	2	220
Manor House Hotel	West Country	1	293
Mansion House Hotel, The	West Country	3	294
Michaels Nook	North	1	122
Mill at Harvington, The	Midshires	1	224
Monk Fryston Hall	North	3	125
Moore's Hotel	Islands	2	459
Mortons House Hotel	West country	2	297
Moyglare Manor	Ireland	3	436
Muchalls Castle	Scotland	3	74
Nare Hotel, The	West Country	2	298
New Hall	Midshires	4	226
Northcote Manor	North	1	129
Old Bell, The	West Country	3	299
Palé Hall Country House	Wales	2	177
Penmaenuchaf Hall	Wales	2	179
Peterstow Country House	Midshires	1	235
Plas Penhelig Hotel	Wales	2	181
Roman Camp House	Scotland	1	82
Royal Castle, The	West Country	2	309
Seymour House	Midshires	1	240
Springs Hotel, The	Midshires	3	242
Thornbury Castle	West Country	2	317
Tillmouth Park Hotel	North	2	140

Trengilly Wartha Inn	West Country	2	319
Tyddyn Llan Country House	Wales	2	187
Waterford Castle	Ireland	2	445
Weston Manor Hotel	Midshires	5	249
Whatley Manor	West Country	2	322
White Hart Hotel, The	Midshires	2	250
Whitechapel Manor	West Country	2	323
Whites Hotel	London	2	407
Woolley Grange Hotel	West Country	2	326
Worsley Arms Hotel	North	2	149

CAPACITY: 51 TO 75 PEOPLE

HOTEL	REGION	MEETING ROOMS	PAGE
Alston Hall	West Country	2	260
Audleys Wood	South	5	334
Ballathie House Hotel	Scotland	4	26
Blakes Hotel	London	2	381
Bodysgallen Hall	Wales	2	157
Calcot Manor	Midshires	4	203
Charingworth Manor	Midshires	2	204
Coul House Hotel	Scotland	1	34
Culloden House Hotel	Scotland	2	40
Danesfield House	South	5	342
Dower House	North	4	108
Fallowfields	Midshires	1	211
Feathers, The	Midshires	1	212
Hotel du Vin & Bistro	South	1	352
Hunstrete House	West Country	3	285
Invercauld Arms Hotel	Scotland	1	55
King's Arms Hotel	North	2	118
Lake Country House, The	Wales	1	170
Manor Hotel, The	West Country	2	292
Middlethorpe Hall	North	2	123
Royal Marine Hotel	Scotland	2	83
Sand House Hotel	Ireland	3	441
Shelleys	South	3	363
Shieldhill Hotel	Scotland	2	85
Stocks Golf Hotel & Country Club	Midshires	2	243
Udny Arms Hotel	Scotland	2	90

CAPACITY: 76 TO 100 PEOPLE

HOTEL	REGION	MEETING ROOMS	PAGE
Armathwaite Hall Hotel	North	5	99
Athenaeum Hotel	London	4	375
Audleys Wood	South	5	334
Balfour Castle	Islands	3	451
Ballathie House Hotel	Scotland	4	26
Basil Street Hotel	London	4	377
Blakes Hotel	London	2	381
Bodysgallen Hall	Wales	2	157
Bryn Tirion Hotel	Wales	1	159
Bunchrew House Hotel	Scotland	3	29
Bushmills Inn, The	Ireland	2	419
Calcot Manor	Midshires	4	203
Cannizaro House	London	7	385
Charingworth Manor	Midshires	2	204
Chewton Glen	South	3	338
Combe Grove Manor	West Country	3	270
Coul House Hotel	Scotland	1	34
Crabwall Manor	North	3	104
Culloden House Hotel	Scotland	2	40
Danesfield House	South	5	342
Dolphin Square	London	3	388
Dower House	North	4	108
Ettington Park Hotel	Midshires	5	210
Fallowfields	Midshires	1	211
Feathers, The	Midshires	1	212
Flackley Ash Hotel	South	2	345
Gean House, The	Scotland	3	49
Grants Hotel	North	5	114
Hotel du Vin & Bistro	South	1	352
Hotel Riviera	West Country	1	308
Hunstrete House	West Country	3	285
Invercauld Arms Hotel	Scotland	1	55
Johnstounburn House	Scotland	3	58
King's Arms Hotel	North	2	118
Lake Country House, The	Wales	1	170
Longueville Manor	Islands	3	458
Lygon Arms, The	Midshires	5	222
Manor Hotel, The	West Country	2	292
Marlfield House	Ireland	2	435
Middlethorpe Hall	North	2	123
Montcalm, The	London	3	400
Montgreenan Mansion House	Scotland	2	73
Nailcote Hall	Midshires	7	225
New Park Manor	South	2	356
Nuthurst Grange	Midshires	3	228
Ockenden Manor	South	1	358
Old Manor Hotel	Scotland	2	77
Painswick Hotel, The	Midshires	3	233
Passford House Hotel	South	4	359
Peterstone Court	Wales	2	180
Priory Hotel, the	West Country	3	304
Richmond Gate Hotel	London	6	402
Rookery Hall	North	5	133
Royal Berkshire Hotel, The	South	9	362
Royal Marine Hotel	Scotland	2	83
St Olaves Court Hotel	West Country	4	311
Sand House Hotel	Ireland	3	441
Seckford Hall	Midshires	2	239
Shelleys	South	3	363
Shieldhill Hotel	Scotland	2	85
Soughton Hall	Wales	2	183
Stocks Golf Hotel & Country Club	Midshires	2	243
Studley Priory	Midshires	4	244
Tinakilly House	Ireland	3	443
Tophams Ebury Court	London	3	405
Tylney Hall	South	9	365
Udny Arms Hotel	Scotland	2	90

CAPACITY: 101 TO 150 PEOPLE

HOTEL	REGION	MEETING ROOMS	PAGE
Alderley Edge Hotel, The	North	3	96
Angel Hotel, The	Midshires	5	196
Balbirnie House Hotel	Scotland	5	24
Bath Spa Hotel	West Country	7	262
Brown's	London	7	383
Buxted Park Hotel	South	6	336
Chesterfield, The	London	7	387
Chilston Park	South	4	339
Devonshire, The	North	5	107
Donnington Valley Hotel	South	9	343
Golf View Hotel, The	Scotland	2	51
Hintlesham Hall	Midshires	4	217
Hollington House	South	4	350
Horsted Place	South	5	351
Hotel Eilean Iarmain	Islands	2	454
Lake Vyrnwy Hotel	Wales	3	171
Lakeside Hotel	North	7	119
Masons Arms	West Country	1	295
Normanton Park	Midshires	3	227
Nutfield Priory	South	10	357
Powdermills Hotel	South	3	360
Regency Park Hotel	South	9	361
Salterns Hotel	West Country	3	312
Savoy, The	London	11	403
Sheen Falls Lodge	Ireland	3	442
Spread Eagle, The	South	5	364
St Brides Hotel	Wales	5	182
Sunlaws House Hotel	Scotland	3	87
Trearddur Bay Hotel	Wales	2	186
Warpool Court Hotel	Wales	2	189
Welcombe Hotel	Midshires	6	247
White House Hotel	London	7	406
Wordsworth Hotel, The	North	3	148

CAPACITY: OVER 150 PEOPLE

HOTEL	REGION	MEETING ROOMS	PAGE
Alverton Manor	West Country	5	261
Ashdown Park Hotel	South	15	333
Barnsdale Lodge Hotel	Midshires	3	197
Berkeley, The	London	7	380
Celtic Manor Golf & Country Club	Wales	8	161
Cisswood House Hotel	South	4	340
Coppid Beech Hotel	South	11	341
Dormy House	Midshires	5	209
Dunadry Hotel & Country Club	Ireland	12	424
Dunloe Castle, Hotel	Ireland	4	425
Galgorm Manor	Ireland	4	426
Howard, The	London	4	394
Hyde Park Hotel	London	24	395
Mansion House Hotel	Scotland	2	71
May Fair Inter-Continental	London	6	398
Miskin Manor	Wales	5	175
Mount Murray Country Club	Islands	3	460
Muckross Park Hotel	Ireland	3	437
Nidd Hall	North	7	128
Queens Hotel, The	West Country	3	305
Redworth Hall Hotel	North	16	132
Regent Hotel, The	Midshires	4	237
Savoy, The	London	11	403
St Andrews Golf Hotel	Scotland	2	84
Swainston Manor Hotel	Islands	4	463
Victoria & Albert Hotel	North	10	142
Woodland Park Hotel	North	2	147
Woolacombe Bay Hotel	West Country	3	325

Meeting facilities

Mussenden Temple, Londonderry

"It is a wise man who keeps his friendships in constant repair"

Samuel Johnson

Ports of entry & nearest hotels

Edinburgh

All the hotels on these pages are within 30 miles of the major Ports of Entry into Great Britain and Ireland. The numbers shown in the map correspond to the number of each port of entry shown below.

SEA AND AIR PORTS IN GREAT BRITAIN AND THE REPUBLIC OF IRELAND

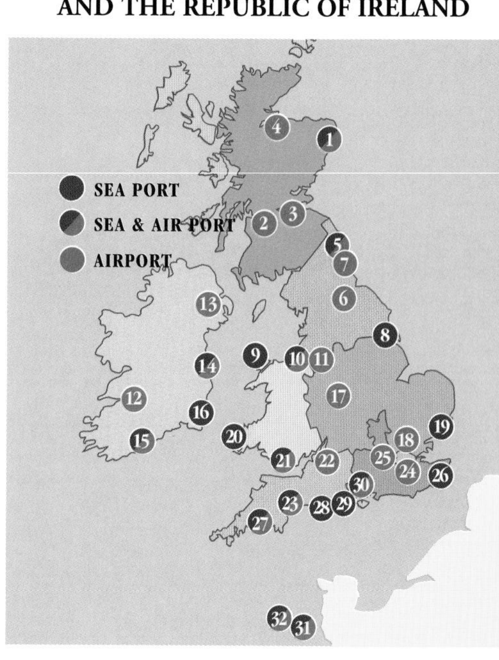

Ports of entry & nearest hotels

Dublin

Tourist Boards' overseas addresses

Dunguaire Castle, Galway

BRITISH TOURIST AUTHORITY

AUSTRALIA
8th Floor,
University Centre
210 Clarence Street
Sydney NSW 2000
Tel 02 267 4555
Fax 02 267 4442

BELGIUM
306 Avenue Louise
1050 Brussels
Tel 02 646 3510
Fax 02 646 3986

CANADA
111 Avenue Road
Suite 450
Toronto
Ontario M5R 3J8
Tel 416 925 6326
Fax 416 961 2175

DENMARK
Montergade 3
1116 Copenhagen K
Tel 33 33 91 88
Fax 33 14 01 36

ENGLAND
Thames Tower
Black's Road
Hammersmith
London W6 9EL
Tel 0181 846 9000
Fax 0181 563 0302

GERMANY
Taunusstrasse 52-60
60329 Frankfurt
Tel 069 238 0711
Fax 069 238 0717

IRELAND
18-19 College Green
Dublin 2
Tel 01 670 8000
Fax 01 670 8244

ITALY
Corso Magenta 32
20123 Milano
Tel 02 7201 0078
Fax 02 7201 0086

JAPAN
Tokyo Club Bldg
3-2-6 Kasumigaseki
Chiyoda-ku
Tokyo 100
Tel 03 3581 3603/4
Fax 03 3581 5797

NETHERLANDS
Aurora Gebouw (5e)
Stadhouderskade 2
1054 ES Amsterdam
Tel 020 685 5051
Fax 020 618 6868

NEW ZEALAND
Suite 305, 3rd Floor
Cnr Queen & Customs Streets
Auckland 1
Tel 09 303 1446
Fax 09 377 6965

NORWAY
Nedre Slotts Gt 21,
4 Etasje
N-0157 Oslo
Postbox 1554 Vika
N-0117 Oslo
Tel 022 42 47 45
Fax 022 42 48 74

SINGAPORE
24 Raffles Place
#19-06 Clifford Centre
Singapore 048621
Tel 535 2966
Fax 534 4703

SOUTH AFRICA
PO Box 41896
Craighall 2024
Tel 011 325 0343
Fax 011 325 0344

SPAIN
Torre de Madrid 6/5
Pza de Espana 18
28008 Madrid
Tel 91 541 1396
Fax 91 542 8149

SWEDEN
Box 745
S 101 35 Stockholm
Tel 08 21 24 44
Fax 08 21 31 29

SWITZERLAND
Limmatquai 78
CH-8001 Zurich
Tel 01 261 4277
Fax 01251 4456

USA - Chicago
625 N Michigan Avenue
Suite 1510
Chicago IL 60611

USA - New York
551 Fifth Avenue
New York NY 10176-0799
Tel 800 GO 2 BRITAIN
Fax 212 986 1188

BORD FAILTE

AUSTRALIA
Bord Fáilte
5th Level, 36 Carrington Street
Sydney NSW 2000
Tel 02 299 6177
Fax 02 299 6323

BELGIUM
Irish Tourist Board
Avenue de Beaulieu 25
1160 Brussels
Tel 2 673 99 40
Fax 2 672 1066

BRITAIN
Bord Fáilte
150 New Bond Street
London W1Y 0AQ
Tel 0171 493 3201
Fax 0171 493 9065

CANADA
Bord Fáilte
Suite 1150
160 Bloor Street East
Toronto
Ontario M4W 1B9
Tel 416 929 2777
Fax 416 929 6783

DENMARK
Det Irske Turistkontor
"Klostergarden"
Amagertorv 29,3
DK 1160 Copenhagen K
Tel 33 158 045
Fax 33 936 390

FINLAND
Irlannin Matkailutoimisto
Embassy of Ireland
Erottajankatu 7A
00130 Helsinki
Tel 0 608 966
Fax 0 646 022

GERMANY
Irische Fremdenverkehrszentrale
Untermainanlage 7
D 60329 Frankfurt/Main
Tel 69 23 64 92
Fax 69 23 46 26

IRELAND
Bord Fáilte
Baggot Street Bridge
Dublin 2
Tel 01 602 4000
Fax 01 602 4100

ITALY
Irish Tourist Board
Via Maria Segreta, 6
20123 Milano
Tel 02 869 05 43
Fax 02 869 03 96

NETHERLANDS
Irish Tourist Board
Spuistraat 104
1012 VA Amsterdam
Tel 020 622 31 01
Fax 020 620 80 89

NORWAY
Irlands Turistkontor
Holmenkollveien 120 B
PO Box 65
Holmenkollen
0324 Oslo
Tel 022 92 00 80
Fax 022 92 00 30

SWEDEN
Irlandska Turistryran
Sibyllegatan 49
S-114 42 Stockholm
Tel 08 662 85 10
Fax 08 661 75 95